François Cardarelli

Electrowinning Iron and Recycling Sulfuric Acid from Iron Sulfates: a Zero-Carbon Iron-Making Process

Electrochem Technologies & Materials Inc.

François Cardarelli, President & Owner
Electrochem Technologies & Materials Inc.
2037 Aird Avenue, Suite 201
Montréal (QC) H1V 2V9, Canada
www.electrochem-technologies.com
Member of ACS, AIChE, CIC, ECS, MSA, OCQ, OS, and TMS

Email: contact@electrochem-technologies.com
contact@francoiscardarelli.ca

ISBN 978-1-7775769-3-6 (Softcover)

ISBN 978-1-7775769-5-0 (Hardcover)

ISBN 978-1-7775769-4-3 (eBook)

Legal deposit: Library and Archives Canada, Ottawa, 2023.

Printed on acid-free paper.

The Electrochem Technologies & Materials Inc. imprint is published by the Canadian corporation Electrochem Technologies & Materials Inc.

The registered company address is: 2037 Aird Avenue, Suite 201, Montréal (QC) H1V 2V9, Canada

Units Policy

In this monograph all the units of measure used for describing physical quantities and properties were those recommended by the *Système International d'Unités* (SI) except in some few instances where some units from the *US Customary System* (USCS) are used in conjunction. For accurate conversion factors between these units and the other non SI units (e.g., cgs, fps, Imperial, and US customary systems) please refer to the reference book of the same author:

CARDARELLI, F. (2005) *Encyclopaedia of Scientific Units, Weight and Measures. Their SI Equivalences and Origins.* Springer, New York, London, xxiv, 848 pages; ISBN 978-1-85233-682-0.

Books by the same author:

CARDARELLI, F. (2022) *Sulfuric Acid Digestion, Sulfuric Acid Baking, and Sulfation Roasting in Mineral and Chemical Processing, and Extractive Metallurgy.* Electrochem Technologies & Materials Inc., Montreal, Canada, xvi, 285 pages, 93 tables, 76 black and white figures. ISBN 978-1-7775769-0-5.

CARDARELLI, F. (2018) *Materials Handbook. A Concise Desktop Reference, Third edition.* Springer, Cham, London, New York. cxxxii, 2254 pages, 150 black and white figures, 25 illustrations in color in two volumes. ISBN 978-3-319-38923-3.

CARDARELLI, F. (2008) *Materials Handbook. A Concise Desktop Reference, Second edition.* Springer, London, xxxviii, 1340 pages, 55 figures; ISBN 978-1-84628-689 (Out-of-Print).

CARDARELLI, F. (2005) *Encyclopaedia of Scientific Units, Weight and Measures. Their SI Equivalences and Origins.* Springer, New York, London, xxiv, 848 pages; ISBN 978-1-85233-682-0.

CARDARELLI, F. (2000) *Materials Handbook. A Concise Desktop Reference.* Springer, London, New York, ix, 595 pages, 7 figures; ISBN 978-1-85233-168-2 (Out-of-Print).

CARDARELLI, F. (1999) *Scientific Unit Conversion. A Practical Guide to Metrication, Second edition.* Springer, London, New York, xvi, 488 pages; ISBN 978-1-85233-043-0 (Out-of-Print).

CARDARELLI, F. (1997) *Scientific Unit Conversion. A Practical Guide to Metrication.* Springer, London, Heidelberg, xvi, 456 pages, ISBN 978-3-540-76022-9 (Out-of-Print).

Author Biography

François Cardarelli
Canadian & French citizen

Academic Background

Ph.D. (Doctorat), Chemical Engineering (Université Paul Sabatier, Toulouse, 1996)

DEA in Electrochemistry (Université Pierre et Marie Curie, Paris, 1992)

M.Sc. (Maîtrise), Physical Chemistry (Université Pierre et Marie Curie, Paris, 1991)

B.Sc. (Licence), Physical Chemistry (Université Pierre et Marie Curie, Paris, 1990)

DEST (Credits) in Nuclear Sciences and Technologies (CNAM, Paris, 1988)

DEUG B in Geophysics and Geology (Université Pierre et Marie Curie, Paris, 1987)

Baccalaureate C (Mathematics, Physics, and Chemistry) (CNED, Versailles, France, 1985)

Working Areas

The author has worked in the following areas since 1990 until present:

2010-Present President and owner, Electrochem Technologies & Materials Inc., Montreal (Quebec), Canada, manufacturing industrial electrodes and electrolyzers, producing vanadium, tantalum, and tungsten chemicals, inventing, patenting, and commercializing electrochemical, chemical, and metallurgical processes for recycling by-products.

2008-2010 Recycling manager, 5N Plus Inc., Ville Saint-Laurent (Quebec), Canada, in charge of the recycling of end-of-life cadmium telluride (CdTe) thin-film photovoltaic solar panels and the hydrometallurgical recovery of tellurium and cadmium.

2007-2008 Principal electrochemist, Materials and Electrochemical Research (MER) Corp., Tuscon (Arizona), USA, working on the electrowinning of titanium metal powder from composite Ti_2OC anodes in molten salts, and other materials-related projects.

2000-2007 Principal chemist (materials), technology department, Quebec Iron and Titanium (QIT) now Rio Tinto, Sorel-Tracy (Quebec), Canada, invented the electrowinning of titanium metal from molten titanium slags and on other novel electrochemical processes.

1998-200 Materials expert and industrial electrochemist, lithium department, Avestor (now Blue Solutions), involved in the metallurgy and processing of lithium metal anodes and the recycling of spent lithium metal polymer batteries.

1997-1998 Battery product leader, technology department, Argotech Productions, Inc. (Avestor), Boucherville (Québec), Canada, in charge of electric-vehicle, stationary, and down-hole oil-drilling applications of lithium metal polymer batteries.

1996-1997 Registered consultant in chemical and electrochemical engineering (Toulouse, France) providing scientific advices on electrochemical processes and electrode materials.

1993-1996 Research scientist, Laboratory of Electrochemical Engineering (Université Paul Sabatier, Toulouse, France) for the electrodeposition of tantalum in molten salts and the preparation and characterization of iridium-based industrial electrodes for oxygen evolution in acidic media (sponsored by Electricité de France).

1992-1993 Design engineer, Institute of Marine Biogeochemistry (CNRS & École Normale Supérieure, Paris, France) for the environmental monitoring of heavy-metal pollution by electroanalytical techniques and by alpha spectrometry.

1990-1992 Research scientist, Laboratory of Electrochemistry (Université Pierre & Marie Curie, Paris, France) for the development of a beta nuclear scintillation detector used for electrochemical experiments involving radiolabelled compounds.

"Nothing is too wonderful to be true if it be consistent with the laws of nature."

Michael Faraday (1791-1867)

"Il y a une analyse selon laquelle, d'une vérité compacte, on déduit des vérités plus simples."

André-Marie Ampère (1775-1836)

"Ogni metallo ha un determinato potere, diverso da metallo a metallo, di mettere in moto il fluido elettrico."

Alessandro Volta (1745-1827)

"Connaître, découvrir, publier, tel est le destin d'un scientifique."

Dominique François Jean Arago (1786-1853)

Preface

This comprehensive monograph is primarily intended to describe the patented FerWIN® technology, a green and zero-carbon iron-making process, which consists to perform the electrowinning of iron metal and the recycling of sulfuric acid from iron sulfates that are by-produced at the million tonnes scale worldwide while releasing pure oxygen gas.

The information has been presented in such a form that industrial electrochemists, chemical engineers, metallurgists, and other practicing engineers, scientists, professors, and technologists will have access to relevant scientific and technical information supported by key experimental data that were obtained from extensive laboratory, prototype, and pilot testing. It also includes comprehensive electrochemical and engineering calculations, costs and benefits analysis, a financial and sensitivity analysis.

I hope this monograph will be of value also to men and women engaged in the traditional iron and steelmaking industries that want to understand this novel electrochemical approach outside their conventional blast furnace, direct reduced iron, and electric arc smelting processes.

Finally, the monograph may be of interest to persons in the steelmaking industries occupying managerial positions such as chief executives, chief operating officers, and V.P. of operations.

Montréal, Québec, Canada François Cardarelli, November 2023

Dedication

I dedicate this monograph to my late mother Claudine, my father Antonio who together with my late uncle Consalvo supported me in the early 1980s in establishing a basic mineralogical, chemical, and metallurgical laboratory, and scientific library and to Louise St-Amour for her continuous support and understanding during all these years.

Acknowledgements

I want to express my deepest thanks to the companies in North America, South America, Europe, and Asia who tested and assessed the patented electrochemical process over the last decade and supplied various feedstocks originating from their commercial operations.

Table of Contents

List of Tables

List of Figures

1 Introduction

1.1 Background

The patented ***FerWIN®*** ***process*** (Trademark of *Electrochem Technologies & Materials Inc.*) [1, 2] is a novel electrochemical process, more precisely an iron electrowinning process that produces pure electrolytic iron (99.995 wt.% Fe) or iron-rich alloys (e.g., Fe with Ni, Cr, Mn, and V) from industrial wastes, and liquid effluents containing iron sulfate(s) such as copperas, spent pickling liquors (SPLs), pregnant leach solutions (PLS) while regenerating concentrated sulfuric acid, and releasing pure oxygen gas according to the overall electrochemical reaction below:

$$FeSO_4 + H_2O = Fe(s) + H_2SO_4 + 0.5O_2(g)$$

The core technology behind the process will be described in great details in Section 14, but in the meantime and in short, the electrowinning of iron consists to electrolyze a catholyte made of warm iron-rich sulfate solution inside a electrolytic cell (i.e., electrolyzer) divided by means of an anion exchange membrane acting as separator, with a steel or titanium cathode, and a mixed metals oxides (MMO) coated-titanium anode.

Before to enter the electrolyzer, the iron-rich sulfate solution is pH-adjusted, and then fed to the cathode compartment. The pH adjustment is necessary to avoid the deleterious evolution of hydrogen gas at the cathode, a competing process to avoid because it reduces the cathode current efficiency.

Upon electrolysis metallic iron deposits as plate or metal powder onto the titanium, a cathode material selected to prevent the evolution of hydrogen while sulfate anions migrate through the anion-exchange membrane towards the anode compartment where they combine with protons to yield concentrated sulfuric acid.

Pure oxygen gas, a by-product from the oxidation of water at the anode, evolves from the MMO anode and might be either recovered or released into the atmosphere after sulfuric acid mists have been removed by scrubbing. For the sake

[1] CARDARELLI, F. (2009) *Electrochemical process for the recovery of metallic iron and sulfuric acid values from iron-rich sulfate wastes, mining residues, and pickling liquors.* PCT International Patent Application WO 2009/124393 (A1) (Electrochem Technologies & Materials Inc.), October 15th, 2009.

[2] CARDARELLI, F. (2016) *Electrochemical process for the recovery of metallic iron and sulfuric acid values from iron-rich sulfate wastes, mining residues, and pickling liquors.* Canadian Patent CA 2,717,887 C (Electrochem Technologies & Materials Inc.), June 14th, 2016.

of clarity, a schematic of the iron electrowinning process using a two-compartment divided electrolyzer is depicted in Figure 1.

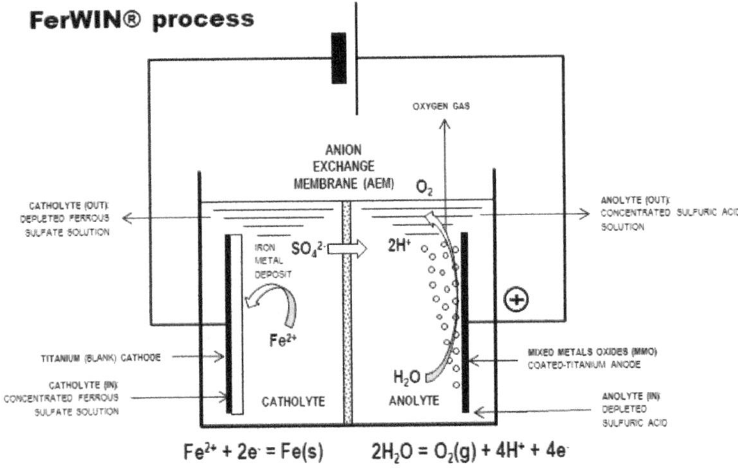

Figure 1 – Schematic of the FerWIN® process (Two-compartment electrolyzer)

The initial sulfuric acid concentration in the anolyte can be as low as five mass percent, and it can reach thirty mass percent before a bleed is performed and replaced by weak sulfuric acid.

In case other reducible metallic impurities such as nickel, zinc, vanadium, manganese, or chromium, are present, they are all co-deposited along with the iron yielding an iron-rich alloy of high commercial value. On the other hand, non-reducible metals such as sodium, potassium or magnesium if present do not participate to the electrochemical reactions, and it is just required to perform a bleed of the catholyte when their concentration reaches a certain threshold.

In certain peculiar situations, it is also possible to perform the FerWIN® process using a three-compartment electrolyzer configuration depicted in Figure 2.

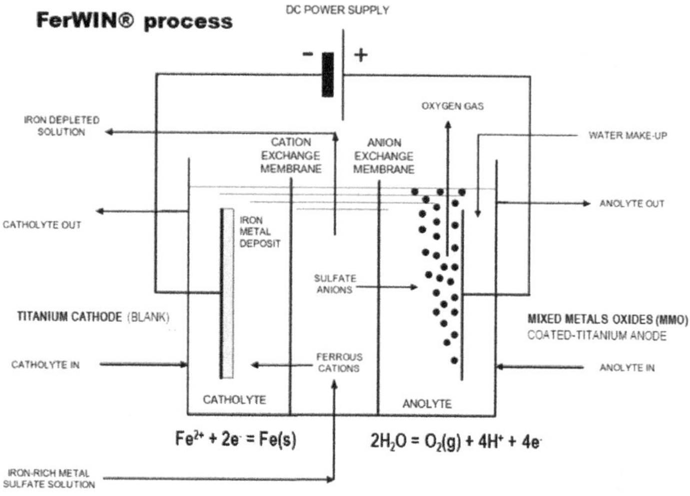

Figure 2 – Schematic of the FerWIN® process (Three-compartment electrolyzer)

1.2 Environmental Benefits

Electrolytic iron is one of the purest forms of metallic iron. Moreover, by contrast with most iron products, it is absolutely devoid of carbon that means it is the pure alpha-iron allotrope (α-Fe) while other pure iron products are always made of ferrite (i.e., solid solution of carbon into alpha-iron). The elevate purity of electrolytic iron makes it suitable for various purposes such as in iron cores for electromagnets, diamond tools manufacturing, chemicals, food additives and pharmaceutical industries.

Despite nowadays electrolytic iron is a tiny niche market (ca. 60,000 tonnes per year) by comparison of the other iron metal products, the aim of electrowinning iron is to largely widen its use and to offer a greener alternative to conventional iron- and steelmaking by matching the current price for high quality steel due to the low production costs in order to offer a sustainable and affordable alternative to steelmaking.

From the overall electrochemical reaction, we can see clearly that electrowinning iron from iron sulfate(s) has a carbon negative footprint releasing 283 kilograms of oxygen gas to the atmosphere per tonne of electrolytic iron for a 98.7% cathode current efficiency.

By contrast, the prevailing ***blast furnace process*** produces pig iron from iron ore using metallurgical coke (i.e, a source of carbon) as reductant; the process releases carbon dioxide to the atmosphere as a by-product while the pig iron produced is further refined inside a ***basic oxygen furnace*** (BOF) by blowing oxygen gas to yield low carbon steel. Moreover, the energy consumed during the smelting and slagging steps together with the carbon dioxide emissions are rather significant.

Actually, from a report from Fruehan et al. [3], the actual specific energy consumption for producing a steel slab by smelting, steelmaking, and hot rolling is on average 22.95 GJ per tonne of steel slab (6.38 MWh/tonne) while the greenhouse gases (GHGs) emission is on average 1.8 tonne of CO_2 per tonne of steel.

This must be compared with a specific energy consumption that can be as low as 10.8 GJ per tonne of pure electrolytic iron (3.00 MWh/tonne) with only pure oxygen gas as by-product with a relatively low production cost. That makes the FerWIN® technology a true green and zero-carbon ironmaking process

Thus, in addition to monetize all the iron values, and to regenerate the sulfuric acid, the FerWIN® process can also bring additional incentives by offsetting carbon taxes for major polluters.

However, we must remain realistic, and we cannot expect steelmakers to tear down their existing facilities but rather promote the new technology for either expanding their current production capacity or when building new facilities by accessing the large pool of copperas, and ferrous sulfates currently available worldwide.

1.3 Sustainable Development Benefits

The novel electrochemical technology being essentially a recycling process with the goal of recovery added value iron metal from wastes and concurrently regenerating sulfuric acid which is send back to the process, results are expected in the recovery of resources, and the reuse of raw material and chemicals expensive and energy-demanding to produce industrially. It is clear that if the technology is implemented commercially, it will reduce or prevent the release of hazardous emissions. Thus *in fine* it reduces the quantity of non-renewable resources or materials used.

Not only, the FerWIN® process will solve environmental issues that the mining, metallurgical and chemical industries are facing today but once integrated vertically with the direct sulfation of iron ores (e.g., hematite and magnetite) or

[3] FRUEHAN, R.J.; FORTONI, O.; PAXTON, H.W.; and BRINDLE, R. (2000) *Theoretical Minimum Energies to Produce Steel for Selected Conditions*. Carnegie Mellon University, Pittsburgh, PA.

iron-rich residues (e.g. bauxite residues, steelmaking slags) it will also offers a huge potential as a novel zero-carbon iron-making technology as it will be cost affordable, less energy demanding, and labor intensive than the current iron making process taking into account both the coking and pelletizing processes together with the blast furnace operation.

Finally, on the long term this electrochemical technology could potentially lead to significant industrial changes in the steelmaking industry not yet envisioned as a novel environmentally friendly alternative route for iron making in replacement of the CO_2-emitting blast furnace.

1.4 Regulatory Compliance and Environmental Liability

All large scale industrial activities are subject to extensive federal and provincial laws and regulations governing development, production, taxes, labour standards, waste disposal, protection, and conservation of the environment, reclamation, plant safety and occupational health.

The costs of evaluating, planning, designing, developing, constructing, operating and closing an industrial plant and other facilities in compliance with such laws and regulations are rather significant. These costs and delays associated with compliance with such laws and regulations could become prohibitive in some jurisdictions. Moreover, insurance against environmental risks including potential liability for pollution or other hazards as a result of the disposal of waste products occurring from production is rather expensive. Finally, laws and regulations intended to ensure the protection of the environment are constantly changing, and are generally becoming more restrictive as time passes.

In this monograph, we will emphasized in many instances, that electrowinning iron from iron sulfates is a true zero-carbon and green iron-making process that either significantly reduces or even offsets the potential risks and liabilities associated with pollution of the environment and the disposal of waste products occurring as a result of production. Therefore, we believe that the roll out and implementation of this green technology is a game changer with great benefits for the environment and thus it will be little impacted by these stringent regulations and will gain the acceptance of licences and permits from various governmental authorities in key jurisdictions.

1.5 Economic Benefits

The costs and benefits analysis of the technology that will be described in details in Section 17, suggests a favorable economics for certain targeted locations with a low operating cost for producing electrolytic iron mostly related to access to affordable hydro- or nuclear electricity combined with reasonable capital expenditures. Based on these figures, the preliminary financial analysis and discounted cash flows calculations that will provided in Section 18 for an electrowinning plant with a 25-year lifetime shows attractive financial indicators such as a net present value (NPV), an internal rate of return (IRR), and a short payback time (PBT).

1.6 Implementation Strategy

The patented technology which is now granted and enforced globally (i.e., Canada, India, Brazil, China, Japan, South Africa, and the European Union) (see Section 1.7) is suitable from an economic and environmental standpoint to be implemented commercially in the following geographical locations: Canada, Scandinavia, Brazil, India, South Africa, and China, and for the following three industrial scenarios:

[1] When large amounts of metallurgical wastes, and chemical effluents containing iron sulfate(s) are by-produced annually at a given production facilities posing environment issues, it allows avoiding the neutralization, disposal, and landfill costs;

[2] When shortages of sulfuric acid are experienced and because the sulfuric acid consumed by a chemical or metallurgical process ends-up as iron sulfate(s) in the effluents, the iron electrowinning process allows regenerating efficiently all the sulfuric acid values that are recycled back in the upstream process thus reducing the working capital, and operating costs significantly;

[3] Finally, the process allows to monetize all the iron values contained in the wastes, and to obtain the maximum value for the iron product as the commercial price for pure metallic iron is by far higher than the price for any of the other iron products generated using other processing routes (e.g., copperas, hematite).

Despite the technology is not yet commercial, it has been tested successfully in the last decade at the laboratory, at the prototype, and finally at the pilot scale [1:50]. The extensive processing of various solid wastes, by-products, and liquid effluents originating from the mining, chemical, and metallurgical industries did confirm the excellent performances, and robustness of the technology which is now technically proven, and de-risked.

1.7 The FerWIN® Patents

Electrochem Technologies & Materials Inc. (Montreal, Quebec) owns the exclusive rights for the patented FerWIN® process worldwide. The patent is now granted and enforced in key jurisdictions for the project such as Brazil (BR), Canada (CA), China (CN), Japan (JP), Europe (EU): France (FR), Italy (IT), Spain (ES), Slovenia (SI), Belgium (BE), Germany (DE), the United Kingdom (UK),

Norway (NO), Sweden (SE) and Finland (FI), South Africa (RSA), India (IN) and Brazil (BR).

Table 1 – Worldwide patents and patents applications

Country	Patent number	Title in the country language
Australian Patent Application	AU 2009/235914	Electrochemical process for the recovery of metallic iron and sulfuric acid values from iron-rich sulfate wastes, mining residues and pickling liquors
Belgian Patent	BE/EP2268852	Procédé électrochimique de récupération de valeurs de fer métallique et d'acide sulfurique à partir de déchets sulfatés riches en fer, de résidus d exploitation et de lessives de décapage
Brazilian Patent	BR 0911653 B	Processo eletroquímico para a recuperação de valores de ferro metálico e de ácido sulfúrico a partir de resíduos de sulfato ricos em ferro, resíduos de mineração e líquidos de decapagem
Canadian Patent	CA 2,717,887 C	Electrochemical process for the recovery of metallic iron and sulfuric acid values from iron-rich sulfate wastes, mining residues and pickling liquors
Chinese Patent	CN 102084034 B	电化学方法从富铁硫酸盐废料，矿渣和酸洗液中回收金属铁和硫酸值
European Patent	EP 2268852 B1	Electrochemical process for the recovery of metallic iron and sulfuric acid values from iron-rich sulfate wastes, mining residues and pickling liquors
Finnish Patent	FI/EP2268852	Sähkökemiallinen prosessi arvokkaiden rautametalli- ja rikkihappojäämien talteenottoon runsasrautaisista sulfaattijätteistä, kaivostoiminnan jätteistä ja peittausnesteistä
French Patent	FR/EP2268852	Procédé électrochimique de récupération de valeurs de fer métallique et d acide sulfurique à partir de déchets sulfatés riches en fer, de résidus d exploitation et de lessives de décapage
German Patent	DE 60 2009 056 032.8	Elektrochemisches verfahren zur rückgewinnung metallischen eisens und schwefelsäurewerte aus eisenreichen schwefelabfällen, abbaureststoffen und altbeizlösungen
Indian Patent	IN 294,372	इलोन-रिक् सलफेट वेस्ट, मिनिंग रेसिड्यूज और पिकल लाइकर्स से मेटालिक इयरन और सौलिड एसीड वैल्यू के अधिग्रहण के लिए मुख्य प्रक्रिया।
Italian	IT/EP2268852	Processo elettrochimico per il recupero di valori di ferro metallico e acido solforico da rifiuti di solfato ricco di

Country	Patent number	Title in the country language
Patent		ferro, residui di attività mineraria e liquidi di decapaggio
Japanese Patent	JP 5469157 B2	鉄に富む硫酸塩廃棄物、鉱業残渣、およびピクリング液からの金属鉄および硫酸の値を回収するための電気化学プロセス
Norvegian Patent	NO/EP2268852 B1	En elektrokjemisk prosess for gjenvinning av metallisk jern eller en jernrik legering, oksygen og svovelsyre fra en jernrik metallsulfatløsning, idet nevnteprosess
Slovenian Patent	SI/EP2268852 B1	Elektrokemični postopek za pridobivanje vrednosti kovinskega železa in žveplove kisline iz odpadnih žveplovih odpadkov, rudarskih ostankov in luščenja
South African Patent	ZA 2010/07214	Electrochemical process for the recovery of metallic iron and sulfuric acid values from iron-rich sulfate wastes, mining residues and pickling liquors
Spanish Patent	ES 2712722 T3	Procedimiento electroquímico para la recuperación de valores de hierro metálico y ácido sulfúrico a partir de desechos de sulfatos ricos en hierro, residuos de minería y licores decapantes
Swedish Patent	SE 2268852 T3	Elektrokemisk process för utvinning av metalliskt järn och svavelsyravärden från järnrikt sulfatavfall, gruvrester och betningslocko
UK Patent	GB/EP2268852	Electrochemical process for the recovery of metallic iron and sulfuric acid values from iron-rich sulfate wastes, mining residues and pickling liquors
US Patent Application	US 2011/00089045 (A1)	Electrochemical process for the recovery of metallic iron and sulfuric acid values from iron-rich sulfate wastes, mining residues and pickling liquors

1.8 Road Map: How to Read this Book?

In order to cover all the aspects of the electrowinning of iron, and the regeneration of sulfuric acid from effluents containing iron sulfate(s), this book contains a plethora of scientific, technical, and economical information. Therefore, depending on the scientific and technical background of the readers, and their particular interest, it could be possible to access directly to the relevant chapters.

For that purpose, to navigate the content of the book, we have provided a simplified road map (Figure 3) by categorizing three groups as follows: (1) readers with a chemical and engineering background such as industrial chemists, chemical engineers, and metallurgists; (2) readers with a background in electrochemistry such as electrochemists, electrochemical engineers, and electrometallurgists, and finally

(3) readers with a non-technical background such as corporate executives, company lawyers, patent attorneys, and decision makers.

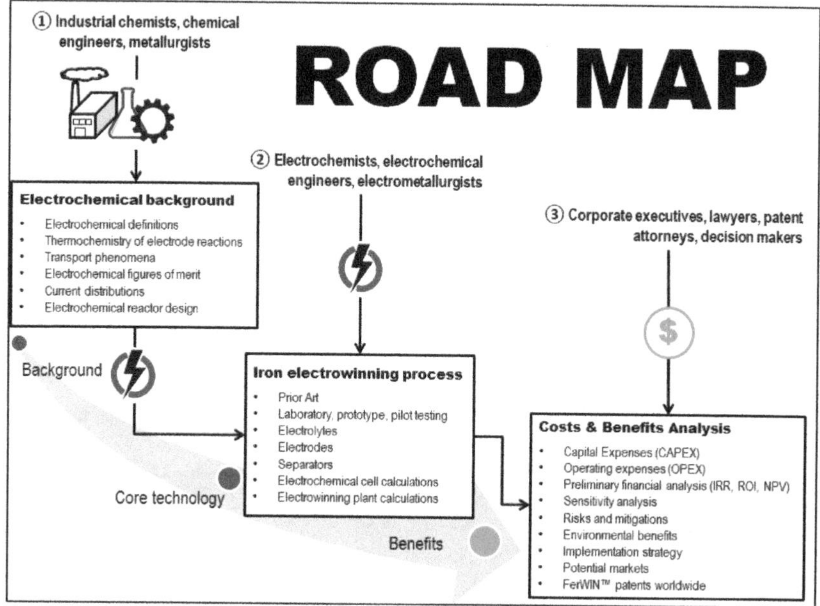

Figure 3 – Road map for navigating through this book

For instance, we recommend to readers from the first group to go through the entire content of the book to become acquainted with the electrochemical concepts necessary to understand the electrowinning of iron while readers from the second group can go directly to the core of the electrowinning technology, and then eventually continue with the cost and benefit analysis. Finally, non-technical readers will be interested by the cost and benefits analysis along with the financial and sensitivity analysis, the potential markets, and the implementation strategy.

2 Markets

Each year, an estimated total of at least 4.6 million tonnes of iron equivalents are by-produced worldwide as iron-rich sulfates mining residues, metallurgical effluents, and industrial wastes originating from the mining, metallurgical, and chemical industries. From that figure about eighty percent are neutralized, disposed-off or simply landfilled.

Owing to the numerous ways for reporting these quantities in liquid effluents, solid wastes, and by-products, it is common practice in the trade to normalize the amount of iron by expressing it as ***ferrous sulfate heptahydrate*** with the chemical formula $FeSO_4 \cdot 7H_2O$, CAS No. [7782-63-0], which is also called ***copperas*** or ***green vitriol*** or even ***melanterite*** when found as a mineral in nature. In this case the above figure corresponds to 23 million tonnes of ferrous sulfate heptahydrate (i.e., copperas) equivalents produced annually worldwide.

The most important sources are: (i) the titanium dioxide white pigment industry, (ii) the iron and steel making industries, and (iii) the hydrometallurgical processing of nonferrous metals.

Actually, it is estimated that about 9 million tonnes of copperas are by-produced worldwide from the titanium dioxide white pigment industry alone.

In addition, another 6 million tonnes of copperas equivalents are contained in ***spent pickling liquors*** (SPLs) that are by-produced from the iron and steel making industries especially from mid-size steel pickling plants [4].

Finally, it is estimated that another 8 million tonnes of copperas mostly contained in ***pregnant leach solutions*** (PLSs) from the hydrometallurgical processing of ores and concentrates of nonferrous metals such as zinc, copper, uranium, and gold, to name a few are also by-produced at various plant locations.

Therefore, we will briefly describe hereafter the by-production of copperas in these three sectors.

---

[4] KLADNIG, W.F. (2010) Acid recycling in steel pickling plants: state-of-the-art and new developments in environmental protection. *International Journal of Environment and Waste Management*, **5**(3-4)(2010)368-378.

2.1 Titanium Dioxide Pigment Industries

2.1.1 Copperas from the Sulfate Process

During the manufacture of titanium dioxide white pigment by the ***sulfate process*** from titanium-rich feedstock such as beach sand ilmenite (52 wt.% TiO_2), large amount of copperas are by-produced, and iron-rich sulfate liquid effluents are generated.

These by-products mostly comprise copperas, ferrous sulfate, and spent sulfuric acid or their combination. The actual by-products are in fact much more complex as these consist of wastes which are essentially made of the above salts often contaminated with other metal sulfates. Most of these wastes contain ubiquitous iron in the chemical form of ferrous sulfate and in lesser extent as ferric sulfates.

Actually, the ground ilmenite concentrate is digested batch wise with concentrated sulfuric acid (85-96 wt.% H_2SO_4) inside brick lined steel vessel called ***digester***. The exothermic sulfation reaction is triggered by injecting water into the pre-heated slurry of concentrated sulfuric acid and oven-dried ilmenite. The baking process proceeds quasi-autogenous for few hours at a temperature above 180°C. After completion, the sulfation cake obtained is cooled, and it is dissolved in cold water to avoid premature hydrolysis of Ti(IV). Because, the Fe(III) present in the original beach sand ilmenite ends-up in the pregnant liquor it must be reduced to Fe(II). Actually, the ferric cations are deleterious chromophore impurities that imparts color to the precipitated titanium oxihydrate $TiO(OH)_2$. Therefore, after clarification for removing suspended solids and some unreacted ilmenite, the pregnant liquor containing 200-300 g/L of titanyl sulfate ($TiOSO_4$) is then reduced with scrap iron metal.

Once the reduction is completed, the total iron concentration ranges from 120 to 150 g/L Fe(II) with at least 3 g/L of Ti(III). The latter species is mandatory for preventing the air oxidation of Fe(II) during handling, and storage. Afterwards, the elevate content of iron is removed by evaporative cooling, and crystallization of ferrous sulfate heptahydrate ($FeSO_4.7H_2O$). The pale green crystals are recovered by centrifugation. The remaining iron-depleted liquor containing about 170-230 g/L of TiO_2, 20-30 g/L of iron, and 20-28 wt.% H_2SO_4 is further processed downstream to recover the titanium values. For a detailed description of the entire process, we recommend to read a book from the same author [5].

The amount of copperas produced by a titanium producer using the sulfate process is thus directly related to the total iron content of the feedstock used. Four main scenarios must be distinguished: (i) at the lower end, sulfate plants utilizing

---

[5] CARDARELLI, F. (2022) *Sulfuric Acid Digestion, Sulfuric Acid Baking, and Sulfation Roasting in Mineral and Chemical Processing, and Extractive Metallurgy*. Electrochem Technologies & Materials Inc., Montreal, QC, Canada, *Chapter 9: Industrial Sulfation Processes*, pages 107-117.

only titanium sulfate slag (i.e., 80 wt.% TiO_2) generate roughly one tonne of copperas per tonne of titanium dioxide pigment, (ii) plants using Australian beach sand ilmenite (i.e., 52 wt.% TiO_2) produce generally around 2.5 tonnes copperas per tonne of titanium dioxide pigment. (iii) At the higher end, sulfate plants using almost exclusively cheaper Norwegian hard rock ilmenite (i.e., 35 wt.% TiO_2) generates a much higher amount of copperas in the order of 4.0 to 4.5 tonnes per tonne of titanium dioxide pigment. Finally, (iv) plants processing both titanium slag and ilmenite separately but mixing the resulting black liquors after the sulfuric digestion is completed have figures in between these two extreme scenarios.

2.1.2 Limited Commercial Applications

In practice, only a small fraction, estimated to less than thirty percent of these iron-rich sulfate wastes, is reused or recycled back. The following chemical compounds such ferrous sulfate heptahydrate, $FeSO_4 \cdot 7H_2O$, ferrous sulfate monohydrate, $FeSO_4 \cdot H_2O$, and finally anhydrous ferrous sulfate, $FeSO_4$ are sold as commercial products. It is important to mention that the commercialization of copperas is greatly hampered by the important volume of the product compared to its iron content (20.1 wt.% Fe), and its low market value.

The total amount of copperas equivalents sold commercially is about 3 million tonnes that distribute as follows for various applications such as:

> 67% of the demand for copperas is consumed for wastewater treatment as flocculating agent used either directly or after conversion to an iron (III) product. The estimated amount of copperas sold annually as flocculating agent is roughly 2 million tonnes;
>
> 15% of the demand for copperas is used as raw material for the manufacture of iron oxides used as red pigments or for magnetic storage devices. The current technology is based entirely on an energy demanding thermal roasting process. Thus about 450,000 tonnes are sold annually for the production of red pigments;
>
> 11% of the demand for copperas is used as fertilizer in agriculture for crop production and prevention of iron chlorosis in plants grown on iron deficient soils or for moss control [6, 7]. Thus about 330,000 tonnes are sold annually as fertilizer in agriculture;

---

[6] KOENIG, R. and KUHNS, M. (1996) *Control of Iron Chlorosis in Ornamental and Crop Plants.* Utah State University, Salt Lake City, UT.

[7] HANDRECK, K. (2002) *Gardening Down Under: A Guide to Healthier Soils and Plants, 2nd edition.* Collingwood, Victoria, Australia: CSIRO Publishing. pp. 146-147.

Only 2.3% of the total demand for copperas is used as an additive in the cement manufacturing process [8, 9]. Actually ferrous sulfate or better moist copperas is used as reducer of hexavalent chromium [i.e., Cr(VI)] that causes serious occupational issues and health hazards and which is present in traces in cement into insoluble and innocuous trivalent chromium, Cr(III). This is achieved in order to eliminate the risk of chrome dermatitis for exposed workers, and end users. This utilization consumes only 69,000 tonnes.

Finally, the remaining 4.7% is used in the preparation of specialty chemicals, in the pharmaceutical industry, as dyeing mordant in the textile industry, as a reducing agent in several chemical processes, and in the food industry as an iron supplement for the treatment of iron deficiency anaemia.

2.1.3 Thermal Roasting Issues

Currently, the only technology used since the 1980s especially in North America, and Europe is a highly energy demanding thermal roasting process with a high carbon footprint and negative environmental impact. The roasting process consists to decompose the iron sulfates by thermal roasting using the heat supplied by the combustion of a fuel. The decomposition yields a salable iron oxides product and sulfur dioxide gas. Afterwards, the sulfur dioxide (SO_2) needs to be converted into sulfur trioxide (SO_3) by means of a nearby and expensive sulfuric acid plant using the contact process. Unfortunately, because nowadays the market for magnetic storage devices such as recording tapes or floppy disks is in severe decline, and the market of iron oxide pigment is very limited, the commercial value of the ferric oxide drastically decreases making the process less profitable and some plants must even blend the copperas with spent pickling liquors to keep their installation running.

The regeneration of sulfuric acid by the roasting process requires to 5,895 kWh/tonne of copperas that must be compared to the 2,376 kWh/tonne from the electrochemical process including also the energy consumed by the concentration of the sulfuric acid by vacuum evaporation.

In addition, besides the thermal roasting; few companies did explore processes to recycle sulfuric acid from iron-rich sulfate liquors such as thermal evaporation with mechanical vapor recompression, nano-filtration, dialysis, ion exchange resins, and solvent extraction. All these processes were only capable to regenerate the sulfuric acid values without recovering any value from the iron

---

[8] MANNS, W.; and LASKOWSKI, Ch. (1999) Eisen(II)sulfat als Zusatz zur Chromatreduzierung. BE-Z: *Beton Journal*, **2**(1999)78-85.

[9] KEHRMANN, A (2008) *Hydraulic Binder and a Chromate Reducer and Use Thereof.* U.S. Patent Application 2008/0282939, November 20th, 2008 (Kerr-McGee Pigment International GmbH.).

which is often irretrievably wasted. In addition, they are energy demanding, and labor intensive.

Therefore, the remaining copperas is simply stockpiled, or in the worst cases dumped into the ocean, disposed-off, deep welled, or land-filled posing serious environmental issues worldwide.

This allows sufficient room for the profitable and successful first rollout and implementation of the new electrochemical technology in locations having access to large amount of iron sulfate(s) wastes, and access to affordable electricity.

2.1.4 Oversupply of Copperas

The oversupply of copperas is particularly important today especially in mainland China, Northern Europe (e.g., Finland), South East Asia, and in a lesser extent North America.

Chinese Market (74%) China with about 70 sulfate plants is by far the largest producing country of titanium dioxide by the sulfate process, totalizing about 6.73 million tonnes of copperas produced each year. Moreover, except two companies all the plants utilize almost exclusively ilmenite as feedstocks, and twenty five plants exhibit nameplate production capacities above 100,000 tonnes of copperas per year, and among them 10 by-produced more than 200,000 tonnes of copperas. Therefore, the Chinese market represents about 74% of the world production of copperas from the titanium pigment industry. However, because of increasing stringent regulations imposed by both the Chinese government and Provincial governments the recycling has to be prioritized. Moreover, because of the affordable wages and building costs in mainland China, the capital expenses for constructing an iron electrowinning plant in China is about the third of the cost for a similar plant built either in North America or Europe and this represents a major advantage to implement successfully this technology.

European Market (15%) In Europe, the total production capacity is about 1.7 million tonnes of copperas dropped since the closure of plant of *Venator* (formerly *Hunstman Pigment*, *Sachtleben GmbH*, and *Kemira Pigment Oy*) located in Pori Finland that was the world largest single plant for producing titanium pigment by the sulfate process using exclusively Norwegian ilmenite as raw material. Actually, the estimated amount of copperas that was produced annually in Pori was 580,000 tonnes. The plant of *Venator* (formerly *Hunstman Tioxide*) in Huelva, Spain, with 216,000 tonnes are good prospects for implementing this novel technology. On the other hand, the two German plants of *Kronos NL* in Nordenham and Leverkusen that produce 270,000 and 142,000 tonnes respectively already regenerates the acid by the thermal roasting technology.

Asia (without China)(6%) When we consider tonnages above 100,000 tonnes of copperas annually in the rest of the world, it restricts mostly to the two Japanese plants of ISK and SAIC.

Based on this analysis, the targeted titanium pigment plants for implementing this novel technology must use beach sand ilmenite and generate above two tonnes of copperas per tonne of titanium dioxide pigment. Moreover because some of these plants are already selling copperas for specific applications, it remains only a selected number of plants having to deal to large oversupply of copperas.

From the above figures, it is obvious that in order to penetrate aggressively the titanium dioxide pigment industry, we need to target the majority of plants worldwide having a similar production of copperas. Therefore, a conservative approach will consist to build a brown field iron electrowinning plant capable to recycle annually 200,000 tonnes of copperas. This benchmark will satisfy most of the Chinese plants, and European plants. Later, if the commercialization of this technology is successful much larger iron electrowinning plants with a treatment capacity of 500,000 tonnes of copperas could be built in China, and Scandinavia.

2.2 Iron and Steel Making Industries

2.2.1 Acid Pickling of Iron and Steel

In the iron and steel industries, 1,840 million of ***crude steel*** are produced annually worldwide [10]. A large portion of the steel is produced in some intermediate forms such as ingots and billets that are later sent to steel mills for further processing into wires, coils, rods, tubes, or flat products such as strips, sheets, and plates.

In order to obtain these steel products, raw steel products require further heat treatment such as annealing, rolling, and forging usually performed in air at temperatures ranging between 800°C and 900°C. It is estimated that 800 million tonnes of steel is heat treated annually.

During heat treatment steel readily oxidizes forming a thick scale consisting of a non-protective layered structure 1 to 10 mm-thick (0.04 to 0.40 mils) made of a mixture of iron oxides. The basic layers constituting the scale from the iron surface are mainly *wustite* (FeO), followed by *magnetite* (Fe_3O_4), and finally *hematite* (Fe_2O_3).

Therefore, acid pickling is a mandatory operation for removing mill scales and unwanted metallic deposits onto steel mill products. During the traditional pickling process, steel mill products are usually pickled through a series of processing tanks containing a concentrated aqueous solution of a strong and hot mineral acid either 20 wt.% HCl or 30 wt.% H_2SO_4 at a temperature of 88°C (190°F) or more heated by means of closed circuit steam-acid PTFE coated heat exchangers.

---

[10] *World Steel Association*, 2023 (www.worldsteel.org).

After a certain number of reuses, the pickling liquor becomes ineffective and must be replaced. It is commonly accepted in the pickling industry that the acid bath is considered ineffective when it contains more than 13 wt.% total iron (65 wt.% copperas) and reaches a mass density of 1,432 kg/m^3. These spent acid baths are known in the steelmaking industry as ***spent pickling liquors*** (SPLs).

Historically, sulfuric acid was extensively used until the 1980s; however, it has been replaced stepwise, and nowadays in large steel mills it has been supplanted almost entirely by hydrochloric acid.

Actually, hydrochloric acid is highly effective for dissolving all the scale and consistently leaves a uniform light gray finish on both low and high carbon steels. It does not leave behind a coating of carbon fine particles remaining onto the surface of the metal which is called ***smut***. Moreover, rinsing is facilitated because of the high solubility of metal chlorides compared to that of metal sulfates. Over pickling is also less likely to occur with hydrochloric acid than with other mineral acids. Finally, the threshold limit for the amount of iron contained in the pickling solution is much higher because metal chlorides are more soluble than metal sulfates than with sulfuric acid without any deleterious effect on pickling.

However, sulfuric acid is still used by smaller and secondary steel finishers, and also in galvanizing plants. It is estimated that 20 percent of the steel heat treated worldwide is still pickled with sulfuric acid. This represents 160 million tonnes of steel.

2.2.2 Spent Pickling Liquors Market

The average loss of iron resulting from acid pickling also called pickling losses ranges usually between 0.3 to 1.0 wt.% of the original steel. It is common practice, to use a conservative average for pickling losses of 10 kg of iron per tonne of steel pickled. This corresponds to 50 kg of copperas per tonne of steel. Hence, the total amount is 1.6 million tonnes of iron lost during acid pickling, that translates itself into 8 million tonnes of copperas generated each year worldwide by the iron and steel pickling industries.

Based on the previous figure of 8 million tonnes of copperas equivalents are by-produced annually for the sulfuric acid pickling of steel, the tonnage of SPLs is about 12.308 million tonnes of liquid wastes. This corresponds to 8,595,000 m^3 (2.27 billion US gallons per year).

In the United States only, about 75 million tonnes of crude steel are produced annually while in Canada about 11 million tonnes are produced during the same period. Therefore, the total amount of copperas, which is by-produced in North-America from the pickling industries, is 750,000 tonnes in the USA and 110,000 tonnes in Canada.

For instance, a common size US steel mill produces 730,000 tons per year (350 working days) of steel mill products, and generates from its pickling operations about 40,000 gallons per day (i.e., 151 m^3 per day) of spent pickling liquors. If we normalize these figures for a hypothetical plant producing one million tonnes of steel mill products pickled per year, we obtain the following mass equivalence factors:

1,000,000 tonnes/year of steel $\cong$ 72,597 m^3/year of SPLs

$\cong$ 23,736 tonnes/year of H_2SO_4

$\cong$ 67,573 tonnes/year copperas

2.3 Hydrometallurgical Processing of Nonferrous Metals

Most of the time, sulfuric acid is the leaching (i.e., lixiviating) agent of choice in the hydrometallurgy of copper, nickel, zinc, lithium, rare earths, and uranium. Actually, sulfuric acid is much cheaper than the other strong mineral acids, and it is largely available commercially as it is often being by-produced on-site or by nearby smelters with large oversupply especially in the USA, Canada, and Scandinavia. Moreover, sulfuric acid poses less occupational safety and environmental issues than its counterpart, that is, hydrochloric acid. The latter has a higher cost due to the scarcity of hydrogen chloride production facilities near the processing plants or a local source of by-produced hydrochloric.

Sometimes however, hydrochloric has to be used for specific purposes. Actually, hydrochloric acid is highly effective for dissolving metal oxides because of the higher solubility of several metal chlorides compared to metal sulfates and because calcium, that often occurs in gangue minerals, precludes the use of sulfuric acid that does form insoluble calcium sulfate dihydrate (e.g., gypsum).

After completion of the processing of the ground concentrate by sulfuric acid, the process yields an aqueous solution containing the metal to recover along with unwanted impurities. Such processing solutions are called ***pregnant leach solutions*** denoted by the acronym PLS, in the mining and metal industries. Because iron is a ubiquitous impurity in most ores, the PLS always contains iron-rich sulfates from which copperas can be easily recovered by crystallization upon evaporative cooling.

Overall, it is estimated that 7 million tonnes of copperas equivalents are generated during the sulfuric acid leaching of non-ferrous ores worldwide and this amount might be even more considering that a plethora of minor operations that are not considered in general market survey or that are not reported yet.

Unfortunately, at present, most of the unwanted iron and other deleterious metal sulfates are simply neutralized, stabilized (e.g., as natrojarosite), and finally disposed-off, and land filled on-site.

2.4 Novel Hydrometallurgical Processing Routes

The economic feasibility of many novel hydrometallurgical and chemical processes currently under intense development in the USA, Canada, Brazil, Australia, and Europe for the extraction of strategic non-ferrous metals (i.e., lithium, rare earths, vanadium, niobium, tantalum, tungsten, and uranium) relies on the recycling of their waste streams for the regeneration of the sulfuric acid values used in the hydrometallurgical process.

In this case, due to obvious economic factors and strict environmental regulations, none of these projects are economically viable without avoiding both neutralization and disposal costs, and regenerating sulfuric acid are as valuable as the recovery of electrolytic iron itself.

Therefore the only alternative is to recycle these wastes by an environmentally friendly, zero-carbon and cost affordable, and energy efficient process using proven technologies and equipment that are already commercially available.

2.4.1 Processing of Bauxite Residues

Another future potential huge source of iron-rich wastes is in the alumina industry with ***bauxite residues*** (BRs) that are by-produced during the chemical processing of alumina from bauxite ores by the Bayer process. With no successful large-scale commercial uses found thus far, the majority of the residue produced continuously during the 117-year-long history of the alumina industry has ended up stored on land in disposal areas.

Actually, these bauxite residues also called when wet ***red mud*** pose several important environmental issues as they are dumped in huge containment ponds (i.e., tailings dams) around the world without further treatment. This was exemplified when a huge spill of red mud from a damaged dam that occurred in Western Hungary on October 2010. The catastrophe forced hundreds of local dwellers out of their homes, contaminated the soil and decimated wildlife irretrievably.

Today, the worldwide inventory of bauxite residues had reached 5 billion tonnes in 2022, and will hit 6 billion tonnes around 2027 at its current growth rate of about 200 million tonnes per annum [11].

---

[11] XUE, S.; JIANG, Y.; and ZHU, F. (2022) Ecological disposal and large-scale utilization of bauxite residue: a long way to go, *Bulletin of Environmental Contamination and Toxicology* **109**(2022)1–2.

Given the large volumes of residue, finding sustainable solutions for residue use is a desirable goal. A number of potential options for re-use of bauxite residues have been suggested. Some of these include: (i) an agricultural amendment for improvement of sandy soils, (ii) neutralizing treatment material for acidic mining wastes, (iii) material for construction purposes (e.g. road fill, brick making), (iv) source of raw materials for ceramics and brick manufacture, and finally feedstock for mineral and metal production (e.g., pig iron, titanium dioxide pigment). In this last reuse, chemical processes such as the sulfuric acid leaching or even sulfuric acid digestion with sulfuric acid of the bauxite residue might generates iron-rich sulfate liquors along with sodium sulfate decahydrate (i.e., Glauber salt) that can be recovered first by crystallization and then the iron-rich liquor to be treated by the present electrochemical technology.

For that reason, since 2016, *Electrochem Technologies & Materials Inc.* conducted several prototype and pilot testing campaigns for performing the sulfuric acid digestion of red muds (RMs) and bauxite residues (BRs), originating from an alumina refinery [12].

The process consisted to digest the waste materials with concentrated sulfuric acid (93 wt.% H_2SO_4). From the pregnant solution obtained after dissolution of the reaction mass with warm water, gypsum was first removed by gravity settling and cross-flow filtration, thoroughly washed, and oven-dried yield a pure product.

Secondly after performing the electrochemical reduction of Fe(III) into Fe(II) followed by the crystallization, and removal of ferrous sulfate heptahydrate (copperas), the aluminum and sodium sulfates were recovered as well.

Afterwards, pure electrolytic iron flakes (99.995 wt.% Fe) were produced by electrowinning metallic iron from the copperas using the patented FerWIN® process.

The electrolysis was performed inside a rectangular tank electrolyser with hanging cathodes totalizing 10 ft^2 (0.929 m^2), anion exchange membrane compartments containing the hanging mixed metals oxides (MMO) coated-titanium anodes.

During electrolysis, sulfuric acid was regenerated inside the anode compartment reaches a strength up to 30 wt.% H_2SO_4 that could be recycled upstream at the sulfation stage after conducting a thermal evaporation. The schematic of the flow diagram is depicted in Figure 4.

---

[12] ONDREY, G. (2022) Recycling bauxite residues and electrowinning iron. *Chementator, Chemical Engineering magazine*, New York, NY, June 1, 2022, page 9.

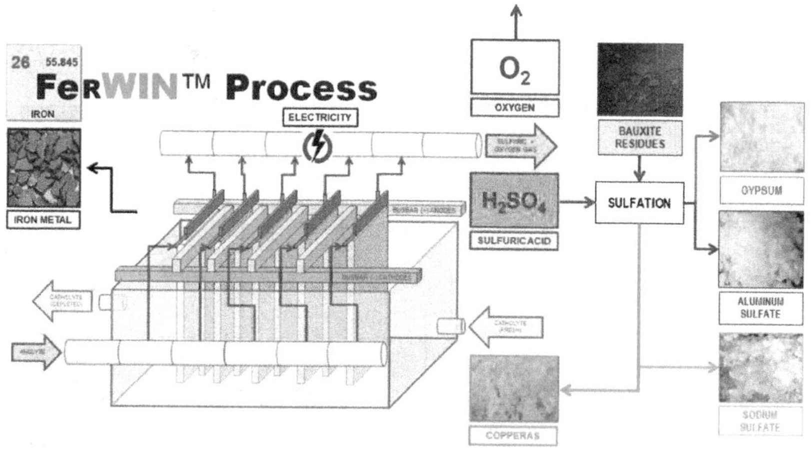

Figure 4 – Vertical integration of FerWIN® with the sulfation bauxite residues

2.4.2 Novel Processing of Titano-Magnetite and Hematite

To address important issues in the current production of vanadium from titano-magnetite by a smelting and roasting, and in order to monetize all the metal values including iron, a novel chemical process was invented by the author, developed, and patented jointly by *Electrochem Technologies & Materials Inc.* (Montreal, Canada) and *VanadiumCorp Resource Inc.* (Vancouver, Canada) [13].

The novel technology called the "*VanadiumCorp-Electrochem Process Technology* (VEPT)"[14] addresses the recovery of vanadium, iron, titanium, and silica values from a plethora of vanadiferous feedstocks such as vanadiferous titano-magnetite, iron ores, and concentrates such as magnetite and hematite, vanadium containing industrial wastes, and other industrial by-products also containing vanadium and iron.

The process is not yet industrial but it was tested successfully at the prototype and semi-pilot scale. A schematic flow diagram is depicted in Figure 5.

The VEPT process consists first to digest the finely ground vanadiferous titano-magnetite into concentrated sulfuric acid inside a brick-lined steel digester.

---

[13] CARDARELLI, F. (2018) *Metallurgical and chemical processes for recovering vanadium and iron values from vanadiferous titanomagnetite and vanadiferous feedstocks.* PCT International Patent Application WO 2018/152628 (A1) (Electrochem Technologies & Materials Inc. and VanadiumCorp Resource Inc.), August 30th, 2018.

[14] CARDARELLI, F. (2021) *Metallurgical and chemical processes for recovering vanadium and iron values from vanadiferous titanomagnetite and vanadiferous feedstocks.* U.S. Patent 10,947,630 B2 (VanadiumCorp Resource Inc.), March 16th, 2021.

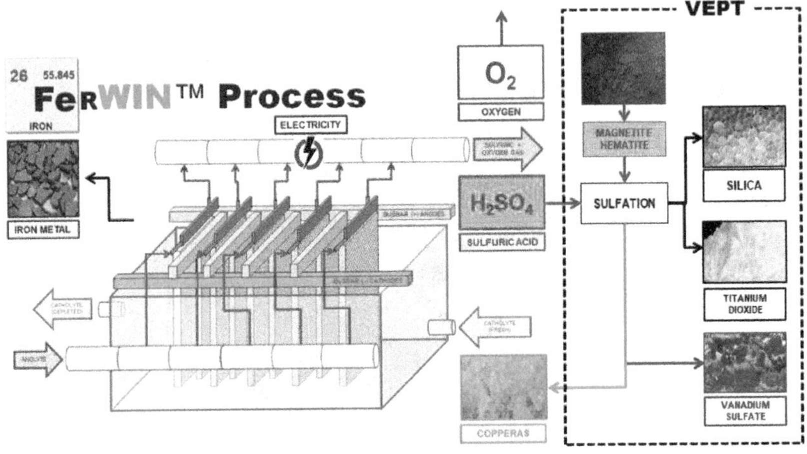

Figure 5 – Vertical integration of the FerWIN® process with the VEPT

The necessary heat required to warm the charge is simply obtained by injecting water directly into the mixture until reaching a final concentration of acid close to 90 wt.% H_2SO_4. The significant heat released by the enthalpy of hydration of the sulfuric acid, brings within few minutes the overall temperature inside the charge to 80-90°C, and then it triggers the exothermic sulfation reaction with the temperature of the charge reaching 180-210°C in a matter of minutes and then lasting for several hours due to the good thermal insulation provided by the refractory and acid proof bricks.

This peculiar behavior allows operating quasi-autogenously until the baking is complete and takes usually 3 to 4 hours with the production of a hard and porous sulfation cake. The dissolution of the sulfation cake is performed with enough warm water to ensure the proper and fast dissolution of all the water soluble metal sulfates. The water is slightly acidic for preventing the hydrolysis of Fe(III), V(IV) and Ti(IV).

After separating the insoluble solids, a concentrated pregnant solution is obtained. Because most of the iron is in the trivalent state, the pregnant solution is reduced electrochemically under high cathode current density using a proprietary divided electrolyzer manufactured by *Electrochem Technologies & Materials Inc.* (Montreal Canada) with a plate and frame configuration. The reduction in performed until some titanium is reduced to Ti(III) to ensure the iron in the reduced pregnant solution is fully reduced and is protected towards air oxidation.

The reduced liquor is then subjected to the chilling down to 5°C and crystallization to yield crystals of copperas (ferrous sulfate heptahydrate). After removing the copperas, the process further comprises removing titanium from the iron depleted solution by hydrolysis thereby producing a vanadium-bearing pregnant solution.

Owing to the large amounts of copperas that are by-produced and the consumption of sulfuric acid for its commercial success the process needs to be integrated vertically with the FerWIN® process.

2.5 World Production of Copperas

In order to summarize all the data and to get the full picture of the total amount of ferrous sulfate heptahydrate by-produced worldwide, either by regions or by countries, and by type of industries, we have reported these figures in Table 2. All the tonnages reported correspond to the amount of iron as copperas equivalents.

Table 2 – World sources for copperas (tonnes per year)

Geographical region	Country	Copperas from titanium pigment industries	Spent pickling liquors from iron and steel industries	Pregnant solutions from the of nonferrous metals	Total per region
North America	USA	none	500,000	1,000,000	**2,580,000**
	Canada	20,000	60,000	1,000,000	
South America	Brazil	20,000	150,000	1,000,000	**1,200,000**
	Argentina		25,000		
	Others		25,000		
Europe	Finland	600,000	1,200,000	500,000	**3,380,000**
	Germany	400,000			
	Spain	230,000			
	Others	450,000			
Australasia	Australia	none	40,000	1,500,000	**1,540,000**
	New Zealand				
	Others				
Asia	China	6,730,000	3,000,000	2,000,000	**12,280,000**
	Japan	250,000	500,000	1,000,000	
	Others	300,000	500,000		
Total worldwide by industries =		**9,000,000**	**6,000,000**	**8,000,000**	**23,000,000**

3 Prior Art

Historically, several attempts have been made regarding the electroplating of iron or the electrowinning of metallic iron from iron sulfates some becoming commercial before being abandoned for economic reasons or due to poor performances. Some information was provided in the scientific and technical literature [15, 16, and 17] but most of the relevant information regarding process conducted at an industrial scale was gathered from patents.

At this point, it is important to distinguish between the electroplating of metallic iron, and the electrowinning iron metal.

3.1 Electroplating Iron from Sulfates

By definition, ***electroplating***, also known as ***electrodeposition***, is an electrochemical process for producing a metal deposit through the reduction of cations of that metal onto a solid metallic substrate which is acting as cathode (i.e., negative electrode) by means of a direct electric current. The cathode of the electrolytic cell is the electrode where the reduction reaction occurs (see Section 4.3); the electrolyte is a solution of a salt of the metal to be electrodeposited; and the anode (i.e. positive electrode) is always made of a soluble or consumable anode made from the metal to be plated.

It appears from the prior art most of the knowledge regarding the electrodeposition of iron originates from the extensive work that has been done since the second half of the eighteenth century on the electroplating of iron metal from iron-containing solutions. Usually, the aim of these processes is to plate electrolytic iron metal of high purity onto a conductive metal substrate, to rebuild worn or damaged steel parts, and to a lesser extent to produce pure iron metal powder. Usually, the first electrolytes investigated were both iron (II) chloride, and on iron (II) sulfate or a mixture of both.

---

[15] MANTEL, C.L. (1950) *Industrial Electrochemistry*. Chemical Engineering Series, McGraw-Hill Book Company, New York, NY, Chapter 16, pp. 333-384.

[16] SCHLESINGER, M.; and PAUNOVIC, M. (eds.)(1992) *Modern Electroplating, Fourth Edition*. John Wiley & Sons, London, UK.

[17] CACERES, C.; NGUYEN, B.; and BARBIER, M.J. Recherches des conditions de dépot électrolytique d'alliages Fe-V en milieu aqueux en vue de la récuperation du vanadium. *Surface Technology* **21**(1984)137-153.

Because electroplating mainly focuses on the cathode product, the anodic reaction usually consisted to the anodic dissolution of a soluble or consumable anode made of impure iron, pig iron, mild steel in bulk form or in pieces or turnings contained inside a bag made of glass cloth, synthetic fabrics such as Orlon® (Trademark of *E. I. Du Pont de Nemours and Company*) and Dynel® (Trademark of *Union Carbide*), and even recently a perforated titanium basket in order to retain the insoluble sludge. In such processes, the use of consumable-type anodes ensures a continuous supply of ferrous cations to the plating bath and avoids undesirable anodic reactions such as the evolution of corrosive nascent oxygen that normally occurs in sulfate electrolytes.

This makes the electroplating process fundamentally different by essence from the electrowinning of iron metal the latter requiring a separator to isolate the insoluble anode evolving oxygen gas, and concurrently regenerating sulfuric acid values.

3.1.1 Early Developments

Historically, the first attempt for electroplating iron from ferrous sulfate electrolyte was reported by Becquerel [18] in 1831. But it was only in 1865, in Russia that Klein devised a commercial process for electroplating iron from a ferrous sulfate bath for "steeling" copper coins. The process was used by the *Russian Mint* until the Bolshevik Revolution in 1917 [19, 20]. The original process consisted to plate iron using a very dilute electrolyte containing 5 g/L of anhydrous ferrous sulfate, $FeSO_4$, and 5 g/L of magnesium sulfate, $MgSO_4$, with a bag containing chunks of magnesite (i.e., magnesium carbonate, $MgCO_3$) that upon reaction with the free acidity to neutralize the plating bath. Because of the low concentration of the iron electroactive species the maximum cathode current density was only -20 A/m^2 and up to six weeks were required to obtain a 2-mm thick deposit plated onto the copper cathode.

---

[18] BECQUEREL, A.C. (1831) *Annales de Chimie et Physique*, **48**(1831)337.

[19] KLEIN, M. (1868) Electroplating of iron onto copper. *Scientific American Patent Agency*, Sept. 29, 1868.

[20] von JACOBI, M.H. (1869) Ueber einige electromagnetische Apparate. *Bulletin de l'Académie impériale des sciences de St.-Pétersbourg*, **13**(1869)40.

Table 3 – First commercial electroplating of iron in Russia (Russian Mint)

Company	Russian Mint	
Year	**1865**	
Inventor(s)	**Klein and Jacobi**	
Process	Electropating iron	
Status	Commercial scale	
Plant location	St. Petersburg, Russia	
Operating parameters	SI unit	USCS unit
Cathode material (-)	Copper	
Cathode current density (j_c)	-20 A/m^2	-1.9 A/ft^2
Cathode current efficiency (CCE)	Unknown	Unknown
Electrolyte		
$FeSO_4$	5.0 g/L	0.67 oz/gal
$MgSO_4$	5.0 g/L	0.67 oz/gal
Temperature	40 °C	104 °F

Company	Russian Mint	
Year	**1868**	
Inventor(s)	**Maximowitch**	
Process	Electropating iron	
Status	Commercial scale	
Plant location	St. Petersburg, Russia	
Operating parameters	SI unit	USCS unit
Cathode material (-)	Silvered copper	
Cathode current density (j_c)	-30 A/m^2	-2.8 A/ft^2
Cathode current efficiency (CCE)		Cathode current efficiency
Electrolyte		
$FeSO_4$	200.0 g/L	26.71 oz/gal
$MgSO_4$	5.0 g/L	0.67 oz/gal
Temperature	40 °C	104 °F

Maximowitch, a close collaborator of Klein at the *Russian Mint*, later improved the plating bath chemistry [21] using 200 g/L of ferrous sulfate and 5 g/L of Epsom salt ($MgSO_4.7H_2O$). Two soluble thick iron anodes were used with a silvered copper cathode that was slightly iodized to allow the easy removal of the iron plate.

The ferric iron was removed by dummying the bath by adding soda ash (i.e., sodium carbonate) in order to precipitate Fe^{3+} as greenish-brown flocks of the ferroso-ferric hydroxide ($Fe(OH)_2$-FeOOH) forming a heavy sludge accumulating at the bottom of the cell. The yellowish scum formed at the surface of the electrolyte prevented further air oxidation. The optimum cathode current density was still only -30 A/m^2. Flexible iron sheets where obtained with a tensile strength of 518 MPa.

In England, in 1910 the British electrometallurgist Cowper-Coles invented and patented an electrolytic process [22] for electroplating iron using electrolytic iron as starter sheet and a soluble anode made of pig iron using an electrolyte made of a solution of ammonium ferrous iron. The formation of a resistive graphite coating onto the anode during the anodic dissolution increasing the cell voltage was prevented by circulating the electrolyte and using metallic brushes on a rotating mandrel to clean the surface by scraping the black graphite tarnish. In order to keep the concentration of ferrous iron constant, the hot plating bath was circulated over iron scrap, steel turnings and cast iron chunks.

In 1918, Schlötter in Berlin, Germany, patented a process [23] for electroplating iron from an electrolyte containing 150 g/L of ferrous sulfate and 100 g/L of sodium sulfate at 100°C despite the excessive evaporation under a

---

[21] MAXIMOWITCH, S. (1905) Ein neues Verfahren zur Herstellung des Elektrolyteisens. *Zeitschrift für Elektrochemie*, **11**(1905)52-43.

[22] COWPER-COLES, S.O. (1910) *An improved process for the production of iron by electro-deposition.* British Patent 28,226, September 28th, 1911.

[23] SCHLÖTTER, M. (1918) Verfahren zu Herstellung von Elektrolytwecheisen. *German Patent* DE 308543 C, February, 7th, 1918.

cathode current density of -200 A/m^2. As for its predecessor, the pH was controlled by adding sodium carbonate while highly reducing conditions were maintained at all times by adding either hydroxylamine or hydrazine to the plating bath.

Table 4 – First commercial electroplating of iron in Germany (Schlötter)

Company	Unknown	
Year	**1918**	
Inventor(s)	**Schlötter**	
Process	Electropating iron	
Status	Commercial scale	
Plant location	Berlin, German Reich	
Operating parameters	SI unit	USCS unit
Cathode material (-)	Copper	
Cathode current density (j_c)	-200 A/m^2	-18.6 A/ft^2
Cathode current efficiency (CCE)	unknown	unknown
Electrolyte		
$FeSO_4$	150.0 g/L	20.03 oz/gal
Na_2SO_4	100.0 g/L	13.35 oz/gal
Temperature	100 °C	212 °F
pH	pH adjusted by adding soda ash (sodium carbonate)	

Most of these early electroplating processes were used either for building up undersized machined parts [24], and also to apply a hard facing to stereotype [25].

3.1.2 The Ferrous Ammonium Sulfate Baths

The first industrial production of electrolytic iron from plating baths of either mixed ferrous and ammonium sulfate or using directly ferrous ***ammonium sulfate hexahydrate*** (***Mohr's salt***), $(NH_4)_2Fe(SO_4)_2.6H_2O$, CAS No. [7783-85-9] started in Germany with Hoepner and Klie in 1895 [26]. They utilized a mixed electrolyte containing 17 wt.% of ferrous sulfate, and 28 wt.% of ammonium sulfate, $(NH_4)_2SO_4$, the remaining balance being water, and operating under a

[24] KELLOG, D.R. (1922) *Min. Metall.*, **3**(1922)61.

[25] LAMB, V.A.; and BLUM, W. (1942) *Proceedings of the American Electroplaters' Society*, **39**(1942)106.

[26] ARNDT K. (1912) Zur Geschichte des Elektrolyteisens. *Zeitschrift für Elektrochemie*, **18**(1912)233-234.

cathode current density of -300 A/m^2 at an operating temperature of 75°C. The soluble iron anode was surrounded by a porous diaphragm. The overall cell voltage was 0.75V.

Table 5 – Electroplating of iron from mixed sulfates (Hoepner and Klie)

Company	Unknown	
Year	**1895**	
Inventor(s)	**Hoepner and Klie**	
Process	Electropating iron	
Status	Unknown	
Plant location	Germany	
Operating parameters	SI unit	USCS unit
Cathode material (-)	Copper	
Cathode current density (j_c)	-300 A/m^2	-27.9 A/ft^2
Cathode current efficiency (CCE)	95%	95%
Electrolyte		
$FeSO_4$	467 g	17.1 wt.%
$(NH_4)_2SO_4$	759 g	27.8 wt.%
H_2O	1500 g	55.0 wt.%
Temperature	75 °C	167 °F
pH	pH adjusted by adding soda ash	
Soluble anode material (+)	Iron plate with porous diaphragm	

However, it is not until the work of Burgess and Hambuechen [27] that iron electroplating was conducted at a much larger scale in the USA. The commercial plating bath consisted of 275 g/L of ferrous sulfate with 30 g/L of ammonium sulfate with a cathode current density of -86 A/m^2 at 30°C with a cell voltage of 1.0 V. They were able to perform continuous electroplating and to achieve the production of ¾-inch (19.05 mm) thick iron plates in only four weeks. The electrolyte was maintained in good conditions during two months by regular dummying of the bath.

[27] BURGESS, C.F.; and HAMBUECHEN, C. (1903) Adherence of Electrolytic Metal Deposits. *Journal of Physical Chemistry*, **7**(6)(1903)409-415.

Table 6 – Commercial electroplating in the US (Burgess and Hambuechen)

Company	Unknown	
Year	**1903**	
Inventor(s)	**Burgess and Hambuechen**	
Process	Electropating iron	
Status	Unknown	
Plant location	USA	
Operating parameters	SI unit	USCS unit
Cathode material (-)	Copper	
Cathode current density (j_c)	-86 A/m^2	-8.0 A/ft^2
Cathode current efficiency (CCE)	95%	95%
Electrolyte		
$FeSO_4$	275.0 g/L	36.72 oz/gal
$(NH_4)_2SO_4$	30.0 g/L	4.01 oz/gal
Temperature	30 °C	86 °F
pH	pH adjusted by adding soda ash	
Soluble anode material (+)	Iron plate	

MacFadyen optimized the previous operating conditions [28] using an electrolyte containing 350 g/L of ferrous ammonium sulfate kept at pH 3.0, using bagged iron anodes. Electrolysis was performed with a cathode current density of -170 A/m^2 at 60°C, the cathode current efficiency was 98%, put decreased to 95% at pH 2.3 and then 90% at pH 2. The process was utilized in England to support war effort during World War II.

[28] MACFADYEN, W.A. (1920) An aspect of electrolytic iron deposition *Transactions of the Faraday Society*, **15**(3)(1920)98.

Table 7 – Commercial electroplating in the UK (MacFadyen)

Company	Unknown	
Year	**1914-1918**	
Inventor(s)	MacFadyen	
Process	Electropating iron	
Status	Unknown	
Plant location	UK (England)	
Operating parameters	SI unit	USCS unit
Cathode material (-)	Copper	
Cathode current density (j_c)	-170 A/m^2	-15.8 A/ft^2
Cathode current efficiency (CCE)	98%	98%
Electrolyte		
$(NH_4)_2Fe(SO_4)_2.6H_2O$	350.0 g/L	46.73 oz/gal
Temperature	60 °C	140 °F
pH	3.0	
Soluble anode material (+)	Iron plate	

The industrial process utilized in England was later taken to the USA and further improved by Westinghouse Electrical & Manufacturing Company [29].

[29] KELLOG, D.R. (1922) *Min. Metall.*, **3**(1922)61.

Table 8 – Commercial electroplating in the UK (Westinghouse)

Company	Westinghouse Electric & Manufacturing Company	
Year	**1920**	
Inventor(s)	MacFadyen	
Process	Electropating iron	
Status	Unknown	
Plant location	USA	
Operating parameters	SI unit	USCS unit
Cathode material (-)	Copper	
Cathode current density (j_c)	-650 A/m^2	-60.4 A/ft^2
Cathode current efficiency (CCE)	98%	98%
Electrolyte		
$(NH_4)_2Fe(SO_4)_2.6H_2O$	350.0 g/L	46.73 oz/gal
Temperature	70 °C	158 °F
pH	3.5	
Soluble anode material (+)	Iron plate	

From the above operating conditions used for electroplating iron, we observe that the electrolyte often consists of an aqueous solution of ferrous sulfate but mixed with a supporting electrolyte such as ammonium, magnesium or sodium sulfates. These metal sulfates are either added intentionally or indirectly resulting from the pH adjustment using bases such as aqueous ammonia, sodium carbonate, or magnesia.

In the 1930s in the US, in order to meet the increasing demand of iron powder, *Plastic Metals Inc.* a division of the *National U.S. Radiator Corp.* started the production of powder of electrolytic iron in Johnstown, PA [30] with the operating conditions reported in Table 9.

[30] SHAFER, W.M.; and HARR, C.R. (1958) Electrolytic Iron Powders-Production and Properties. *Journal of The Electrochemical Society*, **105**(7)(1958)413.

Table 9 – Production of iron powder (Plastic Metals)

Company	Plastic Metals Inc.	
Year	**1920**	
Inventor(s)	Unknown	
Process	Electropating iron	
Status	Unknown	
Plant location	Johnstown, PA, USA	
Operating parameters	SI unit	USCS unit
Cathode material (-)	Stainless seel	
Cathode current density (j_c)	-269 A/m^2	-25.0 A/ft^2
Cathode current efficiency (CCE)	90%	90%
Electrolyte		
$FeSO_4$	135.0 g/L	18.03 oz/gal
Temperature	50 °C	122 °F
pH	4.5	
Soluble anode material (+)	Steel plate (99 wt.% Fe)	

Despite it is out of the topic covered in this book, it is however worth to mention that industrially the electroplating of ductile iron started in Germany in 1905 with Fischer [31] and Langbein who used instead a bath made of 26.4 mass percent of $FeCl_2$, and 29.4 mass percent $CaCl_2$. The electroplating of iron was conducted close to the boiling point of the electrolyte at 95°C with a high cathode current density of -1500 A/m^2 resulting in a high production rate. Because of the elevated temperature, the iron metal plate produced was ductile due to extremely low hydrogen contamination.

In 1914, an iron electroplating plant was implemented in Grenoble, France. The plant produced high purity iron (99.967 wt.% Fe) until the 1920s [32]. The electroplating was performed from neutral solutions of ferrous chloride with a cathode current density of -1100 A/m^2 and at a temperature of 90°C. The

[31] FISCHER, F. (1911) *Process for the manufacture of ductile electrolytic iron*. U.S. Patent 992,951, October 23th, 1909.

[32] GUILLET, L. (1914) Electroplating pure iron from neutral chloride bath. *The Journal of the Iron & Steel Institute*, XC (90)(II)(1914).

dummying of the bath was achieved by using iron turnings, and ground hematite was used to replenish the bath in iron. The iron plate was then annealed at 900°C.

In 1979, Samal and Klar from the *SCM Corporation*, patented an electroplating process [33] for producing iron metal powder from a nearly neural plating bath with a low concentration of ferrous iron.

Table 10 – Production of iron powder (SCM Corp.)

Company	SCM Corporation	
Year	**1979**	
Inventor(s)	Samal and Klar	
Process	Electropating iron	
Status	Unknown	
Plant location	Johnstown, PA, USA	
Operating parameters	SI unit	USCS unit
Cathode material (-)	Stainless seel AISI 304	
Cathode current density (j_c)	-237 A/m^2	-22.0 A/ft^2
Cathode current efficiency (CCE)	90%	90%
Electrolyte		
$FeSO_4$	38.0 g/L	5.07 oz/gal
$(NH_4)_2SO_4$	175.0 g/L	23.37 oz/gal
Temperature	40 °C	104 °F
pH	5.7	
Soluble anode material (+)	Armco® iron	

Later in the late 1950s, René Audubert, then Professor of Electrochemistry at the *Conservatoire National des Arts et Metiers*, and the *Faculté des Sciences de Paris de la Sorbonne*, and his co-worker Henri de Lacheisserie invented a process patented by the *Société d'Électrochimie, d'Électrométallurgie et des Aciéries Électriques d'Ugine* [34].

Therefore simply based on more than 100 years of iron electroplating experience, it seems that a practical pH range comprised between 2.0 and 4.0 and

---

[33] SAMAL, P.K.; and KLAR, E. (1979) *Process for electrolytic iron powder*. U.S. Patent 4,134,800, December 7th, 1977 (SCM Corp.)

[34] AUDUBERT, R.; and LACHEISSERIE, H. (1962) *Electrolytic preparation of iron powder*. U.S. Patent 3,041,253 (Société d'Électrochimie, d'Électrométallurgie et des Aciéries Électriques d'Ugine), June 26th, 1962.

an operating temperature ranging between 40°C and 60°C will guarantee the best results with a saturated and fully reduced electrolyte and by mitigating air oxidation.

3.2 Electrowinning Iron

The fundamental difference between iron electroplating and iron electrowinning in sulfate media is a process whereby the iron metal or an iron-rich alloy is electrodeposited at the cathode while the oxidation occurring at the anode consists of an electrochemical reaction usually the oxidation of water into protons and evolution of nascent oxygen gas or by oxidizing another electroactive (depolarizing) species (e.g., Fe(II), H_2).

Because for obvious reasons, the oxidation of ferrous cations at the anode must be prevented to avoid a never ending loop, it is mandatory to prevent such side reaction by using a divided electrolyzer having a separator either a diaphragm or a membrane. This specificity for electrowinning iron distinguishes the process from other industrial electrowinning processes for copper, nickel or zinc.

3.2.1 Pyror Process

The only reported industrial attempt to recover electrolytic iron metal from an iron-bearing sulfate solution was the process patented by the *Pyror Limited* [35] that was invented in the early 1950s by Aanerud, Mostad, and Verk, which has been reviewed in 2008 by Mostad et al. [36].

In this process, the iron-rich sulfate liquors originating from the acid leaching of chalcopyritic ores as performed by the Norwegian company *Orkla Grube AB*, and that was patented by Aanerud in 1953 [37], were electrolyzed in a two compartment electrolyzer comprising steel cathodes, lead anodes and diaphragms made of various fabric materials. Owing to the low concentration of ferrous iron (25 g/L Fe) in the catholyte, sodium sulfate decahydrate (*Glaubert's salt*), was added as a supporting electrolyte to reach a final concentration of about 90-100 g/L Na_2SO_4.

---

[35] AANERUD, S.A.; MOSTAD, E.; and VERK, L. (1954) *Method for electrolytic production of iron from iron sulfate solutions.* U.S. Patent 2,667,455, January 26th, 1954.

[36] MOSTAD, E.; ROLSETH, S.; and THONSTADT, J. (2008) Electrowinning of iron from sulphate solutions. *Hydrometallurgy*, 90(2-4)(2008)213-220.

[37] AANERUD, S.A. (1953) *Process for total treatment of copper-containing iron pyrites.* U.S. Patent 2,653,905, September 29th, 1953.

Table 11 – Electrowinning iron from pregnant leach solutions (Pyror)

Company	Pyror	
Year	**1950**	
Inventor(s)	**Aanerud, Mostad, and Verk**	
Process	Electrowinning iron	
Status	Commercial scale	
Plant location	Porsgrun, Norway	
	SI unit	USCS unit
Cathode material	Mild steel (-)	
Cathode current density (j_c)	-250 A/m^2	-23.2 A/ft^2
Cathode current efficiency (CCE)	85%	85%
	Catholyte	Catholyte
$FeSO_4$	5.0 g/L	0.67 oz/gal
Na_2SO_4	100.0 g/L	13.35 oz/gal
Temperature (avg.)	70 °C	158 °F
pH	pH adjusted by adding sodium carbonate	
Separator	Porour diaphragm	
	Anolyte	Anolyte
$FeSO_4$	25.0 g/L	3.34 oz/gal
Na_2SO_4	60.0 g/L	8.01 oz/gal
H_2SO_4	60 g/L	8.01 oz/gal
Anode material	Lead anode (+)	
Anode current density (j_a)	-250 A/m^2	-23.2 A/ft^2
Overall cell voltage (U_{cell})	3.75 V	3.75 V
Specific energy consumption (e_m)	4,235 kWh/kg	1,921 kWh/lb
Space time yield (Y)	0.221 kg.m^{-2}.h^{-1}	0.045 lb/(ft^2-hour)

The anolyte was composed of 55-60 g/L sulfuric acid, 55-65 g/L sodium sulfate and 25 g/L ferrous iron the latter being used as an electroactive species (i.e., depolarizer) to be oxidized at the anode to prevent the oxygen evolution reaction and thus reducing the overall cell voltage. The ferric anolyte was then recirculated to the metallurgical plant to oxidize the pyrite.

The electrolysis was performed at a temperature ranging from 70°C to 80°C under a low cathode current density of -250 A/m^2, with an overall cell voltage of 3.75V and a cathode current efficiency of 85%. The schematic of the electrolytic cell is depicted in Figure 6.

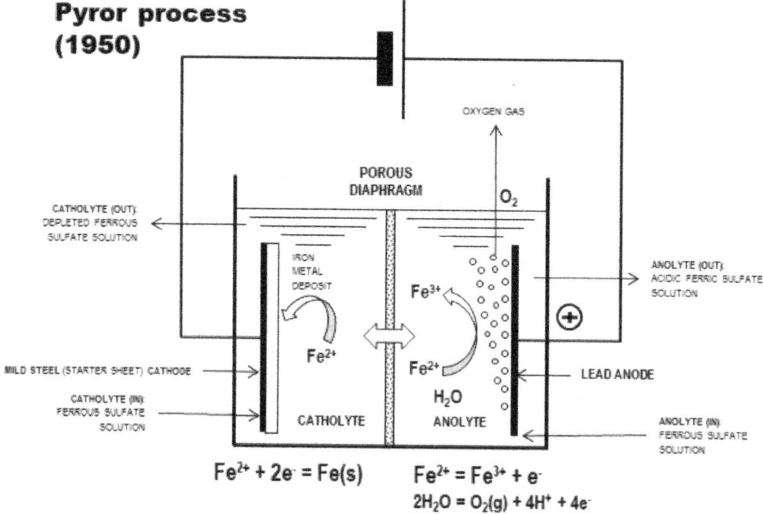

Figure 6 – Schematic of the Pyror process

The major limitations of this process are the following: (1) a low space time yield of 0.221 $kg.m^{-2}h^{-1}$ because of the low cathode current density and current efficiency; (2) the impossibility of recovering pure sulfuric acid from the anolyte because of the presence of sodium sulfate which has to be removed and the noticeable concentration of ferric iron, lead, antimony, and tin coming from the corrosion product of the lead anode; and (3) the high specific energy consumption of 4.235 kWh per kg of iron metal due to the elevated overall cell voltage reported.

In view of the strict specifications regarding the impurity content of sulfuric acid, the above drawbacks have prevented the use of such a process for the recovery of both iron and sulfuric acid values from iron-rich sulfate wastes. The only alternative to electrolysis has been the recovery of sulfuric acid and iron by means of solvent extraction. However, up to the present time, such a process has never reached a commercially useful scale because of the prohibitive cost of the organic solvents involved.

3.2.2 Rohm & Haas Process

In the late 1950s, Bodamer and Horner from the *Rohm & Haas Company* in Philadelphia, PA, invented an electrolytic process [38] to recover electrochemically both metallic iron and sulfuric acid values from spent pickling liquors originating from the steelmaking industries. They used either a two-

[38] BODAMER, G.W.; and HORNER, C. (1957) *Electrolytic treatment of waste sulfate pickle liquor.* U.S. Patent 2,810,686 (Rohm & Haas Company), October 22, 1957.

compartment divided electrolyzer using an anionic perm-selective membrane (i.e., anion exchange membrane, AEM), or a three-compartment electrolyzer using the central compartment separated from the cathode compartment and the anode compartment by means of two anion exchange membranes. The anion exchange membranes used were originally those manufactured by *Ionics Incorporated*. Later heterogeneous anion exchange membranes, commercialized under the tradename *Amberplex*®, consisting of fine colloidal ion-exchange particles embedded in a suitable inert binder (e.g. polyethylene, phenolic resins, PVC) [39], were manufactured directly in-house by *Rohm & Hass*.

The acidic catholyte consisted of spent pickling liquors (SPLs) containing at least 10 mass percent of ferrous sulfate, and about 10 mass percent of free sulfuric acid. Upon electrolysis, at the cathode due to the initial free acidity, protons are reduced first evolving hydrogen gas until the pH rises to 1.8 at which hydrogen evolution ceases and then iron starts to plate. The inventors emphasized that without using an AEM, the protons will irretrievably migrate through a diaphragm toward the cathode thus keeping an acidic pH promoting the hydrogen gas evolution while preventing the electrodeposition of iron. At the end of the electrolysis, the depleted catholyte contained from 1 to 5 mass percent of $FeSO_4$. It was observed that because of the consumption of protons, the electrical conductivity of the catholyte decreased until a lower threshold where the resistance becomes too high with an overall cell voltage imposing excessive energy consumption.

The anolyte consisted of a diluted aqueous solution of sulfuric acid. During electrolysis the sulfate anions cross the AEM towards the anode where protons are produced following the oxidation of water with the release of oxygen gas. Thus the concentration of sulfuric acid inside the anode compartment continuously increases up to 18 mass percent.

The operating conditions used for electrowinning iron by means of the two compartment electrolyzer are reported in Table 12. The cathode current density was -969 A/m^2 (90 A/ft^2). The initial temperature was 23°C and reached up to 75°C after which cooling by immersing coils was necessary for maintaining the operating temperature within 75°C and 82°C. At the beginning of the electrolysis the overall cell voltage was 4.0 V and due to the decrease of the catholyte conductivity with an increasing pH, it reached 5.2 V after a period of 3.1 hours. Note that the level of the catholyte was 1 inch (25.4 mm) higher than that of the anolyte for favoring the permeation of catholyte through the membrane.

---

[39] BODAMER, G.W. (1954) *Permselective films of anion exchange resins*. U.S. Patent 2,681,319 (Rohm & Haas Company), June 15th, 1954.

Table 12 – Electrowinning of iron from spent pickling liquors (Rohm & Haas Co.)

Company	Rohm & Haas Company	
Year	**1957**	
Inventor(s)	**Bodamer and Horner**	
Process	Electrowinning iron	
Status	Commercial scale	
Plant location	Philadelphia, PA, USA	
	SI unit	USCS unit
Cathode material	Stainless steel AISI 316 (-)	
Cathode current density (j_c)	-969 A/m^2	-90.0 A/ft^2
Cathode current efficiency (CCE)	85%	85%
	Catholyte (IN)	Catholyte (OUT)
$FeSO_4$	15.6 wt.%	1.8 wt.%
H_2SO_4	3.9 wt.%	0.4 wt.%
Temperature (avg.)	75 °C	167 °F
pH	pH adjusted by adding sodium carbonate	
Separator	Anion exchange membrane (Amberplex®)	
	Anolyte (IN)	Anolyte (OUT)
H_2SO_4	3.0 wt.%	17.7 wt.%
Anode material	Antimonial lead anode (+)	
Anode current density (j_a)	-969 A/m^2	-90.0 A/ft^2
Overall cell voltage (U_{cell})	4.6 V	4.6 V
Specific energy consumption (e_m)	5,194 kWh/kg	2,356 kWh/lb
Space time yield (Y)	0.858 kg.m^{-2}.h^{-1}	0.176 lb/(ft^2-hour)

However, in order to solve the issue related to the back-migration of protons, it was thus decided first to modify the original process by circulating a fraction of the partially reduced catholyte into the anode compartment. Actually, as for the *Pyror process* the electrochemical oxidation of the ferrous iron in to ferric iron was intended to reduce the overall cell voltage by switching the oxidation reaction. Furthermore, it was found that the presence of significant amount ferric iron in the concentrated sulfuric acid thus produced was not objectionable for performing the sulfuric acid pickling of steels.

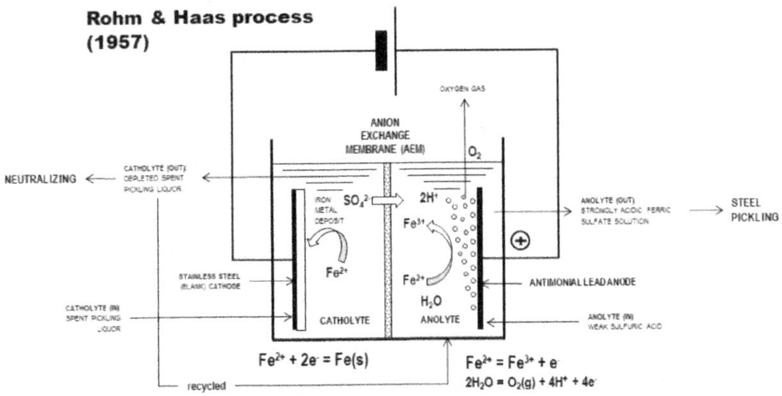

Figure 7 – Schematic of the Rohm & Haas process

Afterwards, a third and narrow central compartment was utilized to act as a buffer zone between the catholyte, and the strong acidity of the anolyte thus shielding the back-migration of the protons. The electrolyte circulating in the central compartment was a diluted aqueous solution of sulfuric acid.

3.2.3 Othmar Ruthner

In 1960, Othmar Ruthner invented a process for regenerating steel mordancing (i.e., pickling) solutions that was patented [40]. The spent pickling solution containing sulfuric acid, and ferrous sulfate was regenerated by crystallizing, and separating by centrifugation the crystals of ferrous sulfate heptahydrate (i.e., copperas). Then the copperas was dissolved into water for preparing a concentrated neutral solution of ferrous sulfate. The electrolyte thus obtained was then circulated through the central compartment of a three-compartment divided electrolyzer. The compartments were separated by two porous diaphragms. The aim of using a central compartment was to delay the acidification of the catholyte by protons from the anolyte. Therefore, the pH of the catholyte was maintained at pH of 3.0 by regulating the flow rate.

Upon electrolysis, electrolytic iron was deposited onto the cathode with ferrous cations replenished in the catholyte from the ***midlyte*** (i.e., central electrolyte) while in the iron-depleted midlyte sulfate anions left behind were reacting with the protons from the anolyte and thus becoming enriched in sulfuric acid. The chemical composition of the acidic midlyte was then adjusted by removing some the residual ferrous sulfate by cooling and then recycled to the pickling tanks.

---

[40] RUTHNER, O. (1963) *An electrolytic process for regenerating iron sulphate mordants.* British Patent 940,517 A, October 10th, 1963.

3.2.4 Licencia Talalmanyokat Ertekesito Vallalat

In Hungary, the multistage and continuous regeneration of spent pickling liquors was patented in 1976 by *Licencia Talalmanyokat Ertekesito Vallalat* [41]. The processing utilized a similar approach to that used by *Rohm & Hass* but with some peculiar differences. The electrolysis was conducted through a cascade of several two-compartment divided electrolyzers connected in series and using only a porous diaphragm as separator.

The catholyte consisted of a spent pickling liquor with a maximum concentration of 100 g/L H_2SO_4 and a minimum of ferrous iron of 25 g/L Fe(II), with 0.5 to 1.0 M of ammonium or sodium sulfates are added intentionally.

At that time, this new approach of adding intentionally ammonium sulfate for acting as a source of bisulfate anions proved to be extremely efficient for the regeneration of sulfuric acid from spent pickling liquors. This allowed obtaining the highest strength sulfuric acid concentration in the rejuvenated solution with only half the amount of electricity this latter point is worth explaining.

Actually, under the strongly acidic conditions existing in spent pickling liquors, at that very low pH usually below 0.5, the sulfate anions become the minor species while the hydrogen sulfate (i.e., bisulfate) anions HSO_4^- predominate with almost 88 percent of all the sulfate species [42]. Thus by contrast with the electrowinning of iron from ferrous sulfate performed at pH 3-4, for each sulfate anion crossing the separator one mole sulfuric acid is formed at the anode while for the same amount of electricity, that is two Faradays, for catholyte having a pH below 0.5 two moles of bisulfate anions migrate instead towards the anode forming two moles sulfuric acid

At pH > 2-3 $SO_4^- + 2H^+ = H_2SO_4$

At pH < 0.5 $2HSO_4^- + 2H^+ = 2H_2SO_4$

The spent pickling liquor was pumped from the pickling tanks and then circulated through all the cathode compartments until it becomes depleted in iron with at the end only 10 g/L Fe(II) and enriched with 165 g/L of ammonium sulfate. The pH increased and reached 1.8-2.0 that ensured that most of the iron was electroplated.

Then the iron-depleted catholyte exiting the last cathode compartment was circulated through the anode compartments where the bisulfate anions after

---

[41] KERT, J.; MANDOKI, A.; and SZEKY, M. (1976) *Method for the cyclic electrochemical processing of sulfuric acid-containing pickle waste liquors.* U.S. Patent 3,969,207 (Licencia Talalmanyokat Ertekesito Vallalat)

[42] CARDARELLI, F. (2022) *Sulfuric Acid Digestion, Sulfuric Acid Baking, and Sulfation Roasting in Mineral and Chemical Processing, and Extractive Metallurgy.* Electrochem Technologies & Materials Inc., Montreal, QC, Canada, *Chapter 2: Physical and Chemical Properties of Pure Sulfuric Acid*, pages 10-11

migrating through the porous diaphragm towards the anode combined with protons leftover by the oxidation of water into oxygen thus producing high strength sulfuric acid directly reusable in the pickling tanks.

Table 13 – Electrowinning of iron from spent pickling liquors (Hungary)

Company	Licencia Talalmanyokat Ertekesito Vallalat	
Year	**1976**	
Inventor(s)	**Kert, Mandoki, and Szeky**	
Process	Electrowinning iron	
Status	Commercial scale	
Plant location	Budapest, Hungary	
	SI unit	USCS unit
Cathode material	Iron starter sheet (-)	
Cathode current density (j_c)	-1800 A/m^2	-167.2 A/ft^2
Cathode current efficiency (CCE)	67%	67%
	Catholyte (IN)	Catholyte (OUT)
$FeSO_4$	25.0 g/L	10.0 g/L
H_2SO_4	100.0 g/L	5.0 g/L
$(NH_4)_2SO_4$	80.0 g/L	165.0 g/L
Temperature (avg.)	85 °C	185 °F
pH	0.5	2.0
Separator	PP porous diaphragm	
	Anolyte (IN)	Anolyte (OUT)
$FeSO_4$	10.0 g/L	10.0 g/L
H_2SO_4	5.0 g/L	294.0 g/L
$(NH_4)_2SO_4$	165.0 g/L	80.0 g/L
Anode material	Lead-silver anode (1 wt.% Ag) (+)	
Anode current density (j_a)	-1800 A/m^2	-167.2 A/ft^2
Overall cell voltage (U_{cell})	4.25 V	4.25 V
Specific energy consumption (e_m)	6,089 kWh/kg	2,762 kWh/lb
Space time yield (Y)	1.256 $kg.m^{-2}.h^{-1}$	0.257 $lb/(ft^2$-hour)

Because the porous diaphragm was not selective toward anions and cations, the ammonium cations also crossed the separator towards the cathode thus diminishing their concentration until reaching the concentration that was originally found in the spent pickling liquor entering the first electrolyzer as equal amount of salt that do not take part in the electrochemical reaction enter and leave the compartments per unit time.

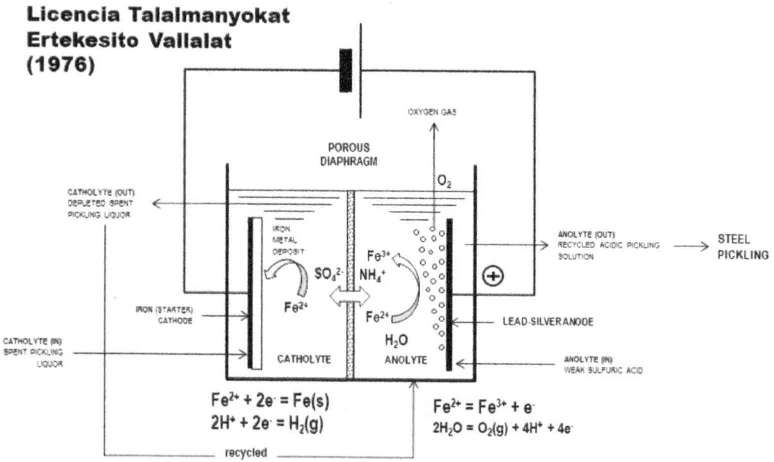

Figure 8 – Schematic of the Hungarian process

According to the inventors a precise balance and an accurate control of the operating parameters was the key to the performances.

Actually, they noticed that concentration below 0.5 M of the bisulfate forming salt is insufficient to ensure the proper salt exchange while above 1.0 M, the solubility of the ferrous sulfate decreases along with a much lower pickling ability.

When the free sulfuric acid in the spent pickling liquor is above 100 g/L the pH is too low resulting in an important hydrogen gas evolution and the total current consumed to raise the pH, and then obtain the proper electrodeposition of iron becomes too high and the specific energy consumption to obtain acceptable performances is unrealistic.

For the depleted catholyte exiting the last electrolyzer, a minimum of 10 g/L of $FeSO_4$ and at least 5 g/L H_2SO_4 are required These conditions are necessary prevent an excessive alkalinisation above pH 5-6 that will favor the fast air oxidation of Fe(II) into Fe(III). With 100 g/l H_2SO_4, by conducting the electrowinning with cathode current densities below -1500 A/m^2 results in poor performances as the cathodic deposition rate for iron cannot compensate for the diffusion across the diaphragm. On the other hand, above -2,200 A/m^2 an iron metal deposit of poor quality is obtained.

The operating temperature must be maintained above 70°C to prevent the crystallization of copperas and promote the kinetics effects and below 90°C to avoid the copious foaming of the bath.

3.2.5 Davis Walker Corp.

In 1979, Burke from the *Davis Walker Corp* invented and patented a process [43] aiming to rejuvenate by electrolysis spent pickling liquors removing iron as electrolytic metal while producing sulfuric acid.

The electrolytic cell as the previous invention was a two-compartment divided electrolyzer with the anode and the two cathode chambers separated by a perfluorinated cation exchange membrane (CEM), of the type Nafion® 415 (Trademark of *Chemours*). The major difference with the prior art is the fact that the anolyte consisted entirely of an aqueous solution of ammonium sulfate.

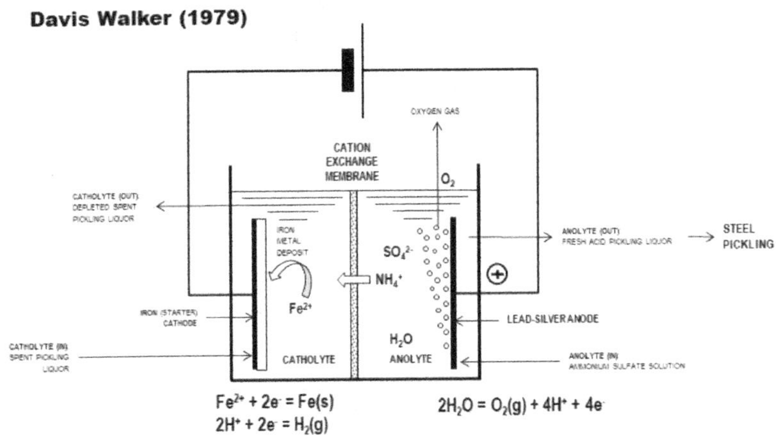

Figure 9 – Schematic of the Davis Walker process

During electrowinning iron was plated out on the cathode while ammonium cation crossed through the membrane into the cathode compartment to form a mixture of ammonium and ferrous sulfates while the anolyte depleted in ammonium sulfate is converted to concentrated sulfuric acid useful for the pickling.

[43] BUKE, Z.L. (1979) *Recovery of spent pickle liquor and iron metal.* U.S. Patent 4,149,946 (Davis Walker Corp.), April 17, 1979.

Table 14 – Electrowinning of iron from spent pickling liquors (Davis Walker)

Company	Davis Walker Corp.	
Year	**1979**	
Inventor(s)	**Burk**	
Process	Electrowinning iron	
Status	Commercial scale	
Plant location	Los Angeles, CA	
	SI unit	USCS unit
Cathode material	Stainless steel AISI 316 (Blank)	
Cathode current density (j_c)	-692 A/m^2	-64.3 A/ft^2
Cathode current efficiency (CCE)	96.3%	96.3%
	Catholyte (IN)	Catholyte (OUT)
$FeSO_4$	296.8 g/L	g/L
H_2SO_4	247.9 g/L	g/L
$(NH_4)_2SO_4$	55.0 g/L	275.0 g/L
Temperature (avg.)	50 °C	122 °F
pH		
Separator	Cation exchange membrane (Nafion® 415)	
	Anolyte (IN)	Anolyte (OUT)
$FeSO_4$	0.0 g/L	g/L
H_2SO_4	247.9 g/L	g/L
$(NH_4)_2SO_4$	312.0 g/L	35.2 g/L
Anode material	Antimonial lead anode (6 wt.% Sb) (+)	
Anode current density (j_a)	-692 A/m^2	-64.3 A/ft^2
Overall cell voltage (U_{cell})	4.59 V	4.59 V
Specific energy consumption (e_m)	4,576 kWh/kg	2,076 kWh/lb
Space time yield (Y)	0.694 kg.m^{-2}.h^{-1}	0.142 lb/(ft^2-hour)

3.2.6 Eddlemann

In the 1970s, Eddleman invented an electrochemical process that was patented in 1979 [44] to address the regeneration of spent pickling liquors originating from the cleaning tanks used for dezincing and pickling improperly coated or partially galvanized steel plates discarded from a zinc galvanizing process.

[44] EDDLEMAN, W.L. (1979) *Frame filter press and apparatus.* U.S. Patent 4,149,951 A, April 17th, 1979.

Actually during the stripping of the zinc coating with sulfuric acid, the pickling liquor became enriched in zinc, iron, and in lesser extent other metals such as manganese, copper, chromium, lead, tin, molybdenum, titanium, nickel, strontium. When the sulfuric acid pickling bath became substantially contaminated, it was no longer able to perform its task and it was replaced with a fresh batch of sulfuric acid. However, the remaining sulfuric acid concentration in the spent pickling liquor was still high, and it was then necessary to neutralize it before dumping making the disposal of large volumes of spent acid exceedingly difficult from economic and environmental standpoints.

The electrolytic process utilized a three-compartment plate and frame divided electrolyzer. The cathode, central, and anode compartments were all separated by means of a diaphragm made of microporous polypropylene named *Celgard®* (Trademark of *Celanese Corporation*) which allows anions and cations to migrate through, but prevented water from diffusing. The anode was made of chemical lead while the preferred cathode material was pure aluminum. The spent pickling liquor was feed to the central compartment while water was generally introduced in the anode compartment to the anolyte where nascent oxygen evolved, and sulfuric acid was produced. The catholyte initially very dilute became enriched in ferrous and zinc cations that electrodeposited onto the aluminum cathode.

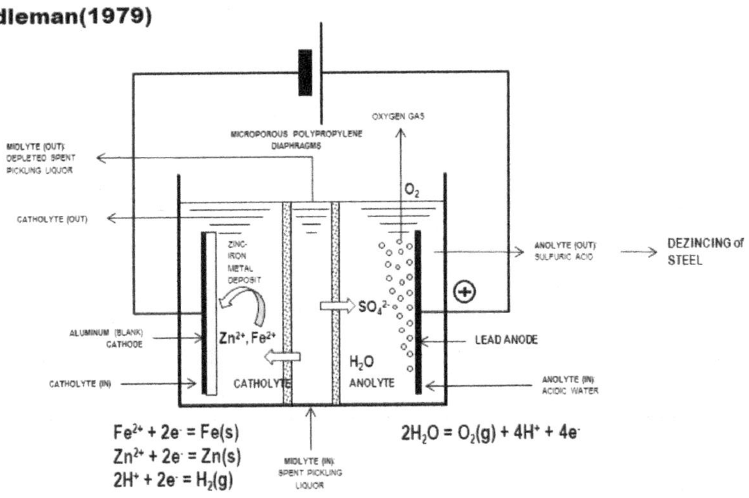

Figure 10 – Schematic of the Eddleman process

The individual cells were designed to be used in a filter press assembly with an array of other cells. The size for each compartment was approximately one inch (2.54 cm) in thickness and 30 inches (0.762 m) in width to 60 inches (1.524 m) in length. A typical electrolyzer comprised seven unit cells of three compartments totalizing ca. 10 square meter of cathode active surface area. However, no information was provided neither on the operating conditions (i.e., current density, voltage, temperature) nor the cell performances (i.e., current efficiencies, yields) regarding the electrowinning of iron and zinc.

3.2.7 Oronzio De Nora Impianti Elettrochimici S.p.a.

In the 1970s, the Italian company *Oronzio De Nora Impianti Elettrochimici S.p.a.* invented a process that was later patented in 1987 [45] to address the treatment of iron-rich solutions originating from the production of titanium dioxide pigment by the sulfate process at the *Montedison* plant in Scarlino (GR), Tuscany, Italy (*Tioxide Europe Srl*, *Hunstman Pigments*, now *Venator*). At that time, the former *Montecatini* plant was processing Australian beach sand ilmenite with 55 wt.% TiO_2 as feedstocks thus generating large amount of iron-bearing residues posing serious environmental and disposal issues.

Actually, the pregnant liquors obtained after the dissolution of the sulfation cake contained significant concentration of Fe(III) a deleterious contaminant during the further hydrolysis of the titanyl sulfate (see Section 2.1.1). The aim was then to completely reduce electrochemically all the ferric cations with a two-compartment divided electrolyzer using an anion exchange membrane. The electrochemical reduction was conducted until reaching at least 4 g/L of Ti(III) to prevent the air oxidation of ferrous cations during handling and storage. This first part of the process will be also discussed again in details in Section 11.1.14.2 regarding the dummying, and electro-reduction of the catholyte prior iron electrowinning.

Afterwards, the copperas was crystallized upon cooling and the crystals removed by centrifugation while the black liquor containing titanyl sulfate was hydrolyzed to yield titanium hydrolysate. The remaining weak acid solution still containing free sulfuric acid values was enriched with some copperas from the previous step to build the concentration of Fe(II) and was used as anolyte. The ferrous cations were necessary to offset the oxygen evolution reaction (OER) by shifting the anode reaction to the electrochemical oxidation of Fe(II) into Fe(III) which is thermodynamically more favorable and having a 100 percent Faradaic efficiency.

Not only this approach allows reducing the overall cell voltage by several hundred of millivolts $[E^0(O_2/H_2O) - E^0(Fe^{3+}/Fe^{2+}) = 0.523\ V]$ but because the oxygen evolution is prevented, it was possible to use graphite anodes instead of expensive anode materials such as their own proprietary ***dimensionally stable anodes***, DSA® (Trademark of *De Nora Elettrodi S.p.A.*).

---

[45] DE NORA, O. (1987) *Procedimento industrial per la produzione di biossido di titanio da ilmenite.* Italian Patent IT 1159931, Mars 14th, 1987 (Oronzio De Nora Impianti Elettrochimici Spa.).

According to the inventors, 70 percent of the original iron content of the beach sand ilmenite was recovered as copperas while the remaining 30 percent was converted to an acidic solution of ferric sulfate.

Therefore, the second step consisted to electrolyze the catholyte solution exiting from the first electrolyzer to which the copperas was dissolved. The electrolysis was performed inside a second divided electrolyzer equipped with a cation exchange membrane. The anolyte consisted of the anolyte exiting from the first electrolyzer still containing enough ferrous cations to act as anode depolarizer. During this second step electrolytic iron was obtained at the cathode while the anolyte became more concentrated in sulfuric acid.

3.2.8 Gewerkschaft Keramchemie

In the 1980s, Heimhard, and Simon both from the German engineering company *Gewerkschaft Keramchemie* invented and patented an electrochemical process for rejuvenating spent pickling liquors by regenerating sulfuric acid from and removing iron by electrodeposition [46]. The method resembles to the two previous patented processes.

Actually, the spent pickling liquor containing 100 g/L H_2SO_4, 40 g/L Fe(II), and 50 g/L of ammonium sulfate added intentionally as bisulfate forming salt in order to boost the sulfuric acid concentration in the anolyte. The catholyte circulates through all the cathode compartments of a series of electrolyzers arranged in cascades one behind the other as already claimed in the patent from *Licencia Talalmanyokat Ertekesito Vallalat.* The Fe(II) content of the iron-depleted decreases down to 7-15 g/L. The iron-depleted catholyte is then conveyed back into the anode compartments of all the electrolyzers where the bisulfate anions HSO_4^-, cross the diaphragm thus combining with the protons left over from the oxidation of water to yield strengthened sulfuric acid.

[46] HEIMHARD, H.-J.; and SIMON, H.-J. (1982) *Verfahren zur elektrolytischen Regenerierung von verbrauchter Schwefelsäure-Beizflüssigkeit.* German Patent DE 3206538 C2 (Gewerkschaft Keramchemie), February 24th, 1982.

Table 15 – Electrowinning of iron from spent pickling liquors (Keramchemie)

Company	Gewerkschaft Keramchemie	
Year	**1980**	
Inventor(s)	**Heimhard and Simon**	
Process	Electrowinning iron	
Status	Commercial scale	
Plant location	Siershahn, Germany	
	SI unit	USCS unit
Cathode material	Iron starter sheet (-)	
Cathode current density (j_c)	-1500 A/m^2	-139.4 A/ft^2
Cathode current efficiency (CCE)	85%	85%
	Catholyte (IN)	Catholyte (OUT)
$FeSO_4$	40.0 g/L	10.0 g/L
H_2SO_4	90.0 g/L	g/L
$(NH_4)_2SO_4$	50.0 g/L	g/L
Temperature (avg.)	60 °C	140 °F
pH	0.5	2.0
Separator	PP porous diaphragm	
	Anolyte (IN)	Anolyte (OUT)
$FeSO_4$	10.0 g/L	10.0 g/L
H_2SO_4	90.0 g/L	250.0 g/L
$(NH_4)_2SO_4$	300.0 g/L	30.0 g/L
Anode material	Lead-silver anode (1 wt.% Ag) (+)	
Anode current density (j_a)	-1500 A/m^2	-139.4 A/ft^2
Overall cell voltage (U_{cell})	4.25 V	4.25 V
Specific energy consumption (e_m)	4,799 kWh/kg	2,177 kWh/lb
Space time yield (Y)	1.328 $kg.m^{-2}.h^{-1}$	0.272 $lb/(ft^2$-hour)

3.2.9 National Aeronautics and Space Administration (NASA)

In 1993, Sullivan from the *National Aeronautics and Space Administration* (NASA) invented and patented a fully integrated process [47] to be used by future extraterrestrial colonies established on the Moon or Mars for producing pure oxygen gas with electrolytic iron as co-product from ferrous sulfate. The ferrous sulfate is obtained by the slurrying and sulfation of iron-rich bearing minerals from the lunar regolith such as ilmenite with hot concentrated sulfuric acid. Once

[47] SULLIVAN, T. (1993) *Method for producing oxygen from lunar materials*. U.S. Patent 5,227,032 (National Aeronautics and Space Administration, NASA), July 13th, 1993.

reacted, the solid sulfation cake is dissolved into hot water and the solution of ferrous sulfate thus produced is electrolyzed inside a divided electrolyzer thus regenerating the sulfuric acid to be reused upstream in the sulfation process and generating oxygen gas.

3.3 Conclusions from the Prior Art

After close examination of the prior art described above, it teaches us important lessons, from which we can draw a certain number of remarks and conclusions especially regarding the optimum operating parameters for electrowinning iron from spent pickling liquors.

- First, the strongly acidic spent pickling liquor with 90-100 g/L H_2SO_4 and 50 g/L Fe when used as catholyte was pumped directly from the pickling tanks and electrolyzed during long periods of time by circulating through a series of two-compartment divided electrolyzers arranged in cascade. The electrolysis was conducted until the pH increased and ranged between 1.8 and 2.0 and the catholyte was depleted in iron with about 10 g/L Fe(II). At that pH, the iron was electrodeposited with a cathode current efficiency usually greater than 90 percent.
- In order to favor the plating of electrolytic iron, and offset the discharge of protons with the hydrogen gas evolution reaction (HER), it is mandatory to conduct the electrolysis at an elevate current density above -1,500 A/m^2 but below -2,000 A/m^2 especially at the beginning of the electrolysis when the concentration of free sulfuric acid is still high as the dendritic deposits exhibit a poor quality.
- Ammonium sulfate is always added to the catholyte with a molarity ranging from 0.5 M and 1.0 M. The addition of ammonium sulfate plays two important roles. First, from decades of experience with the electroplating of iron from mixed sulfates, ammonium cations act as an efficient complexing agent for stabilizing the ferrous cations. Secondly, ammonium sulfate, and in a lesser extent magnesium and alkali-metal sulfates, act as a bisulfate forming salt thus improving the production yield of concentrated sulfuric acid in the anolyte. This allowed obtaining the highest strength sulfuric acid concentration in the rejuvenated solution with only half the amount of electricity consumed.
- Actually, under strongly acidic conditions such as those existing in spent pickling liquors, with a very low pH usually below 0.5, the sulfate anions become the minor species while the hydrogen sulfate (i.e., bisulfate) anions HSO_4^- predominate representing almost 88

percent of all the sulfate species [48]. Thus when electrolysis a catholyte having a pH below 0.5, after circulating a total electric charge of two Faradays, two moles of bisulfate anions migrate and cross the separator towards the anode forming with the protons two moles sulfuric acid according to: $2HSO_4^- + 2H^+ = 2H_2SO_4$. By contrast, when electrolyzing a catholyte made of ferrous sulfate at pH 3-4, sulfate anions are the predominant species. Thus after passing a total charge of two Faradays, only one mole of sulfate anion migrates and crosses the separator forming with the two protons, one mole sulfuric acid at the anode according to: $SO_4^- + 2H^+ = H_2SO_4$.

- In most cases, the anolyte often consisted of a weak sulfuric acid solution to which ferrous sulfate was added intentionally. The presence of ferrous cations was necessary to offset the oxygen evolution reaction (OER) by shifting the anode reaction to the electrochemical oxidation of Fe(II) into Fe(III) which is thermodynamically more favorable and having a 100 percent Faradaic efficiency. Not only this approach allows reducing the overall cell voltage by several hundred of millivolts [$E^0(O_2/H_2O) - E^0(Fe^{3+}/Fe^{2+}) = 0.523$ V] but because the oxygen evolution is prevented, it was possible for the inventions described the 1960s to use cheaper lead or graphite anodes instead of expensive anode materials such as mixed metal oxides (MMO) coated-titanium anodes that were invented in the 1950s by Henri B. Beer [49] and later commercialized in the 1970s for evolving oxygen under the tradename ***Dimensionally Stable Anodes*** (DSA®) (Trademark of *De Nora Permelec Ltd.*).
- With highly concentrated solutions, the operating temperature must be maintained at least above 50°C for preventing the unwanted crystallization of copperas and to favor kinetics effects along with increasing the electrical conductivity of both electrolytes.

---

[48] CARDARELLI, F. (2022) *Sulfuric Acid Digestion, Sulfuric Acid Baking, and Sulfation Roasting in Mineral and Chemical Processing, and Extractive Metallurgy*. Electrochem Technologies & Materials Inc., Montreal, QC, Canada, *Chapter 2: Physical and Chemical Properties of Pure Sulfuric Acid*, pages 10-11

[49] BEER, H.B. (1963) *Noble metal coated titanium electrode and method of making and using it.* U.S. Patent 3,096,272 A, July 2nd, 1963 (Amalgamated Curacao Patents Co.)

4 Electrochemical Definitions

Electrochemistry is a particular field of physical chemistry that studies the transfer of electric charge across an interface between two distinct phases. The first phase called ***electrode*** is always an electronic conductor, and the second phase is an ionic conductor called the ***electrolyte***.

4.1 Electrochemical Reaction

An ***electrochemical reaction***, is a particular heterogeneous chemical reaction involving a charge transfer during which electrons are either provided (i.e., reduction) or removed (i.e., oxidation) from a compound (e.g., ion, atom, molecule, or cluster) by means of an ***electrode***. The kinetic of the charge transfer occurring at the electrode is considered heterogeneous owing to the existence of a physical interface between two phases the electrode (solid) and the electrolyte (liquid).

Therefore, an electrochemical reaction must never be confused with homogeneous oxidation-reduction reactions (i.e., ***redox reactions***), during which the exchange of electrons occurs between the reducing species of one redox couple and the oxidizing species of the second couple. This leads to the modern concept that electron can be considered as a particular reactant contained in huge quantities inside an electrode material acting both as reservoir and/or sink of electrons.

4.2 Electroactive Species

Any chemical species capable to react directly with electrons at the surface of the electrode is called an **electroactive species**, or sometimes ***depolarizer*** or ***depolarizing substance*** in some old textbooks. Electroactive species can be either electrically charged such as anions (e.g., SO_4^{2-}) or cations (e.g., Fe^{2+}) or neutral atoms and molecules (e.g., H_2O), free radicals (e.g., $OH^{\cdot}$), solids, liquids (e.g., $SOCl_2$), or even gases (e.g., H_2, O_2) and plasmas. Electroactive species can be split into two main categories:

Oxidizing (or ***electro-reducible***) species, i.e., entities (e.g., ion, atom, cluster or molecule) capable to capture electron(s) from a cathode according to the general reaction scheme:

$\nu_O O + ne^- \rightarrow \nu_R R$

Reducing (or ***electro-oxidizable***) species, i.e., entities (e.g., ion, atom, cluster or molecule) capable to release electron(s) to the electrode according to the general reaction scheme:

$$\nu_R R \rightarrow \nu_o O + ne^-$$

Therefore, a ***reduction*** (i.e. electro-donation) is always a gain of electrons, while an ***oxidation*** (i.e., de-electronation) is always a removal of electrons.

4.3 Electrodes

The modern concept of an ***electrode*** is an electronic conductor either solid (e.g., Fe, Pt, C) or liquid (e.g., pool of mercury, molten aluminum) in contact with an ionic conductor called electrolyte (e.g., molten salt, aqueous or organic solution, ionized gas, plasma). Some typical examples of electrodes are but not restricted to a copper plate immersed into an aqueous solution of copper sulfate or a platinum wire immersed into an electrolyte containing hydronium cations (H^+) and dissolved hydrogen gas (H_2) or also a platinum wire in contact with a pool of liquid mercury itself immersed into an aqueous solution containing mercuric cations Hg(II). More accurately, an electrode can also be defined as several electronic conducting phases connected in series with at least one phase directly in contact with an ionic conductor. Two types of electrodes can be distinguished:

The ***cathode*** is the electrode at which the reduction (i.e, eltectro-donation) reaction occurs.

The ***anode*** is the electrode at which the oxidation (i.e., de-electronation) reaction takes place.

The sign of the polarization of the electrode is determined only by the type of electrochemical cell.

For an ***electrolyzer***, the anode is the positive electrode where the oxidation occurs while the cathode where the reduction occurs is polarized negatively.

Conversely, for a ***power source*** (i.e., battery, fuel cell), the anode is the negative electrode, and the cathode the positive.

4.4 Sign Convention for the Electric Current

The ***active sign convention*** is used for power sources that deliver voltage to a circuit, for instance, batteries, fuel cells, or discharging capacitors. For active components, the sign convention is that the positive terminal is the terminal that delivers current (i.e., current flows out of it), and the negative terminal is the terminal that current flows back into. Conversely, the flow of electrons occurs in the opposite direction (Figure 11).

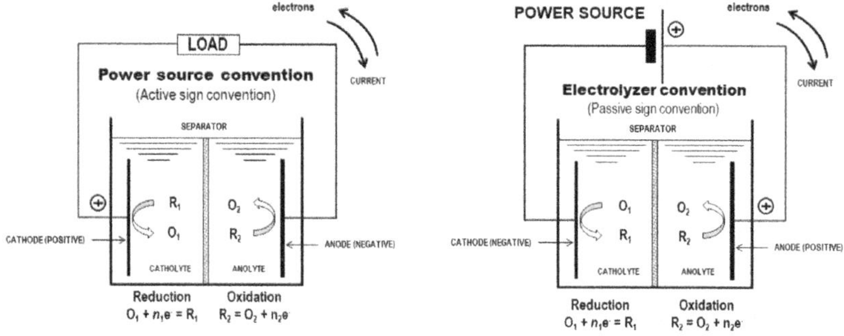

Figure 11 – Sign convention for the electric current (Power source)

Figure 12 – Sign convention for the electric current (Electrolyzer)

By contrast, electrolyzers follow the ***passive sign convention***. The point on a passive component where current flows into the component is considered its positive terminal, and the point where current flows out of the component is considered its negative terminal (Figure 12). Conversely, the flow of electrons occurs in the opposite direction.

4.5 Separators

Separators are physical barriers that split the electrochemical cell into two distinct compartments, and that prevent the contact between reactive species produced at the electrodes. Separators must be electronic insulator while good ionic conductors. The anode (anodic) compartment contains both the ***anolyte*** and the anode while the cathode (cathodic) compartment contains the cathode immersed into the ***catholyte***. Two kinds of separators can be clearly distinguished these are diaphragm and membranes.

4.5.1 Diaphragms

Diaphragms are passive separators acting only as a physical barrier and the proper mass transfer (e.g., porous ceramics, asbestos felt, microporous polymers, and impregnated fabrics). Hence the transport of electroactive species is only achieved by permeation through the material. Diaphragms are usually made of inert porous materials such as: microporous polypropylene, glass wool, asbestos, fiberglass, and ceramics.

4.5.2 Membranes

Membranes are active separators which are chemically selective, i.e., capable to allow the transport of specific ions across the barrier. They are made from chemically active polymers to which special chemical functions are attached (e.g., sulfonic or quaternary ammonium) in order to be ***permselective*** or ***ion selective***.

As a general rule, all separators represent an important contribution to the ohmic drop inside electrochemical cells.

4.6 Electrolytes

Electrolytes are distinguished from pure electronic conductors as the electric current is ensured by the migration of charged species called ***ions*** (i.e., anions or cations) under the electric field imposed by the electrodes. Therefore, electrolytes are entirely ***ionic conductors*** without any electronic conductivity (i.e., no free electrons). They can be found either in the solid state (e.g., fluorite, beta-alumina's, yttria-stabilized zirconia, and silver iodide), the liquid state (e.g., aqueous solutions, organic solvents, or molten salts), and finally in the gaseous state (e.g., ionized gases, and plasmas). Electrolytes can be grouped in three main classes.

4.6.1 Pure Electrolytes

This class is entirely represented by molten (i.e., fused) salts (e.g., molten cryolite, Na_3AlF_6 or molten eutectic mixtures such as LiF-NaF, and usually required high temperatures largely above the melting point or liquidus temperature of the salts to provide sufficient ionic conductivity.

4.6.2 Ionic Solutions

This class is represented by electrolytic solutions and is also split in two subclasses according to their ionic conductivity and dissociation constant.

Strong electrolytes (***ionophores***) Potassium chloride (KCl) is the main example of the class of ionophores, that is, pure ionic compounds (e.g., solids, liquids or gases) already made of anions and cations. Therefore, the dissolution of these ionophores simply consists to the dispersion of pre-existing ions of the crystal lattice into an appropriate solvent followed by a reorganization of solvent molecules around ions (i.e., solvation process). This phenomenon strongly depends on the relative electric permittivity ε_r (i.e., formerly the dielectric constant) of the solvent. Actually, in ionizing solvents, i.e., having a high electric permittivity such as water (ε_r = 78.36 at 298.15K) the coulombic interaction between ions is strongly decreased. Hence, ions maintain a certain independence in their displacement, and they are totally dissociated (i.e., ionized).

By contrast, in inert solvents (e.g., benzene), i.e., exhibiting a low electric permittivity, ionic entities form such as pairs or clusters losing their freedom. For instance, in a series of solvents having a decreasing permittivity, ions form double, triple, quadruples, associations such as $LiBF_4$ into dimethoxyethane ($\varepsilon_r = 7.15$ at 298.15K).

Weak electrolytes. In this case the solute is partially ionized (e.g., NH_4Cl in water). Usually, all the salts obtained by the neutralization of: (i) a weak acid by a strong base (e.g., $CH_3COO^-Na^+$), (ii) a weak base by a strong acid (e.g., NH_4Cl), or (iii) a weak acid by a weak base (e.g., $CH_3COO^-NH_4^+$) are typical examples of weak electrolytes.

4.6.3 Solid Electrolytes

Solid electrolytes correspond to solid materials with the ionic mobility ensured by various intrinsic and extrinsic defects. Common examples are ion conducting solids with the rock salt with the *Strukturbericht* B1-structure (e.g., α-AgI), oxygen conducting solids with the fluorite type C1-structure ($A^{II}O_2$), and yttrium stabilized cubic zirconia (YSZ, ZrO_2 with 8 mol.% Y_2O_3), the pyrochlore structure ($A_2B_2O_7$), the perovskite type oxides ($A^{II}B^{IV}O_3$), $La_2Mo_2O_9$ or solids with the spinel structure such as beta-alumina ($NaAl_{11}O_{17}$). The ionic conductivity of ceria-stabilized zirconia is 60 $mS.cm^{-1}$ at 1200°C while yttria-stabilized zirconia is 20 $mS.cm^{-1}$ at 800°C, 30 $mS.cm^{-1}$ at 900°C, and 100 $mS.cm^{-1}$ at 1000°C.

On the other hand, inorganic and organic salts which on dissociation give an equal numbers of cations and anions of equal charge, such as for instance Na^+Cl^- and $Mg^{2+}SO_4^{2-}$, are called 1-1 and 2-2 ***symmetric electrolytes***. Inorganic and organic salts which on dissociation give ions unequal in either number or charge such as Na_2SO_4 or $MgCl_2$, are called ***asymmetric electrolytes***.

4.7 Electrochemical Cells

An ***electrochemical cell*** consists basically to an arrangement of several interfaces electrode-electrolyte. Usually, it consists to two electrodes separated by at least one or more electrolyte. As a general rule, two types of electrochemical cells must be distinguished.

4.7.1 Galvanic Cells

Galvanic cell is an electrochemical cell where spontaneous electrochemical reactions occur at both electrodes once they are connected electrically using external busbars (i.e., current collectors). At the anode, which is polarized negatively (-), an oxidation takes place leading to the release of electrons flowing in the external circuit to the cathode (+) where a reduction reaction occurs. Hence, when connecting externally the two electrodes of a galvanic cell, the assemblies generates immediately an electric current easy to measure with an ammeter, and for this reason they are mainly used as electric power sources. Galvanic cells include **primary batteries, secondary batteries** (rechargeable), and **fuel cells**.

4.7.2 Electrolytic Cells or Electrolyzers

An ***electrolytic cell*** or in short ***electrolyzer***, the two electrodes are connected externally with busbars to an electric power supply. When the electric potential or cell voltage imposed between the two electrodes is greater than the electromotive force of the cell, *e.m.f.* (See 4.8.1), electrolysis takes place, and an electric current circulates into the cell. At the anode which is polarized positively (+) electrons are removed and the oxidation of electroactive species occurs, while at the cathode (-) electrons provided externally lead to the reduction of electroactive species. Electrolysers are electrochemical cells used for achieving for instance electrolysis, electro synthesis, electrowinning, electrodeposition, electro refining, and electroplating.

Table 16 – International convention of electrochemical cells

Electrochemical cells	Anode (oxidation)	Cathode (reduction)
Galvanic cells (batteries and fuel cells)	Negative (-)	Positive (+)
Electrolytic cells (electrolysers)	Positive (+)	Negative (-)

At this stage, it is worth to mention that in both galvanic and electrolytic cells, the electrons are physically restricted to circulate only inside an electronic conductor (i.e., current collectors, busbars, and electrodes) while into the electrolyte the electric current is only carried by cations and anions. Actually, electrons can never circulate free into ionic conductors such as electrolytes. However, solvated electrons, e^-(aq), can extraordinarily be generated into the electrolyte when the latter is exposed to strong ionizing radiations (e.g., gamma rays) or submitted to elevate electric field strength close to the disruptive voltage of the liquid.

A simplified cell description was introduced by the *International Electrotechnical Commission* (IEC) and consists: (a) to list all the components of an electrochemical cell from the anode where oxidation occurs (left-hand side) to the cathode where reduction takes place (right-hand side), (b) indicating the separation between two distinct phases by a simple slash (/) or better a vertical line (|), a coma between components present in a same phase (,), and a double slash (//) or better double vertical line (||) for separating two phases having a potential difference negligible compared to the *e.m.f* of the overall cell (e.g., liquid junction potential).

For instance, the historical Daniell galvanic cell was composed of an anode made of amalgamated zinc anode immersed in an aqueous solution of zinc sulfate and a cathode of pure copper immersed in a saturated solution of copper(II) sulfate, the anodic and cathodic compartments are separated by a thin porous diaphragm. This galvanic cell can be written as follows:

(-) Zn(Hg) | Zn^{2+}, SO_4^{2-} | | Cu^{2+}, SO_4^{2-} | Cu(s) (+)

4.8 Electric Potentials at the Electrode

An electric potential difference always appears at the boundary of two phases if their electric conductivities are sufficiently high. This potential difference is called the ***electrode potential***. If the electrode is composed of more than two phases in series, the electrode potential is the difference between the electrical potentials of the two terminal phases.

4.8.1 Electromotive Force

The difference between the electrode potentials of the two terminal phases in a galvanic cell without flow of current is called the ***electromotive force*** and denoted by the acronym *e.m.f.* or *emf* [50] also called the ***open circuit voltage*** denoted by the acronym OCV and measured in V.

For example, if a simple ***galvanic cell*** is built with two anodic metallic conductors (M_1, M_2) in contact with an electrolyte (E) also in contact with a semiconductor (S) as depicted in Figure 13 below:

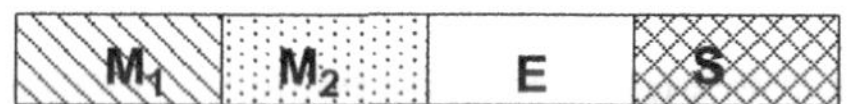

Figure 13 – Galvanic cell

The electrochemical cell can be written schematically as:

(+) M_1 | M_2 | | E | | S (-)

Note the two vertical lines are required for separating two different phases (e.g., solid and liquid) while only one vertical bar is needed when separating similar phases. Thus the *emf* corresponds to the potential difference is simply given by:

$emf = U_{M1} - U_S$

From a practical point, for an accurate measurement, it is important to ensure that the terminal phases used as electrical leads or current collectors consists

[50] LANGE, E. *Zeitschrift für Elektrochemie*. **55**(1951)83 and **56**(1952) 104.

of the same material, this can be achieved in practice by soldering the different electrode materials to leads made of the same metal such as copper or better a chemically inert metal like pure platinum as depicted in Figure 14.

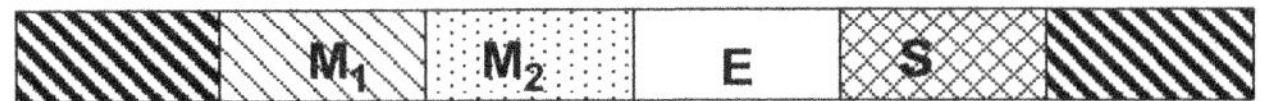

Figure 14 – Electrochemical cell

Therefore, the correct electrochemical cell can be now rewritten using platinum leads as follows:

$(+)(Pt)|M_1|M_2||E||S|(Pt)(-)$

4.8.2 Galvani or Inner Electric Potential

The ***Galvani potential*** or ***inner electric potential*** [51] of a phase α, denoted by the Greek letter, ϕ_α or Φ_α, and expressed in volts (V), corresponds to the inner electric potential of an electric charge, $q_i = Z_i e$, expressed in coulombs (C), positioned inside the electrode material and referenced from a virtual origin located arbitrarily at the infinity in vacuum (i.e., $\Phi(x) = \Phi_{ref} = 0$ for $x \to +\infty$) called the ***Wagner's ground***. The potential energy of the electric charge q_i is then equal to the work, W, in J, required to move it from infinity in vacuum or empty space to the core of the electrode material. Therefore the Galvani's inner potential corresponds to a physical quantity introduced in solid state physics and called the ***electron work function*** of the electrode material denoted W_S, expressed in J (eV) and related by the simple equation to it:

$$W_S = e(\Phi - \Phi_{ref}) = e\Phi$$

Because the Galvani's potential is related to the electron work function of the material it is an intrinsic properties of the electrode material. From a practical point of view only the Galvani potential difference between two phases in contact are measurable in practice. For instance, let's consider, under isothermal conditions, the theoretical galvanic cell depicted in Figure 15.

[51] LANGE, E.; and MISCENKO, K.P. (1930) *Zeitschrift Physikalishe Chemie*, **A149**(1930)1.

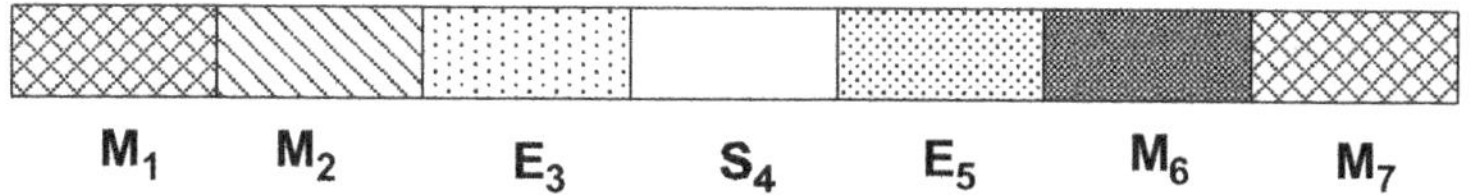

Figure 15 – Theoretical galvanic cell

The electrical assemblies is made of a linear arrangement of a metallic electrode M_1 connected to a second metal M_2 immersed into a compartmented cell with electrolyte E_3 a separator S_4 another electrolyte E_5 and then a metal M_6 itself connected to a metal M_7 similar in nature to M_1. The Galvani potential differences between external busbars, that is, the electromotive force (e.m.f.) of the electrochemical cell is given by the summation of each individual potential differences or Galvani potential of each phase in direct contact.

$$\Phi_7 - \Phi_1 = (\Phi_7 - \Phi_6) + (\Phi_6 - \Phi_5) + (\Phi_5 - \Phi_4) + (\Phi_4 - \Phi_3) + (\Phi_3 - \Phi_2) + (\Phi_2 - \Phi_1)$$

As a general rule, the difference of the Galvani potential between two phases corresponds to the summation of all the Galvani potential differences of each phase in direct contact:

$$\Delta\varphi = \sum_{i=1}^{N} (\varphi_{i+1} - \varphi_i)$$

Therefore, the cell potential corresponds directly to the difference of the Galvani potential of each electrode. It is not possible to measure individual Galvani potential difference but the overall Galvani potential difference is a measurable quantity.

4.8.3 Volta or Outer Electric Potential

Volta potential or ***outer electric potential*** of a phase α, denoted by the Greek letter, Ψ_α is expressed in volts (V) and it corresponds to the electric potential of an electric charge, $q_i = Z_i e$ located at the electrode surface with the reference potential taken as zero at an infinite distance in vacuum (i.e., $\Psi(x) = 0$ for $x \rightarrow +\infty$) called the ***Wagner's ground***. Therefore, the Volta potential corresponds to the potential electric energy required to move an electric charge from infinity to the surface of the phase α. As a general rule, the difference in the two outer electric potential of two different phases, α and β, is called the Volta potential difference, $\Delta\Psi = \Psi_\alpha - \Psi_\beta$ between two phases and it corresponds to the summation of all the Volta potential differences of each phase in direct contact:

$$\Delta\psi = \sum_{i=1}^{N} (\psi_{i+1} - \psi_i)$$

The energy conservation is given by the basic equation, where E_F is the ***Fermi energy*** of an electron located at the Fermi's level: $e(\Phi - \Phi_{ref}) - e(\psi - \psi_{ref}) = e\chi = E_F$

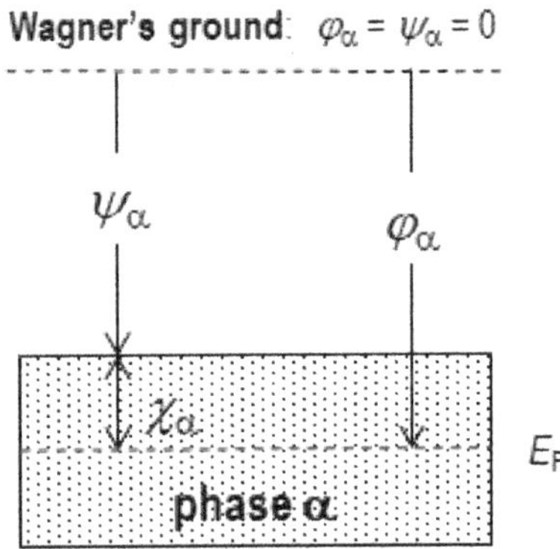

Figure 16 – Volta potential

By definition both reference electric potentials are defined arbitrarily by: $\Phi_{ref} = \psi_{ref} = 0$ (Wagner's ground), hence, the basic relationship between the Galvani and Volta potentials for a given phase α is given by the following equation:

$$\Phi_\alpha - \psi_\alpha = \chi_\alpha$$

With χ_α which is called the ***electrochemical potential*** of an electron, in V, that is, the potential energy of an electron located at the Fermi's level inside the electrode material.

Note that the Galvani and Volta potentials of the same material differ only if a potential difference exists between the interior and the outer surface of the phase. This occurs usually when dipolar molecules are adsorbed onto the outer surface (e.g., H_2O) or if the barycenter of electric charges does not coincide with that of electrons near the surface of the material. Therefore, the surface potential is equal to Galvani inner potential when the Volta potential is zero, that is, when no excess electric charge accumulate on the surface of the electrode.

5 Thermochemistry of Electrochemical Reactions

5.1 Gibbs Enthalpy of Electrochemical Reactions

The ***Gibbs free energy*** is the available free energy of a substance that can be used in a chemical reaction. Substances tend to transform into other substances that have lower Gibbs free energy. The change of ***Gibbs enthalpy*** predicts whether a chemical reaction will occur spontaneously.

The Gibbs free energy change for an incremental reversible process is given by:

$$dG = VdP - SdT + dW_{NPV}$$

Where the differential term dW_{NPV} is the increment of non-pressure–volume work. In the case of an electrochemical cell, the electrical work is non-pressure–volume work.

The maximum amount of work that can be produced by an electrochemical cell denoted W_{max} is equal to the product of the electrochemical cell potential, E, in V, and the total charge per mole transferred during the reaction nF, in C as follows:

$$W_{max}\ (<0) = nF\Delta E^{cell}$$

Work is negative because work is being done by a system an electrochemical cell with a positive potential on its surroundings

Consequently, the relationship between the potential of an electrochemical cell and ΔG is:

$$\Delta G = -nF\Delta E^{cell}$$

A spontaneous redox reaction is therefore characterized by a negative value of ΔG and a positive value of ΔE^{cell}.

When both the reactants and products are in their standard states, the relationship between the two quantities becomes:

$$\Delta G^0 = -nF\Delta E^0$$

A spontaneous redox reaction is therefore characterized by a negative value of ΔG^0 and a positive value of ΔE^0.

From the above equation, it is possible to establish the relationship between the standard cell potential and the equilibrium constant. Actually, the relationship between the standard free-energy change ΔG^0 and the equilibrium constant K_p, for a general reaction of the type: aA + bB = cC + dD are related by the following equation:

$$\Delta G^\circ = -RT\ln K_p = -RT\ln\{[C]^c[D]^d/[A]^a[B]^b\}$$

Therefore, after equalizing the two equations, we obtain:

$$-nF\Delta E^0 = -RT\ln K_p$$

Rearranging the equation we obtain the relationship

$$\Delta E^0 = (RT/nF)\ln K_p = (RT/nF)\ln\{[C]^c[D]^d/[A]^a[B]^b\}$$

5.2 Ion Activity, and Mean Activity Coefficient

The determination of thermodynamic activities of ionic species is required for calculating accurately the ***chemical potentials***, μ_k, and the ***equilibrium constants***, K_p of electrochemical reactions.

Actually, the activities of ionic species are far more important than the activities for non-electrolytes. Actually, the Coulomb electrostatic forces between ions of the type ion-ion, ion-dipole, and dipole-dipole are very large.

5.2.1 Ions in Aqueous Electrolytes

5.2.1.1 Ideal Solutions

When ionic compounds dissolve into water, they are dissociated into anions, and cations. The chemical potentials for the formation of a ionic species *k*, is given by:

$$\mu_k = \mu^0_k + RT\ln a_k$$

Where μ^0 denotes the standard chemical potential for a given standard state of reference.

Where the ***thermodynamic activity*** of a ionic species *k*, in the electrolyte is denoted a_k or (k), is a dimensionless quantity which is the ratio of the molality of the species k, m_k, in mol/kg, to a chosen hypothetical standard state of reference which corresponds to a solution having a molality equals unity ($m_0 = 1$ mol/kg) as follows:

$$a_k = (k) = m_k / m_0$$

The chemical potential of a species k should be written:

$$\mu_k = \mu^0_k + RT \ln (m_k / m_0)$$

5.2.1.2 Actual Solutions and Non-ideality

For actual electrolyte solutions containing ionic species that do not behave ideally even when diluted, it was necessary to account for the non-ideality behavior by introducing a correcting factor required to perform the calculations of the activities of the ionic species. The correction factor is called the ***activity coefficient***, denoted by the Greek symbol γ_k:

$$a_k = (k) = \gamma_k \, m_k / m_0$$

The standard state of reference is based on the limit of the Henry's law, that is, the activity coefficient tends to unity at ***infinite dilution*** when:

$$\gamma_k \rightarrow 1 \text{ in the limit when } m_k \rightarrow 0$$

$$\mu_k = \mu^0_k + RT \ln a_k = \mu^0_k + RT \ln (\gamma_k m_k / m_0)$$

Therefore, in practice, the denominator being equal to unity, it is often omitted in the above equation.

$$\mu_k = \mu^0_k + RT \ln \gamma_k m_k$$

For instance, when iron (II) sulfate dissolves into water, it is dissociated into sulfate anions, and ferrous cations as follows.

$$FeSO_4(aq) = Fe^{2+}(aq) + SO_4^{2-}(aq)$$

The chemical potentials for the formation of ions, is given by:

$$\mu_{FeSO4} = \mu_{Fe^{2+}} + \mu_{SO4^{2-}}$$

The chemical potential of each species is written as a function of the chemical activity of each species as follows:

$$\mu_{FeSO4} = \mu^0_{FeSO4} + RT\ln a_{FeSO4} = \mu^0_{FeSO4} + RT\ln(FeSO_4)$$

$$\mu_{SO4}^{2-} = \mu^0_{SO4}{}^{2-} + RT\ln a_{SO4}{}^{2-} = \mu^0_{FeSO4} + RT\ln(SO_4^{2-})$$

$$\mu_{Fe}{}^{2+} = \mu^0_{Fe}{}^{2+} + RT\ln a_{Fe}{}^{2+} = \mu^0_{FeSO4} + RT\ln(Fe^{2+})$$

$$\mu^0_{FeSO4} = \mu^0_{Fe}{}^{2+} + \mu^0_{SO4}{}^{2-}$$

Introducing, the molalities, and individual activity coefficients of the cations $m_{Fe}{}^{2+}$, $\gamma_{Fe}{}^{2+}$ and sulfate anions $m_{SO4}{}^{2-}$, $\gamma_{SO4}{}^{2-}$ we obtain:

$$\mu^0_{FeSO4} + RT\ln a_{FeSO4} = \mu^0_{Fe}{}^{2+} + RT\ln \gamma_{Fe}{}^{2+} m_{Fe}{}^{2+} + \mu^0_{SO4}{}^{2-} + RT\ln \gamma_{SO4}{}^{2-} m_{SO4}{}^{2-}$$

By regrouping the molalities and activities of the cations and anions in the logarithmic argument, we have:

$$\mu^0_{FeSO4} + RT\ln a_{FeSO4} = \mu^0_{Fe}{}^{2+} + \mu^0_{SO4}{}^{2-} + RT\ln \gamma_{Fe}{}^{2+} m_{Fe}{}^{2+}\ \gamma_{SO4}{}^{2-} m_{SO4}{}^{2-}$$

Thus because of the relation between the standard potentials, we obtain:

$$RT\ln a_{FeSO4} = RT\ln(\gamma_{Fe}{}^{2+} m_{Fe}{}^{2+})\cdot(\gamma_{SO4}{}^{2-} m_{SO4}{}^{2-})$$

Therefore, the activity of the salt is related to the activities of the cations and anions

$$a_{FeSO4} = \gamma_{Fe}{}^{2+} m_{Fe}{}^{2+}\ \gamma_{SO4}{}^{2-} m_{SO4}{}^{2-}$$

Experimentally, it is not possible to measure the individual activity coefficients, $\gamma_{Fe}{}^{2+}$, and $\gamma_{SO4}{}^{2-}$ however, it is possible to calculate from theory a ***geometric mean activity coefficient*** defined as follows:

$$\gamma_{Fe}{}^{2+}\ \gamma_{SO4}{}^{2-} = \gamma_{\pm}{}^{2}$$

Thus we have $a_{FeSO4} = \gamma_{\pm}{}^{2} m_{Fe}{}^{2+} m_{SO4}{}^{2-}$

In the particular case of a 2-2 symmetric electrolyte like ferrous sulfate, the individual molalities, of the cations and anions equals the molality m of the salt:

$$a_{FeSO4} = \gamma_{\pm}{}^{2} m^2$$

The general case of the dissolution of a salt of the type:

$A_xX_y = xA^{y+} + yX^{x-}$

With the initial molality of the salt, m, in mol/kg, the molalities of the cations and anions are as follows:

$m_{A^{y+}} = x \cdot m$ and $m_{X^{x-}} = y \cdot m$

The activity product then becomes:

$$a_A{}^x a_X{}^y = (\gamma_A m_A)^x (\gamma_B m_B)^y = x^x y^y\, m^{(x+y)} (\gamma_A{}^x \gamma_B{}^y)$$

We can define a mean activity coefficient as:

$$\gamma_\pm = (\gamma_A{}^x \gamma_B{}^y)^{1/(x+y)}$$

$$a_A{}^x a_X{}^y = x^x y^y\, m^{(x+y)}\, \gamma_\pm{}^{(x+y)}$$

5.2.2 Debye-Hückel Equations

In order to calculate the mean activity coefficient defined previously, two chemists Peter Debye and Erich Hückel [52] have developed a theoretical model taking into account the electrostatic interaction between ions. They introduced the concept of ionic atmosphere defined as the space around which a charged entity (i.e., ion) is capable to attract an ion of opposite electric charge.

Moreover, the general equation they obtained was based on a physical quantity called the ***ionic strength*** of the solution, denoted I_m, in mol/kg, or I_C, in mol/m^3 depending on the concentration scale used (molality or molarity), and defined as follows:

$I_m = 0.5\sum_k(m_k z_k^2)$ (molality basis)

$I_C = 0.5\sum_k(c_k z_k^2)$ (molar basis)

For instance, for a 2-2 symmetric electrolyte, like $FeSO_4$, the ionic strength (molality basis) is simply given by:

$$I_m = 0.5[m_{Fe^{2+}}(2^2) + m_{SO_4^{2-}}(2^2)] = 2m_{FeSO_4}$$

The form of the ***general Debye-Hückel equation*** is given hereafter:

$$\log_{10}\gamma_\pm = -0.511\ |z^+ z^-|\, I_m{}^{1/2}/[1 + I_m{}^{1/2}]$$

---

[52] DEBYE, P.; and HÜCKEL, E.. Zur Theorie der Elektrolyte. I. Gefrierpunktserniedrigung und verwandte Erscheinungen. *Physikalische Zeitschrift.* **24**(1923)185–206

Where z^+, and z^- are the cation and anion electric charge respectively, and I, the ionic strength of the electrolyte solution.

For low molalities (resp. molarities), the square root of the ionic strength becomes smaller than unity, therefore the simplified ***Debye-Hückel equation*** can be used instead in order to calculate the mean activity coefficient according to:

$$\log_{10}\gamma_\pm = -0.511 \ |z^+z^-| I_m^{1/2}$$

5.3 Thermochemical Data

To establish the equations for the temperature dependence of each thermodynamic function (i.e., enthalpy, entropy, Gibbs enthalpy) they will be calculated using tabulated thermodynamic data widely available in the scientific and technical literature [53, 54, 55, 56, 57, 58].

These data for a set of selected inorganic compounds are reported for convenience in Table 17 hereafter.

---

[53] LIDE, D.R. (ed.) (2001) *Handbook of Chemistry and Physics. 81st Edition.* CRC Press Bocca Raton, FL; pp. 5-85 to 5-88.

[54] WICKS, C.E.; and BLOCK, F.E. (1963) *Thermodynamic Properties of 65 Elements, Their Oxides, Halides, Carbides, and Nitrides.* Bulletin No. 605, U.S. Bureau of Mines, United States Government Printing Office, Washington D.C.

[55] BARIN, I.; and KNACKE, O. (1973) *Thermochemical Properties of Inorganic Substances.* Springer-Verlag, Heidelberg, Germany.

[56] BARNER, H.E.; and SCHEUERMAN, R.V. (1978) *Handbook of Thermochemical Data for Compounds and Aqueous Species.* John Wiley & Sons, New York, NY.

[57] KUBASCHEVSKI, O.; BALBCOK, C.B.; and SPENCER, P.J. (1993) *Materials Thermochemistry, Sixth Edition.* Pergamon Press, Oxford, U.K.

[58] PANKRATZ, L.B. (1983) *Thermodynamic Properties of Elements and Oxides.* Bulletin No. 672, U.S. Bureau of Mines, Washington, DC.

Table 17 – Thermochemical data for selected inorganic substances at 298.15 K

T =	298.15K	25°C	$Cp = a + bT + cT^{-2}$				
Substance	ΔH°	S^{0}	a	b	c	$\Delta H(T)$	$Cp(T)$
	J/mol	J/(mol.K)	J/(mol.K)	J/(mol.K²)	J.K/mol	J/mol	J/(mol.K)
Al (metal)	0	28.33	20.67	0.0124	0.000E+00	0	24
Al_2O_3	-1,673,600	51.04	114.77	0.0128	-3.544E+06	-1,673,600	79
$Al_2(SO_4)_3$	-3,435,064	239.32	366.31	0.0626	-1.116E+07	-3,435,064	259
BeO	-598,730	14.14	35.35	0.0167	-1.326E+06	-598,730	25
$BeSO_4$	-1,200,808	77.97	71.78	0.0997	-1.378E+06	-1,200,808	86
CaF_2	-1,221,310	68.83	59.83	0.0305	-1.966E+05	-1,221,310	67
CaO	-634,294	39.75	49.62	0.0045	-6.945E+05	-634,294	43
$Ca(OH)_2$	-986,211	83.39	105.29	0.0119	-1.897E+06	-986,211	88
$CaSO_4$	-1,432,602	106.69	70.21	0.0987	0.000E+00	-1,432,602	100
$CaSO_4.0.5H_2O$	-1,575,150	130.54	107.93	0.0987	0.000E+00	-1,575,150	137
$CaSO_4.2H_2O$	-2,021,123	193.97	221.08	0.0987	0.000E+00	-2,021,123	251
Cl_2 (gas)	0	223.01	36.90	0.0003	-2.845E+05	0	34
Cr (metal)	0	23.77	19.79	0.0128	-2.594E+04	0	23
Cr_2O_3	-1,129,680	81.17	119.37	0.0092	-1.565E+06	-1,129,680	105
$Cr_2(SO_4)_3$	-2,931,302	258.78	358.07	0.0795	-8.975E+05	-2,931,302	372
Cu (metal)	0	33.35	22.64	0.0063	0.000E+00	0	25
CuO	-155,854	42.59	43.83	0.0168	5.883E+05	-155,854	55
CuSO4	-769,982	109.24	73.41	0.1528	-1.231E+06	-769,982	105
Fe (metal)	0	27.15	17.49	0.0248	0.000E+00	0	25
FeO (wustite)	-272,044	60.75	50.80	0.0086	-3.310E+05	-272,044	50
Fe_2O_3 (hematite)	-825,503	87.45	98.28	0.0778	-1.485E+06	-825,503	105
Fe_3O_4 (magnetite)	-1,118,383	146.44	86.27	0.2089	0.000E+00	-1,118,383	149
$FeSO_4$	-928,848	120.96	122.01	0.0378	-2.929E+06	-928,848	100
$FeSO_4.7H_2O$	-3,014,570	409.20	122.01	0.0378	-2.929E+06	-3,014,570	100
$Fe_2(SO_4)_3$	-2,582,992	307.52	270.63	0.2253	-5.982E+06	-2,582,992	271
$Fe_2(SO_4)_3$, aq.	-2,825,000	-571.00	270.63	0.2253	-5.982E+06	-2,825,000	271
H_2 (gas)	0	130.58	27.28	0.0033	5.021E+05	0	34
HCl (aq)	-167,444	55.10	28.03	0.0035	0.000E+00	-167,444	29
HCl (gas)	-92,312	186.79	26.53	0.0046	1.088E+05	-92,312	29
HF (gas)	-271,100	173.78	26.90	0.0034	1.088E+05	-271,100	29
$H_2Cr_2O_7$	-1,490,300	261.90	118.74	0.0000	0.000E+00	-1,490,300	119
H_2O (liquid)	-285,830	69.50	75.35	0.0000	0.000E+00	-285,830	75
H_2O (vapor)	-242,463	188.72	30.00	0.0107	3.347E+04	-242,463	34
H_2SO_4(liquid)	-813,989	156.90	156.90	0.0284	-2.346E+06	-813,989	139
H_2SO_4(liquid) aq.	-909,267	20.08	58.16	0.1937	0.000E+00	-909,267	116
H_3PO_4(solid)	-1,261,476	110.54	49.83	0.1895	0.000E+00	-1,261,476	106
K_2O	-363,171	94.14	72.17	0.0418	0.000E+00	-363,171	85
K_2SO_4	-1,433,857	175.73	120.37	0.0996	-1.782E-04	-1,433,857	150

Substance	ΔH^0	S^0	a	b	c	$\Delta H(T)$	$Cp(T)$
	J/mol	J/(mol.K)	J/(mol.K)	J/(mol.K^2)	J.K/mol	J/mol	J/(mol.K)
La_2O_3	-1,793,262	128.03	120.75	0.0129	-1.372E+06	-1,793,262	109
$La_2(SO_4)_3$	-3,941,300	0.00	280.00	0.0000	0.000E+00	-3,941,300	280
Li_2O	-598,730	37.89	69.58	0.0179	-1.904E+06	-598,730	53
Li_2SO_4	-1,321,700	115.10	117.60	0.0000	0.000E+00	-1,321,700	118
MgO	-601,241	26.94	48.98	0.0031	-1143905.6	-601,241	37
$MgSO_4$	-1,284,906	91.63	106.44	0.0463	-2189905.6	-1,284,906	96
Mn (Metal)	0	32.01	23.85	0.0141	-1.569E+05	0	26
MnO	-384,928	59.83	46.48	0.0081	-3.682E+05	-384,928	45
$MnSO_4$	-1,065,246	112.13	122.42	0.0373	-2.946E+06	-1,065,246	100
Na_2O	-417,982	75.06	66.22	0.0439	-8.134E+05	-417,982	70
Na_2SO_4	-1,387,205	149.62	82.32	0.1544	0.000E+00	-1,387,205	128
Ni (metal)	0	29.87	32.64	-0.0018	-5.586E+05	0	26
NiO	-240,580	37.99	-20.88	0.1572	1.628E+06	-240,580	44
$NiSO_4$	-889,100	97.07	125.94	0.0415	0.000E+00	-889,100	138
O_2 (gas)	0	205.04	29.96	0.0042	-1.674E+05	0	29
P_4O_{10}	-2,984,029	228.86	140.57	0.3395	-2.675E+06	-2,984,029	212
SO_2 (gas)	-296,813	248.11	43.43	0.0106	-5.941E+05	-296,813	40
SO_3 (gas)	-395,765	256.65	57.15	0.0273	-1.291E+06	-395,765	51
ThO_2	-1,226,749	65.27	69.66	0.0089	-9.372E+05	-1,226,749	62
$Th(SO_4)_2$	-2,541,362	148.11	104.60	0.2310	0.000E+00	-2,541,362	173
TiO_2 (rutile)	-944,747	50.33	62.86	0.0114	-9.958E+05	-944,747	55
Ti_2O_3	-1,520,842	78.78	152.43	0.0000	-5.004E+06	-1,520,842	96
$TiSO_4$	-1,092,024	254.50	272.30	0.0000	0.000E+00	-1,092,024	272
$Ti_2(SO_4)_3$	-3,387,000	254.50	272.30	0.0000	0.000E+00	-3,387,000	272
$TiOSO_4$	-1,637,000	95.50	112.50	0.0000	0.000E+00	-1,637,000	113
V (metal)	0	28.79	20.50	0.0108	8.368E+04	0	25
V_2O_3	-1,225,912	98.32	122.80	0.0199	-2.268E+06	-1,225,912	103
V_2O_4	-1,435,112	102.93	62.59	0.0000	0.000E+00	-1,435,112	63
V_2O_5	-1,557,703	130.96	194.72	-0.0163	-5.531E+06	-1,557,703	128
VSO_4	-1,133,446	-112.52	0.00	0.0000	0.000E+00	-1,133,446	0
$V_2(SO_4)_3$	-3,240,508	-408.78	0.00	0.0000	0.000E+00	-3,240,508	0
$VOSO_4$	-1,203,444	113.99	0.00	0.0000	0.000E+00	-1,203,444	0
$(VO_2)_2SO_4$	-2,208,940	-66.10	0.00	0.0000	0.000E+00	-2,208,940	0
Zn (metal)	0	41.63	22.38	0.0100	0.000E+00	0	25
ZnO	-348,109	43.51	48.99	0.0051	-9.121E+05	-348,109	40
$ZnSO_4$	-978,638	128.03	91.63	0.0761	0.000E+00	-978,638	114

5.4 Standard Molar Enthalpy, and Entropy of Reaction

For a given single chemical species k, at a given absolute temperature T in K, its ***standard molar enthalpy***, denoted $H^0_k(T)$, in J.mol^{-1}, and ***standard molar entropy***, denoted $S^0_k(T)$, in J.K^{-1}.mol^{-1}, can be calculated using the two following equations:

$$H^0_k(T) = H^0_k(T_0) + \int Cp_k dT + \sum\Delta H_{tr}$$

$$S^0_k(T) = S^0_k(T_0) + \int [Cp_k/T]\, dT + \sum\Delta S_{tr}$$

For the two above equations, the temperature dependence of the ***molar heat capacity*** of a single chemical substance k denoted C_{pk}, in $J.K^{-1}.mol^{-1}$, can be described by the following polynomial empirical equation:

$$C_{pk}(T) = a_k + b_k T + c_k/T^2$$

Where the three ***empirical heat capacity coefficients*** a_k in $J.K^{-1}.mol^{-1}$, b_k in $J.K^{-2}.mol^{-1}$, and c_k in $J.K.mol^{-1}$, are determined from accurate calorimetric experiments.

On the other hand, the terms $\sum\Delta H_{tr}$ and $\sum\Delta S_{tr}$ are the sums of the ***latent molar enthalpies*** and ***latent molar entropies*** of all the transitions (e.g., phase change, fusion, vaporization, and sublimation) occurring eventually within the selected temperature range. Because these calculations are aimed to establish thermodynamic equations for aqueous solutions around room temperature most of the time these contributions are not relevant.

Hence, after a straightforward mathematical integration, we obtain:

$$H^0_k(T) = H^0_k(T_0) + a_k(T - T_0) + 0.5b_k(T^2 - T_0^2) + c_k(1/T_0 - 1/T) + \sum\Delta H_{tr}$$

$$S^0_k(T) = S^0_k(T_0) + a_k(\ln T - \ln T_0) + b_k(T - T_0) + 0.5c_k(1/T_0^2 - 1/T^2) + \sum\Delta S_{tr}$$

Regrouping all the constant terms together in bracket followed by the variables, we obtain the following two concise equations for the temperature dependence of the standard molar enthalpy and entropy respectively:

$$H^0_k(T) = [H^0_k(T_0) - a_k T_0 - 0.5b_k T_0^2 + c_k/T_0 + \sum\Delta H_{tr}] + a_k T + 0.5b_k T^2 - c_k/T$$

$$S^0_k(T) = [S^0_k(T_0) - a_k \ln T_0 - b_k T_0 + 0.5c_k/T_0^2 + \sum\Delta S_{tr}] + a_k \ln T + b_k T - 0.5c_k/T^2$$

5.5 Standard Molar Gibbs Enthalpy of Reaction

Afterwards, based on the definition of the molar ***Gibbs molar enthalpy*** below:

$$G^0(T) = H^0(T) - TS^0(T)$$

It is possible to establish the temperature dependence of the standard Gibbs free molar enthalpy of each redox reaction as:

$$G^0_k(T) = H^0_k(T_0) - TS^0_k(T_0) + a_k(T - T_0) + 0.5b_k(T^2 - T_0^2) + c_k(1/T_0 - 1/T) - T[a_k(\ln T - \ln T_0) + b_k(T - T_0) + 0.5c_k(1/T_0^2 - 1/T^2)]$$

As previously, regrouping all the constant terms together in bracket followed by the variables, we obtain the following condensed equation for the temperature dependence of the molar Gibbs enthalpy:

$$G^0_k(T) = [H^0_k(T_0) - a_kT_0 - 0.5b_kT_0^2 + c_k/T_0] + [a_k(1 + \ln T_0) + b_kT_0 - S^0_k(T_0) - 0.5c_k/T_0^2]T - 0.5b_kT^2 - 0.5c_k/T - a_kT\ln T$$

Therefore the temperature dependence of the overall standard Gibbs molar enthalpy is:

$$\Delta G^0(T) = [\Delta H^0(T_0) - \Delta aT_0 - 0.5\Delta bT_0^2 + \Delta c/T_0] + [\Delta a(1 + \ln T_0) + \Delta bT_0 - \Delta S^0(T_0) - 0.5\Delta c/T_0^2]T - 0.5\Delta bT^2 - 0.5\Delta c/T - \Delta aT\ln T$$

If only the first coefficient of the molar heat capacity of each component is available in the tables (i.e., $b_k = c_k = 0$) which is mainly the case for ionic and solvated species then the above equation can be simplified as follows:

$$\Delta G^0(T) = [\Delta H^0(T_0) - \Delta aT_0] + [\Delta a(1 + \ln T_0) - \Delta S^0(T_0)]T - \Delta aT\ln T$$

Based on the three above equations, for $H^0_k(T)$, $S^0_k(T)$, and $G^0_k(T)$, we can now establish the temperature dependence of the standard molar enthalpy, $\Delta_rH^0(T)$, standard molar entropy, $\Delta_rS^0(T)$, and molar Gibbs enthalpy, $\Delta_rG^0(T)$, for a given electrochemical redox reaction of the type:

Cathode: $\nu_O O + ze^- = \nu_R R$

Anode: $H_2(g) = 2H^+ + 2e^-$

Overall: $2\nu_O O + \nu_O H_2(g) = 2\nu_R R + 2\nu_O H^+$

Where ν_O and ν_R are the dimensionless stoichiometric coefficients of the oxidizing, and reducing species respectively, and z the number of electrons involved.

More generally, the Gibbs molar enthalpy of reaction is given by the following equation:

$$\Delta_rG^0(T) = \Delta_rH^0(T) - T\Delta S^0(T)$$

with $\Delta_rH^0(T) = \Sigma_k \nu_kH^0_k(T)$ and $\Delta S^0(T) = \Sigma_k \nu_kS^0_k(T)$

Where ν_k are the stoichiometric coefficients. By convention, these are taken positive for products ($\nu_k > 0$) and negative ($\nu_k < 0$) for reactants. At this point, it is worth to introducing the differential quantities:

$\Delta a = \Sigma_k \nu_k a_k \qquad \Delta b = \Sigma_k \nu_k b_k \qquad \Delta c = \Sigma_k \nu_k c_k$

Based on the above equations, it is then possible to establish the temperature dependence of the standard molar and Gibbs enthalpies for the half-reaction:

$$\Delta_r H^0(T) = [\Delta_r H^0{}_k(T_0) - \Delta a T_0 - 0.5\Delta b T_0^2 + \Delta c/T_0 + \Sigma_k \nu_k \Delta H_{tr}] + \Delta a T + 0.5\Delta b T^2 - \Delta c/T$$

$$\Delta_r G^0(T) = [\Delta H^0(T_0) - \Delta a T_0 - 0.5\Delta b T_0^2 + \Delta c/T_0 + \Sigma_k \nu_k \Delta H_{tr}] + [\Delta a(1 + \ln T_0) + \Delta b T_0 - \Delta S^0(T_0) - 0.5\Delta c/T_0^2]T - 0.5\Delta b T^2 - 0.5\Delta c/T - \Delta a T \ln T$$

We have summarized the two above equations along with their more concise forms utilising their related empirical coefficients A, B, C, D, and E and A^*, B^*, C^*, and D^* in Table 18.

Table 18 – Temperature dependence of molar and Gibbs enthalpies of reaction

Molar Gibbs enthalpy of reaction	$\Delta_r G^0(T) = [\Delta_r H^0(T_0) - \Delta a T_0 - 0.5\Delta b T_0^2 + \Delta c/T_0 + \Sigma_k \nu_k \Delta H_{tr}] + [\Delta a(1 + \ln T_0) + \Delta b T_0 - \Delta_r S^0(T_0) - 0.5\Delta c/T_0^2]T - 0.5\Delta b T^2 - 0.5\Delta c/T - \Delta a T \ln T$ $\Delta_r G^0(T) = \boldsymbol{A} + \boldsymbol{B}T + \boldsymbol{C}T^2 + \boldsymbol{D}/T + \boldsymbol{E}T\ln T$ $\boldsymbol{A} = [\Delta_r H^0(T_0) - \Delta a T_0 - 0.5\Delta b T_0^2 + \Delta c/T_0 + \Sigma_k \nu_k \Delta H_{tr}]$ $\boldsymbol{B} = [\Delta a(1 + \ln T_0) + \Delta b T_0 - \Delta_r S^0(T_0) - 0.5\Delta c/T_0^2]$ $\boldsymbol{C} = -0.5\Delta b$ $\boldsymbol{D} = -0.5\Delta c$ $\boldsymbol{E} = -\Delta a$
Molar enthalpy of reaction	$\Delta_r H^0(T) = [\Delta_r H^0(T_0) - \Delta a T_0 - 0.5\Delta b T_0^2 + \Delta c/T_0 + \Sigma_k \nu_k \Delta H_{tr}] + \Delta a T + 0.5\Delta b T^2 - \Delta c/T$ $\Delta_r H^0(T) = \boldsymbol{A^*} + \boldsymbol{B^*}T + \boldsymbol{C^*}T^2 + \boldsymbol{D^*}/T$ $\boldsymbol{A^*} = [\Delta_r H^0(T_0) - \Delta a T_0 - 0.5\Delta b T_0^2 + \Delta c/T_0 + \Sigma_k \nu_k \Delta H_{tr}]$ $\boldsymbol{B^*} = \Delta a$ $\boldsymbol{C^*} = 0.5\Delta b$ $\boldsymbol{D^*} = -\Delta c$

5.6 Standard Electrode Potential

Therefore, based on the two previous empirical equations, we can now calculate the standard electrode potential for any absolute temperature ranging from 273.15K (0°C) and 363.15K (90°C).

The standard oxidation-reduction potential or standard electrode potential E^0 for a given redox couple: $M^{z+}/M(s)$ is obtained by measuring the electromotive force *emf* of the galvanic cell established between the metallic electrode immersed in an electrolyte containing the metal cations, M^{z+}, and a reference electrode (RE).

The adopted international convention is that the reference electrode is the ***standard hydrogen electrode*** (SHE) at 298.15K with the activity of protons being a_{H+} equals to unity, and the fugacity of hydrogen equals to 101.325 kPa. In this case, the galvanic cell formed is of the type:

$$(+)(Pt) | M(s) | M^{n+} || H^+ || H_2(g) | (Pt)(-)$$

$$emf = E_{anode} - E_{cathode} = E - E_{SHE}$$

When the two electrode of the galvanic cell above are connected at the anode (-), the metal M(s) is oxidized, and it dissolves yielding metal cations M^{z+} going into the solution where z is the dimensionless number of electrons exchanged. The electrons then flow inside the electrical circuit toward the cathode (+) where hydrated protons are reduced, and nascent hydrogen gas evolves according to:

Anode (-): $M(s) = M^{z+} + ze^-$

Cathode (+): $2H^+ + 2e^- = H_2(g)$

Therefore the overall electrochemical reaction becomes, after adding the sulfate anions:

Overall: $2M(s) + zH_2SO_4 = M_2(SO_4)_z + zH_2(g)$

At a given absolute thermodynamic temperature T in K, the standard Gibbs molar enthalpy of the overall reaction given by the equation:

$$\Delta_r G^0(T) = -RT \ln K_p$$

From the Gibbs standard molar enthalpy, $\Delta G^0_{298.15K}$, in J/mol under standard conditions of temperature and pressure (298.15K, 101.325 kPa), it is possible to define the standard electrode potential as follows:

$$\Delta_r G^0(T) = -2zF\Delta E^0(T) = -2zF[E^0(T) - E^0_{H2/H^+}(T)]$$

As already established in Section 4.8.1, it was adopted internationally by the IUPAC in 1970 that the electrode potential of the standard hydrogen electrode at pH = 0 and at an absolute pressure of 101.325 kPa is always zero at all temperatures.

$$E^0_{298.15K}(H^+/H_2) = E^0_T\ (H^+/H_2) = 0.000\ V/SHE$$

Therefore, we obtain the simple equation:

$E^0_{298.15K} = -\Delta G^0_{298.15K}/zF$

From the above equation, we can classify the standard electrode potential of any redox couple vs. the SHE as reference.

Therefore, the standard Gibbs molar enthalpy is simply:

$\Delta_r G^0(T) = -zFE^0(T)$

$\Delta E^0(T) = E^0(T) = (\boldsymbol{A} + \boldsymbol{B}T + \boldsymbol{C}T^2 + \boldsymbol{D}/T + \boldsymbol{E}T\ln T)/(-zF)$

5.7 Sign Convention for Standard Electrode Potentials

The sign convention for the standard electrode potential of a half-reaction was adopted by the *International Union of Pure and Applied Chemistry* (IUPAC) in Stockholm in 1953 [59], called the ***Gibbs-Ostwald sign convention*** that supplanted the ***Nernst–Lewis–Latimer sign convention*** formerly used in North America.

Table 19 – Selected electrochemical reactions involving metal sulfates

1 H_2O					=	1 H_2	+	0.5 O_2		
1 $FeSO_4$	+	1 H_2			=	1 Fe(s)	+	1 H_2SO_4		
1 $FeSO_4.7H_2O$	+	1 H_2			=	1 Fe(s)	+	1 H_2SO_4	+	7 H_2O
1 $Fe_2(SO_4)_3$	+	1 H_2			=	2 $FeSO_4$	+	1 H_2SO_4		
1 $CuSO_4$	+	1 H_2			=	1 Cu(s)	+	1 H_2SO_4		
1 $NiSO_4$	+	1 H_2			=	1 Ni(s)	+	1 H_2SO_4		
1 $Cr_2(SO_4)_3$	+	3 H_2			=	2 Cr(s)	+	3 H_2SO_4		
1 $H_2Cr_2O_7$	+	3 H_2	+	3 H_2SO_4	=	1 $Cr_2(SO_4)_3$	+	7 H_2O		
1 $ZnSO_4$	+	1 H_2			=	1 Zn(s)	+	1 H_2SO_4		
1 $MnSO_4$	+	1 H_2			=	1 Mn(s)	+	1 H_2SO_4		
1 V_2O_5	+	1 H_2	+	2 H_2SO_4	=	2 $VOSO_4$	+	3 H_2O		
1 $(VO_2)_2SO_4$	+	1 H_2	+	1 H_2SO_4	=	2 $VOSO_4$	+	2 H_2O		
2 $VOSO_4$	+	1 H_2	+	1 H_2SO_4	=	1 $V_2(SO_4)_3$	+	2 H_2O		
1 $V_2(SO_4)_3$	+	1 H_2			=	2 VSO_4	+	1 H_2SO_4		
1 VSO_4	+	1 H_2			=	1 V(s)	+	1 H_2SO_4		
2 $TiOSO_4$	+	1 H_2	+	1 H_2SO_4	=	1 $Ti_2(SO_4)_3$	+	2 H_2O		
1 $Ti_2(SO_4)_3$	+	1 H_2			=	2 $TiSO_4$		1 H_2SO_4		

In this sign convention, where the standard electrode potential for the hydrogen electrode at pH = 0 and 101.325 kPa is always zero volt at all temperatures., the electrode potential of half-cell reaction with an electron acceptor

[59] VAN RYSSELBERGHE, P. (1954) Bericht der Kommission für elektrochemische Nomenklatur und Definitionen. *Zeitschrift zur Electrochemie*, **58**(1954) 530-535.

(i.e., oxidant) more oxidizing that the protons is positive while the electrode potential for half-cell reaction with an electron donor (i.e., reducer) more reducing than hydrogen is negative.

, We have reported in Table 20 the calculated empirical coefficients for the standard electrode potential for the selected redox chemical reactions occurring in sulfate media that are listed in Table 19. These redox couples are ordered by decreasing standard electrode potential.

Table 20 – Standard electrode potential for selected redox couples

$\Delta E_0(T) = A + BT + CT^2 + D/T + ET\ln T$								
Redox couple	Nernst potential	Empirical coefficients					T = 298.15K	pH
		A	B	C	D	E	E^0(298K)	**0.0000**
$Cl_2/2Cl^-$	$\Delta E^0(T)$	1.7264	-0.001	9.106E-09	-5.637E-01	-0.00004	**1.358** V/SHE	**1.3583**
Cr(VI)/Cr(III)	$\Delta E^0(T)$	1.5297	-0.006	-4.417E-07	-2.076E+00	0.00088	**1.232** V/SHE	**1.2320**
$O_2/2H_2O$	$\Delta E^0(T)$	1.5389	-0.002	-1.388E-08	-1.084E+00	0.00017	**1.229** V/SHE	**1.2290**
V(V)/V(IV)	$\Delta E^0(T)$	0.9372	-0.003	-5.243E-07	-2.385E+00	0.00051	**0.999** V/SHE	**1.0000**
Fe(III)/Fe(II)	$\Delta E^0(T)$	-0.5904	0.002	-3.225E-07	-9.789E-01	0.00053	**0.771** V/SHE	**0.7710**
Cu(II)/Cu	$\Delta E^0(T)$	0.2979	-0.002	-3.146E-07	1.889E+00	0.00041	**0.342** V/SHE	**0.3419**
V(IV)/V(IIII)	$\Delta E^0(T)$	1.0937	-0.003	-4.965E-07	-2.168E-01	0.00017	**0.338** V/SHE	**0.3370**
Ti(IV)/Ti(III)	$\Delta E^0(T)$	0.8091	-0.004	-9.599E-08	-2.385E+00	0.00024	**0.099** V/SHE	**0.1000**
$2H^+/H_2$	$\Delta E^0(T)$	0.0000	0.000	0.000E+00	0.000E+00	0.00000	0.000 V/SHE	0.0000
V(III)/V(II)	$\Delta E^0(T)$	-0.2678	-0.001	4.935E-07	-1.301E+00	0.00016	**-0.255** V/SHE	**-0.2550**
Ni(II)/Ni	$\Delta E^0(T)$	-0.3252	-0.001	-4.701E-08	-2.748E+00	0.00019	**-0.257** V/SHE	**-0.2570**
Fe(II)/Fe	$\Delta E^0(T)$	0.1678	-0.016	4.597E-07	6.288E+00	0.00235	**-0.447** V/SHE	**-0.4470**
Cr(III)/Cr	$\Delta E^0(T)$	-0.8359	0.000	1.873E-08	-5.706E-01	0.00012	**-0.744** V/SHE	**-0.7440**
Zn(II)/Zn	$\Delta E^0(T)$	-0.7782	-0.002	-1.061E-07	-1.301E+00	0.00031	**-0.762** V/SHE	**-0.7618**
Ti(III)/Ti(II)	$\Delta E^0(T)$	-0.8471	-0.009	4.935E-07	-1.301E+00	0.00157	**-0.900** V/SHE	**-0.9000**
V(II)/V	$\Delta E^0(T)$	-1.1225	-0.001	4.935E-07	-1.301E+00	0.00016	**-1.175** V/SHE	**-1.1750**
Mn(II)/Mn	$\Delta E^0(T)$	-7.7458	0.045	-7.067E-05	7.226E+00	-0.00037	**-1.185** V/SHE	**-1.1850**

5.8 Standard Reversible Cell Voltage

Let's consider two electrode reactions occurring inside an electrolyzer with their respective standard electrode potentials:

Anode (+): $aR_2 = bO_2 + n_2e^-$ $E^0_{298.15K}$ (2)

Cathode (-): $cO_1 + n_1e^- = dR_1$ $E^0_{298.15K}$ (1)

After balancing the two electrode reactions, the overall electrochemical reaction when $E^0_{298.15K}$ (2) > $E^0_{298.15K}$ (1) is given by:

$n_2cO_1 + n_1aR_2 = n_2dR_1 + n_1bO_2$

From the standard electrode potentials at a given absolute thermodynamic temperature T, in K, it is then possible to calculate the ***standard reversible cell voltage***, denoted ΔE^0, in V, for the above electrochemical reaction. It is defined as the algebraic difference between the standard electrode potentials for the oxidation reaction occurring at the anode (+) minus the standard electrode potential for the reduction reaction occurring at the cathode (-).

$$\Delta E^0_{298.15K} = E^0(+) - E^0(-) = E^0_{298.15K}(2) - E^0_{298.15K}(1)$$

5.9 Nernst Electrode Potential

Let's consider two electrode reactions occurring inside an electrolyzer with their respective standard electrode potentials:

Anode (-): $M(s) = M^{z+} + ze^-$

Cathode (+): $2H^+ + 2e^- = H_2(g)$

Therefore the overall electrochemical reaction becomes:

Overall: $2M(s) + 2zH^+ = 2M^{z+} + zH_2(g)$

The stability constant K_p is given by:

$$K_p = (M^{z+})^2 f_{H2}{}^{2z} / [(M)^2(H^+)^{2z}]$$

The relationship between the Gibbs enthalpy and the stability constant is:

$$\Delta_r G^0(T) = -RT \ln K_p$$

Thus we have:

$$\Delta_r G^0(T) = -RT \ln\{(M^{z+})^2 f_{H2}{}^{2z} / [(M)^2(H^+)^{2z}]\}$$

$$\Delta_r G^0(T) = -2RT \ln[(M^{z+})/(M)] - 2zRT \ln f_{H2}/(H^+)$$

$$\Delta_r G^0(T) = -2zF[E^0(T) - E^0_{H2/H^+}(T)]$$

From the standard electrode potentials knowing the activities and fugacity's of involved electroactive species, the Nernstian electrode potentials at a given absolute temperature T, in K, using the well-known Nernst equation:

Anode (+):

$$E_2(T) = E^0_{298.15K}\ (2) + (RT/n_2F)\ \ln[(O_2)^a/(R_2)^b]$$

Cathode (-):

$$E_1(T) = E^0_{298.15K}\ (1) + (RT/n_1F)\ \ln[(O_1)^c/(R_1)^d]$$

5.10 Thermodynamic (Reversible) Cell Voltage

From the Nernst electrode potentials at a given absolute thermodynamic temperature T, in K, it is then possible to calculate the ***thermodynamic cell voltage***, also called the ***reversible cell voltage***, denoted ΔE_{th}, in V, for the above electrochemical reaction. It is defined as the algebraic difference between the standard electrode potentials for the oxidation reaction occurring at the anode (+) minus the standard electrode potential for the reduction reaction occurring at the cathode (-).

$$\Delta E_{th}(T) = [E_2(T) - E_1(T)] = = - \Delta_r G(T)/nF$$

This introducing the standard reversible cell voltage defined previously we obtain the following equations:

$$\Delta E_{th}(T) = [E^0_{298.15K}\ (2) - E^0_{298.15K}\ (1)] + (RT/n_1n_2F) \ln\{[(O_2)^a/(R_2)^b]^{n2}/[(O_1)^c/(R_1)^d]^{n1}\}$$

$$\Delta E_{th}(T) = \Delta E^0_{298.15K} + (RT/n_1n_2F) \ln\{[(O_2)^a/(R_2)^b]^{n2}/[(O_1)^c/(R_1)^d]^{n1}\}$$

5.11 Standard Thermoneutral Potential

The ***thermoneutral electrode potential***, denoted $e^0(T)$, in V, not only ensures that the electrochemical reaction move forward completion but it also generates the amount heat required to maintain a constant temperature by offsetting the rate of entropy production ($\partial S/\partial t$) inside the electrolyzer.

Therefore when conducting the electrolysis at the thermoneutral voltage, the entropy production rate is zero, and the thermoneutral voltage is simply calculated from the enthalpy of the electrochemical reaction as follows:

$$\Delta_r H^0(T) = -zF\Delta e^0(T) = -zF[e^0(T) - e^0_{H2/H+}(T)]$$

As already established in Section 5.6 adopting the same international convention for the thermoneutral electrode potential for the hydrogen electrode at pH = 0 and absolute pressure of 101.325 kPa is always zero at all temperatures:

$$e^0_{H2/H+}(T) = 0.00\ \text{V}$$

Therefore, the standard molar enthalpy is simply:

$$\Delta_r H^0(T) = -zFe^0(T)$$

$$\Delta e^0(T) = e^0(T) = (\boldsymbol{A} + \boldsymbol{B}T + \boldsymbol{C}T^2 + \boldsymbol{D}/T)/(-zF)$$

Table 21 – Standard thermoneutral potential for selected redox couples

$\Delta E_{TN}(T) = \boldsymbol{A} + \boldsymbol{B}T + \boldsymbol{C}T^2 + \boldsymbol{D}/T$						
Redox couple	Thermo-neutral potential	Empirical coefficients				T = 298.15K
		A	**B**	**C**	**D**	E_{TN}(298K)
$Cl_2/2Cl^-$	$\Delta E_{TN}(T)$	1.7275	4.206E-05	-9.106E-09	-1.127E+00	**1.735** V/SHE
Cr(VI)/Cr(III)	$\Delta E_{TN}(T)$	1.4709	-8.818E-04	4.417E-07	-4.152E+00	**1.233** V/SHE
$O_2/2H_2O$	$\Delta E_{TN}(T)$	1.5384	-1.715E-04	1.388E-08	-2.168E+00	**1.481** V/SHE
V(V)/V(IV)	$\Delta E_{TN}(T)$	0.6116	4.103E-04	9.839E-07	2.389E+01	**0.902** V/SHE
Fe(III)/Fe(II)	$\Delta E_{TN}(T)$	0.6574	5.338E-04	-3.225E-07	1.958E+00	**0.795** V/SHE
Cu(II)/Cu	$\Delta E_{TN}(T)$	0.3092	-4.086E-04	3.146E-07	3.777E+00	**0.228** V/SHE
V(IV)/V(IIII)	$\Delta E_{TN}(T)$	-2.6346	3.382E-04	-5.104E-07	2.602E+00	**-2.570** V/SHE
Ti(IV)/Ti(III)	$\Delta E_{TN}(T)$	0.8910	-2.431E-04	9.599E-08	-4.770E+00	**0.811** V/SHE
$2H^+/H_2$	$\Delta E_{TN}(T)$	0.0000	0.000E+00	0.000E+00	0.000E+00	**0.000 V/SHE**
V(III)/V(II)	$\Delta E_{TN}(T)$	-0.2332	-1.600E-04	-4.935E-07	-2.602E+00	**-0.333** V/SHE
Ni(II)/Ni	$\Delta E_{TN}(T)$	-0.3189	-1.882E-04	4.701E-08	-5.496E+00	**-0.389** V/SHE
Fe(II)/Fe	$\Delta E_{TN}(T)$	0.1584	-2.352E-03	-4.597E-07	1.258E+01	**-0.541** V/SHE
Cr(III)/Cr	$\Delta E_{TN}(T)$	-0.8035	-1.216E-04	-1.873E-08	-1.141E+00	**-0.845** V/SHE
Zn(II)/Zn	$\Delta E_{TN}(T)$	-0.7607	-3.129E-04	1.061E-07	-2.602E+00	**-0.853** V/SHE
Ti(III)/Ti(II)	$\Delta E_{TN}(T)$	-1.0009	-1.571E-03	-4.935E-07	-2.602E+00	**-1.522** V/SHE
V(II)/V	$\Delta E_{TN}(T)$	-1.0614	-1.600E-04	-4.935E-07	-2.602E+00	**-1.162** V/SHE
Mn(II)/Mn	$\Delta E_{TN}(T)$	-7.7442	3.744E-04	7.067E-05	1.445E+01	**-1.302** V/SHE

5.12 Thermoneutral Cell Voltage

The ***thermoneutral cell voltage***, denoted ΔE_{TN} or U_{TN}, in V is the cell voltage necessary to conduct the electrochemical reaction while providing the amount of heat necessary to maintain a constant temperature. The thermoneutral voltage is simply given by:

$$\Delta E_{TN}(T) = U_{TN}(T) = -\Delta_R H(T)/zF$$

For instance, this physical quantity is particularly relevant during the electrolysis of pure water according to: $H_2O = H_2(g) + 0.5O_2(g)$ with a standard electrode potential of 1.229 V/SHE and a thermoneutral potential is 1.481 V/SHE for the oxygen gas evolution meaning that the reversible and thermoneutral cell voltage for the decomposition of water at 298.15K are 1.229 V and 1.481 V respectively. The latter figure is the operating voltage mandatory to keep a constant temperature during electrolysis without the need to supply heat externally.

In Table 22 below, we have calculated the reversible and thermoneutral cell voltages for the decomposition of water and ferrous sulfate by electrolysis

Table 22 – Standard reversible and thermoneutral cell voltages for water and $FeSO_4$

		273.15K	283.15K	293.15K	**298.15K**	303.15K	313.15K	323.15K	333.15K	343.15K	353.15K	363.15K
		0°C	10°C	20°C	25°C	30°C	40°C	50°C	60°C	70°C	80°C	90°C
$E_{TN}(O_2/H_2O)$	V/SHE	1.485	1.483	1.482	1.481	1.481	1.479	1.478	1.476	1.475	1.473	1.472
$E^0(O_2/H_2O)$ V/SHE	V/SHE	1.250	1.242	1.233	1.229	1.225	1.216	1.208	1.200	1.191	1.183	1.175
$U_{TN}(H_2O)$	**V**	**1.485**	**1.483**	**1.482**	**1.481**	**1.481**	**1.479**	**1.478**	**1.476**	**1.475**	**1.473**	**1.472**
$U^0(H_2O)$	**V**	**1.250**	**1.242**	**1.233**	**1.229**	**1.225**	**1.216**	**1.208**	**1.200**	**1.191**	**1.183**	**1.175**
$E^0(Fe^{2+}/Fe)$	V/SHE	-0.451	-0.450	-0.448	-0.447	-0.445	-0.442	-0.437	-0.432	-0.425	-0.418	-0.410
$E_{TN}(Fe^{2+}/Fe)$	V/SHE	-0.472	-0.500	-0.528	-0.541	-0.555	-0.583	-0.611	-0.638	-0.666	-0.694	-0.722
$U^0(FeSO_4)$	**V**	**1.701**	**1.692**	**1.682**	**1.676**	**1.670**	**1.658**	**1.645**	**1.631**	**1.617**	**1.601**	**1.585**
$U_{TN}(FeSO_4)$	**V**	**1.957**	**1.983**	**2.010**	**2.023**	**2.036**	**2.062**	**2.088**	**2.115**	**2.141**	**2.167**	**2.194**

From the above table, we can see that conducting the electrolysis of an aqueous solution of ferrous sulfate the thermoneutral cell voltage at 60°C (333.15K) is 2.115 V compared to 1.631 V for the reversible cell voltage.

5.13 Calculated Electrode Potentials vs. Temperature

We have intentionally detailed the calculations for obtaining the temperature dependence of the Gibbs molar enthalpy and molar enthalpy for a set of selected electrochemical reactions occurring during the electrowinning of iron in sulfate media, these calculations are reported in Table 23.

Table 23 – Thermodynamic functions of relevant reactions in sulfate medium

$T_0 =$		298.15 K				$T =$	298.15 K			**O_2**
Reaction	1	H_2O		= 1	H_2	+ 0.5	O_2		Variation	
		18.01528			2.01588		31.9988		0.0	kg/mol
ΔH^0		-285,830			0		0		285,830	J/mol
S^0		69.50			130.58		205.04		163.6	J/(mol.K)
a_k		75.35			27.28		29.96		-33.09	J/(mol.K)
b_k		0			0.003264		0.004184		0.0054	J/(mol.K^2)
c_k		0			502,080		-167,360		418,400	J.K/mol
		A	*B*		*C*		*D*	*E*		
$\Delta G(T)$		296,861.80	-385.999		-0.00267776		-209,200	33.09260	237,052	J/mol
$\Delta E(T)$		1.5383783	-2.00030E-03		-1.38765E-08		-1.084103	1.71490E-04	1.2284	V/SHE
$\Delta E(T)^*$		1.5389410	-2.00030E-03		-1.38765E-08		-1.084103	1.71490E-04	1.2290	V/SHE
									accepted **1.2290**	**V/SHE**

$T_0 =$	298.15 K						$T =$	298.15 K			
Reaction	1 $FeSO_4$	+	1 H_2	=	1 Fe	+	1	H_2SO_4		Variation	**Fe(II)**
	151.9086		2.01588		55.845			98.07948		0.0 kg/mol	
ΔH^0	-928,848		0		0			-813,989		114,859 J/mol	
S^0	120.96		130.58		27.15			156.90		63.1 J/(mol K)	
a_k	122.01		27.28		17.49			156.90		25.10 J/(mol K)	
b_k	0.03782		0.003264		0.024769			0.02843		0.0121 J/(mol.K^2)	
c_k	-2,928,800		502,080		0			0		2,426,720 J.K/mol	
	A		*B*		*C*			*D*	*E*		
$\Delta G(T)$	114,976.697		94.969		-6.05593E-03			-1,213,360	-25.099		96,046 J/mol
$\Delta E(T)$	-0.595825		-4.92140E-04		3.13826E-08			6.287797	1.30069E-04		-0.498 V/SHE
$\Delta E(T)^x$	-0.545100		-4.92140E-04		3.13826E-08			6.287797	1.30069E-04		-0.447 V/SHE
										accepted	-0.447 V/SHE

$T_0 =$	298.15 K						$T =$	298.15 K			
Reaction	1 $FeSO_4.7H_2O$	+	1 H_2	=	1 Fe	+	1	H_2SO_4 (a.i)	+ 7 H_2O	Variation	**Fe(II)**
	278.01556		2.01588		55.845			98.07948	18.01528	0.0 kg/mol	
ΔH^0	-3,014,570		0		0			-909,267	-285,830	104,493 J/mol	
S^0	409.20		130.58		27.15			20.08	69.50	55.0 J/(mol K)	
a_k	122.01		27.28		17.49			58.16	75.35	453.82 J/(mol K)	
b_k	0.03782		0.003264		0.024769			0.19372	0	0.1774 J/(mol.K^2)	
c_k	-2,928,800		502,080		0			0	0	2,426,720 J.K/mol	
	A		*B*		*C*			*D*	*E*		
$\Delta G(T)$	-30,557.775		3023.686		-8.87025E-02			-1,213,360	-453.816		88,084 J/mol
$\Delta E(T)$	0.158355		-1.56692E-02		4.59668E-07			6.287797	2.35174E-03		-0.456 V/SHE
$\Delta E(T)^x$	0.167818		-1.56692E-02		4.59668E-07			6.287797	2.35174E-03		-0.447 V/SHE
										accepted	-0.447 V/SHE

$T_0 =$	298.15 K						$T =$	298.15 K			
Reaction	1 $Fe_2(SO_4)_3$	+	1 H_2	=	2 $FeSO_4$	+	1	H_2SO_4		Variation	**Fe(III)**
	399.8808		2.01588		151.9086			98.07948		0.0 kg/mol	
ΔH^0	-2,825,000		0		-928,848			-813,989		153,315 J/mol	
S^0	-571.00		130.58		120.96			156.90		969.8 J/(mol K)	
a_k	270.63		27.28		122.01			156.90		103.02 J/(mol K)	
b_k	0.22528		0.003264		0.03782			0.02843		-0.1245 J/(mol.K^2)	
c_k	-5,981,865		502,080		-2,928,800			0		-377,815 J.K/mol	
	A		*B*		*C*			*D*	*E*		
$\Delta G(T)$	126,866.801		-314.859		6.22404E-02			188.908	-103.01502		-135,838 J/mol
$\Delta E(T)$	-0.657441		1.63164E-03		-3.22538E-07			-0.978945	5.33838E-04		0.704 V/SHE
$\Delta E(T)^x$	-0.590370		1.63164E-03		-3.22538E-07			-0.978945	5.33838E-04		0.771 V/SHE
										accepted	0.771 V/SHE

5.14 Influence of pH

Several electrochemical reactions reported in Table 19 involve oxygenated cations and protons are taking with the oxygen and hydrogen evolution reactions. Therefore, the Nernst electrode potential for these reactions depends on the pH. Common examples are the discharge of the protons with evolution of nascent hydrogen gas and the oxidation of water with evolution of oxygen:

$$2H_2O = O_2(g) + 4H^+ + 4e^-$$

$$E(O_2/H_2O) = E^0_{298.15K}(O_2/H_2O) + (RT\ln 10/4F)\log_{10} f_{O2} - (RT\ln 10/F)\text{pH}$$

$$2H^+ + 2e^- = H_2(g)$$

$$E(2H^+/H_2) = -(RT\ln 10/F)\text{pH} - (RT\ln 10/2F)\log_{10} f_{H2}$$

We have reported in Table **24** the standard electrode potentials as a function of the temperature and pH for several half electrochemical reactions.

Table 24 – Standard electrode potential vs. pH and temperature

Practical temperature		25°C	30°C	40°C	50°C	54°C	60°C	70°C	80°C	90°C
Absolute thermodynamic temperature	pH	298.15 K	303.15 K	313.15 K	323.15 K	327.15 K	333.15 K	343.15 K	353.15 K	363.15 K
Redox half-cell		Nernst electrode potentials (E^0/V vs.SHE)								
$O_2/2H_2O$	**0.00**	**1.2290**	**1.2248**	**1.2163**	**1.2079**	**1.2046**	**1.1996**	**1.1913**	**1.1830**	**1.1748**
$O_2/2H_2O$	-0.15	1.2297	1.2257	1.2175	1.2094	1.2062	1.2014	1.1934	1.1854	1.1775
$O_2/2H_2O$	-0.25	1.2302	1.2263	1.2183	1.2104	1.2073	1.2026	1.1948	1.1870	1.1793
$O_2/2H_2O$	-0.50	1.2315	1.2277	1.2203	1.2129	1.2100	1.2056	1.1982	1.1910	1.1838
$O_2/2H_2O$	-1.00	1.2340	1.2307	1.2243	1.2179	1.2153	1.2115	1.2052	1.1989	1.1927
VO_2^+/VO^{2+}	0.80	0.806	0.806	0.806	0.805	0.805	0.805	0.805	0.805	0.805
VO_2^+/VO^{2+}	1.00	0.782	0.782	0.781	0.780	0.779	0.779	0.778	0.777	0.776
VO_2^+/VO^{2+}	1.50	0.723	0.722	0.719	0.716	0.714	0.713	0.710	0.707	0.704
VO_2^+/VO^{2+}	2.00	0.664	0.661	0.656	0.651	0.649	0.646	0.642	0.637	0.632
VO_2^+/VO^{2+}	2.25	0.634	0.631	0.625	0.619	0.617	0.613	0.608	0.602	0.596
VO_2^+/VO^{2+}	2.50	0.605	0.601	0.594	0.587	0.585	0.580	0.573	0.567	0.560
Fe^{3+}/Fe^{2+}		0.787	0.813	0.864	0.915	0.935	0.966	1.017	1.068	1.120
Cu^{2+}/Cu		0.214	0.214	0.214	0.214	0.214	0.214	0.214	0.215	0.215
VO^{2+}/V^{3+}	0.80	0.144	0.128	0.097	0.065	0.052	0.033	0.001	-0.030	-0.062
VO^{2+}/V^{3+}	1.00	0.120	0.104	0.072	0.039	0.026	0.007	-0.026	-0.058	-0.091
VO^{2+}/V^{3+}	1.50	0.061	0.044	0.010	-0.025	-0.039	-0.059	-0.094	-0.129	-0.163
VO^{2+}/V^{3+}	2.00	0.002	-0.016	-0.052	-0.089	-0.104	-0.125	-0.162	-0.199	-0.235
VO^{2+}/V^{3+}	2.25	-0.027	-0.046	-0.084	-0.121	-0.136	-0.158	-0.196	-0.234	-0.271
VO^{2+}/V^{3+}	2.50	-0.057	-0.076	-0.115	-0.153	-0.168	-0.192	-0.230	-0.269	-0.307
$2H^+/H_2$	**0.00**	**0.000**	**0.000**	**0.000**	**0.000**	**0.000**	**0.000**	**0.000**	**0.000**	**0.000**
$2H^+/H_2$	0.50	-0.030	-0.030	-0.031	-0.032	-0.032	-0.033	-0.034	-0.035	-0.036
$2H^+/H_2$	0.66	-0.039	-0.040	-0.041	-0.042	-0.043	-0.044	-0.045	-0.046	-0.048
$2H^+/H_2$	0.80	-0.047	-0.048	-0.050	-0.051	-0.052	-0.053	-0.054	-0.056	-0.058
$2H^+/H_2$	1.00	-0.059	-0.060	-0.062	-0.064	-0.065	-0.066	-0.068	-0.070	-0.072
$2H^+/H_2$	1.50	-0.089	-0.090	-0.093	-0.096	-0.097	-0.099	-0.102	-0.105	-0.108
$2H^+/H_2$	2.00	-0.118	-0.120	-0.124	-0.128	-0.130	-0.132	-0.136	-0.140	-0.144
$2H^+/H_2$	2.25	-0.133	-0.135	-0.140	-0.144	-0.146	-0.149	-0.153	-0.158	-0.162
$2H^+/H_2$	2.50	-0.148	-0.150	-0.155	-0.160	-0.162	-0.165	-0.170	-0.175	-0.180
TiO^{2+}/Ti^{3+}	0.80	-0.033	-0.048	-0.073	-0.096	-0.107	-0.124	-0.149	-0.175	-0.037
TiO^{2+}/Ti^{3+}	1.00	-0.057	-0.073	-0.099	-0.122	-0.134	-0.151	-0.177	-0.203	-0.037
TiO^{2+}/Ti^{3+}	1.50	-0.117	-0.135	-0.163	-0.187	-0.200	-0.219	-0.247	-0.276	-0.037
TiO^{2+}/Ti^{3+}	2.00	-0.177	-0.197	-0.227	-0.252	-0.266	-0.287	-0.318	-0.348	-0.037
TiO^{2+}/Ti^{3+}	2.25	-0.207	-0.228	-0.259	-0.284	-0.299	-0.322	-0.353	-0.384	-0.037
TiO^{2+}/Ti^{3+}	2.50	-0.237	-0.259	-0.291	-0.317	-0.332	-0.356	-0.388	-0.420	-0.037
V^{3+}/V^{2+}		-0.354	-0.354	-0.353	-0.352	-0.352	-0.351	-0.350	-0.349	-0.348
Ni^{2+}/Ni		-0.354	-0.353	-0.351	-0.350	-0.349	-0.348	-0.347	-0.345	-0.344
Fe^{2+}/Fe		**-0.439**	**-0.437**	**-0.433**	**-0.430**	**-0.428**	**-0.426**	**-0.422**	**-0.418**	**-0.414**
Cr^{3+}/Cr		-0.795	-0.793	-0.790	-0.788	-0.786	-0.785	-0.782	-0.779	-0.776
Zn^{2+}/Zn		-0.846	-0.845	-0.844	-0.843	-0.843	-0.842	-0.841	-0.840	-0.839
V^{2+}/V		**-1.224**	**-1.224**	**-1.224**	**-1.224**	**-1.224**	**-1.224**	**-1.223**	**-1.223**	**-1.222**
Mn^{2+}/Mn		-1.257	-1.257	-1.270	-1.297	-1.312	-1.338	-1.393	-1.463	-1.546

5.15 Reference Electrodes

Reference electrodes can be grouped into three main categories: (i) electrode of the first kind, (ii) electrode of the second kind, and (ii) electrode of the third kind. For a comprehensive coverage of the subject, we recommend the comprehensive monograph edited by Ives and Janz [60]

[60] IVES, D.J.G.; and JANZ, G.J. (eds.)(1961) *Reference Electrodes: Theory and Practice.* Academic Press, New York, NY.

5.15.1 Reference Electrode of the First Kind

A ***reference electrode of the first kind*** involves only two electroactive species of the same chemical element, and it can be split into three sub-classes according to the nature of one of the electroactive species: (i) redox electrodes were both electroactive species are dissolved into an electrolyte; (ii) metallic electrodes were one electroactive species is in the metallic state; and finally (iii) gas electrodes where one electroactive species is in the gaseous state.

5.15.1.1 Redox or Inert Electrode

This type of reference electrodes is made of an inert electronic conductor that does not participate to the electrochemical reaction which is immersed or in contact with an electrolyte containing a homogenous redox system consisting of a mixture of two electroactive species of the same chemical element either anions or cations but with different oxidation states (e.g., Fe^{3+}/Fe^{2+}). The electrode must be made of an inert material made of noble or precious metals (e.g., Ag, Au) or of platinum group metals (e.g., Pt, Ir), carbon-based materials (e.g., impervious graphite, pyrolytic graphite, glassy or vitreous carbon, boron doped diamond), or even semiconducting advanced ceramics (e.g., SiC, Si_3N_4, B_4C).

For instance for a platinum wire immersed into a solution containing Fe(III) and Fe(II) cations, the half electrochemical cell can be written as:

$$(Pt) \mid Fe^{3+}(aq) \mid Fe^{2+}(aq)$$

That corresponds to the basic electrochemical reaction:

$$Fe^{3+} + e- = Fe^{2+} \qquad E^0_{298.15}(Fe^{3+}/Fe^{2+})$$

The electrode potential is then given by the Nernst equation:

$$E = E^0_{298.15}(Fe^{3+}/Fe^{2+}) + (RT\ln 10/F)\log_{10}(Fe^{3+})/(Fe^{2+})$$

Due to the conservation of the iron element Fe, the sum of all the activities must be equal to the total concentration of Fe into the electrolyte:

$$(Fe^{3+}) + (Fe^{2+}) = (Fe_{total})$$

Therefore activities of both species are interrelated and the Nernst equation can be rearranged as follows:

$$E = E^0_{298.15}(Fe^{3+}/Fe^{2+}) + (RT\ln 10/F)\log_{10}\{(Fe^{3+})/[(Fe_{total}) - (Fe^{3+})]\}$$

For studying the variations of metallic electrode potential versus activities of the redox species, the first and second partial derivatives vs. the activity of (Fe^{3+}) $= a$:

$$\partial E/\partial a = (RT/F)(Fe_{total})/[(Fe^{3+})(Fe_{total}) - (Fe^{3+})^2]$$

The first partial derivative is always positive over the entire range of activities from zero to (Fe_{total}), therefore the electrode potential strictly follows the activity of oxidizing species (Fe^{3+}).

$$\partial^2 E/\partial a^2 = (RT/F)(Fe_{total})[(Fe_{total}) - 2(Fe^{3+})]/\{(Fe_{total}) - (Fe^{3+})]^2(Fe^{3+})^2\}$$

Moreover, because the second partial derivative equal zero when the activities verify (Fe^{3+}) = (Fe^{2+}) = (Fe_{total})/2, the plot of the electrode potential curve $E = f[(Fe^{3+})]$ exhibits a point of inflexion with a minimal slope around equimolar conditions.

Therefore, any addition of electroactive species into the equimolar electrolyte does not impact strongly the electrode potential, and this behavior can be compared with the buffer effect in acid-base theory.

Redox electrodes are usually called comparison electrodes or also ***quasi-reference electrodes***. These electrodes are especially suited and utilized as reference electrodes when no other reference electrodes can be used due to critical technical issues (i.e., severe corrosion of materials, high temperatures), for instance in highly corrosive electrolytes.

5.15.1.2 Metallic Electrodes

If one of the electroactive species is in the metallic state (e.g., copper rod, liquid mercury pool, or wire of pure iron metal) immersed into an electrolyte containing cations of the same metal we obtained a so-called metallic electrode (e.g., $Cu^{2+}/Cu(s)$). For instance, consider a rod of a pure copper immersed into an electrolyte with cupric , the half electrochemical cell can be written:

$$Cu(s) \mid Cu^{2+}$$

The electrode potential of the copper electrode is given by the Nernst equation:

$$E = E^0_{298.15}(Cu^{2+}/Cu) + (RT\ln 10/2F)\log_{10}(Cu^{2+})$$

5.15.1.3 Gas Electrodes

A gas electrode can be regarded as a particular redox electrode system at which the thermodynamic equilibrium is established between: (i) free electrons of a chemically inert electronic conductor such as of noble or precious metals (e.g., Ag,

Au) or of platinum group metals (e.g., Pt, Ir), carbon-based materials (e.g., impervious graphite, pyrolytic graphite, glassy or vitreous carbon, boron doped diamond), or even semiconducting advanced ceramics, (ii) a dissolved polyatomic molecular gas of a chemical element (e.g., hydrogen, oxygen, or chlorine) under a standard pressure, bubbling into an electrolyte solution containing either anions or cations of this element. The well-known example is the standard hydrogen electrode that will be described in details Section 5.15.4 and in a lesser extent the chlorine electrode.

5.15.2 Reference Electrode of the Second Kind

This type of reference electrode corresponds to an extension of the first kind metallic electrodes. Actually, a second kind electrode consists to a metal {M} either solid (e.g., Zn) or liquid (e.g., Hg) covered by an adherent layer of an insoluble salt of the metal ($M^{n+}{}_pX^{p-}{}_n$), this system being then immersed into an electrolyte in which the metallic salt is insoluble but that contains the anions X^{p-}. The half electrochemical cell can be written:

$$(\mathrm{Pt})\,|\,\mathrm{M(s,l)}\,|\,\mathrm{M}^{n+}{}_p\mathrm{X}^{p-}{}_n\mathrm{(s)}\,||\,\mathrm{N}^{m+},\ \mathrm{X}^{p-}$$

That corresponds to the electrochemical, and precipitation chemical reactions:

$$M^{n+} + ne^- = M(s) \qquad E^0_{298.15}[M^{n+}/M(s)]$$

$$pM^{n+} + nX^{p-} = M^{n+}{}_pX^{p-}{}_n(s) \qquad Ks = (M^{n+})^p(X^{p-})^n$$

If we combine the two above reactions, we obtain then the scheme of the overall electrochemical reaction:

$$M^{n+}{}_pX^{p-}{}_n(s) + npe^- = pM(s) + nX^{p-} \qquad E^0_{298.15}[M^{n+}{}_pX^{p-}{}_n(s)/M(s)]$$

The electrode potential of this system is given by the Nernst equation:

$$E = E^0_{298.15}[M^{n+}{}_pX^{p-}{}_n(s)/M(s)] - (RT\ln 10/pF)\log_{10}(X^{p-})$$

The above equation indicates that under constant temperature and pressure condition, the electrode potential of the system depends only on the activity of the anion involved in the precipitate or insoluble salt. This type of electrode can be used as ***ion-selective electrode***.

If we introduce the Nernst equation of the corresponding first kind metallic electrode is introduce:

$$E = E^0_{298.15}(M^{n+}/M) + (RT\ln 10/nF)\log_{10}(M^{n+})$$

$$E = E^0_{298.15}(M^{n+}/M) + (RT\ln 10/npF)\log_{10}[Ks/(X^{p-})^n]$$

$$E = E^0_{298.15}(M^{n+}/M) + (RT\ln 10/npF)\log_{10}Ks - (RT\ln 10/pF)\log_{10}(X^{p-})$$

By identification of the two equations we obtain the relationship between the standard electrode potential of the metal/cation couple and that of the second kind electrode:

$$E^0_{298.15}[M^{n+}{}_pX^{p-}{}_n(s)/M(s)] = E^0_{298.15}[M^{n+}/M(s)] + (RT\ln 10/npF)\log_{10}Ks$$

Because the potential of this type of electrode is highly stable, they are extensively used for making practical reference electrodes (e.g., Ag/AgCl, Ag/Ag_2SO_4, Hg/Hg_2Cl_2, Hg/Hg_2SO_4) that will be discussed hereafter.

5.15.3 Reference Electrode of the Third Kind

This type of reference electrode corresponds to a generalization of the electrode of the second kind. Actually, a third kind electrode consists to a metal {M} covered by an adherent layer of its inorganic or organic salt $M^{n+}{}_pX^{p-}{}_n(s)$, itself covered by another layer of a second salt having the same anion in common but a different cation $N^{m+}{}_pX^{p-}{}_m(s)$, this system being then immersed into an electrolyte in which the second metallic salt is insoluble, and that contains the cations N^{m+}. The half electrochemical cell can be written:

$$(Pt)\,|\,M(s,l)\,|\,M^{n+}{}_pX^{p-}{}_n(s)\,|\,N^{m+}{}_pX^{p-}{}_m(s)\,||\,N^{m+}(aq), Y^{p-}(aq)$$

Therefore, the electrode potential these reference electrodes depends on the activities of the cations into the electrolyte, and hence is used to measure the activity of metallic cations. The most common third kind electrode is the system: $Zn(s)|ZnC_2O_4|CaC_2O_4||Ca^{2+}$.

5.15.4 Standard Hydrogen Electrode

The ***standard hydrogen electrode*** (SHE) sometimes called the ***normal hydrogen electrode*** (NHE) is a first kind gas electrode invented in 1893 by the French chemist Le Blanc. The thermodynamic equilibrium is established between the free electrons of a chemically inert platinized-platinum electrode, the dissolved hydrogen gas is obtained by sparging high purity hydrogen gas previously saturated with water vapor under standard pressure into an aqueous acid electrolyte having an activity of hydronium cations equal to unity. The half electrochemical cell of such system can be written:

The half electrochemical cell can be written:

$$(Pt)\,|\,H_2(gas)\ [p_0 = 101.325\ kPa]\,|\,H^+(aq)\ (a_{H^+} = 1)$$

That corresponds to the basic electrochemical reaction:

$$2H^+ + 2e^- = H_2(gas) \qquad E^0_{298.15}(2H^+/H_2) = 0.00V/SHE$$

The electrode potential is then given by the Nernst equation using the activity of the hydronium cations and the fugacity of the hydrogen gas:

$$E = E^0_{298.15}(2H^+/H_2) + (RT\ln 10/2F)\log_{10}[(H^+)^2/f_{H2}]$$

With $a_H^+ = (H^+)$ being the activity of hydronium cations, and f_{H2} the fugacity of hydrogen gas. For further simplification, it is possible to rearrange the above Nernst equation introducing the ***Sørensen hydrogen potential*** function:

$$pH = colog_{10}a(H^+)$$

$$E = [E^0_{298.15}(2H^+/H_2) - (RT\ln 10/2F)\log_{10} f_{H2}] - (RT\ln 10/F)pH$$

With an activity of hydronium cations equal to unity and under a partial pressure of hydrogen gas equal to 101.325 kPa the electrode potential of the SHE is fixed and it is equal to the standard electrode potential of the redox couple $E^0_{298.15}(2H^+/H_2)$. From the above equation, we can see clearly that the SHE electrode potential decrease by -59.16 mV/decade per increase of a pH-unit

For that reason, the SHE was internationally adopted as the primary and universal standard with which all other electrodes are compared. As already mentioned in Section 5.6 the internationally adopted convention states that the standard equilibrium potential of the redox couple $2H^+/H_2$ is defined as zero at any given temperatures but under a standard pressure of 101.325 kPa.

$$E^0_{298.15}(2H^+/H_2) = 0.00\ VSHE\ (T, p_0 = 101.325\ kPa).$$

Moreover, the pressure dependence of the electrode potential is

Actually, the pressure dependence of the standard electrode potential for the hydrogen electrode at 298.15K is defined as follows:

$$E^0_{298.15}(2H^+/H_2)(101{,}325\ Pa) = E^0_{298.15}(2H^+/H_2)(10^5\ bar) + (\partial E/\partial p)_T$$

However in theory, the absolute electrode potential of the SHE is temperature dependent, but in order to establish the temperature correlation equation of the SHE a non-isotherm galvanic cell with two SHEs maintained at two distinct temperatures must be built as follows which is experimentally impractical:

$(Pt)|H_2(g)\ (T,\ 101.325\ kPa)|H^+(aq)(a_H^+ = 1)||H^+(aq)(a_H^+ = 1)|H_2(g)(298.15, 101.325\ kPa)|(Pt)$

It is worth to mention that in practice, several experimental corrections must be considered when using a SHE in order to ensure the accuracy of the *e.m.f* measured. First of all the partial pressure of the hydrogen gas above the solution of electrolyte must be accurately determined. At 298.15K the pressure coefficient, of the *e.m.f.*, is $(\partial E/\partial p)^0 = 29.2\ \mu V/Pa$. The second important factor is the vapor pressure of water that must be subtracted to the hydrogen partial pressure.

5.15.5 Silver-Silver Chloride Electrode

The ***silver-silver chloride electrode*** denoted by the common acronym SSCE is a reversible reference electrode of the second kind. Its potential relies on the equilibrium between solid silver metal, Ag(s), coated with insoluble silver chloride, AgCl(s), immersed into a solution of an alkali-metal chloride with a fixed concentration of chloride anions according to the following half electrochemical cell:

(Pt) | Ag(s) | AgCl(s) | | Ag^+, Cl^-

The reference electrode is normally in contact with the solution in which the other electrode is immersed using a liquid junction or salt bridge that is in practice a porous sintered glass (i.e, glass frit) or porous ceramics.

Table 25 – Potential of silver-silver chloride electrodes

Electrochemical half-cell	Acronym	E_R (V/SHE)
Ag | AgCl | | KCl (0.1N)	SSCE(0.1N)	+0.2881
Ag | AgCl | | KCl (1N)	SSCE(1N)	+0.22234
Ag | AgCl | | KCl (3.0M)	n.a.	+0.208
Ag | AgCl | | KCl (3.5M)	n.a.	+0.205
Ag | AgCl | | KCl (Satd.)	SSCE(satd.)	+0.198
Ag | AgCl | | KCl (sea water)	SSCE(sea water)	+0.250
Ag | AgCl | | NaCl (Satd.)	SSCE(Na)	+0.197

It is commonly used in electrochemical measurements, especially in chloride based electrolytes, brines and sea water, as internal reference electrode in pH meters and ORP probes, and finally it is often used as reference electrode for redox titration or cathodic protection of structure. For environmental reasons, it has replaced the saturated calomel electrode.

5.15.6 Standard Calomel Electrode

The ***saturated calomel electrode*** denoted by the acronym SCE, is a reversible reference electrode of the second kind. Its potential relies on the equilibrium between a paste of liquid mercury and crystals of mercurous chloride, Hg_2Cl_2 (i.e., calomel) immersed into a solution of an alkali-metal chloride with a fixed concentration of chloride anions according to the following half electrochemical cell:

(Pt) | Hg(l) | Hg_2Cl_2(s) | | Hg^+, Cl^-

Table 26 – Potential of calomel electrodes

Electrochemical half-cell	Acronym	E_R (V/SHE)
Hg | Hg_2Cl_2 | | KCl (0.1N)	DNCE	+0.3356
Hg | Hg_2Cl_2 | | KCl (1N)	NCE	+0.2830
Hg | Hg_2Cl_2 | | KCl (3.5M)	n.a.	+0.2501
Hg | Hg_2Cl_2 | | KCl (Satd.)	SCE	+0.24453
Hg | Hg_2Cl_2 | | NaCl (Satd.)	SCE(NaCl)	+0.2360

5.15.7 Mercury-Mercurous Sulfate Electrode

When the leakage of chloride anions from the reference electrode can pose a contamination issue or when working with concentrated sulfate-based electrolytes such as in the case of the electrowinning of copper, nickel, cobalt, iron, manganese, and zinc, the utilization of a reference electrode using a sulfate solution is highly recommended.

The ***mercury-mercurous sulfate electrode***, is a reversible reference electrode of the second kind. Its potential relies on the equilibrium between a paste of liquid mercury and crystals of mercurous sulfate, Hg_2SO_4 immersed into a solution of sulfuric acid or potassium sulfate with a fixed concentration of sulfate anions according to the following half electrochemical cell:

(Pt) | Hg(l) | Hg_2SO_4(s) | | Hg^+, SO_4^{2-}

Table 27 – Potential of mercury sulfate electrodes

Electrochemical half-cell	Acronym	E_R (V/SHE)
$Hg \mid Hg_2SO_4 \mid\mid H_2SO_4$ (30 wt.%)	MSSA	+0.635
$Hg \mid Hg_2SO_4 \mid\mid K_2SO_4$ (0.5M)	MSKS	+0.682
$Hg \mid Hg_2SO_4 \mid\mid K_2SO_4$ (1M)	MSKS(1M)	+0.674
$Hg \mid Hg_2SO_4 \mid\mid K_2SO_4$ (satd.)	MSKS(Sat.)	+0.658

5.15.8 Silver-Silver Sulfate Electrode

The ***silver-silver sulfate electrode***, is a reversible reference electrode of the second kind. Its potential relies on the equilibrium between silver metal, Ag(s), coated with insoluble silver sulfate, Ag_2SO_4(s), immersed into a solution of sulfuric acid or potassium sulfate with a fixed concentration of sulfate anions according to the half electrochemical cell:

$$(Pt) \mid Ag(s) \mid Ag_2SO_4(s) \mid\mid Ag^+, SO_4^{2-}$$

Table 28 – Potential of silver-silver sulfate Electrodes

Electrochemical half-cell	Acronym	E_R (V/SHE)
$Ag \mid Ag_2SO_4 \mid\mid H_2SO_4$ (0.5M)	NSSE	+0.720
$Ag \mid Ag_2SO_4 \mid\mid H_2SO_4$ (1M)	MSSE	+0.710
$Ag \mid Ag_2SO_4 \mid\mid K_2SO_4$ (Satd.)	SSSE	+0.690

5.15.9 Copper-Copper Sulfate Electrode

If a metallic copper rod or wire of iron metal is immersed into an electrolyte containing cupric cations, we obtain a so-called ***copper reference electrode*** (e.g., $Cu^{2+}/Cu(s)$) of the first kind, the half electrochemical cell can be written:

$$Cu(s) \mid Cu^{2+}(aq)$$

The electrode potential of the copper electrode is simply given by the Nernst equation:

$$E = E^0_{298.15}(Cu^{2+}/Cu) + (RT\ln 10/2F)\log_{10}(Cu^{2+})$$

Table 29 – Potential of copper sulfate electrode

Electrochemical half-cell	Acronym	E_R (V/SHE)
Cu | $CuSO_4$ (Satd.)	SCSE	+0.316

5.15.10 Temperature Coefficients of Reference Electrodes

The empirical equations with their temperature coefficients for three selected reference electrodes that were obtained experimentally are provided below with the temperature t expressed in degrees Celsius:

$$E_{MSKS}\ (V/SHE) = 0.658 - 2.54 \times 10^{-4}(t-25) - 1.22 \times 10^{-6}(t-25)^2 - 6.1 \times 10^{-10}(t-25)^3$$

$$E_{MSSA}\ (V/SHE) = 0.63495 - 7.8144 \times 10^{-4}(t-25) - 4.2689 \times 10^{-6}(t-25)^2$$

$$E_{SSCE}\ (V/SHE) = 0.219 - 4.8564 \times 10^{-4}t - 3.4205 \times 10^{-6}\, t^2 + 5.869 \times 10^{-10}t^3$$

Based on these practical equations, we have calculated for convenience the electrode potentials (V/SHE) for the three reference electrodes at temperatures ranging from 25°C up to 90°C. These figures are reported in Table 30.

Table 30 – Potential of selected reference electrodes vs. temperature (V/SHE)

Practical temperature Absolute thermodynamic temperature		25°C 298.15 K	30°C 303.15 K	40°C 313.15 K	50°C 323.15 K	54°C 327.15 K	60°C 333.15 K	70°C 343.15 K	80°C 353.15 K	90°C 363.15 K
RE = $Hg/Hg_2SO_4//K_2SO_4$ (satd.)	MSKS	0.658	0.657	0.654	0.651	0.650	0.648	0.644	0.640	0.636
RE = $Hg/Hg_2SO_4//H_2SO_4$ (30 wt.%)	MSSA	0.635	0.631	0.623	0.615	0.612	0.608	0.600	0.592	0.584
		-0.023	-0.026	-0.031	-0.035	-0.037	-0.040	-0.044	-0.048	-0.052
RE = Ag/AgCl//KCl(3.5M)		0.205	0.202	0.194	0.187	0.184	0.179	0.170	0.161	0.152

5.16 Pourbaix Diagram for Iron

Over the entire range of pH and redox potential, the following iron species: Fe(s), Fe^{2+}, Fe^{3+}, FeO_4^{2-}, $Fe(OH)_2$(s), $HFeO_2^-$, $Fe(OH)^{2+}$, $Fe(OH)_2^+$, $Fe(OH)_3$(s), are involved thus it is important to establish the predominance and limits between of all these iron species according to the redox and pH conditions existing in solution.

For that purpose it is worth using potential-pH diagrams (E-pH) for the iron system called ***Pourbaix diagrams*** after the Belgian electrochemist Marcel Pourbaix who was the first to devised them for almost all the elements of the periodic chart [61].

---

[61] POURBAIX, M. (1966) *Atlas of electrochemical equilibria in aqueous solutions.* (CEBELCOR, Brussels, Belgium), First English translation Pergamon Press Ltd., New York, NY.

In this section, we will briefly establish a simplified version of the Pourbaix diagram for the iron system (see Figure 17) according to data found in the literature [62] and constructed by using fourteen reduction and oxidation reactions over a pH range from -2 to +16, and electrode potentials ranging from -1.5/SHE to +2.0 V/SHE. For establishing more complex and comprehensive potential-pH diagrams for the system Fe-H_2O-H_2SO_4-$FeSO_4$, we strongly recommend the article of Yokokawa et al. [63].

For the sake of clarity, the Pourbaix diagram is established under standard conditions of temperature and pressure (298.15K and 101.325 kPa) and for a molarity of total dissolved iron: $[Fe(total)] = [Fe^{3+}] + [Fe^{2+}] = C_{Fe} = \mathbf{1.0}$ mol/L. The circled numbers denote lines in the simplified E-pH diagram in Figure 17.

5.16.1 Hydrolysis, Complexation and Precipitation Reactions

Prior to describe all the possible redox reactions, we consider first the chemical equilibria (e.g., hydrolysis, complexation, and precipitation reactions) that depend only with pH.

The first chemical equilibrium to consider is the complete hydrolysis of ferric cations into ferric hydroxide according to:

$$Fe^{3+} + 3H_2O = Fe(OH)_3(s) + 3H^+$$

$$Fe^{3+} + 3OH^- = Fe(OH)_3(s) \qquad pK_{s3} = \mathbf{37.5}$$

The above chemical equilibrium is only controlled by the solubility product of the ferric hydroxide. The solubility product is written as follows:

$$K_{s3} = (Fe^{3+})(OH^-)^3 = 10^{-37.5}$$

By introducing the ***auto-protolysis constant of water***: $K_w = (H^+)(OH^-) = 10^{-14}$, we obtain the equation for calculating the pH of precipitation as a function of the molarity of ferric cations and the solubility product of the ferric hydroxide:

$$K_{s3} = (Fe^{3+})K_w^3/(H^+)^3$$

Therefore, the pH can be calculated by the following simple equation below:

$$pH = \text{colog}_{10}(H^+) = \text{colog}_{10}[(Fe^{3+})K_w^3/K_{s3}]^{1/3}$$

---

[62] CHARLOT, G. (1963) *L'analyse qualitative et les reactions en solutions, cinquième edition.* Masson & Cie, Paris, France.

[63] YOKOKAWA, H.; SAKAI, N.; KAWADA, T.; and DOKIYA, M. (1990) Generelized electrochemical potential diagrams for complex aqueous (M-X-H-O-e-) systems. *Journal of the Electrochemical Society* (JECS) **137**(2)(1990)388-398.

$pH = pK_w - pK_{s3}/3 + (1/3)colog_{10}(Fe^{3+})$

$pH = 1.5 + (1/3)colog_{10}(Fe^{3+})$

Because the molarity of $[Fe^{3+}]$ is **1.0** M, the limit between the ferric iron cations and ferric hydroxide corresponds to a vertical line with abscissa: **pH 1.50**.

However, in practice, upon increasing the pH, there is a succession of hydrolysis, and complexation reactions, the first reaction of hydrolysis of ferric cations proceeds according to the chemical reaction as follows:

④ $Fe^{3+} + H_2O = FeOH^{2+} + H^+$ $pK_4 = \mathbf{2.2}$

The above chemical equilibrium is only controlled by the stability constant of the complex species, $FeOH^{2+}$. The stability constant can be written as follows:

$K_4 = (FeOH^{2+})(H^+)/(Fe^{3+}) = 10^{-2.2}$

Therefore, the pH is simply given by the following equation below:

$pH = colog_{10}(H^+) = colog_{10}[(Fe^{3+})K_4/(FeOH^{2+})]$

$pH = pK_4 - log_{10}[(Fe^{3+})/(FeOH^{2+})]$

$pH = 2.2 - log_{10}[(Fe^{3+})/(FeOH^{2+})]$

Because the molarity of $[Fe^{3+}] = [FeOH^{2+}] = \mathbf{0.5}$ M, the limit between the ferric iron cations and $FeOH^{2+}$ corresponds to a vertical line with abscissa: $\mathbf{pH = pK_4 = 2.2}$.

With a further pH increase, a second hydrolysis and complexation reaction takes place as follows:

⑤ $FeOH^{2+} + H_2O = Fe(OH)_2^+ + H^+$ $pK_5 = \mathbf{4.69}$

The above equilibrium is only controlled by the stability constant of $Fe(OH)_2^+$. The stability constant can be written as follows:

$K_5 = (Fe(OH)_2^+)(H^+)/(FeOH^{2+}) = 10^{-4.69}$

Therefore, the pH is simply given by the following equation below:

$pH = colog_{10}(H^+) = colog_{10}[(FeOH^{2+})K_5/(Fe(OH)_2^+)]$

$pH = pK_5 - log_{10}[(FeOH^{2+})/(Fe(OH)_2^+)]$

$pH = 4.69 - \log_{10}[(FeOH^{2+})/(Fe(OH)_2^+)]$

Because the molarity of $[Fe(OH)_2^+] = [FeOH^{2+}] =$ **0.5** M, the limit between $FeOH^{2+}$, and $Fe(OH)_2^+$ species corresponds to a vertical line with abscissa: **pH = 4.69**.

A final increases in pH results to the precipitation of ferric hydroxide as follows:

⑥ $Fe(OH)_2^+ + H_2O = Fe(OH)_3(s) + H^+$ $pK_6 = \mathbf{2.28}$

The above equilibrium is controlled by the stability constant of $Fe(OH)_3$. The equilibrium constant can be written as follows:

$$K_6 = (H^+)/(Fe(OH)_2^+) = 10^{-2.28}$$

Therefore, the pH is simply given by the following equation below:

$$pH = \text{colog}_{10}(H^+) = \text{colog}_{10}[K_6(Fe(OH)_2^+)]$$

$$pH = pK_6 - \log_{10}[Fe(OH)_2^+]$$

$$pH = 2.28 - \log_{10}[Fe(OH)_2^+]$$

Because the molarity of $[Fe(OH)_2^+] =$ **1.0** M, the limit between $Fe(OH)_2^+$ and $Fe(OH)_3(s)$ corresponds to a vertical line with abscissa **pH = 2.28.**

Similarly, the limit between the regions containing ferrous cations and ferrous hydroxide is controlled by the precipitation reaction as follows:

⑦ $Fe^{2+} + 2H_2O = Fe(OH)_2(s) + 2H^+$

$Fe^{2+} + 2OH^- = Fe(OH)_2(s)$ $pK_{s2} = \mathbf{15.1}$

The above equilibrium is only controlled by the solubility product of the ferrous hydroxide. The solubility product of $Fe(OH)_2(s)$ can be written as follows:

$$K_{s2} = (Fe^{2+})(OH^-)^2 = 10^{-15.1}$$

By introducing the ***auto-protolysis constant of water*** $K_w = (H^+)(OH^-) = 10^{-14}$, we obtain:

$$K_{s2} = (Fe^{2+})K_w^2/(H^+)^2$$

Therefore, the equation for calculating the pH of precipitation as a function of the molarity of ferrous cations, and the solubility product of the ferrous hydroxide is simply given by the following equation below:

$$pH = colog_{10}(H^+) = colog_{10}[(Fe^{2+})K_w^2/K_{s2}]^{1/2}$$

$$pH = pK_w - 0.5\ pK_{s2} - 0.5\ \log_{10}(Fe^{2+})$$

$$pH = 6.45 - 0.5\ \log_{10}(Fe^{2+})$$

Because the molarity of $[Fe^{2+}]$ is **1.0** M, the limit between the ferrous iron and ferrous hydroxide corresponds to a vertical line with abscissa: **pH 6.45**.

At elevate pH and under reducing conditions, the possibility to have the chemical formation of ***hypoferrite anions***, $HFeO_2^-$, must be taken into account as follows:

(11) $Fe(OH)_2(s) = HFeO_2^- + H^+$ $pK_{11} =$ **10.53**

The above equilibrium is only controlled by the solubility product of the ferrous hydroxide, and it can be written as follows:

$$K_{11} = (HFeO_2^-)(H^+) = 10^{-10.53}$$

Therefore, the equation for calculating the pH as a function of the molarity of hypoferrite anion is simply given by the following equation below:

$$pH = colog_{10}(H^+) = colog_{10}[K_{11}/(HFeO_2^-)]$$

$$pH = pK_{11} + \log_{10}(HFeO_2^-)$$

$$pH = 10.53 + \log_{10}(HFeO_2^-)$$

Because the molarity of $[HFeO_2^-]$ is **1.0** M, the limit between the ferrous hydroxide and the hypoferrite anions corresponds to a vertical line with abscissa: **pH 10.53**.

5.16.2 Reduction and Oxidation Reactions

The first redox reaction occurring at an acidic pH low enough to prevent the hydrolysis and precipitation of ferrous hydroxide (*vide supra*) is as follows:

(1) $Fe^{2+} + 2e^- = Fe(s)$ $E^0_{298.15K}(Fe^{2+}/Fe) =$ **-0.447** V/SHE

The Nernst equation of the above half-electrochemical reaction can be written as follows:

$E_1(T) = E^0_{298.15K}(Fe^{2+}/Fe) + (RT\ln 10/2F)\log_{10}(Fe^{2+})$

$E_1(T) = -0.447 + 0.0296 \log_{10}(Fe^{2+})$

Because in that region $[Fe^{2+}] = C_{Fe} = 1.0$ mol/L, we obtain:

$E_1 = -0.447$ V/SHE

Therefore, the limit between ferrous cations and metallic iron is a horizontal line extending up to the pH corresponding to the precipitation of $Fe(OH)_2$.

The second redox reaction occurring at an acidic pH low enough to prevent the hydrolysis and precipitation of ferric hydroxide (*vide supra*) is as follows:

② $Fe^{3+} + e^- = Fe^{2+}$ $E^0_{298.15K}(Fe^{3+}/Fe^{2+}) =$ **+0.771** V/SHE

The Nernst equation of the above half-electrochemical reaction can be written as follows:

$E_2(T) = E^0_{298.15K}(Fe^{3+}/Fe^{2+}) + (RT\ln 10/F)\log_{10}[(Fe^{3+})/(Fe^{2+})]$

$E_2(T) = 0.771 + 0.0592 \log_{10}[(Fe^{3+})/(Fe^{2+})]$

Considering that the molarity of both cations are equals and based on the molarity of total iron: $[Fe^{3+}] + [Fe^{2+}] = C_{Fe}/2 =$ **0.5** mol/L

$E_2 = +0.771$ V/SHE

Therefore, the limit between ferrous cations and metallic iron is a horizontal line extending up to the pH corresponding to the precipitation of $Fe(OH)_3$.

It is worth to mention, that if needed, it is then possible to calculate using the ***Latimer's rule***, the standard electrode potential the direct reduction of Fe^{3+} into metallic iron:

$Fe^{3+} + 3e^- = Fe(s)$

$E^0_{298.15K}(Fe^{3+}/Fe) = [E^0_{298.15K}(Fe^{3+}/Fe^{2+}) + 2E^0_{298.15K}(Fe^{2+}/Fe)]/3 =$ **-0.041** V/SHE

In the particular case of highly oxidizing conditions, it is also necessary to consider the possible formation of Fe(VI) species occurring as ***ferrate anions***, FeO_4^{2-}, as follows:

③a $FeO_4^{2-} + 8H^+ + 3e^- = Fe^{3+} + 4H_2O$

$E^0_{298.15K}[FeO_4^{2-}/Fe^{3+}]$= **+1.700** V/SHE

The Nernst equation of the above half-electrochemical reaction can be written as follows:

$$E_{3a}(T) = E^0_{298.15K}[FeO_4^{2-}/Fe^{3+}] + (RT\ln 10/3F)\log_{10}[(FeO_4^{2-})(H^+)^8/(Fe^{3+})]$$

$$E_{3a}(T) = E^0_{298.15K}[FeO_4^{2-}/Fe^{3+}] - (8RT\ln 10/3F)pH + (RT\ln 10/3F)\log_{10}[(FeO_4^{2-})/(Fe^{3+})]$$

$$E_{3a}(T) = 1.700 - 0.158pH + 0.0197\log_{10}[(FeO_4^{2-})/(Fe^{3+})]$$

Considering that the molarity of both iron species are equals and based on the molarity of total iron: $[Fe^{3+}] + [FeO_4^{2-}] = C_{Fe}/2 =$ **0.5** mol/L, the limit between the two domains is the equation of the electrode potential vs. pH, is a straight line with a slope of -0.158 V/pH-unit at 298.15K and extending up to the pH corresponding to the precipitation of $Fe(OH)_3$ (*vide supra*):

$$E_3 = 1.700 - 0.158\ pH$$

When the pH is increased enough to trigger the hydrolysis of Fe^{3+} with the formation of $FeOH^{2+}$, the above homogeneous redox reaction takes places as follows:

③b $FeO_4^{2-} + 7H^+ + 3e^- = FeOH^{2+} + 3H_2O$

$E^0_{298.15K}(FeO_4^{2-}/FeOH^{2+})$ = **+1.656** V/SHE

The Nernst equation of the above half-electrochemical reaction can be written as follows:

$$E_{3b}(T) = E^0_{298.15K}[FeO_4^{2-}/FeOH^{2+}] + (RT\ln 10/3F)\log_{10}[(FeO_4^{2-})(H^+)^7/(FeOH^{2+})]$$

$$E_{3b}(T) = E^0_{298.15K}[FeO_4^{2-}/FeOH^{2+}] - (7RT\ln 10/3F)pH + (RT\ln 10/3F)\log_{10}[(FeO_4^{2-})/(FeOH^{2+})]$$

In order to calculate the above ***apparent standard electrode potential*** $E^0_{298.15K}(FeO_4^{2-}/FeOH^{2+})$, we can introduce the equilibrium constant of the hydrolysis reaction (4): $Fe^{3+} + H_2O = FeOH^{2+} + H^+$ described in Section 5.16.1, we obtain:

$$E_{3b}(T) = E^0_{298.15K}[FeO_4^{2-}/FeOH^{2+}] - (8RT\ln 10/3F)pH + (RT\ln 10/3F)pK_4 + (RT\ln 10/3F)\log_{10}[(FeO_4^{2-})/(Fe^{3+})]$$

By comparison with the previous equation for the electrode potential of the system, FeO_4^{2-}/Fe^{3+}, we obtain the relation between the apparent standard electrode potentials and the standard electrode potential:

$$E^0_{298.15K}[FeO_4^{2-}/FeOH^{2+}] = E^0_{298.15K}[FeO_4^{2-}/Fe^{3+}] - (RT\ln 10/3F)pK_4$$

Therefore, the apparent standard electrode potential is:

$$E^0_{298.15K}(FeO_4^{2-}/FeOH^{2+}) = (1.700 - 0.044) = \mathbf{+1.656}\ \text{V/SHE}$$

$$E_{3b}(T) = 1.656 - 0.138\ \text{pH} + 0.0197\ \log_{10}[(FeO_4^{2-})/(FeOH^{2+})]$$

Considering that the molarity of both iron species are equals and based on the molarity of total iron: $[FeOH^{2+}] + [FeO_4^{2-}] = C_{Fe}/2 = \mathbf{0.5}$ mol/L, the limit between the two domains is the equation of the electrode potential vs. pH which is a straight line with a slope of -0.138 V/pH-unit at 298.15K starting at a pH corresponding to the formation of $FeOH^{2+}$ up to the pH corresponding to the formation of $Fe(OH)_2^+$:

$$E_{3b} = 1.656 - 0.138\ \text{pH}$$

When the pH is increased further, the hydrolysis of $FeOH^{2+}$ occurs with the formation of the complex cation: $Fe(OH)_2^+$, the homogeneous redox reaction becomes then:

③c $$FeO_4^{2-} + 6H^+ + 3e^- = Fe(OH)_2^+ + 2H_2O$$

$$E^0_{298.15K}(FeO_4^{2-}/FeOH^{2+}) = \mathbf{+1.564}\ \text{V/SHE}$$

The Nernst equation of the above half-electrochemical reaction can be written as follows:

$$E_{3c}(T) = E^0_{298.15K}(FeO_4^{2-}/Fe(OH)_2^+) + (RT\ln 10/3F)\log_{10}[(FeO_4^{2-})(H^+)^6/(Fe(OH)_2^+)]$$

$$E_{3c}(T) = E^0_{298.15K}(FeO_4^{2-}/Fe(OH)_2^+) - (2RT\ln 10/F)\text{pH} + (RT\ln 10/3F)\log_{10}[(FeO_4^{2-})/(Fe(OH)_2^+)]$$

As for the previous redox reaction, if we introduce in the above equation the stability constants of the first and second hydrolysis and complexation reaction of Fe(III), we obtain the direct relation between the apparent standard electrode potential of the couple, $FeO_4^{2-}/Fe(OH)_2^+$, and the standard electrode potential for the couple: FeO_4^{2-}/Fe^{3+} as follows:

$$E^0_{298.15K}(FeO_4^{2-}/FeOH^{2+}) = E^0_{298.15K}[FeO_4^{2-}/Fe^{3+}] - (RT\ln 10/3F)[pK_4 + pK_5]$$

Thus the apparent standard electrode potential is:

$E^0_{298.15K}(FeO_4^{2-}/FeOH^{2+}) = (1.700 - 0.136) = \mathbf{+1.564}$ V/SHE

$E_{3c}(T) = 1.564 - 0.118$ pH $+ 0.0197 \log_{10}[(FeO_4^{2-})/(Fe(OH)_2^+)]$

Considering that the molarity of both iron species are equals and based on the molarity of total iron: $[Fe(OH)_2^+] + [FeO_4^{2-}] = C_{Fe}/2 =$ **0.5** mol/L, the limit between the two domains is the equation of the electrode potential vs. pH which is a straight-line with a slope of -0.118 V/pH-unit at 298.15K starting at a pH corresponding to the formation of $Fe(OH)_2^+$ up to the pH corresponding to the formation of hypoferrite anion $HFeO_2^-$:

$E_{3c} = 1.564 - 0.118$ pH

For strongly alkaline conditions, at pH well above 12.5, the ferrate anion, FeO_4^{2-}, can be reduced directly into the hypoferrite anion, $HFeO_2^-$, according to the following homogeneous redox reaction:

③d $FeO_4^{2-} + 5H^+ + 4e^- = HFeO_2^- + 2H_2O$

$E^0_{298.15K}(FeO_4^{2-}/ HFeO_2^-) = \mathbf{+1.001}$ V/SHE

The Nernst equation of the above half-electrochemical reaction can be written as follows:

$$E_{3d}(T) = E^0_{298.15K}(FeO_4^{2-}/HFeO_2^-) + (RT\ln 10/4F)\log_{10}[(FeO_4^{2-})(H^+)^5/(HFeO_2^-)]$$

$$E_{3d}(T) = E^0_{298.15K}(FeO_4^{2-}/HFeO_2^-) - (5RT\ln 10/4F)\mathrm{pH} + (RT\ln 10/4F)\log_{10}[(FeO_4^{2-})/(HFeO_2^-)]$$

As for the previous redox reaction, if we introduce in the above equation the stability constants of the first and second hydrolysis and complexation reaction of Fe(II), we obtain the direct relation between the apparent standard electrode potential of the couple, $FeO_4^{2-}/HFeO_2^-$, and the standard electrode potential for the couple: FeO_4^{2-}/Fe^{3+} as follows:

$$E^0_{298.15K}(FeO_4^{2-}/FeOH^{2+}) = E^0_{298.15K}[FeO_4^{2-}/Fe^{3+}] - (RT\ln 10/3F)[pK_4 + pK_5]$$

Considering that the molarity of both iron species are equals and based on the molarity of total iron: $[HFeO_2^-] + [FeO_4^{2-}] = C_{Fe}/2 =$ **0.5** mol/L. We have the equation of the following straight line separating the two regions as a function of pH, with a slope of -0.074 V/pH-unit at 298.15K:

$E_{3d} = 1.001 - 0.074$pH

Now if we consider the redox equilibria involving ferric and ferrous hydroxides. We have first the reduction of ferric hydroxide into ferrous cations:

⑧ $$Fe(OH)_3(s) + 3H^+ + e^- = Fe^{2+} + 3H_2O$$

$$E^0_{298.15K}[Fe(OH)_3/Fe^{2+}] = \mathbf{+1.307}\ V/SHE$$

The Nernst equation of the above half-electrochemical reaction can be written as follows:

$$E_8(T) = E^0_{298.15K}[Fe(OH)_3/Fe^{2+}] + (RT\ln 10/F)\log_{10}[(H^+)^3/(Fe^{2+})]$$

Introducing the solubility product of the ferric hydroxide in the above equation: $K_{s3} = (Fe^{3+})K_w^3/(H^+)^3$, we obtain:

$$E_8(T) = E^0_{298.15K}[Fe(OH)_3/Fe^{2+}] + (RT\ln 10/F)\log_{10}[K_{s3}/K_w^3] + (RT\ln 10/F)\log_{10}[(Fe^{3+})/(Fe^{2+})]$$

By comparison with the electrode potential of the reduction of ferric cations into ferrous cations: $E_2(T) = E^0_{298.15K}(Fe^{3+}/Fe^{2+}) + (RT\ln 10/F)\log_{10}[(Fe^{3+})/(Fe^{2+})]$, we obtain the following equation between the two standard electrode potentials:

$$E^0_{298.15K}[Fe(OH)_3/Fe^{2+}] = E^0_{298.15K}(Fe^{3+}/Fe^{2+}) - (RT\ln 10/F)\log_{10}(K_{s3}/K_w^3)$$

$$E^0_{298.15K}[Fe(OH)_3/Fe^{2+}] = E^0_{298.15K}(Fe^{3+}/Fe^{2+}) - (RT\ln 10/F)(pK_{s3} - 3pK_w)$$

Therefore, the numerical value of the apparent standard potential is:

$$E^0_{298.15K}[Fe(OH)_3/Fe^{2+}] = \mathbf{+1.037}\ V/SHE$$

$$E_8(T) = E^0_{298.15K}[Fe(OH)_3/Fe^{2+}] - (RT\ln 10/F)[3pH - \log_{10}(Fe^{2+})]$$

Considering that the molarity of ferrous iron is: $[Fe^{2+}] = C_{Fe} = \mathbf{1.0}$ mol/L, we have the equation of a straight-line separating the two regions as a function of pH, with a slope of with a slope of: -0.178 V/pH-unit as follows:

$$E_8 = 1.037 - 0.178\ pH$$

The reduction of the ferric hydroxide into and ferrous hydroxide can be written as follows:

⑨ $$Fe(OH)_3(s) + H^+ + e^- = Fe(OH)_2(s) + 3H_2O$$

$$E^0_{298.15K}[Fe(OH)_3/Fe(OH)_2] = +0.274\ V/SHE$$

The above equilibrium is controlled by both the precipitation and redox reactions:

$$E_9(T) = E^0_{298.15K}[Fe(OH)_3/Fe(OH)_2] + (RT\ln 10/F)\log_{10}(H^+)$$

If we introduce the ratio of solubility products of the ferric and ferrous hydroxides:

$$K_{s3}/K_{s2} = K_w(Fe^{3+})/[(H^+)(Fe^{2+})] \qquad (H^+) = (K_wK_{s2}/K_{s3})[(Fe^{3+})/(Fe^{2+})]$$

Hence, replacing the hydronium concentration in the above equation, we obtain:

$$E_9(T) = E^0_{298.15K}[Fe(OH)_3/Fe(OH)_2] - (RT\ln 10/F)(pK_w + pK_{s2} - pK_{s3}) + (RT\ln 10/F)\log_{10}[(Fe^{3+})/(Fe^{2+})]$$

By comparison with the electrode potential for the reduction of ferric iron into ferrous iron: $E_2(T) = E^0_{298.15K}(Fe^{3+}/Fe^{2+}) + (RT\ln 10/F)\log_{10}[(Fe^{3+})/(Fe^{2+})]$, we obtain the relation between the apparent and standard electrode potentials:

$$E^0_{298.15K}[Fe(OH)_3/Fe(OH)_2] = E^0_{298.15K}(Fe^{3+}/Fe^{2+}) + (RT\ln 10/F)[pK_w + pK_{s2} - pK_{s3}]$$

Therefore, the numerical value of the standard electrode potential is:

$$E^0_{298.15K}[Fe(OH)_3/Fe^{2+}] = \mathbf{+0.274}\ V/SHE$$

$$E_9(T) = +0.274 - 0.059\ pH + 0.059\log_{10}[(Fe^{3+})/(Fe^{2+})]$$

Considering that the molarity of ferrous iron is: $[Fe^{2+}] = C_{Fe} = \mathbf{1.0}$ mol/L, we have the equation of a straight-line separating the two regions as a function of pH, with a slope of: -0.059 V/pH-unit as follows:

$$E_9 = +0.274 - 0.059\ pH$$

The direct reduction of ferrous hydroxide into metallic iron is described by the following redox reaction:

(10) $Fe(OH)_2(s) + 2H^+ + 2e^- = Fe(s) + 2H_2O$

$E^0_{298.15K}[Fe(OH)_2/Fe] = -0.066$ V/SHE

The Nernst equation of the above half-electrochemical reaction can be written as follows:

$$E_{10}(T) = E^0_{298.15K}[Fe(OH)_2/Fe] + (RT\ln 10/2F)\log_{10}(H^+)^2$$

Introducing the solubility product of the ferrous hydroxide in the above equation: $K_{s2} = (Fe^{2+})K_w^2/(H^+)^2$, we obtain the equation:

$$E_{10}(T) = E^0_{298.15K}[Fe(OH)_2/Fe] + (RT\ln 10/2F)\log_{10}[(Fe^{2+})K_w^2/K_{s2}]$$

$$E_{10}(T) = E^0_{298.15K}[Fe(OH)_2/Fe] - (RT\ln 10/2F)[2pK_w - pK_{s2}] + (RT\ln 10/2F)\log_{10}(Fe^{2+})$$

By comparison with the equation for the electrode potential of the reduction of ferrous cations: $E_1(T)= E^0_{298.15K}(Fe^{2+}/Fe) + (RT\ln 10/2F) \log_{10}(Fe^{2+})$, we obtain the relation between the apparent and standard electrode potentials as follows:

$$E^0_{298.15K}[Fe(OH)_2/Fe] = E^0_{298.15K}(Fe^{2+}/Fe) + (RT\ln 10/F)[pK_w - pK_{s2}/2]$$

Therefore, the numerical value of the apparent standard electrode potential is:

$$E^0_{298.15K}[Fe(OH)_2/Fe] = \mathbf{-0.066}\ V/SHE$$

$$E_{10}(T) = E^0_{298.15K}[Fe(OH)_2/Fe] + (RT\ln 10/F)pH$$

Therefore, the variation of the electrode potential with the pH is given by a straight line with a slope of -0.059 V/pH-unit with the equation:

$$E_{10} = -0.066 - 0.059\ pH$$

Finally, at very alkaline pH, the redox reaction for reduction of hypoferrite anions into metallic iron must be considered:

⑫ $HFeO_2^- + 3H^+ + 2e^- = Fe(s) + 2H_2O$

$$E^0_{298.15K}[HFeO_2^-/Fe] = \mathbf{+0.493}\ V/SHE$$

The Nernst equation of the above half-electrochemical reaction can be written as follows:

$$E_{12}(T) = E^0_{298.15K}[HFeO_2^-/Fe] + (RT\ln 10/2F)\log_{10}[(HFeO_2^-)(H^+)^3]$$

The equation for calculating electrode potential as a function of the molarity of hypoferrite anions and the pH is given below:

$$E_{12}(T) = E^0_{298.15K}[HFeO_2^-/Fe] + (RT\ln 10/2F)[\log_{10}(HFeO_2^-) - 3pH]$$

$$E_{12}(T) = E^0_{298.15K}[HFeO_2^-/Fe] - (3RT\ln 10/2F)\ pH + (RT\ln 10/2F)[\log_{10}(HFeO_2^-)$$

Because the molarity of $[HFeO_2^-]$ is **1.0** M, Therefore, the variation of the electrode potential with the pH is given by a straight-line with a slope of:-0.089 V/pH-unit with the equation:

$$E_{12} = +0.493 - 0.089pH$$

⑬ $Fe(OH)_2^+ + 2H^+ + e^- = Fe^{2+} + 2H_2O$

$E^0_{298.15K}[Fe(OH)_2^+/Fe^{2+}] = \mathbf{+1.179}$ V/SHE

The Nernst equation of the above half-electrochemical reaction can be written as follows:

$$E_{13}(T) = E^0_{298.15K}[Fe(OH)_2^+/Fe^{2+}] + (RT\ln 10/F)\log_{10}[(Fe(OH)_2^+)(H^+)^2/(Fe^{2+})]$$

Therefore, the equation for calculating electrode potential as a function of the molarity of the ionic species and the pH is given below:

$$E_{13}(T) = E^0_{298.15K}[Fe(OH)_2^+/Fe^{2+}] - (2RT\ln 10/F)pH + (RT\ln 10/F)\log_{10}[(Fe(OH)_2^+)/(Fe^{2+})]$$

Introducing the two stability constants: $K_5 = (Fe(OH)_2^+)(H^+)/(FeOH^{2+})$ and $K_4 = (FeOH^{2+})(H^+)/(Fe^{3+})$ into the above equation, we obtain the new equation:

$$E_{13}(T) = E^0_{298.15K}[Fe(OH)_2^+/Fe^{2+}] + (RT\ln 10/F)\log_{10}[K_4K_5(Fe^{3+})/(Fe^{2+})]$$

$$E_{13}(T) = E^0_{298.15K}[Fe(OH)_2^+/Fe^{2+}] - (RT\ln 10/F)(pK_4 + pK_5) + (RT\ln 10/F)\log_{10}[(Fe^{3+})/(Fe^{2+})]$$

By comparison with the equation for the electrode potential of the reduction of ferrous hydroxide: $E_2(T) = E^0_{298.15K}(Fe^{3+}/Fe^{2+}) + (RT\ln 10/F)\log_{10}[(Fe^{3+})/(Fe^{2+})]$, we obtain the relation between the apparent and standard electrode potentials as follows:

$$E^0_{298.15K}[Fe(OH)_2^+/Fe^{2+}] = E^0_{298.15K}(Fe^{3+}/Fe^{2+}) + (RT\ln 10/F)(pK_4 + pK_5)$$

Therefore, the numerical value of the apparent standard electrode potential is:

$E^0_{298.15K}[Fe(OH)_2^+/Fe^{2+}] = \mathbf{+1.179}$ V/SHE

Because the molarity of $[Fe(OH)_2^+] = [Fe^{2+}] = \mathbf{0.5}$ M, the variation of the electrode potential with the pH is given by a straight-line with a slope of:-0.118 V/pH-unit with the equation:

$E_{13} = 1.179 - 0.118$ pH

⑭ $FeOH^{2+} + H^+ + e^- = Fe^{2+} + H_2O$

$E^0_{298.15K}[FeOH^{2+}/Fe^{2+}] = \mathbf{+0.901}$ V/SHE

The Nernst equation of the above half-electrochemical reaction can be written as follows:

$$E_{14}(T) = E^0_{298.15K}[FeOH^{2+}/Fe^{2+}] + (RT\ln 10/F) \log_{10}[(FeOH^{2+})(H^+)/(Fe^{2+})]$$

Therefore, the equation for calculating electrode potential as a function of the molarity of the ionic species and the pH is given below:

$$E_{14} = E^0_{298.15K}[FeOH^{2+}/Fe^{2+}] - (RT\ln 10/F)\text{pH} + (RT\ln 10/F)\log_{10}[(FeOH^{2+})/(Fe^{2+})]$$

Introducing the stability constant: $K_4 = (FeOH^{2+})(H^+)/(Fe^{3+})$ into the above equation, we obtain:

$$E_{14}(T) = E^0_{298.15K}[FeOH^{2+}/Fe^{2+}] + (RT\ln 10/F)\log_{10}[K_4(Fe^{3+})/(Fe^{2+})]$$

$$E_{14}(T) = E^0_{298.15K}[FeOH^{2+}/Fe^{2+}] - (RT\ln 10/F)pK_4 + (RT\ln 10/F)\log_{10}[(Fe^{3+})/(Fe^{2+})]$$

By comparison with the equation for the electrode potential of the reduction of ferrous hydroxide: $E_2(T)= E^0_{298.15K}(Fe^{3+}/Fe^{2+}) + (RT\ln 10/F) \log_{10}[(Fe^{3+})/(Fe^{2+})]$, we obtain the relation between the apparent and standard electrode potentials as follows:

$$E^0_{298.15K}[FeOH^{2+}/Fe^{2+}] = E^0_{298.15K}(Fe^{3+}/Fe^{2+})+(RT\ln 10/F)pK_4$$

Therefore, the numerical value of the apparent standard electrode potential is:

$E^0_{298.15K}[Fe(OH)_2^+/Fe^{2+}] = \mathbf{+0.901}$ V/SHE

Because the molarity of $[FeOH^{2+}] = [Fe^{2+}] = \mathbf{0.5}$ M, the variation of the electrode potential with the pH is given by a straight-line with a slope of:-0.059 V/pH-unit with the equation:

$$E_{14} = E^0_{298.15K}[FeOH^{2+}/Fe^{2+}] - (RT\ln 10/F)\text{pH}$$

$E_{14} = +0.901 - 0.059$ pH

From these calculations, we were able to draw a simplified Pourbaix diagram that is depicted in Figure 17.

Note that in in practice, at pH below 4.0, the ***oxidation-reduction potential*** (ORP) provides a direct and useful information regarding the concentration of iron cations. For commercial ORP probes, the potential of the platinum electrode is measured vs. a silver-silver chloride reference electrode. But in sulfate baths, it is strongly advised to use a mercury-mercurous sulfate type reference electrode (see Section 5.15.7). Hence when both ferrous and ferric cations are present in the catholyte, and the total concentration of iron is known, the measured ORP provides a direct measurement of the ratio of the activities of the two iron species according to the following equation:

$$ORP\,(\mathrm{mV}/RE) = E^{\circ}_{298\mathrm{K}}(\mathrm{Fe^{3+}/Fe^{2+}}) + (RT\ln 10/F)\log_{10}(\mathrm{Fe^{3+}})/(\mathrm{Fe^{2+}}) - E_{\mathrm{RE}}$$

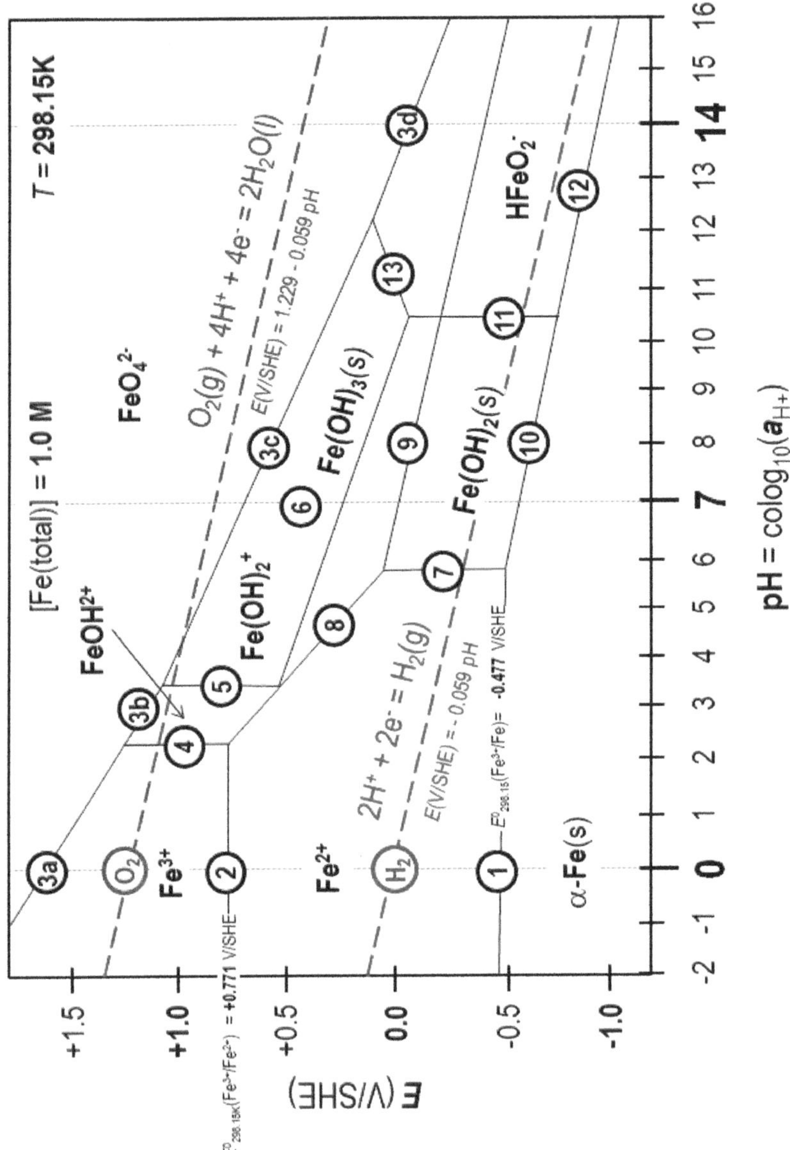

Figure 17 – Simplified Pourbaix (E-pH) diagram for iron

6 Transport Phenomena

The ***transport phenomena*** of ionic, i.e., anions and cations, and non-ionic species occurring during an electrochemical process are directly responsible of the electric current flowing inside the electrochemical cell. Actually, when an electric potential difference, i.e., voltage, is applied between the two electrodes of an electrochemical reactor under isothermal conditions, an electric current circulates through the electrolyte. The corresponding mass transfer is mainly carried by the acting or driving forces also called fluxes of three following transport phenomena: (1) the ***diffusion***, (2) the ***electro-migration***, and (3) ***natural convection*** (i.e., free convection) or ***forced convection***.

Diffusion and convection are common transport phenomena well-known to chemical engineers. By contrast, the migration is specific to electrochemical engineering and in a lesser extent to plasma physicists because it applies only to ionized media. Depending on the hydrodynamic conditions occurring inside the electrochemical reactor, the physical and chemical properties of the electrolyte, one of the above mentioned mass transfer mechanism dominates but usually the three are intimately interconnected, and they participate together in the overall mass transfer.

6.1 Fluxes of Electroactive Species

Because the electric current circulating inside an electrochemical reactor is directly related to the mass transfer of electroactive species, it is important to quantify the mass transfer of a given species by introducing the vector physical quantity named the ***flux of the electroactive species*** and denoted by the general symbol J_k. The modulus of the flux represents the amount of an electroactive species, X, that flow per unit time across a given surface with an area, A.

$$J_k = \partial X_k/(\partial A \cdot \partial t)$$

The dimension of the flux $[XL^2T^{-2}]$ depends on the dimension of the physical quantity X used to measure the amount of species k.

In practice, if we consider a stream of electrolyte, the flow rate of the species k is related to its concentration X_k times the linear velocity of the species in the fluid stream, denoted u_k, in $m.s^{-1}$ by the general equation:

$$J_k = X_k \cdot u_k$$

The Table 31 summarizes the names, symbols and SI units for the flux as a function of the physical quantity adopted for describing the concentration of the species. The relations between the fluxes are:

$J_k N_A = \phi_k$; $J_k M_k = G_k$; and $N_A(G_k/M_k) = \phi_k$

Table 31 – Names, symbols and SI units of various fluxes

Physical quantity, symbol and SI unit for concentration	Dimension of the flux	Name, symbol and SI unit for the flux
Particle density (n_k /m^{-3})	[$L^{-2}T^{-1}$]	Particle flux (ϕ_k/m^{-2}.s^{-1})
Molarity (c_k /mol.m^{-3})	[$NL^{-2}T^{-1}$]	Molar flux (J_k /mol.m^{-2}.s^{-1})
Mass of species per unit volume of solution (C_k/kg.m^{-3})	[$ML^{-2}T^{-1}$]	Mass velocity (G_k /kg.m^{-2}.s^{-1})

The overall flux of the electroactive species, k, inside an electrolyte is the sum of three contributions: the flux of diffusion, migration, and convection.

$J_{total} = J_{diffusion} + J_{migration} + J_{convection}$

6.2 Electro-Migration

The ***electro-migration*** or simply migration is only restricted to the transport of electrically charged species, i.e., charged particle such as electrons and protons, and ions. It takes place under an existing gradient of electrical potential such as the potential difference existing between two electrodes. Therefore, this mechanism is only observed in ionized media such as electrolytes, but also in metals, semiconductors, and plasmas.

Consider an ionic electroactive species k (e.g., anion or cation) with a mass m_k, in kg, and having an electric charge $q_k = z_k e$ expressed in C, where z_k is the algebraic valence of the ion, and e is the elementary electrostatic charge (ca. 1.6021×10^{-19} C).

If an electric voltage ΔU in V is applied between two plane, parallel, and rectangular electrodes, it appears inside the inter-electrode gap, d in m, an electric field strength, denoted $\boldsymbol{E} = -\nabla V$, in V.m^{-1} orientated according to the decreasing potentials and having the value $\Delta U/d$. Under this electric field, the ion is submitted to an external electrostatic force, $\boldsymbol{F}_e = z_k e\boldsymbol{E}$ expressed in N and it moves towards the electrode having the opposite sign with a terminal velocity $\boldsymbol{v}_k$.

During the motion of the ion in the electrolyte, it also undergoes a drag force $\boldsymbol{F}_d$ opposite to the displacement. This viscous force results from the microscopic collisions (i.e., friction) with the atoms and molecules constitutive of the electrolyte. Therefore, the equation of displacement must verify the second Newton's law of motion:

$$\boldsymbol{F}_e + \boldsymbol{F}_d = m_k \mathrm{d}\boldsymbol{v}_k/\mathrm{d}t$$

If we assume that the electrolyte is an ideal fluid having a dynamic or absolute viscosity η expressed in Pa.s, and that the ion is a quasi-spherical particle with a ionic radius r_k, in m, the viscous force can be expressed with a good approximation by the ***Stokes' law*** describing the motion of a spherical particle into an ideal hydrodynamic medium [64]: $\boldsymbol{F}_d = -(6\pi\eta r_k)\boldsymbol{u}_k$. Hence the general equation of motion for the ion can be written:

$$z_k e\boldsymbol{E} - (6\pi\eta r_k)\boldsymbol{v}_k = m_k \mathrm{d}\boldsymbol{v}_k/\mathrm{d}t$$

Once the steady state is reached (i.e., $\boldsymbol{v}_k$ = constant), the ion reaches a terminal velocity $\boldsymbol{v}_k$ which is given by the simple equation:

$$\boldsymbol{v}_k = (z_k e/6\pi\eta r_k)\boldsymbol{E} = u_k\boldsymbol{E}$$

Therefore, there is a direct linear relationship between the terminal velocity of the ion in motion into an electrolyte and the electric field strength existing between the two electrodes. The proportional coefficient defined by the equation below corresponds to the drift velocity per unit electric field strength.

This scalar physical quantity is called the conventional ***electrical mobility*** of the ionic species k or simply the ***ionic mobility***, denoted by the symbol u_k, and expressed in the SI in $m^2.s^{-1}.V^{-1}$:

$$u_k = (|z_k|e)/6\pi\eta r_k = (|z_k|F)/6\pi N_A\eta r_k$$

The ionic mobility characterizes the ability of an ion to move freely under an electric field, and its value corresponds to the velocity of the ion divided by the intensity of the electric field.

The electric mobility is an important characteristics related to: (i) the intrinsic properties of the ionic species (e.g., ionic radius, and electric charge), (ii) the physical properties of the solvent in which it migrates (e.g., dynamic or absolute viscosity), and (iii) the temperature, and pressure conditions.

---

[64] STOKES, G.G. (1845) On the theories of the internal friction of fluids in motion and of the equilibrium and motion of elastic solids. *Transactions of the Cambridge Philosophical Society*, **8**(1845)287-305.

The order of magnitude for the ionic mobility in aqueous electrolytes is about 10^{-8} $m^2.s^{-1}.V^{-1}$ (i.e., 10^{-4} $cm^2.s^{-1}.V^{-1}$). For convenience, we have listed the electrical mobility of selected cations and anions that are relevant in the electrowinning of iron in Table 32 hereafter. Note that is common practice to choose the entity to be $1/z_k$ of an ion of valence z_k, thus for example molar conductivities for sodium cation, ferrous and ferric cations would be quoted as: $\lambda(Na^+)$, $\lambda(1/2Fe^{2+})$, or $\lambda(1/3Fe^{3+})$.

Table 32 – Ionic mobility of selected cations and anions

Cation or anion	u (10^{-8} $m^2.s^{-1}.V^{-1}$)	Cation or anion	u (10^{-8} $m^2.s^{-1}.V^{-1}$)
H^+	**36.2**	Fe^{2+}	5.5
Li^+	4.0	Co^{2+}	5.7
Na^+	5.2	Ni^{2+}	5.1
K^+	7.6	Cu^{2+}	5.9
NH_4^+	7.6	Zn^{2+}	5.5
Mg^{2+}	5.5	OH^-	**20.5**
Al^{3+}	6.3	SO_4^{2-}	8.3
Notes: measured at 25°C, 1 $cm^2.s^{-1}.V^{-1}$ = 10^{-4} $m^2.s^{-1}.V^{-1}$ (E)			

Note that other definitions of the electric mobility of ionic species are also used in the literature, especially in old textbooks causing some confusion. Actually, another derived quantity called the ***absolute electric mobility*** with the symbols B_k, and ω_k respectively, and expressed in $kg^{-1}.s$ or $mol.kg^{-1}.s$ and related to the conventional mobility by the two following equations:

$$B_k = u_k/(|z_k|e) = 1/6\pi\eta r_k$$

$$\omega_k = u_k/(|z_k|F) = 1/6\pi N_A\eta r_k$$

Based on the previous equations, it is now possible to express the flux of electro-migration of the ionic species i:

$$\phi_{k\ \text{migration}} = n_k\, u_k\, \boldsymbol{E} = n_k\, z_k e\, B_k\, \boldsymbol{E} \qquad \text{(particle basis)}$$

$$J_{k\ \text{migration}} = c_k\, u_k\, \boldsymbol{E} = c_k\, z_k F\, \omega_k\, \boldsymbol{E} \qquad \text{(molar basis)}$$

$$G_{k\ \text{migration}} = C_k\, u_k\, \boldsymbol{E} = c_k\, M_k\, z_k F\, \omega_k\, \boldsymbol{E} \qquad \text{(mass basis)}$$

6.3 Mass Diffusion

The ***diffusion*** ensures the mass transfer under an existing gradient of chemical potential of all the species without regards to the electric charge of the entities transported (i.e., particles, ions, atoms, free radicals, and molecules). Thus diffusion takes place when there is a concentration gradient between two regions inside a medium (e.g., plasma, gas, liquid, and solid). The motion of a definite species always occurs irreversibly from the highest concentration regions to the depleted regions until a homogeneous concentration of this species is reached in the entire solution.

The flux of diffusion which is often located close to the electrode surface is related to the gradient of the chemical potential which is defined as follows:

$$\mu_k(T, P) = \mu_k^0(n_k) + kT \ln f_k.n_k \qquad \text{(particle basis)}$$

$$\mu_k(T, P) = \mu_k^0(c_k) + RT \ln \gamma_k \, c_k \qquad \text{(molar basis)}$$

$$\mu_k(T, P) = \mu_k^0(b_k) + RT \ln g_k.b_k \qquad \text{(molality basis)}$$

Where μ_k^0 is the standard chemical potential of the pure constituent k with the properties of an ideal solution at infinite dilution. Hence, the flux of diffusion can be related to the gradient of chemical potential by the following equation:

$$\boldsymbol{\phi}_{k\ \text{diffusion}} = -(n_k D_k / kT)\ \nabla \mu_k \qquad \text{(particle basis)}$$

$$\boldsymbol{J}_{k\ \text{diffusion}} = -(c_k\ D_k / RT)\ \nabla \mu_k \qquad \text{(molar basis)}$$

$$\boldsymbol{G}_{k\ \text{diffusion}} = -(C_k D_k / M_k RT)\ \nabla \mu_k \qquad \text{(mass basis)}$$

After replacing the chemical potential of the species by its equation, it is possible to express the flux of diffusion of the species k by the well-known ***Fick's first law*** expressed as follows:

$$\boldsymbol{\phi}_{k\ \text{diffusion}} = -n_k D_k\ \nabla \ln n_k = -D_k\ \nabla n_k \qquad \text{(particle basis)}$$

$$\boldsymbol{J}_{k\ \text{diffusion}} = -\ c_k\ D_k\ \nabla \ln c_k = -D_k\ \nabla[\text{k}] \qquad \text{(molar basis)}$$

$$\boldsymbol{G}_{k\ \text{diffusion}} = -C_k D_k / M_k\ \nabla \ln(C_k / M_k) = -D_k\ \nabla C_k \qquad \text{(mass basis)}$$

The negative sign indicates that the flux of diffusion is always directed from higher concentration regions (i.e., higher chemical potential) to depleted regions (i.e., lower chemical potential) in accordance with the second law of thermodynamics. For instance, a diffusional flux appears near the electrode surface when a charge transfer reaction causes a depletion of ions leading to a concentration gradient.

The proportional coefficient denoted with the symbol D_k is the ***diffusion coefficient***, sometimes called ***mass diffusivity***, of the species k, which is expressed in $m^2.s^{-1}$. Usually, the order of magnitude for diffusion coefficients of ionic species in aqueous electrolytes is about 10^{-9} $m^2.s^{-1}$ (i.e., 10^{-5} $cm^2.s^{-1}$).

6.4 Natural and Forced Convection

As a general rule, free convection is the direct consequence of the existence of a temperature gradient in the solution leading to the creation of density gradients. In the case of forced convection, the flux of matter results from the input of external mechanical energy (e.g., mixing, bubbling). In both cases the flux is equal to the concentration of species times the average centroid velocity, $\boldsymbol{v}_G$ of the entire fluid, in $m.s^{-1}$, i.e., the velocity of the solvent with respect to the laboratory coordinate system. This velocity can be obtained by the resolution of the ***Navier-Stokes*** hydrodynamic equation. Hence, the flux of convection can be expressed by:

$\phi_{k\ \mathrm{convection}} = n_k \boldsymbol{v}_G$ (particle basis)

$J_{k\ \mathrm{convection}} = c_k \boldsymbol{v}_G$ (molar basis)

$G_{k\ \mathrm{convection}} = C_k \boldsymbol{v}_G$ (mass basis)

6.5 Thermodiffusion

When non-isothermal conditions are encountered, it is necessary to consider the ***thermodiffusion*** also called the ***Ludwig-Soret*** effect or formerly ***thermophoresis*** induced by the existence of thermal gradients **grad**T arising in different regions of the electrolyte. The ***Soret effect*** tends to move light species to hot regions and heavy species to cold regions. This acting force is significant at very low fluid velocities (e.g., stagnant electrolyte) with natural convection. The corresponding thermodiffusion flux is given by:

$\phi_{k\ \mathrm{thermodiffusion}} = D_k \nabla n_k + n_k (1 - n_k) D_T \nabla T$ (particle basis)

$\boldsymbol{J}_{k\ \mathrm{thermodiffusion}} = D_k \nabla c_k + c_k (1 - c_k) D_T \nabla T$ (molar basis)

$\boldsymbol{G}_{k\ \mathrm{thermodiffusion}} = D_k \nabla C_k + C_k (1 - C_k) D_T \nabla T$ (mass basis)

Where D_T is the ***thermodiffusion coefficient*** expressed in $m^2.s^{-1}.K^{-1}$, and D_k, the mass diffusion coefficient expressed in $m^2.s^{-1}$.

The ***Soret coefficient*** of the species denoted, S_T, expressed in K^{-1}, is the ratio of thermodiffusion and diffusion coefficients.

$$S_T = D_T / D_k$$

On the other hand, the ***thermodiffusion factor***, denoted α_T, is defined as follows:

$$\alpha_T = T \times S_T = \ = T \times (D_T / D_k)$$

6.6 The Nernst-Planck's Equation

The total flux of a given electroactive species k in motion inside an electrolyte corresponds to the vector sum of all the individual contributions responsible of the transport of the species by diffusion, migration, and convection:

$$\boldsymbol{J}_{k,\ total} = \boldsymbol{J}_{k,\ diffusion} + \boldsymbol{J}_{k,\ migration} + \boldsymbol{J}_{k,\ convection}$$

Replacing each flux contribution by their previous equation, we obtained the so-called ***Nernst-Planck's equation***:

$$\boldsymbol{\phi}_{k\ total} = -D_k\, \nabla n_k - n_k\, u_k\, \nabla V + n_k \mathbf{v}_G \qquad \text{(particle basis)}$$

$$\boldsymbol{J}_{k\ total} = -D_k\, \nabla c_k - c_k\, u_k\, \nabla V + c_k \mathbf{v}_G \qquad \text{(molar basis)}$$

$$\boldsymbol{G}_{i\ total} = -D_k\, \nabla C_k - C_k\, u_k\, \nabla V + C_k \mathbf{v}_G \qquad \text{(mass basis)}$$

This general equation describes the transport of an electroactive species by diffusion-migration-convection in an isothermal electrochemical reactor when an electric potential difference is applied between two electrodes. Note that for concentrated solutions, it is important to replace the concentrations by the corresponding activities.

6.7 Liquid Junction Potential

6.7.1 Origins

When an external flow of electric current occurs, there must be a compensating current within the electrochemical cell ensured by the transport of ionic species through the electrolyte and the separator. A ***liquid junction*** consists of a porous diaphragm separating two different liquids. Because the concentrations of ionic species are not the same apart the separator, a diffusion flow occurs from the concentrated compartment to the dilute region. Because usually the transference number of ions inside the porous medium are unequal, a potential difference appears across the diaphragm, such potential difference is called ***liquid junction potential***.

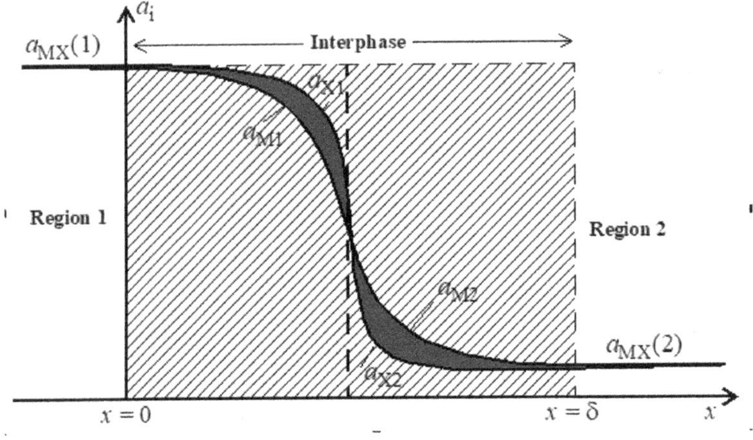

Figure 18 – Interphase

6.7.2 Types of Liquid Junction Potentials

According to Guggenheim [65] four types of liquid junction systems can be identified: (i) continuous mixture junction; (ii) constrained diffusion junction; (iii) flowing junction; and finally (iv) free diffusion junction. For an electrowinning process using a separator only the continuous diffusion liquid junction is relevant.

It consists to separate the two phases physically by either a porous separators such as diaphragms or impervious such as ion exchange membranes. The forced convection ensured by the mixing on each side maintains constant activities of each ionic species. Therefore, the liquid junction potential is strictly maintained inside the ***physical interphase*** and a real steady state can be reached with activities and potential becoming time-independent. Hence, the diffusion occurs across a constant-thickness transition layer.

6.7.3 Planck Equation

Planck assumed that for a constrained diffusion liquid junction i.e., the catholyte and anolyte are physically separated by a separator. The forced convection ensures the mixing on each side and maintains constant activities of each species .Therefore, the liquid junction potential is strictly restricted inside the physical interphase and a real steady state can be reached with activities and potential becoming time-independent. Hence, the diffusion occurs across a constant-thickness transition layer an expression for a boundary of the constrained diffusion type.

---

[65] GUGGENHEIM, E.A. (1930) A study of cells with liquid-liquid junctions. *Journal of the American Chemical Society*, **52**(4)(1930)1315-1337.

Because of the difference of both activities and diffusion coefficient of the ionic species, it appears a gradient of activities in the contact zone. This gradient leads to the mass diffusion of the ionic species. However, the flux of diffusion of each species is different because their activity and ionic mobility are different for each compartment. Even without current, an electric potential appears that impedes ions having an opposite charge to migrate while allowing the other ions to migrate.

The liquid junction potential cannot be measured directly but calculated. The electromotive force of a concentration cell with transference includes the liquid junction potential.

The *emf* of a concentration cell without transport where the activities of the electroactive species for instance a metal cation M^{z+} across the separator are a_1 and a_2 respectively is given by:

$$E_{conc} = (RT/zF)\ln(a_2/a_1)$$

On the other hand, the *emf* of a concentration cell with transport:

$$E_{trans} = 2t_+(RT/zF)\ln(a_2/a_1)$$

The liquid junction potential denoted ΔE_J in V, is the difference between these two potentials as follows:

$$\Delta E_J = E_{trans} - E_{conc} = (2t_+ - 1)(RT/zF)\ln(a_2/a_1)$$

More generally, when a Faraday passes, a corresponding amount of species k migrates according to its ionic mobility, u_k, across the separator in a direction depending on its electric charge z_k. The amount of total current carried by the ionic species is given by its transference number, t_k. This migrating flux of ionic species creates changes in their thermodynamic activities, and thus their chemical potential μ_k on each sides of the separator, and hence the change in the Gibbs molar enthalpy in $J.mol^{-1}$ in the contact zone is given by:

$$d\Delta G = -(t_k/z_k)d\mu_k$$

Because, the chemical potential for an ionic species k is given by:

$$\mu_k = \mu_k^0(T,P) + (RT/F)\ln a_k$$

The potential change for a species k is given by:

$$dE_J = -(RT/F)(t_k/z_k)d\ln a_k$$

In practice, a satisfactory approach for calculating with a good accuracy the liquid junction potential is to use the following integral equation between the phase I and II called the ***Planck equation***:

$$\Delta E_J = \int dE_J = -(RT/F)\int \Sigma_k(t_k/n_k)d\ln a_k = -(RT\ln 10/F)\int \Sigma_k(t_k/n_k)d\log_{10} a_k$$

With

ΔE_J	liquid junction potential in V,
t_k	dimensionless transference number of ionic species k,
n_k	dimensionless number of electric charge of species k,
a_k	activity of ionic species k expressed in $mol.m^{-3}$.

Assuming that the concentrations are equivalent to the activities, and the concentration of each ion follows a linear transition between the two phases, the above equation becomes after integrating over the entire contact zone, we obtain, the general equation of Planck for the liquid junction potential.

6.7.4 Binary Electrolyte

For instance, if we consider the binary electrolyte $M^{p+}{}_nX^{n-}{}_p$ at two different activities apart a separator:

$M^{p+}{}_nX^{n-}{}_p(a_1) \;||\; M^{p+}{}_nX^{n-}{}_p(a_2)$

We have the relationship between charge numbers and stoichiometric coefficients: $n|z_M| = p|z_X|$.

The transference numbers are independent on the activities of the ionic species and are only related by the equation: $t_M + t_X = 1$, and the activities of ionic species are: $a_{M+} = n\, a_\pm$ and $a_{X-} = p\, a_\pm$

Therefore, the liquid junction potential is given by the equation:

$$\Delta E_J = (RT/F)\{(t_M/z_M)\ln[a_M(1)/a_M(2)] + (t_X/z_X)\ln[a_X(1)/a_X(2)]\}$$

$$\Delta E_J = (RT/F)[(n^2t_M - p^2 + p^2t_M)/nz_M]\ln[a_\pm(1)/a_\pm(2)]$$

For a binary and symmetrical electrolyte of 2-2 type such as $Fe^{2+}SO4^{2-}$, we obtain the simplified equation:

$$\Delta E_J = (2t_M - 1)(RT/F)\ln[a_\pm(1)/a_\pm(2)] = (1 - 2t_X)(RT/F)\ln[a_\pm(1)/a_\pm(2)]$$

6.7.5 Henderson Equation

Henderson [66, 67] assumed that the interphase consists to a region where the linear mixing of the two different electrolytes occurs. If we introduce the thermodynamic activities a_k of the species k in the region A comprised between 0 at $x = \delta$ (i.e., interface between the mixing zone and the electrolyte j) and $a_i(A)$ at (i.e., interface of the mixing zone and electrolyte i) and a_j the molar fraction of electrolyte j in the region B varying between 0 and $a_j(B)$.

Because the activity of ionic species follows a linear variation inside the interphase region, the equation giving the molar fraction of each species as a function of position is given by:

$$a_j(x) = [a_j(B)/\delta]\, x \qquad \text{and} \qquad a_i(x) = -[a_i(A)/\delta]\, x + a_i(A)$$

Injecting these two relations into the equation of the transference number of the ionic species i we obtain:

$$t_k = z_k\, u_k\, a_k/(z_k\, u_k\, a_k + z_j\, u_k\, a_j)$$

It is also necessary to assume that thermodynamic activities and ionic mobility's are independent from the location x of the species. This is true when the ionic strength is low (I <0.1 M).

In a liquid cell by contrast with a concentration cell, the concentration of the intermediate layers influences the *e.m.f.* Thus it is possible to calculate the *e.m.f.* assuming an intermediate layer consisting of a continuous mixture of two contiguous liquids. A general formula is derived for the case where the contiguous solutions have the same concentration. However, in practical situations, a more sophisticated equation called the general ***Henderson equation*** should be used for calculating the liquid junction potential:

$$\Delta E_J = (RT/F)\{\sum(u_k/z_j)[[a_j(B) - a_j(A)]\}/\{\sum u_k[[a_j(B) - a_j(A)]\}\ln\{[\sum u_k\, a_j(A)]/[\sum u_k a_j(B)]\}$$

The Henderson equation is satisfactory only for binary electrolytes. It can be corrected for incomplete dissociation for weak electrolytes. Historically, Henderson conducted numerous measurements on the following liquid cells at various concentrations such as:

K_2SO_4 | | Na_2SO_4

---

[66] HENDERSON, P. (1907) The thermodynamics of liquid cells. *Zeitschrift Physikalische Chemie*, **59**(1907)118-127.

[67] HENDERSON, P. (1908) On the thermodynamics of liquid cells. *Zeitschrift Physikalische Chemie*, **63**(1908)325-345.

H_2SO_4 | | K_2SO_4,

H_2SO_4 | | Na_2SO_4

In the particular case of binary electrolytes, the above equation satisfies to the equation found previously. However, in the case of systems that consists of two different binary electrolytes with an anion in common such as:

$M^{p+}{}_nX^{n-}{}_p(a_2)$ | | $N^{q+}{}_nX^{n-}{}_q(a_1)$

With the following relationships:

$n\|z_M\| = p\|z_X\|$	and	$n\|z_N\| = q\|z_X\|$
$a_{M^+} = n\, a_\pm(2)$	and	$a_{X^-} = p\, a_\pm(2)$
$a_{N^+} = n\, a_\pm(1)$	and	$a_{X^-} = q\, a_\pm(1)$

Therefore the Henderson-Planck equation becomes as follows:

$$\Delta E_J = (RT/F)[(n^2u_M+p^2u_X)qa_2-(n^2u_N+q^2u_X)pa_1]/\{pqz_X[(nu_M+pu_X)a_2-(nu_N+qu_X)a_1]\}\ln\{(nu_N+qu_X)a_1/(nu_M+pu_X)a_2\}$$

For instance for two different but electrolytes with a common anion such as the cell: $FeSO_4$ | | H_2SO_4, we can express the Henderson equation in its simplified form:

$$\Delta E_J = (RT/F)[(u_M+u_X)a_2-(u_N+u_X)a_1]/[(u_M+u_X)a_2-(u_N+u_X)a_1]\ \ln\{(u_N+u_X)a_1/(u_M+u_X)a_2\}$$

If activities of the two electrolytes are equal, the equation of the liquid junction potential becomes:

$$\Delta E_J = (RT/F)\ \ln\{(u_N+u_X)/(u_M+u_X)\} = (RT/F)\ \ln(\Lambda_{NX}/\Lambda_{MX})$$

Where Λ_{NX}, and Λ_{MX} are the equivalent conductivities of the two solutions at the concentration employed. This simple equation was first introduced in 1909 by Sargent et Lewis [68].

In practice, the order of magnitude for a liquid junction potential ranges from few millivolts up to 50 mV, depending on the nature of the electroactive species, and the concentrations of the electrolyte.

---

[68] LEWIS,G.N.; and SARGENT, L.W. (1909) Potentials between liquids. *Journal of the American Chemical Society*, **31**(1909)363-367.

6.8 Continuity Equations

For a definite electroactive species k contained inside a volume of electrolyte V, the universal principle of the mass conservation at a given time can be generally written as follows:

$$[\text{Accumulation}]_k = [\text{Flux in}]_k - [\text{Flux out}]_k + [\text{Production/Consumption}]_k$$

If we consider a small element of volume of electrolyte dV having a cross section area dA, the mass balance equation applied to the single species k can be written as follows:

$$(\partial n_k/\partial t)dV = -\phi_k dA + \sigma_k dV \quad \text{(particle basis)}$$

$$(\partial c_k/\partial t)dV = -J_k dA + s_k dV \quad \text{(molar basis)}$$

$$(\partial C_k/\partial t)dV = -G_k dA + S_k dV \quad \text{(mass basis)}$$

Where the first algebraic term corresponds to the net rate of accumulation of the species, the second member is the net difference between the incoming and out coming fluxes of the species, finally the third algebraic member corresponds to the net rate of production (i.e., source) or consumption (i.e., sink) of the species inside the system for instance by a chemical reaction in homogeneous phase or an electrochemical reaction involving the species. The latter term, it is expressed depending on the concentration scale used in $m^{-3}.s^{-1}$, $mol.m^{-3}.s^{-1}$, or $kg.m^{-3}.s^{-1}$ respectively.

If we applied the ***Liebnitz theorem*** to the left member and the ***Gauss theorem*** (i.e., ***Green-Ostrogradsky***) to the right member we obtained the so-called ***continuity equation*** for the single species k:

$$\partial n_k/\partial t + \mathrm{div}\phi_k = \sigma_k \quad \text{(particle basis)}$$

$$\partial c_k/\partial t + \mathrm{div}\boldsymbol{J}_k = s_k \quad \text{(molar basis)}$$

$$\partial C_k/\partial t\ t + \mathrm{div}\boldsymbol{G}_k = S_k \quad \text{(mass basis)}$$

Introducing the Nernst-Planck's equation into the continuity equation we obtain the following set of equations:

$$\partial n_k/\partial t - \mathrm{div}[D_k \nabla n_k + n_k u_k \nabla V - n_k \mathbf{v}_G] = \sigma_k \quad \text{(particle basis)}$$

$$\partial c_k/\partial t - \mathrm{div}[D_k \nabla c_k + c_k u_k \nabla V - c_k \mathbf{v}_G] = s_k \quad \text{(molar basis)}$$

$$\partial C_k/\partial t - \mathrm{div}[D_k \nabla C_k + C_k u_k \nabla V - C_k \mathbf{v}_G] = S_k \quad \text{(mass basis)}$$

Developing the member in brackets using the tools of vector analysis, we obtain the set of three equations:

$$\partial n_k/\partial t - \mathrm{div}(D_k \nabla n_k) - u_k (\nabla n_k \nabla V + n_k \nabla^2 V) + \mathbf{v}_G \cdot \nabla n_k + n_k \mathrm{div}\boldsymbol{u}_G = \sigma_k$$

$$\partial c_k/\partial t - \text{div}(D_k \nabla c_k) - u_k (\nabla c_k \nabla V + c_k \nabla^2 V) + \boldsymbol{v}_G \cdot \nabla c_k + c_k \text{div} \boldsymbol{u}_G = s_k$$

$$\partial C_k/\partial t - \text{div}(D_k \nabla C_k) - u_k (\nabla C_k \nabla V + C_k \nabla^2 V) + \boldsymbol{v}_G \cdot \nabla C_k + c_k \text{div} \boldsymbol{u}_G = S_k$$

This is the ***general continuity equation*** taking into account the diffusion, the migration, and the convection of the electroactive species. When possible the mathematical resolution of this global continuity equation using the ***Laplace transform*** allows obtaining the equation for the concentration profile of the species k as a function of time. From a practical point of view, most of the situations encountered in industrial electrochemistry and electrochemical engineering based on particular boundaries conditions allows simplifying the continuity equation into more solvable and easy to handle equations.

When the diffusion coefficient of the species D_k is independent of its concentration and position, and there is neither production nor consumption of the species (i.e., σ_k, s_k, and $S_k = 0$) the general continuity equation can be simplified as follows:

$$\partial n_k/\partial t - \text{div}(D_k \nabla n_k) - u_k (\nabla n_k \nabla V + n_k \nabla^2 V) + \boldsymbol{v}_G \cdot \nabla n_k + n_k \text{div} \boldsymbol{v}_G = 0$$

$$\partial c_k/\partial t - \text{div}(D_k \nabla c_k) - u_k (\nabla c_k \nabla V + c_k \nabla^2 V) + \boldsymbol{v}_G \cdot \nabla c_k + c_k \text{div} \boldsymbol{v}_G = 0$$

$$\partial C_k/\partial t - \text{div}(D_k \nabla C_k) - u_k (\nabla C_k \nabla V + C_k \nabla^2 V) + \boldsymbol{v}_G \cdot \nabla C_k + c_k \text{div} \boldsymbol{v}_G = 0$$

In the particular case, where the electroactive species are not electrically charged, the continuity equation simplify to the diffusion-convection equation common in hydrodynamics:

$$\partial n_k/\partial t - \text{div}(D_k \nabla n_k) + \boldsymbol{u}_G \cdot \nabla n_k + n_k \text{div} \boldsymbol{v}_G = 0 \qquad \text{(particle basis)}$$

$$\partial c_k/\partial t - \text{div}(D_k \nabla c_k) + \boldsymbol{u}_G \cdot \nabla c_k + c_k \text{div} \boldsymbol{v}_G = 0 \qquad \text{(molar basis)}$$

$$\partial C_k/\partial t - \text{div}(D_k \nabla C_k) + \boldsymbol{u}_G \cdot \nabla C_k + c_k \text{div} \boldsymbol{v}_G = 0 \qquad \text{(mass basis)}$$

These equations are extremely useful in electrochemical engineering when the electroactive species is present at a low concentration, and when a supporting electrolyte is used in large excess allowing to neglect the electro-migration of the electroactive species. For symmetric electrolytes of type 2-2 (i.e., Fe^{2+} and SO_4^{2-}) the equation applies rigorously. When the convection can be neglected, we obtain the ***Fick's second law*** of diffusion:

$$\partial n_k/\partial t = D_k \nabla^2 n_k \qquad \text{(particle basis)}$$

$$\partial c_k/\partial t = D_k \nabla^2 c_k \qquad \text{(molar basis)}$$

$$\partial C_k/\partial t = D_k \nabla^2 C_k \qquad \text{(mass basis)}$$

6.9 The Nernst-Einstein's Equation

For very dilute solutions, the coefficient of diffusion, D_k and the absolute ionic mobility u_k of charged species are interdependent, and this relation is called the Nernst-Einstein equation:

$$D_k = \omega_k kT = u_k kT/z_k e = u_k RT/z_k F$$

The Nernst-Einstein's equation gives reasonable results if the ionic species diffusing is roughly spherical and much larger than the solvent molecules and it can be used for calculations of the diffusion coefficients of charged species when tabulated data are not available.

6.10 Electroneutrality

Many inorganic and organic salts, when dissolved in water, dissociate to some extent into charged species called ions. The dissociation is a chemical equilibrium which depends on the substance, and the solvent in which it dissolves. Since a compound or mixture of compounds is electrically neutral, a solution made by dissolving a compound or mixture in water, must also satisfy the electrical neutrality. This means that the total number of positive charges (i.e., cations) must be equal to the total number of negative charges (i.e., anions). This statement is known as the ***law of electroneutrality for electrolytes.*** Hence, in order to meet the electroneutrality of the electrolyte, the concentrations of ions must satisfy the following general equation:

$$e\Sigma n_k.z_k = \Sigma n_k.z_k = 0 \qquad \text{(particle basis)}$$

$$F\Sigma c_k.z_k = \Sigma c_k.z_k = 0 \qquad \text{(molar basis)}$$

$$F\Sigma C_k.z_k/M_k = \Sigma C_k.z_k = 0 \qquad \text{(mass basis)}$$

This simple principle of electroneutrality is consistent with the ***Poisson's law*** commonly used in classical electromagnetism, and described below by the equation:

$$\mathrm{div}(\varepsilon_0\varepsilon_r \boldsymbol{E}) = \rho_e \quad \text{or} \quad -\mathrm{div}\,\boldsymbol{E} = \nabla^2 V = -\rho_e/\varepsilon_0\varepsilon_r$$

ε_0 vacuum electric permittivity, in $F.m^{-1}$,

ε_r relative electric permittivity of the solvent,

ρ_e electric charge density, in $C.m^{-3}$.

6.11 Current Density

The ***electric current density*** vector which is associated with the transport of a single ionic species k is denoted by the symbol j_k and its value is expressed in $A.m^{-2}$. The equation of the current density is obtained by multiplying the total flux of the species by diffusion-migration-convection times the electric charge of the given species:

$$j_k = z_k e \phi_{k\ total} = -z_k e D_k \nabla n_k - z_k e n_k u_k \nabla V + z_k e n_k \mathbf{v}_G$$

$$j_k = z_k F J_{k\ total} = -z_k F D_k \nabla c_k - z_k F c_k u_k \nabla V + z_k F c_k \mathbf{v}_G$$

$$j_k = (z_k F G_{k\ total})/M_k = (-z_k F D_k \nabla C_k - z_k F C_k u_k \nabla V + z_k F C_k \mathbf{v}_G)/M_k$$

Therefore the total current density corresponds to the vector summation over all charged species present into the electrolyte:

$$j = \Sigma_k j_k = -e[(\Sigma_k z_k D_k \nabla n_k) + (\Sigma z_k n_k u_k)\nabla V]$$

$$j = \Sigma_k j_k = -F[\Sigma_k z_k D_k \nabla c_k + (\Sigma z_k c_k u_k)\nabla V]$$

$$j = \Sigma_k j_k = -F[\Sigma_k (z_k D_k \nabla C_k/M_k) + (\Sigma z_k C_k u_k/M_k)\nabla V]$$

Note that in the above equation, the convective contribution is canceled due to the electroneutrality principle applied to the entire volume of solution.

In the particular case where there is no concentration gradient near the electrode, the diffusion of the species is negligible, and the equation for the current density becomes:

$j = -e(\Sigma z_k n_k u_k)\nabla V$ (particle basis)

$j = -F(\Sigma z_k c_k u_k)\nabla V$ (molar basis)

$j = -F(\Sigma z_k C_k u_k/M_k)\nabla V$ (mass basis)

Conversely, if a supporting electrolyte is used the electro-migration of the electroactive species can be neglected, and the current density related to the electroactive species is

$$j_k = -e z_k D_k \nabla n_k$$

$$j_k = -F z_k D_k \nabla c_k$$

$$j_k = -F(z_k D_k \nabla C_k/M_k)$$

6.12 Conservation of the Electric Charge

The fundamental principle of the conservation of the electric charge is a universal principle like the conservation of the mass, which can be written as follows:

$$(\partial \rho_e/\partial t)dV = - \boldsymbol{j}d\mathbf{A} + I_V dV$$

Where ρ_e is the density of electric charges per unit volume of electrolyte, in C.m^{-3}, j the electric current density, in A.m^{-2}, and I_V the net rate for either the production or the consumption of electric charge per unit volume of electrolyte, in A.m^{-3}.

For instance during electrowinning, $I_V = j_c.a_e$ where j_c is the cathode current density of the electrochemical reaction, and a_e the cathode specific active surface area in m^{-1} defined by the relation: $a_e = A_C/V_S$.

$$\partial \rho_e/\partial t + \mathrm{div}\boldsymbol{j} = I_V = j_c.a_c$$

We know that the density of charges is related to the concentration of ionic species by the relation:

$$e\Sigma n_k.z_k = \rho_e \quad \text{(particle basis)}$$

$$F\Sigma c_k.z_k = \rho_e \quad \text{(molar basis)}$$

$$F\Sigma C_k.z_k/M_k = \rho_e \quad \text{(mass basis)}$$

$$e\partial[\Sigma n_k.z_k]/\partial t + \mathrm{div}\boldsymbol{j} = j_c.a_e$$

$$F\partial[\Sigma c_k.z_k]/\partial t + \mathrm{div}\boldsymbol{j} = j_c.a_e$$

$$F\partial[\Sigma C_k.z_k/M_k]/\partial t + \mathrm{div}\boldsymbol{j} = j_c.a_e$$

Based on the electroneutrality of the electrolyte, the general equation for conservation of the electric charge becomes:

$$\mathrm{div}[(\Sigma z_k D_k \nabla n_k) + (\Sigma z_k n_k u_k)\nabla V] = -j_c a_e/e \quad \text{(particle basis)}$$

$$\mathrm{div}[(\Sigma z_k D_k \nabla c_k) + (\Sigma z_k c_k u_k)\nabla V] = -j_c a_e/F \quad \text{(molar basis)}$$

$$\mathrm{div}[(\Sigma z_k D_k \nabla C_k/M_k) + (\Sigma z_k C_k u_k/M_k)\nabla V] = -j_c a_e/F \quad \text{(mass basis)}$$

In the particular case of absence of concentration gradients and there are no electrochemical reactions, we obtain the well-known ***Laplace's equation*** which allows obtaining after integration the primary electric current distribution (see Section 9):

$$\nabla^2 V = 0$$

6.13 Electrical Conductivity

6.13.1 Electrolyte Electrical Conductivity

By comparison of the equation of the current density in the electrolyte with the generalized ***Ohm's law*** which is described by the equation below:

$$j = -\kappa E = -\kappa \nabla V$$

Where

j electric current density, in $A.m^{-2}$,

κ electrical conductivity of the electrolyte, in $S.m^{-1}$,

E electric field strength, in $V.m^{-1}$,

V electrical potential, in V.

It is possible to obtain in the absence of diffusion, the general equation for the ***electrical conductivity*** formerly called the ***specific conductance*** of the electrolyte. Actually, each ion present at infinite dilution contributes to the total ionic conductivity regardless of the nature of any other ions present. This means that the total conductivity of a sufficiently dilute electrolyte solution is given by the sum of the individual ionic conductivities of each ion k present in it according to the following equations:

$$\kappa = \Sigma_k \kappa_k = e\Sigma_k |z_k| n_k u_k = e^2 \Sigma z_k^2 n_k B_k \quad \text{(particle basis)}$$

$$\kappa = \Sigma_k \kappa_k = F\Sigma_k |z_k| c_k u_k = F^2 \Sigma z_k^2 c_k \omega_k \quad \text{(molar basis)}$$

$$\kappa = \Sigma_k \kappa_k = F\Sigma_k |z_k| C_k u_k / M_k = F^2 \Sigma z_k^2 C_k \omega_k / M_k \quad \text{(mass basis)}$$

Owing to the square exponent of the valence of the species in the equation for the electrical conductivity of the electrolyte, all the ions contribute positively to the electric current circulating into the electrolytic cell without regards of their electrical charge.

From the set of the above equations, it is possible to define the individual ionic conductivity of each single ion k:

$$\kappa_k = e|z_k| n_k u_k = e^2 z_k^2 n_k B_k \quad \text{(particle basis)}$$

$$\kappa_k = F|z_k| c_k u_k = F^2 z_k^2 c_k \omega_k \quad \text{(molar basis)}$$

$$\kappa_k = F|z_k| C_k u_k / M_k = F^2 z_k^2 C_k \omega_k / M_k \quad \text{(mass basis)}$$

6.13.2 Molar Ionic Conductivity

The ***electrical conductivity***, denoted κ, in S/m, of a strong electrolyte decreases as the solution concentration decreases. For dilute solutions, or solutions sufficiently diluted, that is, the ionic environment remains undisturbed upon further dilution, the electrical conductivity should decrease as it does with concentration only because the number of charge carriers per unit volume of solution decreases.

In order consider the variation of conductivity of each species with concentration, it is possible to normalize it to its molarity, introducing a new physical quantity called the ***molar ionic conductivity*** or the ***molar conductance***, which is defined as the electrical conductivity divided by the molar concentration, denoted by the Greek symbol Λ_m, and expressed in $S.m^2.mol^{-1}$.

$$\Lambda_m = \kappa / c$$

6.13.3 Equivalent Ionic Conductivity

It is standard practice in electrochemistry to normalize the conductivity to the normality rather than molarity, it is then possible to introduce the ***equivalent ionic conductivity*** or formerly the ***equivalent ionic conductance*** of the electrolyte, denoted by the Greek symbol Λ_{eq}, and is expressed in the SI in $S.m^2.eq^{-1}$.

$$\Lambda_{eq} = \kappa / zc$$

The relationship between the molar and equivalent ionic conductivities is given by the simple equation:

$$\Lambda_{eq} = \Lambda_m / z$$

The *International Union of Pure and Applied Chemistry* (IUPAC) recommended the use of equivalent conductivity to be discontinued [69]. The use of molar conductivity was then preferred. However, the theory behind electrolytic conductivity is mainly based on the equivalent thus in order to keep this book consistent with the theory, we use the terms equivalent and equivalent conductivity. Selected values [70] for the equivalent conductivities of electrolytes expressed in $S.cm^2.eq^{-1}$ are reported for convenience in Table 33.

---

[69] PARSONS, R. (1974) Manual of symbols and terminology for physico-chemical quantities and units, appendix iii-electrochemical nomenclature. *Pure and Applied Chemistry,* **37**(1974)499-516.
[70] DOBOS, D. (1975) *Electrochemical Data: a Handbook for Electrochemists in Industry and Universities.* Elsevier, Amsterdam, Oxford, UK, and New York, NY, pp. 49 to 53.

Table 33 – Equivalent ionic conductivities of selected electrolytes at 18°C

$C^{1/2}$		0.0224	0.0316	0.0707	0.1000	0.1414	0.2236	0.3162	0.4472	0.7071	1.0000	1.4142	1.7321	2.0000	2.2361
Normality	Λ_0	**0.0005 N**	**0.001 N**	**0.005 N**	**0.01 N**	**0.02 N**	**0.05 N**	**0.1 N**	**0.2 N**	**0.5 N**	**1.0 N**	**2.0 N**	**3.0 N**	**4.0 N**	**5.0 N**
$^1/_2H_2SO_4$	**429.7**	374.4	361.0	330.0	308.0		253.0	232.9		205.0	198.6	182.7	166.5	150.5	134.6
$^1/_2Li_2SO_4$	**118.7**		96.4		86.9		74.7	68.2		50.5	41.3	30.7	23.3	18.1	13.9
$^1/_2Na_2SO_4$	**129.8**	107.3	106.7	100.8	97.7		83.4	77.6	70.4	59.4	50.3	39.6	33.5		
$^1/_2K_2SO_4$	**153.5**	128.2	126.9	120.3	115.8		101.9	94.8	87.8	78.3	71.5				
$^1/_2(NH_4)_2SO_4$	**153.7**			120.0	116.5			89.0		79.5	73.0	65.0		55.2	
$^1/_2MgSO_4$	**133.1**	104.2	99.8	84.5	76.2		56.9	49.6	43.0	34.8	28.9	21.4	16.1	12.9	8.8
$^1/_2CuSO_4$	**133.6**	103.4	98.5	81.0	72.2		53.6	43.8	36.0	30.7	25.7	20.0	16.2		
$^1/_2FeSO_4$	**133.5**		82.0	75.0	70.0		54.0	44.5		30.8	25.8	19.5	15.4		
$^1/_2MnSO_4$	**133.5**									30.0	24.7	18.5	14.2	10.8	8.1
$^1/_2CoSO_4$	**135.0**		113.0		82.5		51.4	43.9	35.3	29.3	19.5	15.3	11.9		
$^1/_2NiSO_4$	**129.6**	102.0	94.4		69.8			43.8	37.9	30.6	25.4	19.3	15.1		
$^1/_2ZnSO_4$	**137.7**	103.4	95.4	84.9	74.2	61.2	52.6	45.4	39.1	31.4	26.6	20.0	15.6	11.9	9.0

Notes: measured at 25°C, 1 $S.cm^2.eq^{-1} = 10^{-4} S.m^2.eq^{-1}$(E), and $10^{-5} cm^2.s^{-1} = 10^{-9} m^2.s^{-1}$ (E)

In practice, the equivalent conductivity decreases with increasing concentration. With strong acids such as sulfuric acid, strong bases, and neutral inorganic salts such as Na_2SO_4, the change in conductivity is not very large, but with weak acids and bases the equivalent conductivity fall dramatically as the normality is increased, and becomes very low for normality's above 0.1 N. Other substances such as ferrous (II) sulfate exhibit an intermediate behavior.

6.13.4 Limiting Equivalent Conductivity

Close examination of the Table 33 indicates that the equivalent conductivity of strong electrolytes is approaching a limiting value as the normality is diminished. This physical quantity is called the ***equivalent conductivity at infinite dilution*** or simply the ***limiting equivalent conductivity*** of the electrolyte denoted Λ_0 and sometimes by Λ_∞.

It corresponds theoretically of the equivalent ionic conductivity of an electrolyte when it is completely ionized into ions, and the latter are so far apart that they exert no influence on each other. For that reason, interpretation of processes in solution, the value of Λ_0 is of more fundamental importance than that of Λ_{eq} because it is extrapolated to zero concentration (i.e., infinite dilution), and hence it is characteristic only of the ions and solvent, and it is theoretically independent of any ionic interactions.

6.13.5 Individual Equivalent Ionic Conductivity

It is convenient to introduce the ***individual equivalent conductivity*** of each ionic species k in the same manner as equivalent conductivities of electrolytes:

$$L_k = \kappa_k/(|z_k|\, n_k) = e u_k = e^2 z_k B_k \qquad \text{(particle basis)}$$

$$\lambda_k = \kappa_k/(|z_k|\, c_k) = F u_k = F^2 z_k c_k \omega_k \qquad \text{(molar basis)}$$

6.13.6 Law of Independent Migration of Ions

When the limiting equivalent ionic conductivity at infinite dilution of pairs of salts for instance AX and BX having an anion X in common is measured, it is observed experimentally that the difference between the equivalent ionic conductivities is almost constant irrespective to the nature of the anion.

For instance, from the limiting equivalent conductivities at infinite dilution at 18°C of potassium and sodium chlorides, and sulfates both having the same anion in common are presented in Table 34.

Table 34 – Limiting equivalent ionic conductivities of salts with anions in common

Salt AX	Λ_0 (/S.cm^2.eq^{-1})	Salt BX	Λ_0 (/S.cm^2.eq^{-1})	$\Delta\Lambda_0$ (/S.cm^2.eq^{-1})
$1/2K_2SO_4$	133	$1/2Na_2SO_4$	111.9	21.1
KCl	150	NaCl	126.5	23.5

This clearly demonstrates that the cation contributes to a definite amount of the overall conductivity of the electrolyte, irrespective to the nature of the anion. Thus broadly, the limiting equivalent conductivities of two electrolytes with two different cations, and a common anion differ by an amount which is independent of the nature of the anion:

$$\Lambda_0(AX) - \Lambda_0(BX) \approx \Lambda_0(AY) - \Lambda_0(BY)$$

Therefore, the limiting equivalent conductivity of the electrolyte is obtained by the summation of all the individual limiting equivalent ionic conductivities of each ion present in the solution.

This rule was first observed experimentally by the German physicist Friedrich W. Kohlrausch in 1876 and is known today as the ***Kohlrausch's law of independent ionic migration*** that holds only at infinite dilution when mutual ionic interactions are negligible.

Hence the equivalent conductivity at infinite dilution of an electrolyte (Λ_0) is then simply the sum of the limiting equivalent ionic conductivities of all the ions produced from the dissociation of the salt. Therefore, the law can be expressed by the following more general mathematical equation:

$$\Lambda_0 = \Sigma_k \nu_k \lambda_k$$

Where:

λ_k is the limiting equivalent ionic conductivity of k, in S.m^2 eq^{-1},

ν_k is the number of moles of cations and anions per formula unit,

For binary and symmetric 2-2 electrolytes such as $FeSO_4$, the equation becomes simply: $\Lambda_0 = \lambda_{Fe^{2+}} + \lambda_{SO_4^{2-}}$

Many of the values of the individual limiting equivalent ionic conductivities of cations and anions in aqueous solutions were determined experimentally by measuring the ion transport number that will be defined in Section 6.13.12.

For the cation: $\lambda_+ = t_+\Lambda_0/\nu_+$

For the anion: $\lambda_- = t_-\Lambda_0/\nu_-$

Comprehensive tabulated data are available in the scientific literature. For convenience, we have listed in Table 35, the limiting equivalent ionic conductivities of selected cations, and anions at 25°C often encountered during the electrowinning of iron from iron sulfates.

Table 35 – Equivalent ionic conductivity and diffusion coefficients at infinite dilution

Cations and anions	λ_k ($S.cm^2.mol^{-1}$)	D_k ($10^{-5}cm^2.s^{-1}$)	Cations and anions	λ_k ($S.cm^2.mol^{-1}$)	D_k ($10^{-5}cm^2.s^{-1}$)
$1/3Al^{3+}$	61	0.541	$1/2Mg^{2+}$	53.06	0.706
$1/2Cd^{2+}$	54	0.719	$1/2Mn^{2+}$	53.5	0.712
$1/2Co^{2+}$	55	0.732	NH_4^+	73.7	1.957
$1/3Cr^{3+}$	67	0.595	Na^+	50.08	1.334
$1/2Cu^{2+}$	56.6	0.714	$1/2Ni^{2+}$	49.6	0.661
$1/2Fe^{2+}$	53.5	0.719	$1/2Zn^{2+}$	52.8	0.703
$1/3Fe^{3+}$	67.4	0.604	**OH^-**	**198**	**5.273**
H^+	**349.65**	**9.311**	HSO_4^-	52	1.385
K^+	73.48	1.957	$1/2SO_4^{2-}$	80	1.065
Li^+	38.69	1.029	$1/2S_2O_8^{2-}$	86	1.145
Notes: measured at 25°C, $1\ S.cm^2.eq^{-1} = 10^{-4}\ S.m^2.eq^{-1}$(E), and $10^{-5}\ cm^2.s^{-1} = 10^{-9}\ m^2.s^{-1}$ (E)					

From the above table, we can see that most monovalent anions and cations in water exhibits equivalent ionic conductivities ranging from 40 to 90 $S.cm^2.eq^{-1}$ at 25°C. The only exceptions are the hydronium (protons) cations (H^+) with 350 $S.cm^2.eq^{-1}$, and hydroxyl anions (OH^-) with 198 $S.cm^2.eq^{-1}$.

Therefore for a binary 1-1 symmetric and strong electrolyte A^+X^- the limiting equivalent conductivity: $\Lambda_0(AX) = \lambda_{A+} + \lambda_{X-}$ is usually close to 120 $S.cm^2.eq^{-1}$. This rule of the thumb is sometimes useful to the industrial electrochemist in the field for assessing the conductance of an electrolyte without fast and easy access to tabulated data.

6.13.7 Conductivity of Pure Water

Based on the Kohlrausch's law, the theoretical limiting equivalent conductivity of pure water $\Lambda_0(H_2O)$ is then simply the sum of the products of the limiting equivalent ionic conductivities of hydronium and hydroxyl ions times their molarities:

$$\Lambda_0(H_2O) = \lambda_{H+} + \lambda_{OH-}$$

Base of the above equation the limiting equivalent conductivity of pure water is simply: $\Lambda_0(H_2O)$ = (349.65 + 198.0) = 547.65 $S.cm^2.eq^{-1}$. Therefore the electrical conductivity is: $\kappa = \Lambda_0(H_2O)\ [H^+]$

The theoretical molarity of hydronium cations (i.e., protons), and hydroxyl anions can be easily obtained from the value of dissociation product of pure water: $pK_w = \mathrm{colog}_{10}(a_{H+})(a_{OH-})$ as follows: $[H^+] = [OH^-] = 10^{-pK_w}$

This value is constant under standard conditions (298.15K and 101.325 kPa) with the assigned value of 14, that is, $[H^+] = [OH^-] = 10^{-14}$ mol/L (10^{-11} mol/m^3). Base of the above equation the electrical conductivity of pure water is: κ = 5.4765 x 10^{-13} $S.m^{-1}$ = 5.4765 x 10^{-15} $S.cm^{-1}$. This corresponds to the maximum resistivity for pure water of 18.26 MΩ.cm.

6.13.8 Kohlrausch Equation

For dilute aqueous solutions of strong electrolytes, the extrapolation of measured values of Λ_{eq} to infinite dilution vs. the square root of the concentration, $C^{1/2}$, is approximately linear. The resulting linear equation is called the ***Kohlraush equation*** with the empirical slope coefficient α which is characteristic of the electrolyte:

$$\Lambda_{eq} = \Lambda_0 - \alpha c^{1/2}$$

6.13.9 Onsager Equation

Later in 1927, Lars Onsager [71, 72] developed a modern theory of ionic motion in solution, in which he treated ions as small particles travelling in a dielectric medium, in analogy to the theory of Debye and Hückel for the equilibrium properties of electrochemical solutions.

An important result of his theory is expressed by the simple equation now known as the ***Debye-Hückel-Onsager equation*** or in brief as the ***Onsager equation*** as follows:

$$\Lambda_{eq} = \Lambda_0 - (A + B\Lambda_0)I^{1/2}$$

[71] ONSAGER, L. (1926) Zur Theorie der Electrolyte. I. *Physikalische Zeitschrift*, **27**(1926)388-392.
[72] ONSAGER, L. (1927) Zur Theorie der Electrolyte. II. *Physikalische Zeitschrift*, **28**(1927)277-298.

Where the two empirical coefficients, A, and B, for the above equation depend on the fundamental constants, the temperature, and the properties of ions and the solvent. Therefore, knowing A and B, it is possible to determine Λ_0 from Λ_{eq} measured at any concentration. For dilute solutions, the equations for the two coefficients according to the theoretical calculations are:

$$A = 4125(|z^+|+|z|)/[(\varepsilon_r T)^{0.5}\eta]$$

$$B = 2.801\ 10^6(|z^+|\cdot|z|q)/[(\varepsilon_r T)^{1.5}(1 + \sqrt{q})]$$

Where $|z^+|$ and $|z|$ are the absolute values of the valence of cations and anions respectively, ε_r is the relative permittivity of the solvent, η the dynamic (absolute) viscosity of the solvent in mPa.s, T, the absolute (thermodynamic) temperature in K, and the parameter q defined as follows:

$$q = |z^+|\cdot|z|/(|z^+|+|z|)$$

For example, for an aqueous solution at 298.15 K, the water exhibits a relative permittivity of 78.3, and a dynamic viscosity of 0.889 mPa.s, thus the Onsager equation becomes:

$$\Lambda_{eq} = \Lambda_0 - \{30.365\,(|z^+|+|z|) + 0.7852\,[(|z^+|\cdot|z|q)/(1 + \sqrt{q})]\Lambda_0\}\,\sqrt{I}$$

In the particular case of a symmetrical 2-2 electrolyte such as $FeSO_4$, with $|z^+| = |z| = |z| = 2$, then $q = 1$, therefore we can simplify the above equation and then obtain the condensed form below:

$$\Lambda_{eq} = \Lambda_0 - (60.73\,|z| + 0.3926\,|z|^2\Lambda_0)\,\sqrt{I}$$

6.13.10 Influence of Temperature

The limiting equivalent conductivity of a solution at a given temperature T versus a known value at a reference temperature T_0 is given by the following equation:

$$\Lambda(T) = \Lambda(T_0)[1 + a(T-T_0)]$$

Where a is the average temperature coefficient of the electrolyte solution, expressed in K^{-1}. It depends on both the salt and the solvent. Usually, for salts in aqueous solutions a ranges roughly between 0.019 K^{-1} to 0.021 K^{-1}, that is, the limiting equivalent conductivity of electrolytes increases by about two percent by degree Celsius at ordinary temperatures. Note that acids and bases exhibits slightly lower temperature coefficients, of 0.016 $K^{-1}$to 0.018 K^{-1}respectively. In the same manner limiting equivalent ionic conductivities of individual ions follow the same type of equation:

$\lambda(T) = \lambda(T_0)[1 + b(T-T_0)]$

But for nearly all ions, except hydronium cation (0.0142 K^{-1}) and hydroxyl anion (0.0160 K^{-1}) the temperature coefficient b ranges roughly between 0.018 K^{-1} to 0.022 K^{-1}. Roughly, higher is the ionic conductance the smaller the temperature coefficient is, hence differences between the values of different ions become smaller as the temperature is raised.

The results described above hold for infinite dilution, but similar conclusions hold for strong electrolytes at appreciable concentrations. However, weak electrolytes show some abnormalities: the conductivity of such solutions is dependent mainly on the degree of dissociation, and since it usually decreases with increasing temperature, the conductivity increases to a maximum and then decrease as the temperature is raised.

6.13.11 Measurement of the Conductivity of Electrolytes

In theory, the electrolyte conductivity, κ, (resp. resistivity, ρ), in S/m (resp. Ω.m) of an electrolyte can be determined by using two plane and parallel electrodes of identical surface area A, in m^2, immersed in the electrolyte and with a fixed inter-electrode spacing, L, in m (Figure 19) by the measuring the electrical resistance, R in ohm (resp. conductance, C, in S) using the following equations:

$$R = (1/\kappa)(L/A) = \rho(L/A) \qquad C = \kappa(A/L)$$

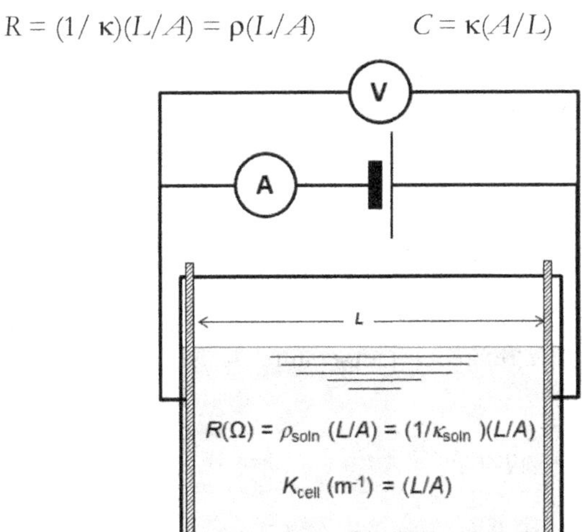

Figure 19 – Electrical resistance of an electrolytic cell

Because in practice the electrodes spacing, and the active surface area is not necessarily kwon with the great accuracy, it is common practice to introduce the physical quantity called the ***cell constant***, denoted K_{cell}, in m^{-1}, and simply defined as: $K_{cell} = (L/A)$. The experimental determination of cell constant for a given the electrolytic cell is obtained by measuring the conductance of the calibrated standard solution (e.g., molal solution of KCl)[73] using for instance a ***Wheatsone bridge*** under direct current (Figure 20).

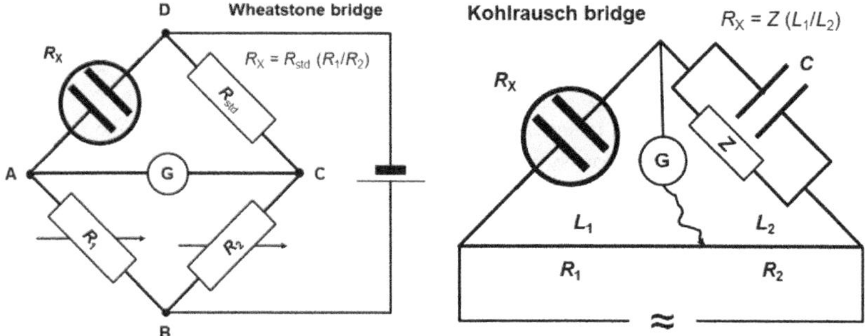

Figure 20 – Wheatsone bridge

Figure 21 – Kohlrausch bridge

However because of the electrochemical reactions occurring at each electrode once the voltage is applied, it is more reliable to measure the resistance of the cell using a source of high frequency alternative current up to 2 kHz by using the ***Kohlrausch bridge*** (Figure 21). More recently the measurement of the electrical conductivity of electrolytes is performed industrially using sturdy ***Toroidal conductivity probes*** very reliable, no affected by fouling, ideal for submersible applications in corrosive media, and electrolytes having a high conductivity up to 2,000 mS/cm.

6.13.12 Transference Number of Ions

Because the electric mobility varies with both the valence and the ionic radius of ionic species, each ion does not contribute identically in the transport of the electric current. The ***transport number*** of an ionic species i also called ***transference number*** or ***migration number*** and denoted t_k is the dimensionless ratio of the electric current transported by the species k to the overall current flowing in the cell. It is defined by the following simple equation:

$$t_k = j_k/j = I_k/I$$

The general and extensive equation is given below:

$$t_k = (|z_k| D_k |\nabla n_k| + |z_k| n_k u_k \ |\nabla V| - |z_k| n_k \mathbf{v}_G) / \{(\Sigma |z_k| D_k |\nabla n_k|) + (\Sigma |z_k| n_k u_k) z_k |\nabla V|\} \text{ (particle basis)}$$

[73] Pratt, K.W.; Koch, W.F.; Wu, Y.C.; And Berezansky, P.A. (2001) Molality-based primary standards of electrolytic conductivity. *Pure and Applied Chemistry*, **73**(11((2001)1783–1793.

$$t_k = (|z_k| D_k |\nabla c_k| + |z_k| c_k u_k |\nabla V| - |z_k| c_k \mathbf{v}_G)/\{(\Sigma |z_k| D_k |\nabla c_k|) - (\Sigma |z_k| c_k u_k) \nabla V|\} \text{ (molar basis)}$$

$$t_k = [(|z_k| D_k |\nabla C_k| - |z_k| C_k u_k \nabla V| + |z_k| C_k \mathbf{v}_G)/M_k]/[\Sigma(|z_k| D_k |\nabla C_k/M_k|) + (\Sigma |z_k| C_k u_k/M_k) |\nabla V|] \text{ (mass basis)}$$

When transport phenomena by convection and diffusion are negligible, we obtain the most common simplified equation:

$$t_k = |z_k| n_k u_k / (\Sigma |z_k| n_k u_k) \qquad \text{(particle basis)}$$

$$t_k = |z_k| c_k u_k / (\Sigma |z_k| c_k u_k) \qquad \text{(molar basis)}$$

$$t_k = (|z_k| C_k u_k / M_k) / (\Sigma |z_k| C_k u_k / M_k) \qquad \text{(mass basis)}$$

For a solution containing a single binary electrolyte $M_n^+X_p^-$, the transport number of each ion is given by the two relationships:

$$t_+ = c_+u_+/(c_+u_+ + c_-u_-) \qquad \text{and} \qquad t_- = c_-u_-/(c_+u_+ + c_-u_-)$$

For a binary and symmetric 1-1 electrolyte such as M^+X^- then $c_+ = c_-$

$$t_+ = u_+/(u_+ + u_-) \qquad \text{and} \qquad t_- = u_-/(u_+ + u_-)$$

Because the values of the mobility of most cations and anions ions are quite similar, the transport numbers of such binary symmetric electrolytes are approximately equal to 0.5. In addition, since an electrolyte solution must always remain electrically neutral, a value of 0.5 is the maximum value which can be achieved with a symmetrical electrolyte.

6.13.13 Role of a Supporting Electrolyte

Transport numbers vary with the nature of the solute and of the solvent as well as with concentration of the electrolyte. Transport numbers do change with concentration in a solution of a single salt, but only slightly. However, since the transport number of an ion is the fraction of the total ionic conductance due to that ion, the transport number of any particular ion or ions can be reduced to virtually zero by addition of a large concentration of some salt which does not contain them to the solution this is called a ***supporting electrolyte***. Electrochemists often make use of this technique for cancelling the migration of a particular electroactive species to study. On the other hand, because, the transport number is the fraction of the total charge transported which is transported by a particular ion, an increase of the relative concentration of any ion will cause its transport number to increase toward one.

7 Electrode Kinetics

The scope of the ***electrode kinetics*** is to study and understand the fundamental mechanisms of electrochemical reactions and to express the corresponding reaction rate as a function of electric current circulating inside the electrolyzer [74]. Therefore, the aim is to establish the equation for the electric current density as a function of the electrode potential, called ***characteristic current-potential curves*** or in short ***E-j* curves**.

7.1 Electrode Potential Measurements

The measurement of the electrode potential is generally conducted using the ***Piontelli's three-electrode system*** consisting of a ***working electrode*** (WE), that is, the electrode to be studied, and a ***counter electrode*** (CE), and finally a ***reference electrode*** (RE).

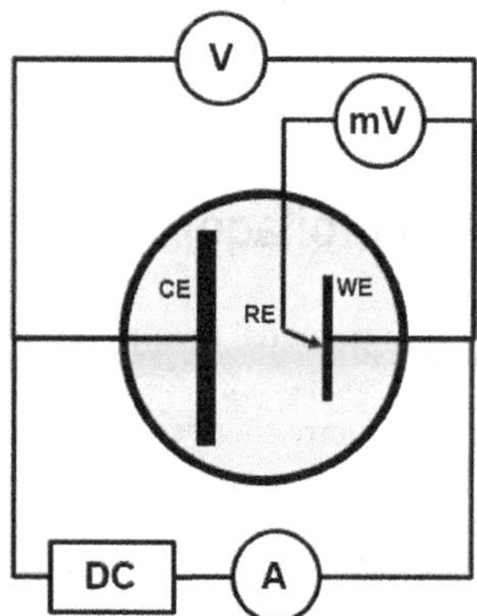

Figure 22 – Piontelli's three-electrode system

In order to minimize the ohmic drop (iR), it is important to use an appropriate supporting electrolyte, and to locate the reference electrode closer to the surface of the working electrode using for instance at the laboratory a ***Haber-Luggin capillary*** or a long probe with a porous plug at the tip for industrial electrolyzers. The potential measurements are performed with a high impedance

[74] CHARLOT, G.; BADOZ-LAMBLING, J.; and TREMILLON, B. (1962) *Electrochemical Reactions. The Electrochemical Methods of Analysis*. Elsevier Publishing Company, Amsterdam, The Netherlands.

voltmeter with the positive terminal of the electrometer connected to the working electrode and the negative terminal (COM) to the reference electrode.

7.2 Rest Potential

When an isolated electrode of a pure metal M is immersed into an electrolyte (e.g., aqueous solution of a soluble salt M^{z+} X^{z-}), without any electric current circulating, the electrode exhibits after a given stabilizing period (e.g., seconds to minutes) a ***rest potential***. This potential is equal to the thermodynamic standard electrode potential given by the Nernst equation corresponding to the half-reaction:

$$M^{z+} + ze^{-} = M(s)$$

$$E(T) = E^{0}_{298.15K} + (RT/zF)\ln(M^{z+}) = E^{0}_{298.15K} + (RT\ln 10/zF)\log_{10}(M^{z+})$$

In fact, at a microscopic scale, a state of equilibrium is reached owing to the simultaneous cathodic reduction of cations and anodic dissolution of metal proceeding in different domains (i.e., crystals or grains) at the electrode surface at equal rates. Since these processes involve the transfer of charge across the electrode-electrolyte (i.e., metal-solution) interface, their rates can be expressed in terms of electric current and hence, this process operates globally at zero net current.

7.3 Overpotential (Overvoltage)

In case a greater electric potential is imposed upon the electrode from an external source, the electrode surface is disturbed from its thermodynamic equilibrium conditions, and an electrochemical reaction occurs, that is, a finite electric current passes. This new electrode potential is called ***polarization***, and the electrode is said to be polarized. In 1899, the German scientist Caspari [75] called the difference between the electrode polarization and its rest potential *Überspannung* translated later as ***overpotential*** or simply ***overvoltage***. Later, two other definitions were introduced.

According to the French electrochemist Audubert in 1950, the overpotential corresponds to the difference between the rest potential and the electrode potential at which the electrochemical reaction is effectively observed, that is, when an electric current is detected with an ammeter. One can easily understand that this definition is imprecise because it is directly related to the sensitivity of the equipment to detect the electric current (i.e., galvanometer, ammeter). For instance, in certain old textbooks, the ***decomposition voltage***, the

[75] CASPARI, W.A. (1899) Über elektrolytische gasentwickelung. *Zeitschrift für Physikalische Chemie.* **30U**(1)(1899)89-97.

gassing overvoltage or ***bubble overvoltage***, are all synonyms of overvoltage in the particular case of gas evolution reactions (e.g., H_2, O_2). They all indicated the electrode potential at which the first bubbles of gases were visually observed!

Later in 1960 the German electrochemist Heinz Gerischer provided the universal and modern definition still used today in electrochemistry. The overpotential or overvoltage corresponds to the algebraic difference between any given potential of the polarized electrode when it carries an electric current, and its rest or equilibrium potential under the same experimental conditions (i.e., T, P, solvent, concentration of species). Hence, the overpotential of an electrode is denoted by the Greek letter, η and it is expressed in volts, at any given current density, j, in $A.m^{-2}$ is given by the simple equation:

$$\eta(j) = E(j) - E_{th}$$

7.4 Types of Overpotential

Many phenomena are associated with an electrochemical reaction, and they can lead to the existence of overpotentials of various origins. Actually, any electrochemical reaction can be described as a combination of consecutive elementary steps (i.e., mass transfer, homogenous chemical reaction, adsorption/desorption, electron transfer processes) as depicted in Figure 23. Therefore the rate for the electrochemical reaction, i.e., the current, is always controlled by the slower reaction (i.e., ***rate determining step***) of the electrode reaction pathway.

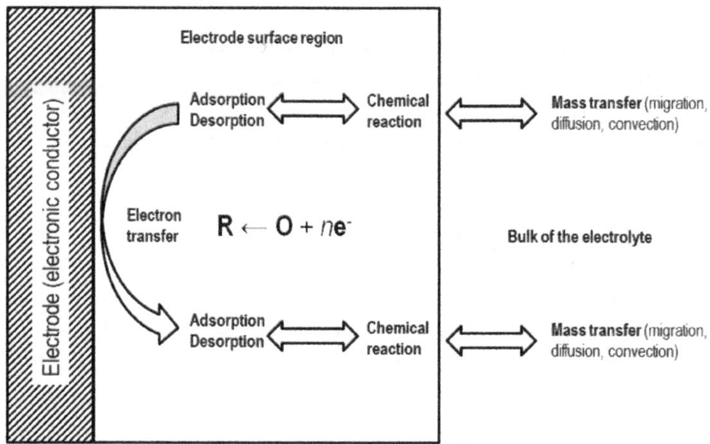

Figure 23 – Schematic of an electrochemical reaction pathway

Therefore, when an electric current circulates across an electrode, the resulting electrode potential is always the algebraic summation of two main terms:

(i) the equilibrium, thermodynamic or Nernstian electrode potential (E_{eq}, E_{th}) which is independent of the current density, and (ii) all the overpotential contributions that are strongly affected by the current.

$$E(j) = E_{th} + \Sigma_k \eta_k$$

Kortüm [76] identified at least five major, and distinct causes of overpotential: (1) the mass transfer by diffusion, (2) the electron transfer of activation, (3) the chemical reaction, (4) the crystallization, and (5) the passivation.

7.4.1 Concentration (Diffusion) Overpotential

During the cathodic electrodeposition of a metal from an electrolyte solution containing the metal cations into a supporting electrolyte, once the electrode is negatively polarized the narrow electrolyte region near the cathode surface is instantaneously depleted in metal cations. Owing to the large excess of inactive cations from the supporting electrolyte, the transference number of electroactive species is so negligible that the electromigration of metal cations is not sufficient to compensate quickly the depletion. Therefore, the apparition of a concentration gradient implies that diffusion is the only mass transfer mechanism capable to supply the electroactive species to the electrode surface. The ***diffusion overpotential*** also called the ***concentration overpotential*** can be drastically decreased if the diffusion layer is reduced by mean of intense forced convection (e.g., stirring or mixing). Actually, the molarity of the electroactive species close to the electrode surface is maintained close to its molarity in the bulk of the electrolyte and hence concentration gradient reaches its maximum.

7.4.2 Activation (Charge Transfer) Overpotential

The ***activation overpotential*** also called the ***charge transfer overpotential*** is due to a slow transfer of electrons across the electrode-electrolyte interface owing to an elevate activation energy for the charge transfer constant rate.

7.4.3 Chemical Overpotential

The ***chemical overpotential*** arises when the electroactive species is involved in a homogeneous chemical reaction before reaching the electrode or after leaving the electrode surface, the chemical reaction is then the rate determining step.

---

[76] KORTÜM, G. (1965) *Treatise in Electrochemistry, Second Edition.* Elsevier, Amsterdam, Netherlands, page 443.

7.4.4 Crystallization Overpotential

When a solid electrodeposit forms, the nucleation followed by two dimensional motions of adsorbed atoms or ***adatoms*** at the cathode surface to reach final lattice positions can induce a ***crystallization overpotential.***

7.4.5 Passivation Overpotential

When a thin passivating layer forms at the electrode surface (e.g., anodization, oxidation, sulfidation), the new insulating interface induces a ***passivation overpotential***.

7.5 International Sign Convention

The ***internationally adopted sign convention*** for both current and potential related to an electrochemical reaction were first introduced by the *Commité International de Corrosion et Technologie Électrochimique* (CICTE), later suggested by the *International Electrotechnical Commision* (IEC), and finally adopted by *The Electrochemical Society* (ECS) in 1952 [77]. It can be summarized as follows:

- Reduction (cathodic reaction) $j < 0$ and $\eta < 0$
- Oxidation (anodic reaction) $j > 0$ and $\eta > 0$

The convention can be depicted graphically using a plot of the current density vs. the electrode potential also called a voltamperometric (i.e., voltammetric) curve as depicted in Figure 24 hereafter.

[77] Journal of the Electrochemical Society, **99**(1952)25C

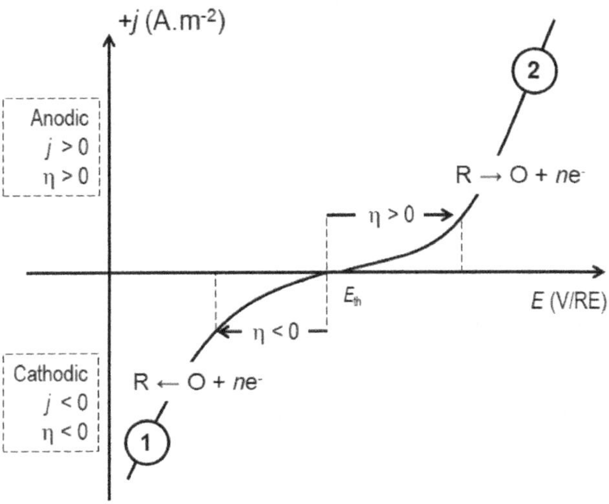

Figure 24 – Plot of the current density vs. electrode potential

Conversely, it is also possible to plot the absolute value of the current density vs. electrode potential as depicted in Figure 25.

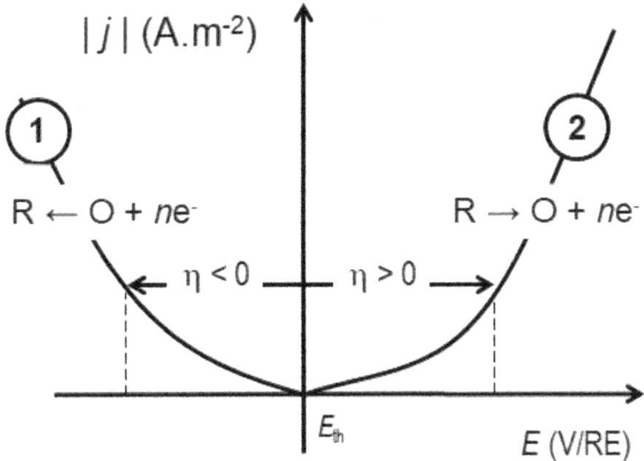

Figure 25 – Plot of the absolute value of current density vs. electrode potential

7.6 De Donder-Pourbaix Inequality

Therefore, the sign of the overpotential indicates clearly the direction taken by the electrochemical reaction. Actually, for a reduction the overpotential will have negative values ($\eta < 0$) while for an oxidation it will exhibits positive values ($\eta > 0$). Therefore whatever the type of electrochemical reaction considered the product of the current density times the overpotential is always positive and must satisfied the ***De Donder-Pourbaix inequality***:

$$\eta . j > 0$$

The first consequence of the De Donder-Pourbaix inequality, is that any electrochemical reaction can only proceed into an oxidation if overpotential is positive while reduction in the contrary. The second consequence is that polarization curves (i.e., E-j curves) are always located in the first and third quadrant of the plane.

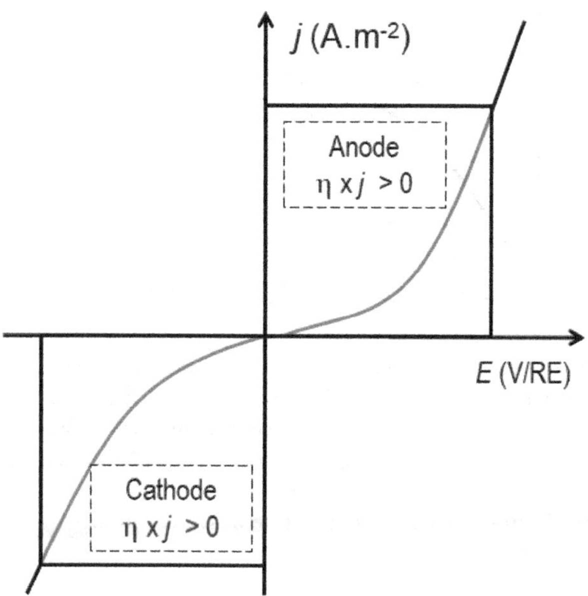

Figure 26 – DeDonder-Pourbaix quadrants

Formerly the first sign convention that introduced historically by Heyrovsky and called the polarography convention consisted to account cathodic currents as positive. This old convention is sometimes used in electro-analysis.

7.7 Reversible (Fast) Electrode Reaction

A ***reversible electrochemical system*** also called a ***fast*** or ***Nernstian system*** indicates that the electron transfer across the electrode-electrolyte interface is fast and hence the kinetics of the electrochemical reaction is only controlled by the mass transfer by diffusion of the electroactive species.

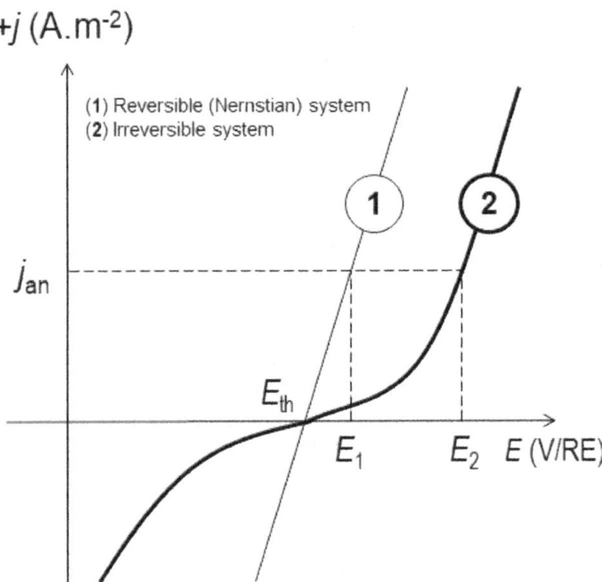

Figure 27 – Polarization plots for reversible and irreversible electrode reactions

In other words, a slight change in the electrode polarization, either anodic or cathodic, is capable to generate an elevate current density through the electrode (see Figure 27). In theory, a system is reversible from an electrochemical standpoint if the partial derivative $[\partial j/\partial \eta]$, that is, the slope of the polarization curve, tends to infinity close to the origin, forming a vertical straight line. For instance, typical quasi-reversible electrochemical systems are represented by the cathode reduction of hydronium cations (e.g., protons) onto platinized platinum.

It is worth to mention that the ***reversibility criterion*** used in electrochemistry is only a kinetic consideration that must not be confused with thermodynamic criterion. Hence pure diffusion regime is usually the preferred term to avoid confusion.

7.8 Irreversible (Slow) Electrode Reactions

An ***irreversible electrochemical system*** is characterized by a slow electron transfer across the electrode-electrolyte interface owing to the elevate activation energy of the potential barrier; it is sometimes called activation controlled. From a practical point of view, only a slight electrode potential is required either at the anode or at the cathode to generate a measurable current density (see Figure 27).

For instance, the reduction of hydronium cations (i.e., protons) at a titanium metal cathode yielding to the evolution of nascent hydrogen gas is a typical example of irreversible electrochemical reaction. On the other hand when the exchange current density is very small then a large value of overpotential (E_j - E_{th}) is required to change the current density. Intermediate behavior is generally referred to as ***quasi-reversible***.

7.9 Electrochemical Span

Observing the polarization curve of a polarized electrode, we can always identify a potential region were no electrochemical reaction occurs significantly, i.e., no electric current is easily detected (i.e., less than a nA.cm^{-2}), the electrode is said to be ***ideally polarized*** or ***electrochemically inert***.. This region is called the ***electrochemical span***, the ***electroactivity domain*** and it depends on the following parameters: (i) on the electrode material, (ii) the type of solvent, (iii) the type of solute, and finally (iv) the operating conditions (T, P, and concentration).

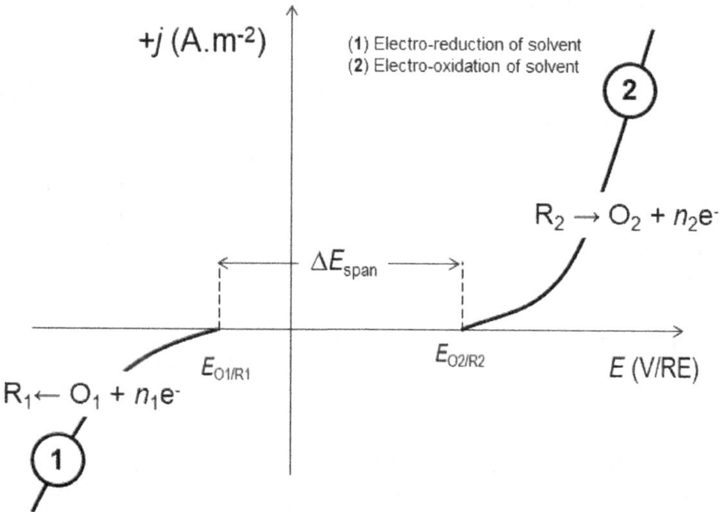

Figure 28 – Electrochemical span of the solvent

7.10 Concentration Overpotential

Consider a cathode immersed into a supporting electrolyte containing an electroactive species as metal cations, when an electric current is applied progressively between the cathode and the anode until the cathode potential stabilizes, above a given amperage, a voltage variation occurs corresponding to the beginning of the reduction of the metal cations.

Depletion of the electroactive species at the electrode surface leads to the spontaneous formation of a concentration gradient between the cathode surface and the bulk of the solution that creates a flux insuring the proper mass transfer of the cations of the metal as depolarizing species. The overall electrochemical reaction rate is the sum of mass transfer rate (i.e., diffusion, electromigration, and convection), and electric charge transfer rate at the cathode-electrolyte interface. However, if the electron transfer is fast across the electrolyte-electrode interface and if no homogenous chemical reaction involving the metal cations occurs, the only rate determining step of the overall electrochemical reaction is the mass transfer of the electroactive species.

Because the electromigration is mainly assumed by ionic species from the dissociation of the supporting electrolyte, the diffusion is the only mean to supply electroactive species at the electrode surface. Therefore concentration overpotential occurs when the kinetics of the electrochemical reaction is entirely controlled by the diffusion of the electroactive species.

7.10.1 Nernst Diffusion Layer

Once the steady-state conditions are reached in the electrochemical reactor (i.e., $\partial C_k/\partial t = 0$), a thin stagnant layer of electrolyte called the ***Nernst's layer*** or ***diffusion layer*** takes place at the electrode surface. The thickness of this boundary layer usually denoted by the Greek letter, δ, and expressed in m, depends on the hydrodynamic conditions (e.g., free and/or forced convection) existing at the electrode-electrolyte interface. It usually ranges between 1 μm (intense mixing) to 100 μm (gentle stirring). Usually, the thickness of the Nernst diffusion layer can be calculated by solving the corresponding transport equations. For instance, for pure diffusion from the bulk of solution to a solid electrode in the absence of convection, the thickness can be calculated with the equation:

$$\delta = (\pi D t)^{1/2}$$

The value of the thickness of the diffusion layer can be calculated using empirical correlations obtained from the dimensional analysis that will be discussed in Section 7.10.6.

Inside this boundary layer, the only process that ensures the proper mass transfer of an electroactive species, k, is the diffusion while outside the layer in the bulk of the solution, forced and/or free convection homogenize permanently the electrolyte. The main approximation assumed by Nernst consisted to consider a linear concentration profile inside the diffusion layer despite the actual concentration profile is not linear (Figure 29).

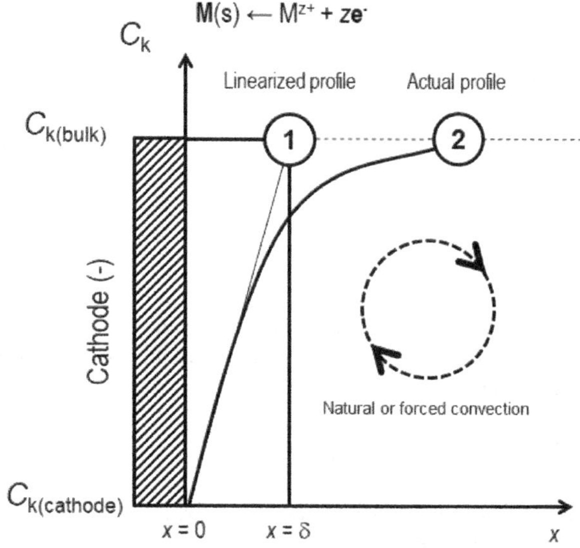

Figure 29 – Nernst diffusion layer

In this case, it is possible to define the two boundary conditions related to the linearized concentration profile assumed by Nernst.

Bulk of the solution: $C_k(x = \delta) = C_k(\delta) = C_{k,bulk}$;

Electrode surface: $C_k(x = 0) = C_k(0) = C_{k,electrode}$

7.10.2 Limiting Current

The overall molar flow rate of the electroactive species is given by the Nernst-Planck equation. Because a supporting electrolyte is often used, the electromigration flux ($\boldsymbol{J}_m$) can be neglected, and because the convection flux ($\boldsymbol{J}_c$) is effective only outside the boundary layer only the mass transfer by diffusion must be considered. Thus the transport of the electroactive species k is well described by the Fick's first law of diffusion:

$$\boldsymbol{J}_k = -D_k \nabla C_k$$

The vector current density is then simply obtained by multiplying the molar flow rate by the molar charge as follows:

$$\boldsymbol{j} = nF\boldsymbol{J}_k$$

It is then possible to express the vector current density existing at the electrode surface:

$$\boldsymbol{j} = -nFD_k(\boldsymbol{\nabla} C_k)_{x=0}$$

In the particular case of one-dimensional planar diffusion, the molarity of electroactive species only varies along the normal axis perpendicular to the planar electrode:

$$j = -nFD_k(\partial C_k/\partial x)_{x=0}$$

Owing to the Nernst assumptions, the gradient of concentration at the electrode surface is linear, thus the first partial derivative can be replaced by the slope of straight concentration profile:

$$(\partial C_k/\partial x)_{x=0} = [C_k(\delta) - C_k(0)]/\delta$$

Therefore, the current density can be expressed as follows, with the sign imposed by the international convention previously described and depending on the type of electrochemical reaction considered such as reduction (-) and oxidation (+):

$$j = \pm nFD_k[C_k(x) - C_k(0)]/\delta_k = \pm nFD_k(C_{k,bulk} - C_{k,electrode})/\delta_k$$

Highest is the difference between the molarity of the electroactive species in bulk of the solution and lowest at the electrode surface, highest is the concentration gradient, and hence the resulting current density.

For a given electrode potential, the molarity of the electroactive species tends to zero at the electrode surface, hence the concentration gradient and current density reach a maximum:

$$j_{max} = j_L = \pm nFD_kC_{k,bulk}/\delta_k = \pm nFD_kC_{k,bulk}/\delta_k$$

$$I_{max} = I_L = \pm nFA_eD_kC_k(\infty)/\delta_k = \pm nFA_eD_kC_{k,bulk}/\delta_k$$

These simple equations points out that the ***maximum current density*** or ***limiting current density*** denoted j_{max} or sometimes j_L and expressed in $A.m^{-2}$ is related to: (i) the intrinsic properties of the electroactive species (e.g., diffusion coefficient, oxidation state), (ii) the molarity of the species in the bulk solution, and finally (iii) the hydrodynamic conditions existing in the electrochemical reactor as the latter directly influences the thickness of the diffusion layer.

In electrochemical engineering, it is common practice to replace the ratio of the diffusion coefficient to the thickness of the diffusion layer by a new physical quantity called the ***mass transfer coefficient***, denoted, k_m, in $m.s^{-1}$ as follows:

$$k_m = D_k/\delta_k$$

In this case, the limiting current density becomes:

$$j_{max} = j_L = \pm nFk_m C_{k,bulk}$$

The limiting current density represents the highest rate per unit surface area of the electrode at which the electrochemical reaction can be conducted. It is therefore a very useful parameter for diffusion controlled reactions because it provides a direct relationship between current density and the production or consumption rate of the electroactive species.

7.10.3 Electroreduction of Metal Cations

If we consider the simple electrochemical reaction that consists to reduce a z-valent metal cation (M^{z+}) to the corresponding metal, M(s), according to following reaction scheme:

$$M^{z+} + ze^- = M(s)$$

When no current flows, the thermodynamic or equilibrium electrode potential is provided by the Nernst equation with the molarity of the metal cation measured in the bulk of the solution:

$$E(j = 0) = E_{eq} = E_{th} = E^0(M^{z+}/M) + (RT/zF)\ \ln[a_{M^{z+}}(\text{bulk})]$$

$$E(j = 0) = E_{eq} = E_{th} = E^0(M^{z+}/M) + (RT/zF)\ \ln[\gamma_{M^{z+}}.C_{M^{z+}}(\text{bulk})]$$

Where

E_{th} (E_{eq})	Nernst electrode potential, in V,
$E^0(M^{z+}/M)$	standard electrode potential, in V,
$\gamma_{M^{z+}}$	activity coefficient of the metal cation (molarity basis),
$C_{M^{z+}}$(bulk)	molarity of metal cation in the bulk solution, in $mol.m^{-3}$,
z	number of electrons involved,
R	ideal gas constant, 8.3145 $J.K^{-1}.mol^{-1}$,
F	Faraday's constant, 96,485.309 $C.mol^{-1}$.

For simplification, it is possible to define an ***apparent standard electrode potential***, denoted E^{0*}, that includes the non-ideality term and which is defined as follows:

$$E^{0*}_{(M^{z+}/M)} = E^0_{(M^{z+}/M)} + (RT/zF)\ln\gamma_{M^{z+}}$$

It is worth to mention that the apparent standard electrode potential is strongly dependent on the activity coefficients of the electroactive species, and hence on the ionic strength of the electrolyte.

The above simplification allows yielding a condensed Nernst equation as follows:

$$E_{th} = E^{0*}(M^{z+}/M) + (RT/zF) \ln C_{M^{z+}}(\text{bulk})$$

Now in order to reduce electrochemically the cation, the electrode (cathode) must be polarized negatively several millivolts below the thermodynamic electrode potential, at least 200 mV are required in practice.

Therefore once the cathode is polarized negatively, the reduction of cations starts with the electrodeposition of the metal onto the cathode, and a cathodic current density appears. The electrode potential is provided by the Nernst equation with the molarity of the metal cation taken at the electrode surface:

$$E(j) = E^{0*}(M^{z+}/M) + (RT/zF) \ln C_{M^{z+}}(0)$$

Because the electrochemical reaction exhibits a perfect Nernstian behavior, that is, it is controlled by the diffusional mass transfer of cations; the cathode and limiting current densities are given by:

$$j_c = -nFD_{M^{z+}}[C_{M^{z+}}(\text{bulk}) - C_{M^{z+}}(0)]/\delta_{M^{z+}}$$

$$j_{c,\max} = -nFD_{M^{z+}}C_{M^{z+}}(\text{bulk})/\delta_{M^{z+}}$$

Hence the molarity of the metal cation in the bulk of the solution and at the electrode surface can be expressed as a function of these cathodic current densities:

$$C_{M^{z+}}(\text{bulk}) = -j_{c,\max}\delta_{M^{z+}}/zFD_{M^{z+}}$$

$$C_{M^{z+}}(0) = [(j_c - j_{c,\max})\ \delta_{M^{z+}}]/zFD_{M^{z+}}$$

It is then possible to establish the mathematical equation for the current density-potential curve: $[j = f(E)]$ also called a polarization curve:

$$E(j) = E^{0*}(M^{z+}/M) + (RT/zF) \ln C_{M^{z+}}(\text{bulk}) + (RT/zF) \ln[(j_{c,\max} - j_c)/j_{c,\max}]$$

7.10.4 Diffusion Overpotential Equation

Therefore from the previous equation for the cathode potential, the corresponding cathode mass diffusion overpotential can be simply written as follows:

$$\eta(j) = E(j) - E_{th} = (RT/zF)\ln[(j_{c,max} - j_c)/j_{c,max}] = (RT/zF)\ln[C_{M^{z+}}(0)/C_{M^{z+}}(bulk)]$$

After further simplification, we finally obtain the Naperian and Briggsian logarithmic equations:

$$\eta(j) = (RT/zF)\ln(1 - j_c/j_{c,max}) = (RT\ln 10/zF)\log_{10}(1 - j_c/j_{c,max})$$

It is then possible to expressed the cathode current density, j_c, as a function of the cathodic overpotential $\eta(j)$ by the general mathematical equation:

$$j_c = j_{c,max}\{1 - \exp[+zF(E_j - E_{th})/RT]\} = j_{c,max}\{1 - \exp[+zF\eta(j)/RT]\}$$

The Figure 30 depicts the E-j plot of the above equation related to the reduction of metal cations. The plot is called a reduction ***voltamperogram*** or by contraction ***voltammogram*** or ***voltammetric curve***.

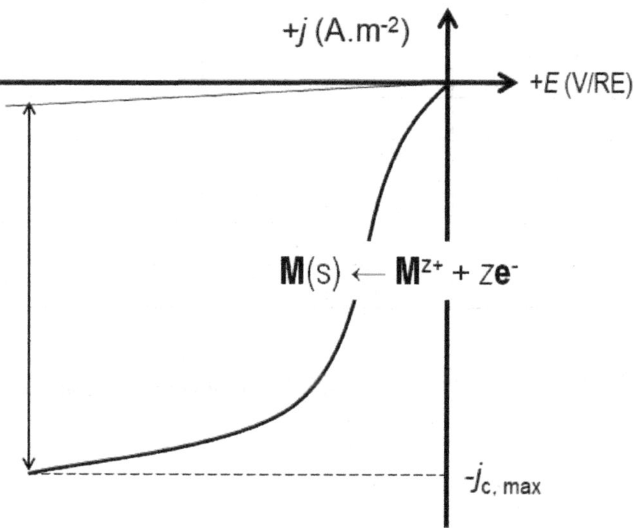

Figure 30 – Polarization plot due to concentration overvoltage

In old textbooks, it is also possible to find the name ***cathodic wave***. Actually, early electrochemists called these E-j plots waves because they look similar to the front of waves described in hydrodynamics. Therefore to minimize the concentration overpotential, industrially the electrolysis must always be conducted near the maximum (i.e., limiting diffusion) current, that is, when the concentration of species k at the electrode surface is nearly zero, and with the maximum concentration of electroactive species compatible with operating conditions and economic considerations.

For instance, we have reported in Table 36 the concentration overpotentials as a function of the dimensionless ratio (j/j_{max}), and the number of electrons exchanged, z, during the cathodic reduction of a metal cation M^{z+}.

Table 36 – Diffusion overpotential vs. ratio of current densities and electrons exchanged

$\eta(j) = (\ln 10 RT/zF) \log_{10}(1 - j/j_{max})$					
n =	2	3	4	5	6
j/j_{max}	Cathode diffusion overpotential (η_c/mV)				
0.001	-0.013	-0.009	-0.006	-0.005	-0.004
0.002	-0.026	-0.017	-0.013	-0.010	-0.009
0.004	-0.051	-0.034	-0.026	-0.021	-0.017
0.008	-0.10	-0.07	-0.052	-0.041	-0.034
0.016	-0.21	-0.14	-0.10	-0.083	-0.069
0.032	-0.42	-0.28	-0.21	-0.17	-0.14
0.064	-0.85	-0.57	-0.42	-0.34	-0.28
0.128	-1.76	-1.17	-0.88	-0.70	-0.59
0.256	-3.80	-2.53	-1.90	-1.52	-1.27
0.512	-9.22	-6.14	-4.61	-3.69	-3.07
0.750	-17.81	-11.87	-8.90	-7.12	-5.94
0.999	-88.74	-59.16	-44.37	-35.49	-29.58

However, when electrolyzing highly concentrated catholyte solutions such as in the case of electrowinning iron from solution of copperas near saturation, the operating cathode current density usually represents only a fraction of the limiting cathode current density, and thus the mass diffusion overpotential must be accounted for in addition to the other overpotential such as the nucleation (i.e., crystallization) overpotential.

7.10.5 Diffusion Polarization Resistance

We have shown previously that the diffusion overpotential is given by the simple equation:

$$\eta(j) = E(j) - E_{th} = (RT/zF)\ln[(j_{c,\,max} - j_c)/j_{c,\,max}]$$

After rearranging we obtain:

$$(1 - j_c/j_{c,\,max}) = \exp[+zF\eta(j)/RT]$$

When the absolute value of the mass diffusion overvoltage is small let say below 50 mV thus the dimensionless ratio $x = [+zF\eta(j)/RT]$ is also small. Then we can use the mathematical equivalence: $e^x = (1 + x)$, the linearized and simplified equation between overpotential and cathode current density becomes:

$$\eta(j) = -[RT/(zFj_{c,\max})]\,j_c = -[RT/(zFj_{c,\max})]\,j_c$$

The above equation is simply the Ohm's law, where the ***mass transfer polarization resistance***, denoted R_m, in $\Omega.m^2$ is given by:

$$R_m = [RT/(zFj_{c,\max})]$$

7.10.6 Mass Transfer Coefficient

It is essential to achieve efficient and uniform mass transport conditions over the whole electrode area within the cell in order to: (1) obtain a high limiting current density, actually the maximum current density for a reaction is proportional to the mass transfer coefficient; (2) achieve an uniform current density, and hence rate of reaction over all the electrode surface area, (3) minimize the local composition changes within the reaction layer at the electrode surface that can lead to precipitates and unwanted side reactions.

The mass flow rate through an electrolyzer with stationary electrodes depends on:

- The electrolyte mass flow rate,
- The design of electrolyte flow distributor at the inlet and outlet of the electrode compartments,
- The design of turbulence promoters properly placed into the electrolyte stream to produce eddies and hence increasing mixing,
- Where applicable gas bubble formation during electrode reaction or roughening of the surface by electrodeposited metals.

For this reason, when designing an electrochemical reactor, the highest value of the ***mass transfer coefficient*** is sought with limiting factors such as expensive pumping costs.

Before to calculate the best operating conditions of the electrolyzer, it is necessary to determine the mass transfer coefficient of each electroactive species (e.g., Fe^{2+} and SO_4^{2-}) involved in electrowinning.

From a practical point of view, it exists several methods to access the numerical value of the ***mass transfer coefficient*** of an electroactive species: (i) the first approach consists to conduct theoretical calculations made from tabulated data of diffusion coefficients using the simple equation: $k_m = (D_k/\delta_k)$, (ii) secondly, it is possible to determine the limiting current from E-j plots obtained by voltammetric measurements, and finally (iii) to use dimensionless ***empirical correlations*** obtained from previous test work, and published in the literature.

Usually, all the empirical correlations have the same mathematical form:

$$Sh = aRe^{\alpha}Sc^{\beta}Gr^{\gamma}$$

Where the relevant dimensionless numbers are:

$Sh = k_m D_h/D$	dimensionless Sherwood number,
$Re = uD_h/\nu$	dimensionless Reynolds number,
$Sc = \nu/D$	dimensionless Schmidt number,
$Gr = g_n h^3(1-\rho_0/\rho_b)/\nu^2$	dimensionless Grashof number.

The empirical constant, a, and the three empirical exponents, α, β, and γ, are usually determined from experiments.

In the particular case of a parallel and vertical plate electrodes inside a rectangular tank such as the type of electrolyzer used industrially for performing the electrowinning of metals such as zinc, copper, and nickel, it is important to distinguish several conditions such plate electrodes with finite or infinite width, forced or natural convection, and finally laminar or turbulent flow.

7.10.6.1 Natural Convection and Laminar Flow

In the particular case of a two compartment rectangular electrolyzer without circulation of the electrolyte because of the free convection conditions existing inside the cell and based on and elevate the Schmidt-Grashof product, a first empirical correlation as follows can be used:

$$k_m D_h/D = a\,[(\nu/D)\,g_n h^3(1-\rho_0/\rho_b)/\nu^2]^{1/4}$$

$$k_m = a g_n^{1/4}\,h^{3/4}\,\nu^{-1/4}\,D_h^{-1}\,D^{3/4}\,(1-\rho_0/\rho_b)^{1/4}$$

Hence, introducing the actual constant and the three empirical exponents, the mass transfer coefficient can be finally expressed numerically as follows:

$$k_m\,(\text{free convection}) = 1.168\,h^{3/4}\,\nu^{-1/4}\,D_h^{-1}\,D^{3/4}\,(1-\rho_0/\rho_b)^{1/4}$$

The exact anode and cathode mass transfer coefficients based on the best estimated physical properties of the anolyte and catholyte are presented in Table 102.

7.10.6.2 Forced Convection

The empirical correlations under convective transfer conditions and corresponding to each of these cases are available from the literature are reported for convenience in Table 37 hereafter.

Table 37 – Correlations for mass transfer coefficients with plane parallel vertical plates

Hydrodynamic conditions	Empirical correlation equation	Conditions of validity
Natural (free) convection:		
• Laminar flow	$Sh = 0.66\ (ScGr)^{0.25}$	$5 \times 10^6 < ScGr < 8 \times 10^{13}$
• Turbulent flow	$Sh = 0.31\ (ScGr)^{0.28}$	$4 \times 10^{13} < ScGr < 10^{15}$
• Narrow gap	$Sh = 0.19\ (ScGr)^{1/3}$	$10^8 < ScGr < 1.4 \times 10^{12}$
Forced convection:		
• Laminar flow	$Sh = 0.66\ Re^{1/2}Sc^{1/3}(x/h)^{1/3}$	$Re < 300{,}000$
• Turbulent flow	$Sh = 2.54\ Re^{1/3}Sc^{1/3}(x/h)^{1/3}$	$Re < 3{,}000$
	$Sh = 0.023\ Re^{0.80}Sc^{1/3}$	$300 < Re < 30{,}000$
		$h = 5.9\ D_H$
Natural (free) convection between plate and separator (Laminar flow): Membrane-electrode gap, x and plate height, h:	$Sh = 0.0225\ (ScGr)^{0.85}(x/h)^2$	$2 \times 10^6 < ScGr < 2 \times 10^8$ $0.005 < x/h < 5.48(ScGr)^{-0.3}$

7.11 Activation Overpotential

When the rate of the electrode process (i.e., electrochemical reaction) is only controlled by the electric charge transfer across the electrode-electrolyte interface, the electron transfer process is the rate determining step compared to all other processes which are then considered faster.

7.11.1 Butler-Volmer Equation

Consider a homogenous and thermodynamically reversible redox electrochemical reaction performed onto an inert electrode material (ideally polarized) and where both reducing and oxidizing species are totally soluble into the electrolyte:

$$aR = bO + ne^-$$

with	R	reducing species (i.e., reductant),
	O	oxidizing species (i.e., oxidant),
	a, b	dimensionless stoichiometric coefficients,
	n	dimensionless number of electrons involved.

When any current circulates, the thermodynamic or equilibrium electrode potential is provided by the Nernst equation were the molarities of electroactive species are measured in the bulk of the solution:

$$E_{th} = E^0_{O/R}{}^* + (RT/nF)\ln(C_{Ob}{}^b/C_{Rb}{}^a)$$

Where

E_{th}	thermodynamic or equilibrium electrode potential, in V,
$E^{0*}_{O/R}$	apparent standard electrode potential, in V,
	with $E^{0*}_{O/R} = E^0_{O/R} + (RT/nF)\ln(\gamma_O{}^b/\gamma_R{}^a)$
$E^0_{O/R}$	standard electrode potential of the redox couple, in V,
a, b	stoichiometric coefficients of electroactive species,
C_{Ob}, C_{Rb}	molarities of species in the bulk of the solution, in $mol.m^{-3}$,
n	number of electrons exchanged,
R	ideal gas constant, 8.3145 $J.K^{-1}.mol^{-1}$,
F	Faraday's constant, 96485.309 $C.mol^{-1}$.

Once current flows, according to chemical kinetics, the overall reaction rate corresponds to the difference between the forward (→) (i.e., oxidation) reaction rate and the backward (←) (i.e., reduction) rate:

$$v = v_a - v_c$$

The electrochemical reaction will proceed to an oxidation when $v > 0$, and conversely to a reduction when the overall reaction rate is negative. The elementary reaction rates can be expressed with the formalism used in chemical kinetics with the orders of the reaction equal to stoichiometric coefficients, and assuming that the molarity of the electrons [e] inside the electrode material, in $mol.m^{-3}$, remains constant owing to the high density of electrons inside metallic electrode materials:

Rate of oxidation: $v_a = k(\rightarrow)C_{Rb}{}^a$

Rate of reduction: $v_c = k(\leftarrow)C_{Ob}{}^b[e]^n \approx k(\leftarrow)C_{Ob}{}^b$

Where

v_a, v_c rate of oxidation (reduction) per unit area, in $mol.m^{-2}.s^{-1}$,

k_a, k_c rate constant of oxidation (reduction), $mol^{(1-a)}.m^{(-2+3a)}.s^{-1}$,

C_{Rb}, C_{OE} molarities of electroactive species at the surface of electrode, in $mol.m^{-3}$.

The two equations for the oxidation (→) and reduction (←) rate constants are calculated from the ***theory of the activated complex*** or ***theory of absolute reaction rates*** first devised in 1935 by H. Eyring [78] that yield the two equations:

$$k(\rightarrow) = k_a \exp(+\alpha nFE_j/RT) \qquad k(\leftarrow) = k_c \exp(-\beta nFE_j/RT)$$

$$v_a = k_a C_{Rb}{}^a \exp(+\alpha nFE_j/RT) \qquad v_c = k_c C_{Ob}{}^b \exp(-\beta nFE_j/RT)$$

Where α is the dimensionless ***anode transfer coefficient*** for the anode reaction, i.e., the fraction of anode overpotential used for the oxidation and β is the dimensionless ***cathode transfer coefficient*** for the cathode reaction, i.e., the fraction of overpotential used for the reduction. The two coefficients being interrelated by the simple equality: $\alpha + \beta = 1$. In practice, the numerical value of the anode transfer coefficient is equal to 0.5, or at least comprised between 0.3 and 0.7.

Therefore, the anode and cathode current densities for each electrochemical reaction are simply related to the elementary reaction rate by using: $j = \pm nFv$

$$j_a = +\ nFk_a C_{Rb}{}^a \exp(+\alpha nFE_j/RT)$$

$$j_c = -\ nFk_c C_{Ob}{}^b \exp(-\beta nFE_j/RT)$$

The overall current density, j, being the sum of the two algebraic contributions: $j = j_a + j_c$.

$$j = nFk_a C_{Rb}{}^a \exp(+\alpha nFE_j/RT) - nFk_c C_{Ob}{}^b \exp(-\beta nFE_j/RT)$$

When no current circulates, we have of course: $j = j_a + j_c = 0$ and because the electrochemical reaction is not mass transfer controlled, the molarities of the electroactive species k in the bulk of the solution, and at the electrode surface must be equals. Hence the electrode potential is equal to the thermodynamic or equilibrium potential, E_{th} provided by the Nernst equation then:

$$|j_a| = |j_c| = j_{eq}$$

---

[78] GLASSTONE, S.; LAIDLER, K.J.; and EYRING, H. (1941) *Theory of Rate Processes*. McGraw-Hill Book Company, New York, NY.

Where j_{eq} is the ***exchange current density*** at equilibrium potential in A/m^2, it is a direct measured of the reversibility of the electrochemical reaction concerned:

$$j_{eq} = nFk_a C_{Rb}{}^{a} \exp(+\alpha nFE_{th}/RT) = nFk_c C_{Ob}{}^{b} \exp(-\beta nFE_{th}/RT)$$

Rewriting the above equation we have:

$$E_{th} = (RT/nF) \ln(k_c/k_a) + (RT/nF) \ln(C_{Ob}{}^{b}/C_{Rb}{}^{a})$$

with $E^{0*}{}_{O/R} = (RT/nF) \ln(k_c/k_a)$

Therefore, the exchange current density at the equilibrium potential is:

$$j_{eq} = nFk_c{}^{\alpha} k_a{}^{\beta} C_{Ob}{}^{\alpha b} C_{Rb}{}^{\beta b}$$

By introducing the exchange constant rate: $k_{eq} = k_c{}^{\alpha} k_a{}^{\beta}$

$$j_{eq} = nFk_{eq} C_{Ob}{}^{\alpha b} C_{Rb}{}^{\beta b}$$

For practical reasons, when the electroactive species are in equimolar ratio (i.e., $C_O = C_R = 1$), it is possible to introduce the ***standard exchange current density***, denoted j_o, in A/m^2, and the ***standard exchange rate constant***, denoted, k_o.

$$j_{eq} = j_o C_{Ob}{}^{\alpha b} C_{Rb}{}^{\beta b} = nFk_o C_{Ob}{}^{\alpha b} C_{Rb}{}^{\beta b}$$

The standard exchange current density reflects the electro-catalytic performance of the electrode active surface towards a specific electrochemical reaction. It varies over many orders of magnitude, for instance, for the reduction of protons into nascent hydrogen, it varies from 3.98 $A.m^{-2}$ for a platinized-platinum cathode down to only 10^{-9} $A.\ m^{-2}$ for a chemical lead cathode.

In similar way, the standard exchange rate constant, k_0, is an intrinsic characteristic of a redox couple that depends on the complexity of the electron transfer mechanism. Thus, an elevate rate constant characterises a reversible system with an electrochemical reaction controlled by the mass transfer of the electroactive species while a low rate constant characterizes an electrode process controlled by the electron transfer across the electrode-electrolyte interface.

On the other hand, we can write:

$$j_{eq} = nFk_a C_{Rb}{}^{a} \exp(+\alpha nFE_{th}/RT) = nFk_c C_{Ob}{}^{b} \exp(-\beta nFE_{th}/RT)$$

Thus we obtain the Butler-Volmer equation giving the current density vs. electrode potential when the electron transfer across the electrode-electrolyte interface controls the electrode kinetic (i.e., activation regime):

$$j = j_{eq}\{\exp[+\alpha nF(E_j - E_{th})/RT] - \exp[-(1-\alpha)nF(E_j - E_{th})/RT]\}$$

If we introduce the overpotential: $\eta = E_j - E_{th}$ defined previously in Section 7.3, we obtained the condensed form:

$$j = j_{eq}[\exp(+\alpha nF\eta/RT) - \exp[-(1-\alpha)nF\eta/RT]]$$

The corresponding plot of the current density vs. the overpotential is depicted schematically in Figure 31 hereafter.

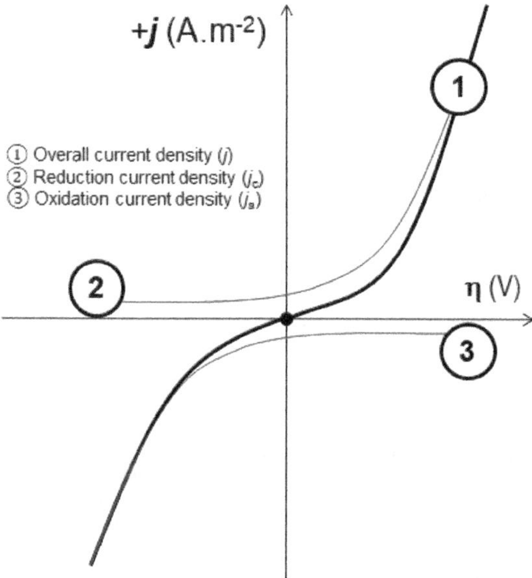

Figure 31 – Pure activation current-potential plot

In the special case, when both anode and transfer coefficients are equal to ½, then the curve of the current density vs. the overpotential adopts a symmetric shape corresponding to the hyperbolic sine function:

$$j = 2j_{eq}\sinh(nF\eta/RT)$$

7.11.2 Generalized Butler-Volmer Equation

When the electrochemical reaction rate is controlled both by the electron transfer, and the diffusion of electroactive species towards the electrodes, a general form of the Butler-Volmer equation must be established to account for this ***mixed activation-diffusion regime***. For that purpose, the concentrations of species are those at the electrodes:

$$j = nFk_aC_{RE}^a\exp(+\alpha nFE_j/RT) - nFk_cC_{OE}^b\exp(-\beta nFE_j/RT)$$

Using the linear approximation Nernst's diffusion layer, the molarities of species at the electrodes are related to the current and limiting current densities:

$$C_{RE} = C_{Rb}(1 - j/j_{a,\,max}) \qquad \text{and} \qquad C_{OE} = C_{Ob}\,(1 - j/j_{c,max})$$

Thus the anode and cathode current densities are:

$$j_a = nFk_a[C_{Rb}(1 - j/j_{a,\,max})]^a\exp(+\alpha nFE_j/RT)$$

$$j_c = -nFk_c[C_{Ob}(1 - j/j_{c,max})]^b\exp(-\beta nFE_j/RT)$$

By introducing the exchange current density defined previous:

$$j_{eq} = nFk_aC_{Rb}^a\exp(+\alpha nFE_{th}/RT) = nFk_cC_{Ob}^b\exp(-\beta nFE_{th}/RT)$$

We obtain:

$$j_a = j_{eq}(1 - j/j_{a,\,max})^a\exp[+\alpha nF(E_j - E_{th})/RT]$$

$$j_c = -j_{eq}(1 - j/j_{c,max})^b\exp[-\beta nF(E_j - E_{th})/RT]$$

The substitution of the above relations yields the equation:

$$j = j_{eq}\{(C_{RE}/C_{Rb})^a\exp[+\alpha nF(E_j - E_{th})/RT] - (C_{OE}/C_{Ob})^b\exp[-\beta nF(E_j - E_{th})/RT]\}$$

If we introduce the overpotential: $\eta = E_j - E_{th}$ defined previously in Section 7.3, we obtained the condensed form:

$$j = j_{eq}[(1 - j/j_{a,\,max})^a\exp(+\alpha nF\eta/RT) - (1 - j/j_{c,max})^b\exp(-\beta nF\eta/RT)]$$

By regrouping the current density on the same side of the equation, we obtain the ***generalized Butler-Volmer equation*** [79], expressing the current density when the electrode reaction is controlled both by activation and diffusion (i.e., mixed regime):

$$j = j_{eq}[\exp(+\alpha nF\eta/RT) - \exp(-\beta nF\eta/RT]/[1 + (j_{eq}/j_{a,\,max})^a\exp(+\alpha nF\eta/RT) - (j_{eq}/j_{c,max})^b\exp(-\beta nF\eta/RT)]$$

---

[79] BUTLER, J.A.V. (1924) *Transaction of the Faraday Society*, **19**(1924)734.

The plot of the current density vs. the overpotential for a mixed activation-diffusion regime is depicted schematically in Figure 32 hereafter.

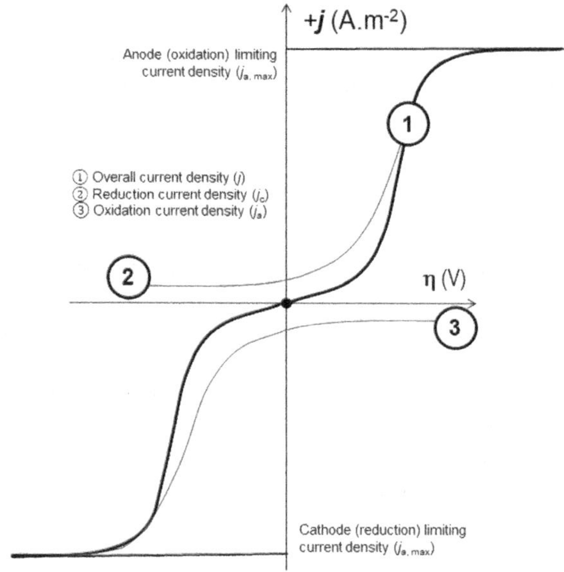

Figure 32 – Mixed activation-diffusion current-potential plot

7.11.3 High Overpotentials

Despite the Butler-Volmer equation is valid over the full potential range; simpler approximate solutions can be obtained over more restricted ranges of potentials.

Actually, as overpotentials, either positive or negative, become larger than about 50 mV, ($|\eta| > 50$ mV) the second or the first term of Butler-Volmer equation becomes negligible, respectively. Hence, simple exponential relationships between the current density (i.e., rate) and the overpotential are obtained and the overpotential can be considered as logarithmically dependent on the current density. This theoretical result is in agreement with the first experimental findings conducted in 1905 by the German physical chemist Julius Tafel [80].

7.11.3.1 Anode Tafel's Coefficients

As the anode potential, E_j, becomes more positive than the thermodynamic electrode potential, E_{th}, (i.e., high anode overpotential), the

[80] TAFEL, J. *Über die Polarisation bei kathodischer Wasserstoffentwicklung*. In: OSTWALD, W.; and VAN'T HOFF J.H. (Eds.) (1905) *Zeitschrift für physikalische Chemie, Stöchiometrie und Verwandtschaftslehre*. Volume 50. Wilhelm Engelmann Verlag, Leipzig, Germany, pp. 641-712.

cathodic current becomes less significant so that the total or net current density approaches the condition of purely anodic current.

The measured increase of the anode overpotential is a clear indicator of the irreversibility of the anode process, and the activation control (i.e., slow electron transfer), and finally for very high anode overpotential the plot exhibits a typical asymptotic plateau related to a mass transfer limiting step.

Actually, for elevate anodic overpotential, the second term in the Butler-Volmer equation becomes negligible and j_a becomes simply expressed by the following equation with C_{RE} and C_R being the concentration of the reducing species to be oxidized at the anode, and in the bulk of the solution respectively:

$$|j_a| = j_{eq}(C_{RE}/C_R)^a \exp[+\alpha nF(E_j - E_{th})/RT] = j_{eq}(1 - j/j_{a,\,max})^a \exp(+\alpha nF\eta/RT)$$

A more rigorous manner to characterize the irreversibility is to utilize the semi-logarithmic transform of the potential-current density curve. This semi-logarithmic diagram $[\eta = \log_{10}|j|]$ is called the ***Horiuti diagram***. The Naperian (natural) logarithmic form is given as follows:

$$\eta_a(j) = E_j - E_{th} = (RT/\alpha nF)[-\ln|j_{eq}| - a\ln(1 - j/j_{a,\,max}) + \ln|j_a|]$$

For practical and historical reasons, industrial electrochemists rather use the Briggs (decadic) logarithmic form to express the anode overpotential:

$$\eta_a(j) = (RT\ln 10/\alpha nF)[-\log_{10}|j_{eq}| - a\log_{10}(1 - j/j_{a,\,max}) + \log_{10}|j_a|]$$

When the anode reaction is only controlled by the charge transfer, and after regrouping the terms, the above equation becomes simply:

$$\eta_a(j) = a_a + b_a\log_{10}|j_a|$$

Where b_a is the ***anode Tafel's slope*** or ***Tafel's first anode coefficient*** that exhibits a positive value obtained from the slope of the linear portion of the logarithmic transform.

$$b_a = \partial\eta_a/\partial|j_a| = RT\ln 10/(\alpha nF)$$

The anodic Tafel's coefficient gives directly access to the value of αn, for instance under standard T and P conditions standards (298.15 K, 101.325 kPa):

1 decade per $\alpha \times 59.1$ mV for $n = 1$ electron involved,

1 decade per $\alpha \times 118.3$ mV for $n = 2$ electron involved,

1 decade per $\alpha \times 177.5$ mV for $n = 3$ electron involved.

On the other hand, the intercept of the linear portion yields the ***Tafel's intercept*** or simply ***Tafel's second anode coefficient***.

$$a_a = b_a[-\log_{10}\lfloor j_{eq}\rfloor$$

$$a_a = -[RT\ln 10/(\alpha nF)][\log_{10}\lfloor j_{eq}\rfloor$$

The Tafel's intercept allows determining the exchange current density at equilibrium, j_{eq}, while when using an equimolar ratio of electroactive species; it allows determining directly the standard exchange current density, j_0 from the simplified equation below:

$$a_a = -[RT\ln 10/(\alpha nF)]\log_{10}\lfloor j_0\rfloor$$

In the case where both the diffusion and activation control the rate of the electrochemical reaction, the anode overvoltage is the sum of the activation and diffusion overpotentials and the linear form is as follows:

$$\eta_a(j) = (a_a + b_a\log_{10}\lfloor j_a\rfloor) - a(RT\ln 10/nF)\log_{10}(1 - j/j_{a,\,max})$$

7.11.3.2 Cathode Tafel's Coefficients

As the cathode potential, E_j, becomes more positive than the thermodynamic electrode potential, E_{th}, (i.e., high cathode overpotential), the anodic current becomes less significant so that the total or net current density approaches the condition of purely cathodic current.

The measured increase of the cathode overpotential is a clear indicator of the irreversibility of the cathode process, and the activation control (i.e., slow electron transfer), and finally for very high cathode overpotential the plot exhibits a typical asymptotic plateau related to a mass transfer limiting step.

Actually, for elevate cathode overpotential, the first term in the Butler-Volmer equation becomes negligible and j_c becomes simply expressed by the following equation with C_{OE} and C_O being the concentration of the oxidizing species to be reduced at the cathode, and in the bulk of the solution respectively:

$$\lfloor j_c\rfloor = j_{eq}(C_{OE}/C_O)^b\exp[-\beta nF(E_j - E_{th})/RT] = j_{eq}(1 - j/j_{c,max})^b\exp(-\beta nF\eta/RT)$$

A more rigorous manner to characterize the irreversibility is to utilize the semi-logarithmic transform of the potential-current density curve. This semi-logarithmic diagram $[\eta = \log_{10}\lfloor j\rfloor]$ is called the ***Horiuti diagram***. The Naperian (natural) logarithmic form is given as follows:

$$\eta_c(j) = E_j - E_{th} = -[RT/(\beta nF)][-\ln\lfloor j_{eq}\rfloor - b\ln(1 - j/j_{c,max}) + \ln\lfloor j_c\rfloor]$$

For practical and historical reasons, industrial electrochemists rather use the Briggs (decadic) logarithmic form to express the cathode overpotential:

$$\eta_c(j) = [RT\ln 10/(\beta nF)][\log_{10}|j_{eq}| + b\log_{10}(1 - j/j_{c,max}) - \log_{10}|j_c|]$$

When the cathode reaction is only controlled by the charge transfer and after regrouping the terms, the above equation can be put in the simplified form:

$$\eta_c(j) = a_c - b_c\log_{10}|j_c|$$

Where b_c is the ***cathode Tafel's slope*** or ***cathode first Tafel's coefficient*** that can be determined from the slope of the linear portion of the logarithmic transform.

$$b_c = \partial\eta_c/\partial|j_c| = RT\ln 10/(\beta nF)$$

The cathode Tafel's coefficient gives directly access to the value of βn, for instance under standard T and P conditions standards (298.15 K, 101.325 kPa):

1 decade per $\beta \times 60$ mV for $n = 1$ electron involved,

1 decade per $\beta \times 120$ mV for $n = 2$ electron involved,

1 decade per $\beta \times 180$ mV for $n = 3$ electron involved.

On the other hand, the intercept of the linear portion yields the ***Tafel intercept*** or simply ***Tafel's second coefficient***:

$$a_c = b_c\,[\log_{10}|j_{eq}|$$

$$a_c = [RT\ln 10/(\beta nF)]\log_{10}|j_{eq}|$$

The Tafel's intercept allows determining the exchange current density at equilibrium, j_{eq}, while when using an equimolar ratio of electroactive species; it allows determining directly the standard exchange current density, j_0.

$$a_c = [RT\ln 10/(\beta nF)]\log_{10}|j_0|$$

In the case where both the diffusion and activation control the rate of the cathode reaction, the cathode overvoltage is the sum of the activation and diffusion overpotentials and the linear form is as follows:

$$\eta_c(j) = (a_c - b_c\log_{10}|j_c|) - b(RT\ln 10/nF)\log_{10}(1 - j/j_{c,\,max})$$

The Horiuti plot of the logarithm transforms of the anode and cathode current density vs. overpotential is depicted in Figure 33.

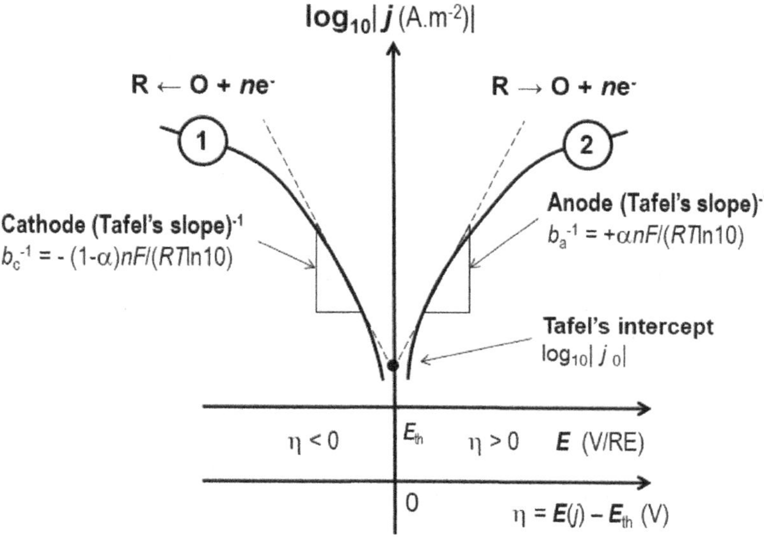

Figure 33 – Horiuti plot showing the anode and cathode Tafel's parameters

7.11.4 Low Overpotentials

At very low electrode overpotentials ($|\eta| < 10$ mV), the exponential term in the Butler-Volmer can be developed into a finite element ($e^x \approx 1 + x$), and assuming that the stoichiometric coefficients are equal to unity and because: $\alpha + \beta = 1$, the equation simply reduces to:

$$j = j_{eq}\,(nF\eta/RT)/[1 + (j_{eq}/j_{a,\,max}) - (j_{eq}/j_{c,max})]$$

Thus the overpotential can be written as a linear function of the current density similar to the Ohm's law:

$$\eta = (RT/nF)(1/j_{eq} + 1/j_{a,\,max} - 1/j_{c,max})\,j$$

The above equation is the Ohm's law ($U = Ri$) applied in the region where the overpotential is extremely small, and the polarization curve (η, j) is linear. It is then possible to introduce a new electrochemical quantity called the ***overall resistance of polarization***, denoted R_p, which is expressed in $\Omega.m^2$. This overall polarization resistance characterizes the ohmic drop due to both activation and diffusion control, and it can be defined as the slope of the polarization curve close to the equilibrium potential:

$$R_p = (\partial\eta/\partial j)_0 = (RT/AnF)(1/j_{eq} + 1/j_{a,\,max} - 1/j_{c,max})$$

We can see that the overall polarization resistance is simply the sum of the activation polarization resistance and diffusion polarization resistance in series:

$$R_p = R_{p,a} + R_{p,d}$$

$$R_{p,a} = (RT/j_{eq}AnF) \quad \text{and} \quad R_{p,d} = (RT/AnF)(1/j_{a,\max} - 1/j_{c,\max})$$

7.11.5 Low Activation Overpotentials

At very low cathode overpotentials ($|\eta| < 10$ mV), the exponential term in the Butler-Volmer can be developed into a finite element ($e^x \approx 1 + x$) and the Butler-Volmer equation simply reduces to:

$$j = j_{eq}\{(1 - j/j_{c,\max})^b[1 - \beta nF(E_j - E_{th})/RT]\}$$

In the particular case of an equimolar ratio of electroactive species, and stoichiometric coefficients equal to unity, the simplified equation reduces to:

$$j = j_{eq}nF(E_j - E_{th})/RT = (j_{eq}nF/\beta RT)\ \eta$$

This equation is the Ohm's law ($U = Ri$) applied in the region where the overpotential is extremely small, and the polarization curve (η, j) is linear. It is then possible to introduce a new electrochemical quantity called the ***activation resistance of polarization***, denoted R_p, which is expressed in $\Omega.m^2$. This polarization resistance characterizes the ohmic drop due to the activation control, and it can be defined as the slope of the polarization curve close to the equilibrium potential:

$$R_p = (\partial\eta/\partial j)_0 = (\partial E/\partial j)_0 = [RT/(\beta j_{eq}nF)]$$

7.12 Electro-Crystallization Overpotential

Electro-crystallization refers to the nucleation and crystal growth of a metal occurring at the cathode surface due to a negative polarization applied. The overall electro-crystallization process is rather complex in nature as it consists of several consecutive steps each controlled by its own kinetics. However, the simplest conditions are realized for the electrodeposition of a metal (e.g., Fe) from a catholyte containing simple metal cations (e.g., Fe^{2+}).

Actually, first the solvated (i.e., hydrated) metal cation $[M(H_2O)_n]^{z+}$ (e.g., octahedral $[Fe(H_2O)_6]^{2+}$) is brought from the bulk of the catholyte to the cathode surface by transport phenomena such as diffusion and migration. Then after the departure of water ligands, the bare adsorbed cation M^{z+} (i.e, ***adion***) is reduced by charge (i.e., electron) transfer across the cathode-catholyte interface to yield an ***adatom*** (i.e., adsorbed atom) at a given site location [S] at the cathode surface:

$[M(H_2O)_n]^{z+} = M^{z+} + nH_2O$

$M^{z+} + ze^- + [S] = M[S]$

The resulting adatom produced then moves in two-dimension at the cathode surface by diffusion to a kink site form a cluster of few atoms nuclei that then continue to growth in three-dimension to form finally an ordered crystal of the metal (e.g., face centered cubic lattice for alpha-iron).

$M[S] = M(crystal) + [S]$

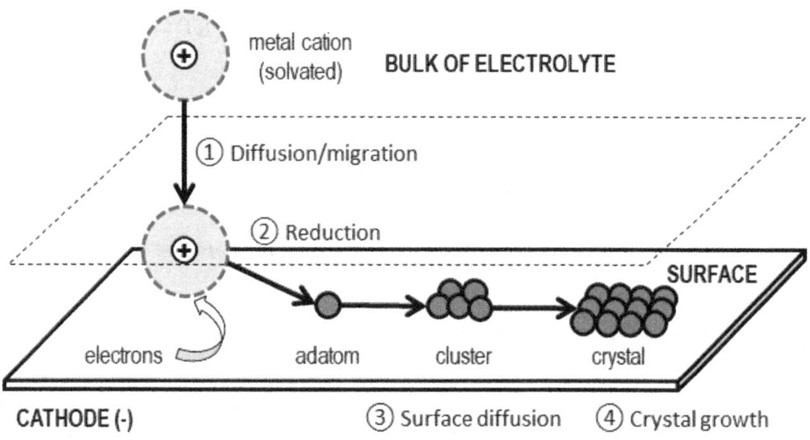

Figure 34 – Schematic of the steps occurring during electro-crystallization

These steps are depicted schematically in Figure 34. Two distinct situations must be considered though: (1) the formation of a metal onto an inert foreign metal substrate (e.g., iron onto a titanium blank cathode), that depends strongly on the deposited metal-substrate interaction, and the departure between the crystal lattices of the two metal (e.g., hexagonal closed packed (*hcp*) for titanium vs. body centered cubic (*bcc*) for alpha-iron); and (2) the electrodeposition onto a substrate of the same metal (e.g., iron onto mild steel starter sheet).

For the metal deposition onto foreign substrates for a relatively weak metal-substrate interaction, the deposition process starts at cathode potentials more negative than the Nernst equilibrium potential of the metal phase with the formation of isolated crystallites on an unmodified foreign substrate. This deposition mechanism which is not affected by the departure in crystal lattices is called the ***Volmer-Weber growth regime***. By contrast, in the case of a strong metal-substrate interaction, the electrodeposition can start even at electrode potentials more positive than the Nernst reversible electrode potential with the formation of two-dimension metal monolayers, a phenomenon called ***underpotential deposition*** (UPD). From an electrode kinetic standpoint, the kinetics of two reactions control the overall reaction rate namely the electroreduction of the metal cation to a metallic adatom at a surface site, and the crystallization.

The mathematical treatment for establishing the equation of the current density vs. overpotential is outside the scope of this monograph. It requires the utilization of a generalized Butler-Volmer equation taking into account de crystallization, and dissolution rate constants, k_c, and k_d, respectively. Hereafter, we are presenting in a first approximation a simplified equation only valid for high cathode overpotential:

$$j = j_{eq}\exp(-\beta nF\eta/RT)/[j_{eq}/nF(k_c + k_d)]\exp(-\beta nF\eta/RT) - 1]$$

Moreover, when the backward dissolution reaction becomes negligible compared to the crystallization reaction:

$$j = j_{eq}\exp(-\beta nF\eta/RT)/[(j_{eq}/nFk_c)\exp(-\beta nF\eta/RT) - 1]$$

$$\eta(j)_{crystal} = -[RT\ln 10/(\beta nF)]\log_{10} j_{eq} + \log_{10}[j/(j - nFk_c)]$$

7.13 Overall Overpotential

In practice, the situations are rather complexes as the overall overpotential is the sum of all the individual overpotentials due to crystallization, activation, and diffusion as depicted in Figure 35.

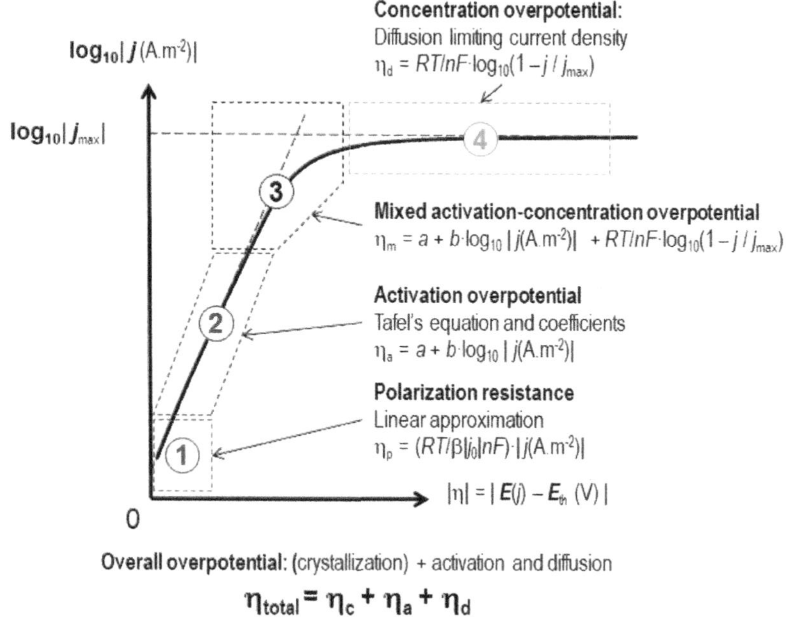

Figure 35 – Breakdown of the electrode overpotential vs. current density

Therefore the overall overpotential for the electrodeposition of a metal onto a cathode can be obtained by calculation using the equation below assuming that the value overpotential for the electro-crystallization of the metal to be electrowon is constant:

$$\eta_{total} = \eta_{crys} + (RT\ln 10/zF)[(1/\beta)(\log_{10}|j_{eq}| + \log_{10}|j_c|) + \log_{10}(1 - j_c/j_{c,\,max})]$$

The above equation can be further simplified by introducing the Tafel's coefficients as follows:

$$\eta_{total} = \eta_{crys} + (a + b\log_{10}|j_c|) + (RT\ln 10/zF)\log_{10}(1 - j_c/j_{c,\,max})]$$

$$\llcorner \text{cryst.} \lrcorner + \llcorner \text{activation} \lrcorner \quad + \quad \llcorner \text{diffusion} \lrcorner$$

8 Electrochemical Figures of Merit

8.1 Faraday's Laws

The relationship between the quantity of electricity passing through an electrolyte and the amount of substance liberated at the electrodes was discovered by Sir Michael Faraday [81] leading to the two laws of electrolysis.

8.1.1 First Faraday's Law

The amount of chemical substance produced (i.e., deposited, evolved, converted, or dissolved) during an electrochemical reaction (e.g., electrolysis) is directly proportional to the quantity of electricity (i.e., electric charges) that had circulated in the cell per unit time, i.e., directly proportional to the electric current.

8.1.2 Second Faraday's Law

The amounts of different substances deposited, evolved or dissolved by the same quantity of electricity are proportional to their electrochemical equivalent masses.

In this case the electrochemical process is defined as a ***Faradaic process.*** By contrast, if a reaction occurs without a charge transfer across the electrolyte-electrode interface, the process is called a ***non-faradaic process*** [82].

8.2 Electrochemical Equivalents

Let's consider an electrochemical reaction occurring at the electrode inside an electrolyser:

---

[81] FARADAY, M. (1834) On electrical decomposition. *Philosophical Transactions of the Royal Society.* **124**(1834)77-122.

[82] GRAHAME, D.C. (1952) Mathematical theory of the faradaic admittance. *Journal of the Electrochemical Society*, **52**(1952)370C–385C.

$\nu_o O + ne^- = \nu_R R$

Where

O	oxidizing species (i.e., oxidant),
R	reducing species (i.e., reductant),
ν_O, ν_R	dimensionless stoichiometric coefficients,
n	dimensionless number of electrons exchanged.

Therefore ν_o moles of the oxidizing species {O} requires a quantity of electricity equal to nF coulombs in order to produce ν_R moles of the reducing species {R}.

8.2.1 Gravimetric Electrochemical Equivalent

From the previous equation, we can introduce a physical quantity denoted the ***specific electrochemical equivalent*** sometimes called the ***gravimetric electrochemical equivalent***, denoted Eq_m, and expressed in the SI in $C.kg^{-1}$(Ah/kg). This quantity corresponds to the amount of electric charge required per unit mass of substance to reduce or oxidize it. The specific electrochemical equivalent is thus given by the following equation:

$$Eq_m = (nF/\nu M)$$

Where, n is the number of electrons exchanged during the oxidation or reduction of the substance, F, is the Faraday's constant of 96,485.309 $C.mol^{-1}$, ν the dimensionless stoichiometric coefficient of the electrochemical reduction or oxidation, M, the atomic or molecular molar mass of the electrode material in $kg.mol^{-1}$. The above equation is the modern form of the second Faraday's law.

> **Example**: Pure iron metal can be electroplated at the cathode from an aqueous solution containing ferrous cations according to the electrochemical half-reaction: $Fe^{2+} + 2\ e^- = Fe(s)$, the relative atomic molar mass for iron is 55.845, hence because reduction of ferrous iron requires two electrons, the iron molar and specific electrochemical equivalent factors are respectively 193 kC/mol, and 960 Ah/kg.

8.2.2 Volumetric Electrochemical Equivalent

Sometimes for practical reasons, it is necessary to indicate the number of electrons available per unit volume of substance or solution, this is the ***volumetric electrochemical equivalent*** denoted Eq_v, and expressed in the SI in $C.m^{-3}$ (Ah/m^3), in this particular case, it can be calculated multiplying the specific electrochemical equivalent by the mass density of the substance in kg/m^3 as indicated by following the equation:

$Eq_V = \rho(nF/\nu M)$

The gravimetric and volumetric electrochemical equivalent factors for selected reducible metals and electroactive species often encountered in solutions of iron sulfates, and iron-rich effluents are listed in Table 38. The calculated values are based on the relative atomic and molecular masses recommended by the IUPAC [83].

Table 38 – Electrochemical equivalents for selected redox couples

Redox couple	Redox half-reaction	n	E^0_{298} (V/SHE)	M_r (^{12}C = 12)	Density (ρ/kg.m^{-3})	Eq (/Ahkg^{-1})	Eq (/Ah.dm^{-3})
$O_2/2H_2O$	**$O_2 + 4H^+ + 4e^- = 2H_2O$**	4	**1.229**	**31.999**	**1.33**	**3,350**	**4.46**
VO_2^+/VO^{2+}	$VO_2^+ + 2H^+ + e^- = VO^{2+} + H_2O$	1	0.999	50.942	6,110	526	**3,215**
Fe^{3+}/Fe^{2+}	$Fe^{3+} + e^- = Fe^{2+}$	1	0.771	55.845	7,874	480	**3,779**
Cu^{2+}/Cu	$Cu^{2+} + 2e^- = Cu(s)$	2	0.342	63.546	2,699	844	**2,277**
VO^{2+}/V^{3+}	$VO^{2+} + 2H^+ + e^- = V^{3+} + H_2O$	1	0.338	50.942	6,110	526	**3,215**
TiO^{2+}/Ti^{3+}	$TiO^{2+} + 2H^+ + e^- = Ti^{3+} + H_2O$	1	0.099	47.867	4,540	560	**2,542**
$2H^+/H_2$	**$2H^+ + 2e^- = H_2(g)$**	2	**0.000**	**2.0159**	**0.084**	**26,590**	**2.23**
V^{3+}/V^{2+}	$V^{3+} + e^- = V^{2+}$	1	-0.255	50.942	6,110	526	**3,215**
Ni^{2+}/Ni	$Ni^{2+} + 2e^- = Ni(s)$	2	-0.257	58.693	8,900	913	**8,128**
Fe^{2+}/Fe	**$Fe^{2+} + 2e^- = Fe(s)$**	2	**-0.447**	**55.845**	**7,874**	**960**	**7,558**
Cr^{3+}/Cr	$Cr^{3+} + 3e^- = Cr(s)$	3	-0.744	51.996	7,190	1,546	**11,118**
Zn^{2+}/Zn	$Zn^{2+} + 2e^- = Zn(s)$	2	-0.762	65.390	7,133	820	**5,847**
Ti^{3+}/Ti^{2+}	$Ti^{3+} + e^- = Ti^{2+}$	1	-0.900	47.867	4,540	560	**2,542**
V^{2+}/V	$V^{2+} + 2e^- = V(s)$	2	-1.175	50.942	6,110	1,052	**6,429**
Mn^{2+}/Mn	$Mn^{2+} + 2e^- = Mn(s)$	2	-1.185	54.938	7,440	976	**7,259**

8.3 Faradaic Current Efficiency

For a given electrochemical reaction involving a particular electroactive species denoted k, the ***faradaic efficiency*** also called in short the ***current efficiency*** of the electrolytic process, is denoted by the Greek symbol ε_I, or by the acronym *CE*, corresponds to the dimensionless ratio of the electric current consumed selectively by the electrochemical reaction involving the species k to the total electric current circulating inside the electrochemical reactor for the same duration of electrolysis.

In practice, the current efficiency is expressed as a fraction or a percentage and it is related directly to the actual mass of electroactive species k consumed or produced compared to the theoretical mass expected. Thus, the faradaic current efficiency is defined by the simple equations listed below:

$$CE = \varepsilon_I = I_k/I = Q_k/Q = m_k Eq/I\Delta t$$

[83] Loss, R.D. Atomic Weights of the Elements 2001. *Pure & Applied Chemistry*, **75**(8)(2003)1107-1111.

Where:

ε_I	dimensionless faradaic or current efficiency,
I_k, I	individual and total electric currents, in A,
Q_k, Q	individual and total electric charges, in C (Ah),
m_k	mass of the electroactive species produced or consumed, in kg,
Eq	gravimetric electrochemical equivalent of k in $C.kg^{-1}$ ($Ah.kg^{-1}$),
Δt	duration of electrolysis, in seconds (h).

Hence, if an electric current I in amperes (A) is provided to the cathode with an external source (e.g., DC power supply) during a given time Δt in hours, the mass of substance of reducing species, m_k, produced is given by the following relation:

$$m_k = \varepsilon_I \nu M(I\Delta t/nF) = \varepsilon_I(I\Delta t/Eq)$$

Where:

m_k	mass of substance produced, in kg,
v	dimensionless stoichiometric coefficient,
I	total electric current, in A,
M	molar atomic or molecular mass of reducing species, $kg.mol^{-1}$,
Δt	duration of electrolysis, in hours,
n	dimensionless number of electrons exchanged,
F	Faraday's constant 96,485.309 $C.mol^{-1}$,
Eq	gravimetric electrochemical equivalent of k in $C.kg^{-1}$ ($Ah.kg^{-1}$),
ε_I	Faradaic current efficiency.

The above equation is the mathematical form of the first Faraday's law.

As a more general rule, if the electric current varies with time, the overall quantity of electricity provided during a given time, denoted $Q(t)$, in C (Ah), is given by the integral equation of the current over the time:

$$Q(t) = \int I(t)dt$$

Hence a more versatile equation must include the above integral. This more sophisticated equation should be used for precise electric measurements (e.g., coulometer):

$$m_k = \varepsilon_I[Q(t)/Eq] = (\varepsilon_I/Eq)\int I(t)dt$$

It is also important to mention, that the Faradaic current efficiency increases with increasing temperature. Actually, from an electrode kinetics standpoint, a high temperature favors the transport of ions towards the electrode; it also decreases the dynamic viscosity of the electrolyte, and the overpotential.

8.4 Overall Cell Voltage

When an ***electric current***, I in A, circulates inside an electrolyzer, the overall cell voltage is equal to the sum of several contributions, and it is usually expressed by the following general equation [84]:

$$\Delta U_{cell} = [E_{th(an.)} - E_{th(cath.)}] + [\Sigma_k (\eta_{an,k} - \eta_{cath,k})] + j \Sigma_k R_k A_k + \Delta U_t = \Delta U_{th} + \Sigma\eta + IR_T + \Delta U_t$$

Where

U_{cell}	overall cell voltage in V,
$E_{th(an.)}$, $E_{th(cath.)}$	Nernstian electrode potentials, in V,
$\eta_{an,k}$, $\eta_{cath,k}$	anodic and cathodic overpotentials, in V,
j	electric current density, in $A.m^{-2}$,
R_k	electrical resistance of the medium k, in Ω,
A_k	cross sectional area of the medium k, in m^2,
ΔU_t	cell potential drift in V.

The first term U_{th} represents the ***reversible cell voltage*** also called the ***thermodynamic cell voltage***, the second term $\Sigma\eta$ is the contribution of both anode and cathode ***overpotentials*** (i.e., concentration, activation, and passivation), the third term, iR_T, is the sum of all the ***ohmic drops*** (i.e., electrolytes, electrodes, separator, contacts, and bus bars), and the finally fourth term ΔU_t, is the ***cell potential drift*** which is a time-dependent variable related to the aging of electrodes, and separator materials.

Therefore, for a targeted electrochemical reaction, which is taking place at the working electrode (i.e., cathode in the case of iron electrowinning), the reversible cell voltage can be minimized by carefully selecting a proper electrochemical reaction occurring at the counter electrode (i.e., anode).

Regarding the reduction of overpotentials, the ***activation overpotential*** can be reduced by selecting the most appropriate electrode materials with enhanced catalytic properties while the ***concentration overpotential*** can be minimized enhancing the mass transfer near the electrode surface by forced circulation and by using turbulent promoters.

---

[84] CARDARELLI, F. (2018) *Materials Handbook: A Concise Desktop Reference, Third Edition*. Springer, Cham, Switzerland, pages .

The ohmic drop is reduced: (1) by using highly conductive electrolytes that are compatible with the chemistry of the process, (2) by designing the narrowest ***inter electrode gap*** or ***membrane-electrode gaps*** allowing the proper fluid flow conditions, and ensuring the harvest of the electrodeposited metal at the cathode, and the escape of oxygen gas bubbles at the anode, (3) by selecting separators with high ionic conductivity, and low thicknesses, and finally (4) by limiting the number of electrical contacts, and by using optimized bus bars and current collectors.

Finally, the potential drift can be reduced using long lasting electrodes, and separator materials with slow corrosion and degradation rates.

8.5 Electrochemical Reaction Rates

8.5.1 Hourly Yield

Based on the previous physical quantities, it is now possible to express the mass production or consumption rate for reducing or oxidizing an electroactive species k, also called the ***hourly yield*** denoted dm/dt, and expressed in the SI in kg/s (kg/hour). It is defined by the following equation:

$$(dm/dt)_{\mathrm{k}} = \varepsilon_I \nu M I / nF = \varepsilon_I I / Eq$$

Where

$(dm/dt)_{\mathrm{k}}$ hourly yields for electroactive species in $\mathrm{kg.s^{-1}}$ (kg/hour),

Eq gravimetric electrochemical equivalent of k in $\mathrm{C.kg^{-1}}$ ($\mathrm{Ah.kg^{-1}}$),

I total electric current, in A,

M molar mass of electroactive species, $\mathrm{kg.mol^{-1}}$,

ε_I Faradaic current efficiency.

8.5.2 Space Time Yield

The productivity of an electrochemical process corresponds to the mass production or consumption rate of an electroactive species k at a given electrode having a geometric surface area A_{e} expressed in $\mathrm{m^2}$. The mass production rate of electroactive substance per unit area of electrode were the reaction occurs is called the ***space-time yield*** denoted by the symbol Y_{k} or by the acronym STY, expressed in the SI in $\mathrm{kg.m^{-2}.s^{-1}}$ ($\mathrm{kg.m^{-2}.h^{-1}}$) which is given by the equation below:

$$STY(k) = Y_{\mathrm{k}} = (1/A_{\mathrm{e}})(dm/dt)_{\mathrm{k}} = \varepsilon_I (I/A_{\mathrm{e}})/Eq = (\varepsilon_I j)/Eq$$

Where:

$STY(k)$ space-time yield of species k in $\mathrm{kg.m^{-2}.s^{-1}}$ ($\mathrm{kg.m^{-2}.h^{-1}}$),

A_c	active surface area of the electrode in m^2,
I	total electric current, in A,
j	Current density in A/m^2,
Eq	gravimetric electrochemical equivalent of k in $C.kg^{-1}$ ($Ah.kg^{-1}$),
ε_I	Faradaic current efficiency.

8.6 Voltage, and Energy Efficiencies

8.6.1 Voltaic or Potential Efficiency

The ***voltaic efficiency*** also called ***potential efficiency***, denoted by the Greek symbol ε_U, is defined as the dimensionless ratio of the thermodynamic or reversible cell voltage to the total cell voltage, and it can be expressed as a fraction or a percentage.

$$\varepsilon_U = U_{th}/U_{cell}$$

Where:

ε_U	dimensionless voltaic or potential efficiency,
U_{th}	thermodynamic or reversible cell voltage in V,
U_{cell}	total cell voltage in V.

8.6.2 Energy Efficiency

The ***energy efficiency***, denoted by the Greek symbol ε_E, is the dimensionless ratio of the electrical energy consumed by the electrochemical process to the total electric energy supplied to the electrochemical reactor. It is the product of the faradaic efficiency times the voltaic efficiency. As for other efficiencies, it can be expressed as a fraction or a percentage.

$$\varepsilon_E = \varepsilon_U \times \varepsilon_I = (U_{th}/U_{cell})(I_k/I)$$

Where:

ε_U	voltaic or potential efficiency,
ε_I	faradaic or current efficiency,
U_{th}	thermodynamic or reversible cell voltage in V,
U_{cell}	overall cell voltage in V,
I	total electric current in A.

8.7 Specific and Volumetric Energy Consumptions

Consider an electrochemical reactor operating at a constant current I during an elapsed time Δt with an average cell voltage $<U_{cell}>$ in volts. Assuming that the steady state is reached, the electric energy consumed by the electrochemical reactor is given by the following equation:

$$E = <U_{cell}> \int I dt = <U_{cell}> \times I\Delta t$$

If we divide this energy per unit mass of the electroactive species k produced or consumed, we obtained the so called the ***specific energy consumption*** denoted by the symbol e_m or by the acronym *SEC*, and expressed in the SI in J/kg (kWh/kg):

$$SEC(k) = e_m = <U_{cell}> \int I dt/m_k = <U_{cell}> I\Delta t/m_k = <U_{cell}> \times Eq/\varepsilon_I$$

Where:

e_m	specific energy consumption in $J.kg^{-1}$ ($Wh.kg^{-1}$),
$<U_{cell}>$	average cell voltage in V,
Eq	electrochemical equivalent of species k in $C.kg^{-1}$ ($Ah.kg^{-1}$),
ε_I	Faradaic or current efficiency.

Therefore for decreasing the specific energy consumption the two options available consist: (i) to increase the ***Faradaic current efficiency***, and (ii) to decrease the ***overall cell voltage***.

The ***volumetric energy consumption*** denoted e_V or by the acronym *VEC*, expressed in the SI in J/m^3 (kWh/dm^3) is simply related to the specific energy consumption using the mass density of the solution, ρ_{soln}, in kg/m^3 (kg/dm^3) as follows:

$$VEC(k) = e_V = \rho_{soln}\, SEC(k) = <U_{cell}> \times \rho_{soln}\, Eq/\varepsilon_I = <U_{cell}> \times Eq_V/\varepsilon_I$$

9 Current Distributions

During iron electrowinning, the thickness, the profile, and the crystalline morphology of electrodeposited iron metal varies with the local cathode current density, and thus it is affected by the spatial current distribution existing at the cathode surface. The latter is imposed by the geometry of the electrodes, the electrolyzer design, and the electrical conductivity of the catholyte, the activation, and concentration overpotential. For a comprehensive discussion on the subject, we suggest to read the following references [85, 86]

9.1 Primary Distribution

The primary current distribution is only controlled by the geometry of the electrodes configuration and shapes as the electrical conductivity of the electrolyte solution has no influence. The primary current distribution predominates when both electrode kinetic effects, and concentration overpotential are negligible. Basically, it consists to solve the Laplace equation for the definite electrode geometry and cell design.

9.1.1 Laplace Equation

The primary current distribution and potential does not consider the mass transfer of the electroactive species and the electron charge transfer across the electrode-electrolyte interface. Hence in steady state conditions ($\partial \rho_e / \partial t = 0$) without generation or consumption of the electroactive species the charge continuity equation becomes a particular case of the well-known ***Poisson equation*** that becomes the simple ***Laplace equation*** instead:

$$\text{div} j = \text{div}(\kappa E) = \text{div}(\kappa \nabla V) = \nabla^2 V = 0$$

Depending on the system geometry and the boundaries limits, the integral solutions are not the same. The one-dimensional Laplace equation can be written for the two coordinate systems of interest in electrowinning (i.e., Cartesian, cylindrical) in the absence of source or disappearance of charge ($I_V = 0$) in the form of an equation with second-order partial derivatives:

[85] POPOV, K.I.; and STEVANOVIĆ, R.M. A new current line division concept for the determination of the current distribution in electrochemical cells. Part I. Theoretical background of the corner weakness effect in electroforming. *Journal of the Serbian Chemical Society*, **65**(2000)905-914.

[86] POPOV, K.I.; DJOKIĆ, S.S., and GRGUR, B.N. (2002) *Fundamental Aspects of Electrometallurgy*. Kluwer Academic / Plenum Publishers, New York, NY.

$$\partial^2 V/\partial x^2 + \partial^2 V/\partial y^2 + \partial^2 V/\partial z^2 = 0$$

The integral solution of this partial differential equation, obtained by introducing the initial and boundary conditions specific to each problem, directly provides the distribution of electric potential. The latter is used in the generalized Ohm's law to obtain the expression of the current density vector.

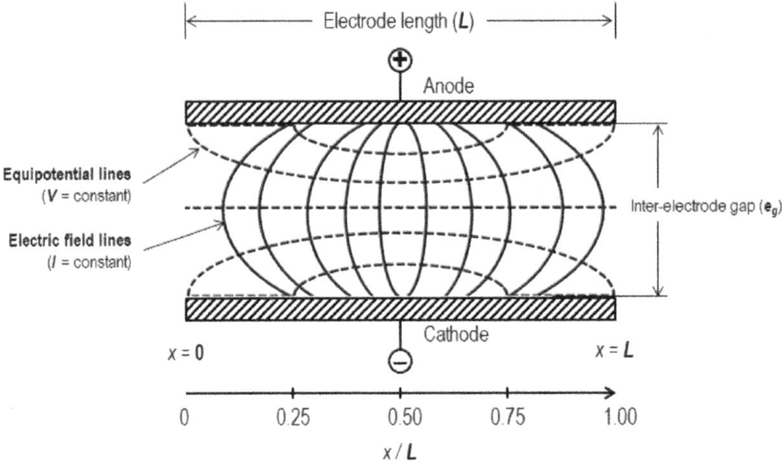

Figure 36 – Primary current distribution with equipotential and electric field lines

In the particular case of a two parallel, and plane electrodes with an inter-electrode gap, e_g, and a length, l, such as the one encountered in undivided electrowinning cells, and depicted in Figure 36, in the absence of a source term, the resolution of the two-dimensional Laplace equation below was obtained by Parris and Newman in 1970 [87, 88, 89]:

$$\partial^2 V/\partial x^2 + \partial^2 V/\partial y^2 = 0$$

$$(j/j_{max}) = [\Phi \mathrm{ch}\Phi / K(\mathrm{th}^2\Phi)]/[\mathrm{sh}^2\Phi - \mathrm{sh}^2[(2x - L)(\Phi/L)]$$

With $\Phi = (\pi L/2e_g)$, and $K(\mathrm{th}^2\Phi)$ an elliptical integral

---

[87] PARRISH, W.R.; and NEWMAN J. (1970) Current Distributions on Plane, Parallel Electrodes in Channel Flow. *Journal of The Electrochemical Society*, **117**(1)(1970)43-49.

[88] NEWMAN, J. (1968) Engineering design of electrochemical systems. *Industrial and Engineering Chemistry*, **60**(4)(1968)12-27.

[89] NEWMAN, J. (1970) Ohmic potential measured by interrupter techniques. *Journal of the Electrochemical Society*, **117**(4)(1970)507-508.

9.1.2 Cathode Edge Effects

For an electrowinning cell consisting of two equal area and parallel-plane cathode and anode both not in contact with the tank walls, because the current lines pass partially around the rectangular space between the cathode and the tank walls hence the cathode current density is much higher at the edges than at the center of the cathode plate.

Actually, between two symmetrically positioned points on the anode and cathode in a homogeneous electric field, between such points on the edges of electrodes there are a number of current lines concentrating. Assuming that each current line is characterized by the same ohmic resistance the phenomenon increases markedly the cathode current density at the edges of the cathode for $x = 0$ and $x = L$. Theoretically, the cathode current density becomes infinite. However, in practice, due to the existence of activation, and concentration overpotentials these impose limited numerical values for the cathode current density.

This result in a different morphology of the metal electrodeposited at the cathode. Often the deposit at the center of the cathode is compact, thicker, and flat whereas the occurrence of dendrites is often observed at the edges. The formation of dendrites at the edges of the cathode could cause short circuits or damage or even piercing to the separator, and damage to the DC power supply.

9.2 Secondary Distribution

The ***secondary current distribution*** is only related to the activation overpotential. It is worth to mention, that even for a simple anode-cathode configuration (e.g., parallel plates), the calculations, for obtaining the numerical solutions for the secondary current distribution, are not simple. This becomes even more complicated for intricate electrode geometry and electrolyzer design (e.g., tubular cell with coaxial electrodes) especially when the limiting diffusion current density and the hydrodynamic conditions vary.

9.2.1 Haring-Blum Cell

Let's consider a conventional electrowinning cell with plane and parallel rectangular plate cathodes and anodes facing each other but excluding the separator for the sake of clarity. This experimental set-up called the ***Haring-Blum cell*** was designed historically in the 1920s to assess the ***throwing power*** of an electroplating process.

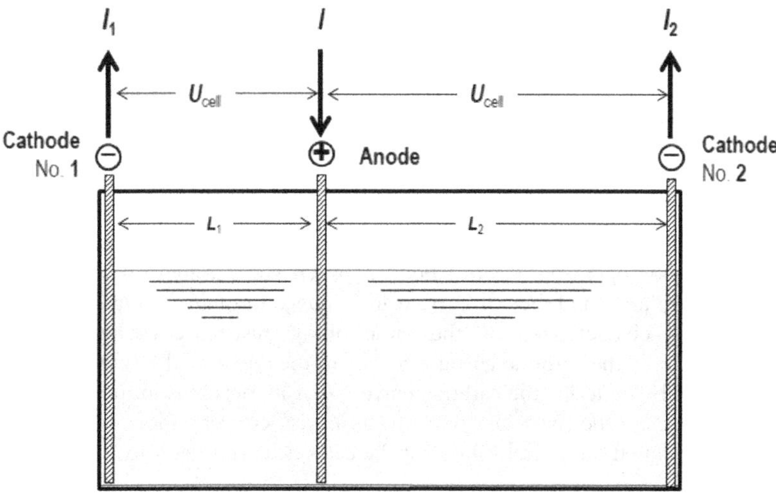

Figure 37 – Schematic of the Haring-Blum cell

In this theoretical case, the electrolytic cell contains two cathodes (-) denoted $\{C_1\}$ and $\{C_2\}$ apart with in between an anode (+) denoted $\{A\}$, but with two different inter-electrode gaps (Figure 37). Moreover, all electrodes having the same active surface area, A_c, in m^2:

$$A_1 = A_2 = A_c$$

When the electrolysis is conducted under a ***galvanostatic mode***, that is, under a constant electric current, I, in A, because the two different anode-cathode electrode gaps, denoted L_1 and L_2, there are two ohmic drops. Thus according to the Kirchhoff law, two electric currents I_1 and I_2 circulate towards each cathode and verify the equality:

$$I = I_1 + I_2$$

When the cathode surface area is taken into account we have the following relation between the cathode current densities:

$$A_1 j_1 + A_2 j_2 = A_T j$$

But because we have the same cathode surface: $A_T = A_1 + A_2 = 2A_c$

$$j = j_1/2 + j_2/2$$

On the other hand, the cell voltage between {C_1} and {A}, denoted U_{AC1}, in V, is the sum of the reversible cell voltage, U_{th}, the activation overpotential, η_{C1}, and the ohmic drop across the electrolyte:

$$U_{AC1} = [U_{th} + \eta_{C1}(j_1) + L_1 j_1/\kappa]$$

Similarly, the cell voltage between {C_2} and {A}, denoted U_{AC2}, in V is given by the following equation:

$$U_{AC2} = [U_{th} + \eta_{C2}(j_2) + L_2 j_2/\kappa].$$

Because both cell voltages are equals, we have:

$$U_{th} + \eta_{C1}(j_1) + L_1 j_1/\kappa = U_{th} + \eta_{C2}(j_2) + L_1 j_1/\kappa$$

Thus: $\eta_{C1}(j_1) + L_1 j_1/\kappa = \eta_{C2}(j_2) + L_2 j_2/\kappa$

After regrouping the terms, we obtain:

$$[\eta_{C2}(j_2) - \eta_{C1}(j_1)] = (L_1 j_1 - L_2 j_2)/\kappa$$

In the particular case, when the absolute values of cathode overpotentials are lower than |-100 mV|, the slope of the polarization plot near the origin is almost linear and it is equivalent to the polarization resistance defined in Section 7.11.4, R_p, and it can be approximated by the following equation:

$$(\partial\eta/\partial j)_{cath} = [\eta_{C2}(j_2) - \eta_{C1}(j_1)]/(j_2 - j_1) = R_p$$

Therefore, after introducing the above equation into the previous we obtain:

$$(j_2 - j_1)(\partial\eta/\partial j)_{cath} = (L_1 j_1 - L_2 j_2)/\kappa$$

Finally, after rearranging, the above equation, we obtain the relation between the two cathode current densities as follows:

$$(j_2/j_1) = [L_1 + \kappa\cdot(\partial\eta/\partial j)_{cath}]/[L_2 + \kappa\cdot(\partial\eta/\partial j)_{cath}] = [L_1 + R_p]/[L_2 + R_p]$$

Based on the above equation, it is possible to draw several conclusions: (1) When the polarization resistance due to the electro transfer becomes negligible, and because the cathode surface area are identical, the ratio between the two cathode current densities is inversely proportional to the cathode-anode gaps ratio: $(j_{C1}/j_{C2}) = (L_1/L_2)$. In this case the situation is identical to the primary distribution as the Ohm's law control the current distribution. (2) Conversely, if the product

$\kappa\cdot(\partial\eta/\partial j)_{cath}$ is much greater than the cathode-anode gaps, then the dimensionless ratio becomes unity and the secondary distribution prevails and remains uniform.

More generally, when the absolute value of the cathode overpotentials are greater than |-100 mV|, the equation becomes more complicated. Indeed, the linearization of the polarization plot is no more valid, and the Tafel's slope must be used instead. In this case, we have:

$$(\partial\eta/\partial j) = b_c/j$$

Thus the equation of the dimensionless ratio of the cathode current densities is

$$(j_2/j_1) = [L_1 + \kappa\cdot 2b_c/(j_1 + j_2)]/[L_2 + \kappa\cdot 2b_c/(j_1 + j_2)]$$

9.2.2 Hull Cell

In practice, the trapezoidal ***Hull cell*** patented by Dr. Richard O. Hull from *E.I Dupont de Nemours and Co.* in 1935 [90] and still used today is usually made of polymetacrylate or Plexiglas® (Trademark to *Röhm GmbH*), polycarbonate or Lexan® (Trademark of *Sabic Global Technologies B.V.*), PTFE, or even PVC eventually equipped with a thermostatic heater, and an air or inert gas sparging.

It provides several technical advantages compared to the previous Haring-Blum cell that facilitate greatly the understanding of the electrodeposition of a metal with only one single experimental setup [91]. For instance, a standard configuration extensively used in North America among electroplaters is depicted in Figure 38 while a custom made cell is depicted in Figure 39.

[90] HULL, R.O. (1935) *Apparatus and process for the study of plating solutions.* U.S. Patent 2,149344 A, (E.I Dupont de Nemours and Co.), March 22, 1935.

[91] NOHSE, W. (1966) *The Hull Cell: The investigation of electroplating and related solutions with the aid of the Hull cell.* Robert Drapert, London, UK.

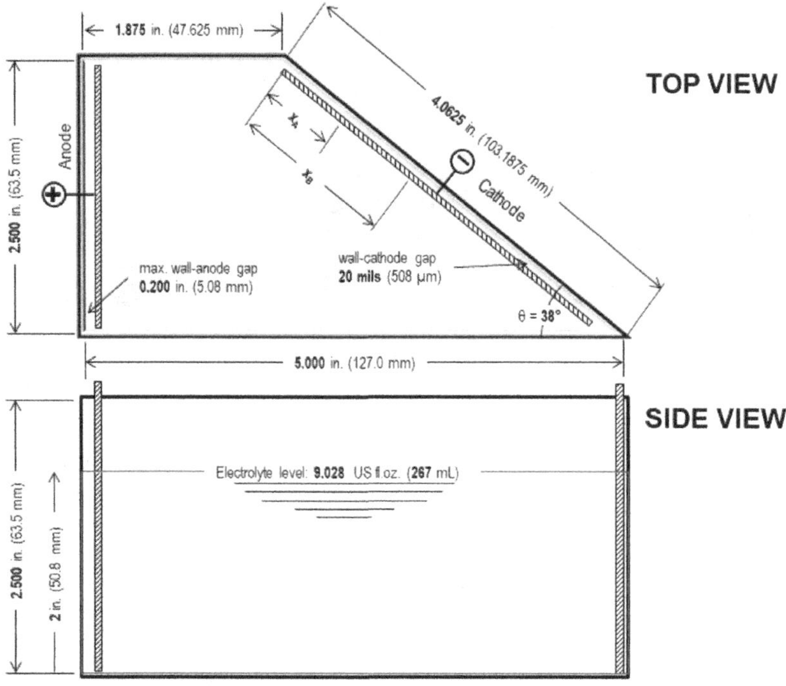

Figure 38 – Schematic of the 267-mL type Hull cell

Actually, the Hull cell allows assessing easily the optimization of the cathode current density, observe visually the type of deposits (e.g., nodular, cracked, flaky, dull, bright, dark), and to evaluate the impact of deleterious impurities, and additives, along with the determination of the throwing power that will be discussed later.

Figure 39 – Sturdy construction of a 267-mL type Hull cell with single use copper foil

The cell is operated at constant current, I_{cell}, in A, and the adopted cell current is usually 2 A that allows to provide a cathode current density ranging from

-26 A/m^2 for an anode-to-cathode spacing of 5 inches (127 mm) up to -900 A/m^2 for an anode to-cathode spacing of only 1.875 in (47.625 mm). Other cell designs are available commercially and standardized methods used in North America [92] and abroad in Europe it is included in the German standard DIN 50957-2 [93].

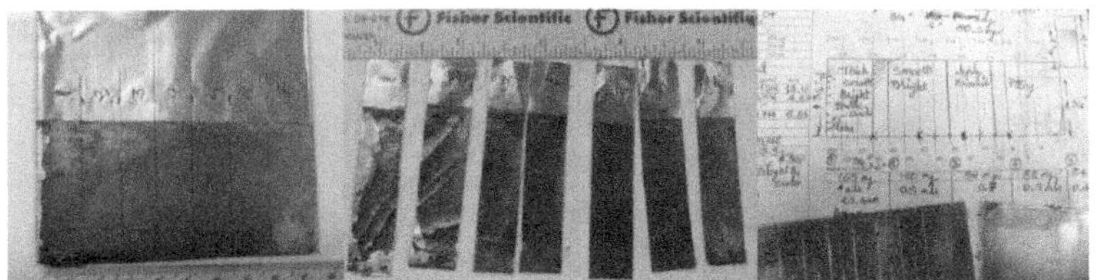

Figure 40 – Cut strips of the iron-plated copper foil used as cathode

The cathode current density, $j_{cathode}$, in A/m^2, at a given abscissa location on the cathode distance, denoted x_c, in cm, can be obtained either graphically from plot of the current density vs. distance or simply by using the simple empirical equation below:

$$j_c\ (\text{A/m}^2) = I_{cell}\ (\text{A}) \times [A - B \log_{10} x_c\ (\text{cm})]$$

With the two empirical constants in SI units equal to:

$A = 510\ \text{m}^{-2}$ and $B = 524\ \text{m}^{-2}$

Selected values of the cathode current density vs. cathode abscissa are provided in Table 39 for a total current of 2 A and 4 A respectively.

On the other hand, the determination of the coating thickness can be measured either by microscopy of an embedded cross-section of the cathode, or by using a high precision caliper, or by using a thin metal foil with a known thickness as cathode.

In the latter case, the electroplated metal foil is detached from the metallic support at the end of the electrolysis, and then cut into strips of equal width and length that are weighted to determine the surface mass density of the electrodeposit (Figure 40). We found this simple technique reliable during extensive screening tests used to assess on the spot the impact of pH, temperature, iron concentration, and addition of additives or for adjusting the operating conditions during pilot testing. For that purpose, thin metal foils made of aluminum, copper, iron, and titanium with a calibrated thickness were particularly useful.

---

[92] ANONYMOUS (1997) IPC-TM-650 test methods manual. *The Institute for Interconnecting and Packaging Electronic Circuits* (IIPEC) Northbrook, IL.

[93] ANONYMOUS (2019) *Testing of electrolytes used for electro-deposited metallic coatings - Test involving electro-deposition - Part 2: Special test cells.* Deutsches Institut für Normung E.V. (DIN), Berlin, Germany, June 2019.

Table 39 – Hull cell cathode current density vs. cathode abscissa

abscissa (x_c)		Cathode current density (j_c/A.m^{-2})	
x_c/cm	x_c/in	I = 2 A	I = 4 A
1.270	0.50	-911	-1822
1.905	0.75	-727	-1454
2.540	1.00	-596	-1192
3.175	1.25	-494	-988
3.810	1.50	-411	-822
4.445	1.75	-341	-682
5.080	2.00	-280	-560
5.715	2.25	-227	-454
6.350	2.50	-179	-358
6.985	2.75	-135	-270
7.620	3.00	-96	-192
8.255	3.25	-59	-118
8.890	3.50	-25	-50

9.2.3 Wagner Number

From the previous paragraph, the secondary current distribution depends on the electrical conductivity κ of the electrolyte, in S/m, the cathode Tafel's slope coefficient in V, obtained from the Horiuti semi-logarithmic plot ($\eta_c = \log_{10}|j_c|$) of the cathode overpotential vs. cathode current density ($\partial\eta_c/\partial j_c$), and finally a characteristic length of the system, denoted L, usually the inter-electrode gap, in m. In the absence of mathematical solutions, electrochemical engineers had to rely on the dimensional analysis. This approach resulted in the introduction of a new dimensionless ***Wagner number*** denoted, W_a, defined by the following equation:

$$Wa = (\partial\eta_c/\partial j_c)(\kappa/L)$$

The Wagner number represents the ratio of the polarization resistance due to the electron transfer to the ohmic resistance due to the ionic transport. Both resistance being in series, the larger of the two control the current distribution. Consequently, if the polarization resistance is zero only the ohmic drop control the current, and thus the primary current distribution prevails.

As a general rule the Wagner number increases with the electrical conductivity of the electrolyte that normalizes the current lines. Conversely, increasing the characteristic length decreases the Wagner number with the current distribution switching from secondary to primary. The reversibility of the cathodic process also influences the number as the secondary current distribution is more uniform for dilute electrolytes.

Therefore, for large values of the Wagner number, the current distribution becomes more even irrespective to the electrode geometry. Conversely, the current distribution is more uniform for smaller characteristic length, with a catholyte solution exhibiting a high ionic conductivity, and with larger cathode Tafel's slope coefficient.

9.2.4 Throwing Power

The ***throwing power***, denoted by the acronym *TP*, refers to the ability of an electroplating electrolyte to electrodeposit a metal uniformly onto a cathode exhibiting an irregular shape. Experimentally, since the 1920s the Haring-Blum cell is used in order to measure the throwing power. As seen in previous paragraphs by changing the cathode-anode gaps, the current density ratio of the two cathodes varies. That means that the masses of deposits on the two cathodes are different.

The ratio of cathode-anode distance (L_1 and L_2) is then related to the mass of metal electrodeposited (m_1 and m_2) respectively or the thickness (t_1 and t_2) of cathode deposit. As seen previously, the difference in mass (resp. thickness) is attributed to the sum of the contributions due to the ohmic drop, and the cathode activation overpotential. Field was the first proposed a formula still used today for the throwing power as follows:

$$TP(\%) = 100\ (P - M)/(P + M - 2)$$

With $P = (j_2/j_1)$ and $M = m_1/m_2$

9.3 Tertiary Distribution

For the ***tertiary current distribution***, the calculations become increasingly complex as both the activation, and diffusion overpotentials must be considered and taken into account.

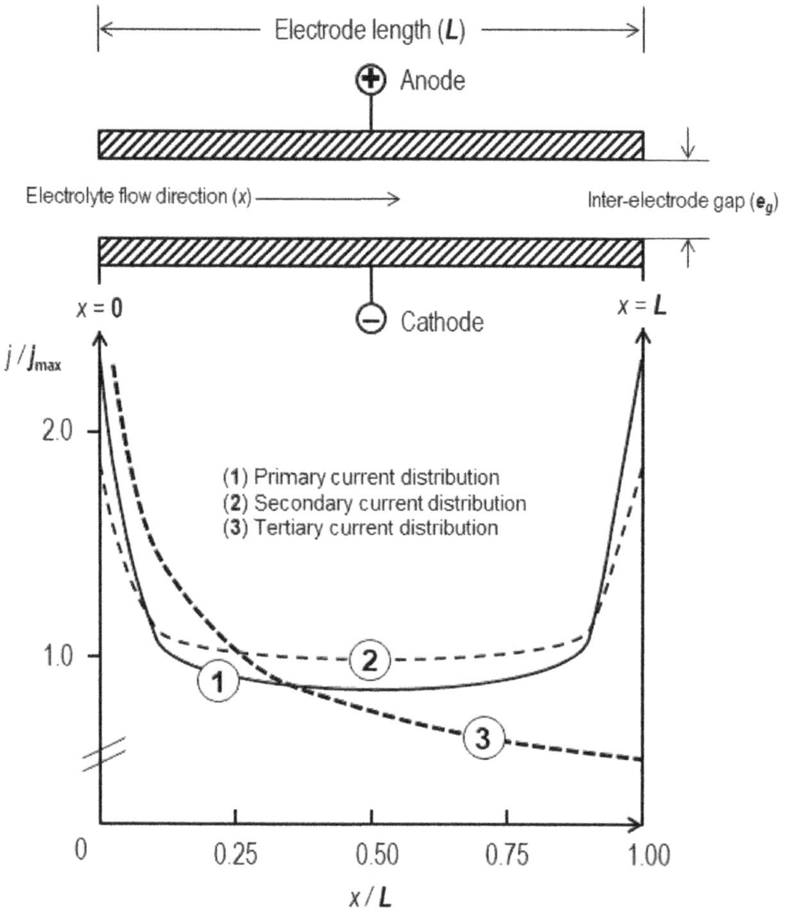

Figure 41 – Primary, secondary, and tertiary current distributions

10 Electrochemical Reactors Design

In this section, we will briefly describe the various types of electrochemical reactors (i.e., electrolyzers) operation commonly used in the industry sometimes referred by some electrochemists as ***macrokinetic models***. For a comprehensive treatment of the subject, we strongly recommend the reader to consults the textbooks on electrochemical engineering that are listed in Section 20.3 and to read dedicated review articles [94, 95].

10.1 Electrochemical Reactors Types

In electrochemical engineering, electrochemical reactors are usually grouped according to three main types based on the flow of the electrolyte: (i) the discontinuous or ***electrochemical batch stirred tank reactor*** or simply the ***batch stirred electrolyzer*** (BSE), (ii) the ***electrochemical plug flow reactor*** or simply the ***plug flow electrolyzer*** (PFE), and finally (iii) the ***electrochemical continuous stirred tank reactor*** or simply the ***continuous stirred electrolyzer*** (CSE). In addition, various sub-types can be derived from the three above design, for instance, by operating the reactors in cascades, by re-circulating the electrolyte in closed loop or by recycling a fraction of the electrolyte.

Prior to describe in details each type of electrolyzer, the general equation for the time variation of the molarity of the electroactive species will be explained.

10.1.1 General Time Dependent Mass Balance Equation

If we consider the general electrochemical reaction scheme occurring at the cathode inside the electrolyzer:

$$\nu O + z e^- = R$$

[94] TRINIDAD, P.; and WALSH, F.C. (1998) Conversion expression for electrochemical reactors which operate under mass controlled reaction conditions, Part I: batch reactor, PFR, and CSTR. *International Journal of Engineering*, **14**(6)(1998)431-41.

[95] WALSH, F.C.; TRINIDAD, P.; and GILROY, D. (2005) Conversion expression for electrochemical reactors which operate under mass controlled reaction conditions, Part II: batch reactor, PFR, and CSTR. *International Journal of Engineering*, **21**(5)(2005)981-992.

with O oxidizing electroactive species,

R reduced electroactive species,

ν Stoichiometric coefficient,

z dimensionless number of electrons exchanged.

Therefore, the time variation of the amount of substance or moles of any electroactive species, k, either produced or consumed at the electrode vicinity inside an electrolyzer can be described by the following basic conservation equation:

$$dn_k/dt = (dn_{IN}/dt - dn_{OUT}/dt) \pm S_k$$

With

n_k amount of substance of electroactive species k, in mol,

dn_{IN}/dt, molar flow rate of species k, entering the reactor, in mol/s,

dn_{OUT}/dt molar flow rate of species k, leaving the reactor, in mol/s,

S_k source term accounting for the production or consumption rates of the electroactive species k, that is, the amount produced or consumed per unit time, mol/s.

If the volume of the electrochemical reactor, V_R, is constant over time, we can expressed the time dependent overall mass balance equation by replacing the amount of substance of any electroactive species, k by the molarity, $C_k = C_k(t)$ at a given time:

$$dn_k/dt = V_R dC_k/dt = (C_{IN} - C_{OUT})Q_v \pm S_k$$

With

$C_k(t)$ molarity of species at a given time, k, in mol,

C_{IN}, molarity of species entering the electrolyzer, in mol/m^3,

C_{OUT} molarity of species leaving the electrolyzer, in mol/m^3,

Q_v volume flow rate of electrolyte, m^3/s.

If no chemical reaction involving the electroactive species occurs, the source term of electroactive species produced or consumed per unit time is only related to the electrochemical reaction rate and it is simply given by the application to the first Faraday's law for the electrolysis:

$$S_k = \pm\varepsilon_I \nu_k |I|/zF$$

With z dimensionless stoichiometric coefficient,

$\lvert I \rvert$	absolute value of the electric current, in A,
z	dimensionless number of electrons exchanged,
F	Faraday's constant, 96,485.309 C/mol,
ν_k	stoichiometric coefficient,
ε_I	Faradaic current efficiency.

If we utilize instead of the absolute value of the electric current, the absolute value of the current density, $\lvert j \rvert$, defined by the ratio of the total current to the active surface area, A_e, of the electrode onto which the electrochemical reaction occurs (i.e., anode or cathode), we obtain:

$$S_k = \pm \varepsilon_I \nu_k \lvert j \rvert A_e / zF$$

The sign ($\pm$) introduced in before the source term in the conservation equation follows the ***thermodynamic sign convention***, that is, it is positive in case of matter entering the system (i.e., generation or production) and negative in the case of matter leaving the system (i.e., disappearing or consumption).

Therefore, the overall time dependent mass balance equation for a given electroactive species, k, implying molarities is as follows:

$$V_R dC_k / dt = (C_{IN} - C_{OUT}) Q_v \pm \varepsilon_I \nu_k \lvert j \rvert A_e / zF$$

10.1.2 Residence Time and Electrode Specific Surface Area

From the previous established overall time dependent mass balance equation, we can simplify and condense it further by dividing the left hand side by the constant volume of the electrochemical reactor:

$$dC_k / dt = (C_{IN} - C_{OUT}) Q_v / V_R \pm \varepsilon_I \nu_k \lvert j \rvert A_e / zFV_R$$

Then, we can now introduce two new physical quantities useful in the design of electrochemical reactors:

(1) The ***residence time*** or ***space-time***, denoted, τ_R, and expressed in s, defined as the ratio of the volume flow rate divided by the volume of the electrolyzer. It corresponds to the average time the electroactive species remains inside the electrolyzer: $\tau_R = V_R/Q_v$.

(2) The ***electrode specific surface area***, denoted a_e, expressed in m^{-1}, that corresponds to the ratio of the active surface area of the electrode where the electrochemical reaction takes place to the volume of the electrochemical reactor: $a_e = A_e/V_R$

Then, the overall condensed time dependent mass balance equation becomes simply:

$$dC_k/dt = (C_{IN} - C_{OUT})/\tau_R \pm \varepsilon_I \nu_k a_e |j|/zF$$

10.1.3 Fractional Conversion Rate

If we introduce the ***fractional conversion rate*** for the electroactive species, k, denoted X_k or sometimes R_k, which is simply defined as the difference between the initial amount of electroactive species, n_o, and the amount of electroactive species at a given time, $n(t)$, divided by the original amount we have:

$$X_k = X_k(t) = [n_o - n(t)]/n_o = 1 - [n(t)/n_o]$$

In the particular case where the volume of the electrolyte inside the electrolyzer remains constant over the time, it is then possible to replace the amount of substance by the molarity of the electroactive species:

$$X_k = X_k(t) = [C_o - C_k(t)]/C_o = 1 - [C_k(t)/C_o]$$

Therefore, the time variation of the fractional conversion rate can be related to that of the molarity simply by:

$$dC_k/dt = - C_o\, dX_k/dt$$

Therefore, the condensed time dependent mass balance can be rewritten as follows:

$$-dX_k/dt = X_k(t)/\tau_R \pm \varepsilon_I \nu_k a_e |j|/zFC_o$$

10.1.4 Batch Stirred Electrolyzer

This simplest type of electrolyzer is usually described by an ***electrochemical batch stirred tank reactor*** or simply the ***batch stirred electrolyzer*** with the acronym BSE and operating under transient state and in which all the reactants are present at the beginning of the electrolysis during which no additional material is neither fed into nor removed from the electrolyzer.

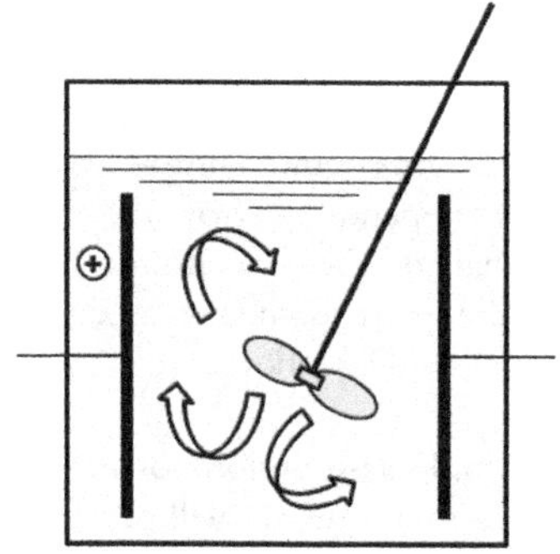

Figure 42 – Schematic of the batch stirred electrolyzer (BSE)

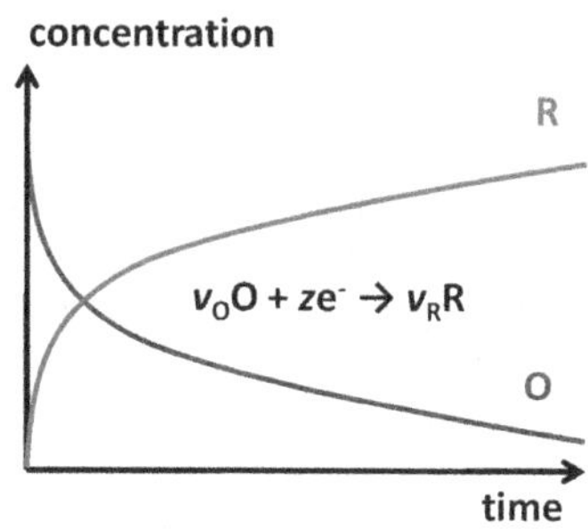

Figure 43 – Concentration of electroactive species vs. time inside the BSE

In practice, the batch electrolyzer consists to a closed tank with or without external mixing (Figure 42). After a definite time, the depleted or enriched electrolyte is discharged from the reactor vessel and the products are recovered by various techniques (e.g., crystallization, precipitation, solid-liquid separation, solvent extraction, ion exchange, etc.).

During the electrochemical reaction, the molarities of reactants decrease progressively with time while those of products increase in the same manner (Figure 43). Permanent and efficient agitation and mixing ensure that molarities are uniform throughout the entire volume of the electrolyzer and that no concentration gradients established inside the electrolyzer except in the narrow Nernst's diffusion layer close to the electrodes surface.

Because a batch operation is always labor intensive, this type of electrolyzer is used primarily at the laboratory or for small-scale industrial processes for producing high value specialty chemicals, and pharmaceuticals, or in closed systems such as electrochemical power sources and energy storage devices especially primary and secondary batteries.

If we apply the previously established equation for the time dependent mass balance for a given electroactive species, *k*, because the mass flow rate of the electrolyte (Q_v) inside the electrolyzer is zero, the equation exhibits it simplest form:

$$-dX_k/dt = \pm\, \varepsilon_I \nu_k a_e |j| / zFC_0$$

Therefore the ***reaction time***, denoted τ_B, required for reaching a given conversion rate is obtained by the solving the integral equation:

$$\tau_B = -\, zFC_0/(\pm\, \varepsilon_I \nu_k a_e) \int (dX_k/|j|) = \tau_R$$

In this particular case, the reaction time above is well established and identical to the residence time, denoted τ_R.

We can see that the above equation seems quite simple from a mathematical standpoint, but in fact the integrand depends also on the current density which itself depends on the electrode potential and the concentration of the electroactive species at the electrode surface, thus the exact mathematical equation of the current density is needed to solve the above integral equation.

Usually, it is possible to solve by using simple assumptions or in simple cases. These cases will be described hereafter and for each one, we will provide the exact equations as a function of time for the fractional conversion rate, the molarities of species, the space-time, the current density under potentiostatic conditions, and eventually the electrode potential under galvanostatic regime.

In case of an electrochemical reaction controlled by the rate of mass transfer of the electroactive species, we can distinguish two important cases relevant to electro synthesis and industrial electrochemical processes that are:

Electrolysis performed at maximum current density, that is, at a fixed electrode potential (i.e., potentiostatic mode).

Electrolysis performed at a constant current density well below limiting current density (i.e., galvanostatic mode).

10.1.4.1 Mass Transfer Limited Electrochemical Reaction

When the overall rate of the electrochemical reaction is controlled by the diffusion of the electroactive species, k, towards the working electrode, and assuming a narrow Nernst diffusion layer with a linear concentration profile, the absolute value of the current density of the electrochemical reaction at a given time, denoted $j(t)$, in A/m^2, can be express in a first approximation (see Section 7.10) as follows:

$$|j| = zFk_m (C - C_E)$$

Where

$|j|$ Absolute current density, in A/m^2,

k_m mass transfer coefficient, in m/s,

z number of electron exchanged,

F Faraday constant, 96,485.309 C/mol,

C molarity of the species in the bulk, mol/m^3.

C_E molarity of the species at the electrode surface, mol/m^3.

10.1.4.1.1 Electrolysis at Limiting Current Density

If the electrolysis is performed at the limiting current by simply fixing the electrode potential (i.e, potentiostatic mode), the molarity of the electroactive species at the electrode surface becomes zero, $C_E(t) = 0$, and thus the concentration gradient inside the diffusion layer reaches a maximum. The equation of the absolute value of the limiting current density, denoted $|j_L(t)|$, in A/m^2, depends now only to the concentration of the electroactive species in the bulk of the solution as follows:

$$|j_L(t)| = zFk_mC_k(t)$$

Because of the previously established definition of the fractional conversion rate, the above limiting current density can also be expressed as a function of the initial molarity of the electroactive species in the bulk of the solution, C_0, and the fractional conversion rate.

$$|j_L(t)| = zFk_mC_0[1 - X_k(t)]$$

Therefore, the initial limiting current density at $t_0 = 0$ is simply given by:

$$|j_L(0)| = zFk_mC_0$$

The overall mass balance equation becomes in this case:

$$-dX_k/dt = \pm \varepsilon_I \nu_k a_e k_m[1 - X_k(t)]$$

Rearranging the above equation, we obtain a logarithmic first order differential equation:

$$-dX_k/(1 - X_k) = d\ln(1 - X_k) = (\pm \varepsilon_I \nu_k a_e k_m)dt$$

The integral solution is simply:

$$\ln|(1 - X_k)| = (\pm \varepsilon_I \nu_k a_e k_m)\, t + \text{constant}$$

Because of the initial conditions, that is, at $t_o = 0$, the fractional conversion rate is: $X_k = 0$, hence $\ln|(1 - X_k)| = 0$ and the integration constant is then equal to zero.

Therefore, the mathematical equation for the fractional conversion rate of the electroactive species, k, inside the batch stirred electrolyzer is given by the general equation:

$$X_k^{BSE}(t) = [1 - \exp(\pm \varepsilon_I \nu_k a_e k_m t)]$$

From the previous equation, we can see clearly, that the fractional conversion rate is a direct function of the faradaic current efficiency, the specific electrode surface area, and the mass transfer coefficient. Therefore, the molarity of the electroactive species can be derived from the equation and written as follows:

$$C_k(t) = C_0 \exp(\pm \varepsilon_I \nu_k a_e k_m t)$$

Regarding the reaction time inside the BSE, substituting the mathematical equation of the limiting current density in the equation, we obtain:

$$\tau_B = \tau_R = -[\pm 1/\varepsilon_I \nu_k a_e k_m] \int dX_k/(1 - X_k) = -[\pm 1/\varepsilon_I \nu_k a_e k_m] \int d\ln(1 - X_k)$$

After integration of this differential logarithmic equation, we obtain the expression of the reaction time in a batch stirred electrolyzer when the electrochemical reaction is mass transfer limited and the electrolysis is performed under potentiostatic mode:

$$\tau_B = [\pm 1/\varepsilon_I \nu_k a_e k_m] \ln[1/(1 - X_k)]$$

Therefore, the limiting current density vs. time is given by the following equation:

$$|j_L(t)| = [zFk_m C_o]\exp(\pm \varepsilon_I \nu_k a_e k_m t) = |j_L(0)|\exp(\pm \varepsilon_I \nu_k a_e k_m t)$$

We can see as expected that in case of disappearing of an electroactive species (minus sign), the limiting current density decreases overtime following the depletion of the electroactive species as the batch electrolyzer is by principle a closed system.

10.1.4.2 Electrolysis below Limiting Current Density

This practical situation is of upmost importance industrially as it concerns all the electrochemical processes and preparative electrolysis performed in concentrated electrolytes where the rate determining step is the electron transfer reaction (i.e., pure activation process). This is especially the case when electrowinning iron metal from concentrated solutions of ferrous sulfate.

Therefore, in this particular case, the operating current density at a given time, denoted $j(t)$, is simply given by the equation assuming a Nernst diffusion layer with a linear concentration profile:

$$|j(t)| = zFk_m[C_k(t) - C_E(t)] = zFk_m[C_o\exp(\pm \varepsilon_I \nu_k a_e k_m t) - C_E(t)]$$

With the $C(t)$ and $C_E(t)$, being the molarities of the electroactive species, k, in the bulk of the electrolyte, and at the electrode surface respectively. Note that the molarity of the electroactive species at the electrode surface vs. time is obtained from chrono-potentiometry and it is related to the initial molarity in the bulk of the electrolyte and the current density as described in the following equation:

$$C_E(t) = C_0 - 2(|j(t)|/zF)(t/\pi D_k)^{1/2}$$

Hence, at each time, the absolute value of the limiting current density is given when the molarity of the electroactive species at the electrode surface becomes zero, $C_E(t) = 0$, hence:

$$|j_L(t)| = zFk_m C_k(t) = zFk_m C_0 \exp(\pm \varepsilon_I \nu_k a_e k_m t)$$

We have seen previously that the time dependent mass balance equation is given by:

$$-dX_k/dt = \pm \varepsilon_I \nu_k a_e |j(t)|/zFC_o$$

At this stage, it is suitable to introduce two dimensionless quantities. The first one is the ***dimensionless current density***, denoted $|j^*|$, corresponding to the ratio of the current density to the initial limiting current density:

$$|j^*| = |j(t)|/|j_L(0)| = |j(t)|/zFk_m C_0 = \exp(\pm \varepsilon_I \nu_k a_e k_m t) - [C_E(t)/C_0]$$

The second dimensionless quantity is the ***electrochemical reactor time constant***, denoted τ_C, and simply defined as follows:

$$\tau_C = 1/k_m a_e$$

Hence, the condensed form of the mass balance equation becomes:

$$-dX_k/dt = \pm \varepsilon_I \nu_k |j^*|/\tau_C$$

The fractional conversion rate can be calculated simply by the integral equation:

$$X_k(t) = -[(\pm \varepsilon_I \nu_k)/\tau_C] \int |j^*|\, dt$$

At this point, two practical modes of operation must be distinguished: (i) the electrolysis performed at constant current density or galvanostatic mode and (ii) the electrolysis performed at a constant electrode potential or potentiostatic mode. We will describe only the former in the following paragraph.

10.1.4.3 Galvanostatic Mode

The galvanostatic mode imposes by definition to conduct the electrolysis at a constant current density, thus: $|j^*| = |j|/|j_L(0)| =$ constant. Therefore, the integral solution of the differential equation is a very straightforward equation:

$$X_k(t) = 1 - [C_k(t)/C_0] = -(\pm\,\varepsilon_I\,\nu_k)\,|j^*|\,(t/\,\tau_C) = -[(\pm\varepsilon_I\,\nu_k)\,|j|\,/\,zFk_mC_0](t/\,\tau_C)$$

Therefore, when conducting the electrolysis at a constant current density well below the initial limiting current density, the fractional conversion rate of the electroactive species varies linearly with time.

This simple situation persists until a *transition time*, denoted τ_t, is reached that corresponds when the molarity of the electroactive species at the electrode surface becomes nil:

$$C_E(\tau_t) = 0$$

At the transition time ($t = \tau_T$), the operating current density $|j|$ equals the limiting current density for the molarity of the electroactive species measured at the transition time, this allows to yield new equations for the actual current density and its related dimensionless quantity:

$$|j| = |j_L(\tau_t)| = zFk_mC_k(\tau_t) = zFk_mC_o\exp(\pm\,\varepsilon_I\,\nu_k\,a_e\,k_m\,\tau_t)$$

$$|j^*| = |j(\tau_t)^*| = |j(\tau_t)|\,/\,|j_L(0)| = C_k(\tau_t)/C_o = \exp(\pm\,\varepsilon_I\,\nu_k\,a_e\,k_m\,\tau_t)$$

Therefore, the fractional conversion rate also reaches a critical value, $X_k(\tau_t)$, which is expressed simply hereafter as a function of the dimensionless current density:

$$X_k^{BSE}(\tau_t) = 1 - [C_k(\tau_t)/C_o] = 1 - |j^*|$$

Equating the above equation with that obtained previously for the fractional conversion rate we obtain:

$$1 - |j^*| = -(\pm\,\varepsilon_I\,\nu_k)\,|j^*|\,(\tau_t/\,\tau_C)$$

This allows to express the practical equation for calculating the transition time as a function of the operating parameters and the kinetic data of the electrochemical reaction.

$$\tau_t = -\,[\tau_C/(\pm\,\varepsilon_I\,\nu_k)](1 - |j^*|)/|j^*| = -\,[\tau_C/(\pm\,\varepsilon_I\,\nu_k)][zFk_mC_o/\,|j| - 1]$$

The above transition time must not be confused with the transition time of the electrochemical reaction that could be calculated by means of equations obtained in chrono-potentiometry namely the ***Sand's equation***.

$$\tau_{Sand} = \pi D_k(zFC_0/2j)^2$$

Actually, the above Sand's equation was established in the particular case when electrolyte is intentionally kept quiet by avoiding any agitation or mixing near the electrode surface in order to avoid disturbance of the transient concentration profiles. Thus, it is not relevant in a batch stirred electrolyzer where mixing is favored. Nevertheless, it can be used as a rough estimate for establishing a minimum threshold for the transition time.

Electrolysis performed under a constant current density below the limiting current density and for period below the transition time, the fractional conversion rate varies linearly with time while from and above the transition time a second electrochemical reaction begins thus decreasing the faradic current efficiency.

In the case, where electrolysis is carried on from the transition time and above, the current density for transforming the electroactive species remaining constant, the limiting current density for the molarity of the electroactive species in the bulk of the electrolyte continue to decrease exponentially with time and the difference in current density between the two values represents the current density used by the second electrochemical reaction:

$$\text{At } t > \tau_t\text{: } |j^*| = |j_L(t)|/|j_L(0)| = C_k(t)/C_o = 1 - X_k(t)$$

Therefore, the differential equation of the overall mass balance becomes:

$$-dX_k/dt = \pm\, \varepsilon_I\, \nu_k\, [1 - X_k(t)]/\, \tau_C$$

After integration we obtain the integral solution:

$$\text{At } t > \tau_t\text{: } \ln[1 - X_k(t)] = \pm\, \varepsilon_I\, \nu_k\, t/\, \tau_C + K$$

The constant of integration is obtained with the initial condition chosen for $t = \tau_T$, where $X_k(\tau_T) = 1 - |j^*|$, hence the constant is given by:

$$K = \ln|j^*| - (\pm\, \varepsilon_I\, \nu_k\, \tau_t/\, \tau_C)$$

Therefore the equation giving the fractional conversion rate for electrolysis performed at a constant current density well below the initial limiting current but for duration period above the transition time is listed below:

$$X_k(t) = 1 - |j^*|\exp[(\pm\, \varepsilon_I\, \nu_k)(t - \tau_t)/\, \tau_C] = 1 - [|j|/zFk_mC_o]\exp[(\pm\, \varepsilon_I\, \nu_k)(t - \tau_t)/\, \tau_C]$$

We see clearly from the above equation that the time variation of fractional conversion rate is less pronounced than the previous linear trend.

Similarly, the Faradaic current efficiency is no longer constant as it is influenced the decreasing fraction of the operating current density. From the original definition of the Faradaic current efficiency, that is, the ratio of the current density actually used by the electrochemical reaction, in this case the limiting current at a given time, to the overall current allows to write:

$$\varepsilon_I''(t) = |j_L(t)|/|j| = \exp[(\pm \varepsilon_I \nu_k)(t - \tau_t)/\tau_C]$$

The potential of the electrode where the electrochemical reaction occurs is obtained by chrono-potentiometry, and it is given by the following equation:

$$E(t) = E^o(O/R) + (RT/2zF)\ln[D_O/D_R] + (RT/zF)\ln[(\tau_T/t)^{1/2} - 1]$$

If the diffusion coefficients of the electroactive species are almost equal, then we have the simplified form:

$$E(t) = E^o(O/R) + (RT/zF)\ln[(\tau_T/t)^{1/2} - 1]$$

If the ohmic drop of the electrolytes and membranes, the anode potentials and overpotential are kept almost constant, then the overall cell voltage follows the same trend.

10.1.5 Plug Flow Electrolyzer

The ***plug flow electrolyzer*** with the acronym PFE is a particular type of continuous electrolyzer, the electrolyte containing the electroactive species (i.e., reactants) flows through the cell cross section without mixing along the direction of flow, and the products are simply extracted at the reactor outlet.

This type of electrolyzer is also called tube or ***piston-flow electrolyzer*** is a continuous and steady state reactor. The PFE describes rather well electrolyzers with a channel flow configuration such as the Kreb's electrolytic cells used for the industrial production of sodium chlorate or flow-through three-dimensional electrodes with packed meshes or packed beds.

From a theoretical point of view, this electrolyzer type is characterized by the perfect mixing in the radial dimension (i.e., uniform cross section concentration) and the fact that for a given flow of electrolyte no elements of volume are mixed axially (i.e., no axial dispersion) nor they are modified the entrance order. The chemical composition changes only with distance through the reactor and the residence time is identical for all species.

Let consider a plug flow electrolyzer made of an electrolyte circulating through a narrow rectangular channel made by two parallel plate electrodes of total length, L, a width b, and inter-electrode gap, h, all expressed in m (Figure 44). The volume flow rate, Q_v, in m^3/s is assumed to be constant.

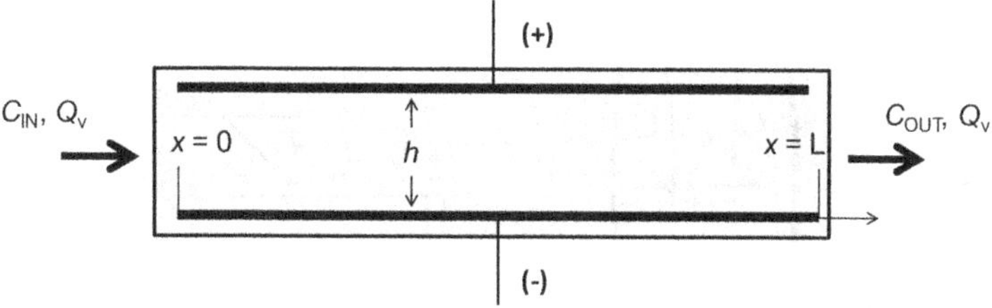

Figure 44 – Schematic of the plug flow electrolyzer (PFE)

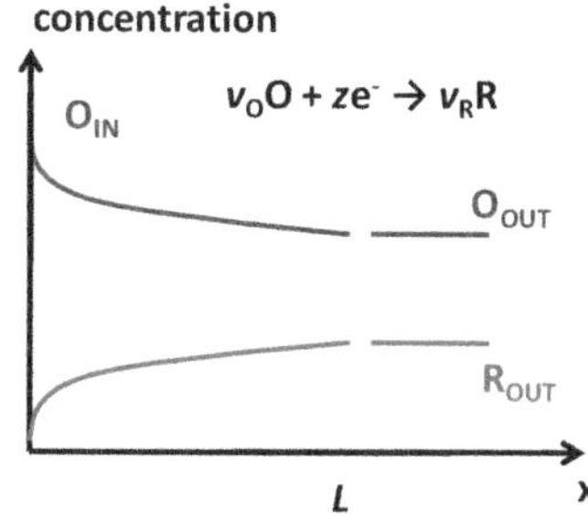

Figure 45 – Concentration of electroactive species vs. distance from the entrance

In this case, the molarity of the electrolyte entering the plug flow reactor is C_{IN} while the molarity of the electrolyte leaving the cell is denoted C_{OUT}, thus, the fractional conversion rate can be written:

$$X_k = X_k(t) = [(C_{IN} - C_{OUT})/C_{IN}] = 1 - (C_{OUT}/C_{IN})$$

Because the molarity of the electroactive species, denoted k, decreases continuously along the length x of the electrodes measured from the feed end ($x = 0$), the molarity of the electroactive species and hence the fractional conversion rates are both a direct function of the distance along the flow path and time:

$$C_k = C_k(x,t) \qquad \text{and} \qquad X_k = X_k(x,t)$$

Therefore, in this case the overall mass balance equation must be considered in a given differential element of volume valid either for a tubular reactor with concentric electrodes depicted in Figure 46 or a rectangular channel with parallel plate electrodes in Figure 47.

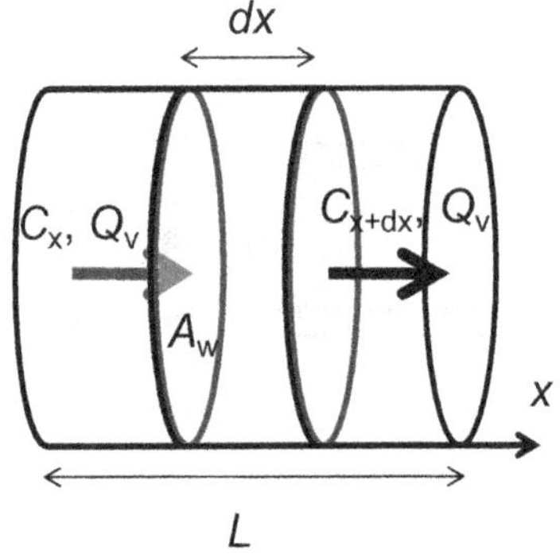

Figure 46 – Differential volume for concentric electrodes

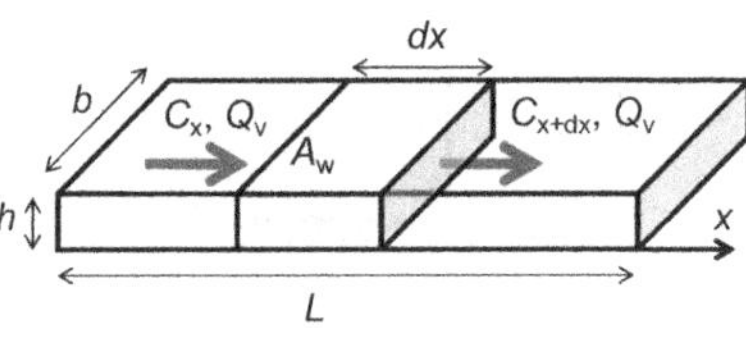

Figure 47 – Differential volume for parallel electrodes

Tubular duct with concentric electrodes:

$$dV = A_w \cdot dx = (\pi D_h^2/4)\ dx$$

Rectangular duct with parallel plate electrodes:

$$dV = A_w \cdot dx = bh\ dx$$

With A_w the wetted or cross sectional area that must not be confused with the electrode area, A_e. Therefore, the mass balance applied to that differential volume and a differential electrode area can be written as follows:

$$dV(dC_k/dt) = (C_{x+dx} - C_x)Q_v \pm \varepsilon_I\ \nu_k\ |j|\ dA_e/zF$$

The differential electrode surface area, dA_e, is defined for a specific geometry as follows:

Tubular duct with concentric electrodes: $dA_e = \pi D_h \cdot dx$

Rectangular channel with parallel plate electrodes: $dA_e = b\ dx$

Hence, we obtain the general equation for the mass balance inside a plug flow electrolyzer:

$$(dC_k/dt) = (dC_k/dV)Q_v \pm \varepsilon_I\ \nu_k\ |j|\ (dA_e/dV)/zF$$

Because the term (dA_e/dV) corresponds to the specific surface area of the electrode where the electrochemical reaction occurs, a_e, introduced earlier in Section 10.1.2, we obtained the condensed form:

$$(dC_k/dt) = (dC_k/dV)Q_v \pm \varepsilon_I \nu_k a_e |j|/zF$$

When the steady state is reached, the above equation is greatly simplified

$$0 = (dC_k/dV)Q_v \pm \varepsilon_I \nu_k a_e |j|/zF$$

$$0 = - C_{IN}(dX_k/dV)Q_v \pm \varepsilon_I \nu_k a_e |j|/zF$$

Therefore, the minimum volume of the electrochemical reactor to obtain a given fractional conversion rate is obtained by integrating:

$$V_R = \int dV = [zFC_{IN}Q_v/(\pm \varepsilon_I \nu_k a_e)]\int dX_k/|j|$$

This corresponds to the ***residence time*** or ***space-time*** for the PFE:

$$\tau_R = V_R/Q_v = [zFC_{IN}/(\pm \varepsilon_I \nu_k a_e)]\int dX_k/|j|$$

10.1.5.1 Mass Transfer Limited Electrochemical Reaction

When the overall rate of the electrochemical reaction is controlled by the diffusion of the electroactive species, k, towards the working electrode, and assuming a narrow Nernst diffusion layer with a linear concentration profile, the absolute value of the current density of the electrochemical reaction at a given time, denoted $j(t)$, in A/m^2, can be express in a first approximation (see Section 7.10) as follows:

$$|j| = zFk_m (C - C_E)$$

Where

$\lvert j \rvert$	Absolute current density, in A/m^2,
k_m	mass transfer coefficient, in m/s,
z	number of electron exchanged,
F	Faraday constant, 96,485.309 C/mol,
C	molarity of the species in the bulk of the solution, mol/m^3.
C_E	molarity of the species at the electrode surface, mol/m^3.

10.1.5.2 Electrolysis at Limiting Current (Potentiostatic)

If the electrolysis is performed by fixing the electrode potential (i.e., potentiostatic mode) the electrochemical reaction will be at a current density equal to the limiting current, the concentration gradient inside the diffusion layer reaches a maximum. This situation corresponds when the concentration of the electroactive species at the electrode surface is nearly zero. Thus, the equation of the absolute value of the limiting current density, denoted j_L, in A/m^2, depends only to the concentration of the electroactive species in the bulk of the solution as follows:

$$|j_L| = zFk_mC = zFk_mC_{IN}(1 - X_k)$$

Therefore, the minimum volume of the electrochemical reactor to obtain a given fractional conversion rate is obtained by integrating:

$$V_R = [Q_v/(\pm \varepsilon_I \nu_k a_e k_m)]\int dX_k/|(1 - X_k)| = [Q_v/(\pm \varepsilon_I \nu_k a_e k_m)]\int d\ln(1 - X_k)$$

After integration of this differential logarithmic equation, we obtain the expression of the volume of the reactor needed to obtain a given fractional conversion rate inside an electrochemical plug flow reactor when the electrochemical reaction is mass transfer limited and the electrolysis is performed at the maximum limiting current density:

$$V_R = [Q_v/(\pm \varepsilon_I \nu_k a_e k_m)] \ln[1/(1 - X_k)]$$

From the above equation, it is then possible to calculate the minimum electrode surface area required to perform the electrolysis for a given fractional conversion rate:

$$A_e = a_e V_R = [Q_v/(\pm \varepsilon_I \nu_k k_m)] \ln[1/(1 - X_k)]$$

This corresponds to the ***residence time*** or ***space-time*** denoted τ_R as follows:

$$\tau_R = V_R/Q_v = [1/(\pm \varepsilon_I \nu_k a_e k_m)] \ln[1/(1 - X_k)]$$

Finally, for an electrolyzer of fixed reactor volume and with a given electrode surface area, the fractional conversion rate and the molarity of the outlet electroactive species are obtained from the two equations:

$$X_k^{PFE} = [1 - \exp(\pm \varepsilon_I \nu_k a_e k_m \tau_R)]$$

$$C_{OUT} = C_{IN} \exp(\pm \varepsilon_I \nu_k a_e k_m \tau_R)$$

We can see clearly from the above equation, that fractional conversion rate for the plug flow electrolyzer and batch stirred electrolyzer will be the same if the residence time inside the PFE is equivalent to the batch processing or reaction time inside the BSE.

The operating limiting current depends on the distance from the entrance of the reactor and it is obtainable by integrating the current between the entrance and the exit of the electrolyzer as:

$$dI_L = |j_L| dA_e$$

$$|I_L| = [zFQ_vC_{IN}/(\pm \varepsilon_I \nu_k)] X_k = [zFQ_vC_{IN}/(\pm \varepsilon_I \nu_k)][1 - \exp(\pm \varepsilon_I \nu_k a_e k_m \tau_R)]$$

Therefore, the limiting current density is simply obtained by dividing the above equation by the electrode active surface area:

$$|j_L| = [zFQ_vC_{IN}/(\pm \varepsilon_I \nu_k A_e)] X_k$$

$$|j_L| = [zFQ_vC_{IN}/(\pm \varepsilon_I \nu_k A_e)][1 - \exp(\pm \varepsilon_I \nu_k a_e k_m \tau_R)]$$

When the fractional conversion rate is extremely low inside the reactor, the limiting current density is:

$$|j_L| = zFk_mC_{IN}$$

Instead, when the fractional conversion rate is almost unity the limiting current density becomes:

$$|j_L| = [zFQ_vC_{IN}/(\pm \varepsilon_I \nu_k A_e)]$$

10.1.5.3 Electrolysis below Limiting Current

This practical situation is of upmost importance industrially as it concerns all the electrochemical processes and preparative electrolysis performed in concentrated electrolytes where the rate determining step is the electron transfer reaction (i.e., pure activation process). Therefore, in this particular case, the operating current density at a given time, denoted $j(t)$, is simply given by the equation assuming a Nernst diffusion layer with a linear concentration profile:

$$|j(t)| = zFk_m[C_{IN} - C_E(t)] = zFk_m[C_{IN}\exp(\pm \varepsilon_I \nu_k a_e k_m \tau_R) - C_E(t)]$$

With the $C(t)$ and $C_E(t)$, being the molarities of the electroactive species, k, in the bulk of the electrolyte and at the electrode surface respectively.

Hence, at each time, the absolute value of the limiting current density is given when the molarity of the electroactive species at the electrode surface becomes zero, $C_E(t) = 0$, hence:

$$|j_L| = [zFQ_vC_{IN}/(\pm \varepsilon_I \nu_k A_e)] X_k$$

$$|j_L| = [zFQ_vC_{IN}/(\pm \varepsilon_I \nu_k A_e)][1 - \exp(\pm \varepsilon_I \nu_k a_e k_m \tau_R)]$$

We have seen previously that the steady state mass balance equation in the PFE is given by:

$$C_{IN} (dX_k/dV)Q_v = (\pm \varepsilon_I \nu_k a_e) |j| / zF$$

As for the case of the CSE, it is suitable to introduce the ***dimensionless current density***, denoted $|j^*|$, corresponding to the ratio of the current density to the initial limiting current density:

$$|j^*| = |j(t)| / |j_L| = |j(t)| / [zFQ_vC_{IN}/(\pm \varepsilon_I \nu_k A_e)]X_k$$

Hence, the condensed form of the mass balance equation becomes a first order differential logarithmic equation of the form:

$$dX_k/X_k = (|j^*| / \tau_R)dt$$

The fractional conversion rate can be calculated simply by the integral equation:

$$X_k(t) = \exp[|j^*| (t/\tau_R)]$$

10.1.5.4 Plug Flow Electrolyzer with Recirculation

From the previous section describing the plug flow electrolyzer, we demonstrated that for a given reactor volume and electrode surface area a maximum fractional conversion rate can be obtained.

If it is necessary to increase the fractional conversion rate further one option described hereafter consists to connect the electrolyzer to a much larger holding tank with its volume, V_T, being much greater than the volume of the electrochemical reactor itself, V_R. Therefore, in the plug flow reactor with recirculation (PFE-R) electrolyte is re-circulated in closed loop a fixed volume flow rate, Q_V, until the targeted conversion rate is reached.

The dimensionless ratio between the residence times, $\tau_R = (Q_v/V_R)$ and $\tau_T = (Q_v/V_T)$, inside the reactor and inside the holding tank respectively is equal to the ratio of their respective volume as follows:

$$\tau_T/\tau_R = (V_T/V_R)$$

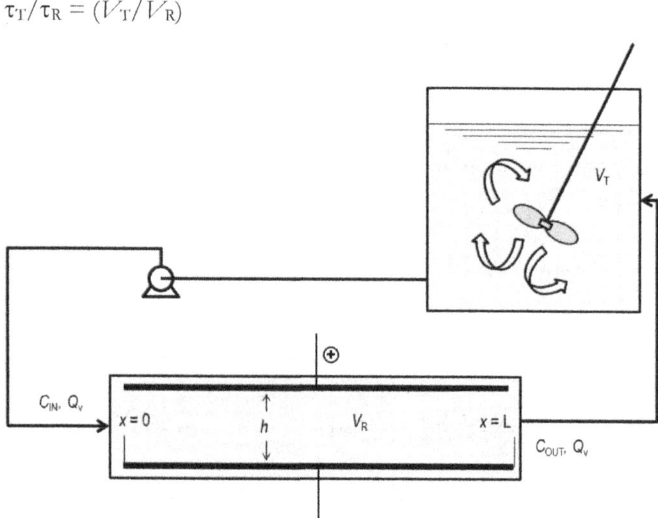

Figure 48 – Schematic of the plug flow electrolyzer with recirculation (PFE-R)

This option offers several advantages from an operation standpoint: (1) to keep the concentration of the electroactive species almost constant by replenishing periodically the reactants and hence allowing to operate the electrolyzer at under potentiostatic mode at the maximum current density, (2) to stabilize both the pH and ORP by adding reagents accordingly, (3) to utilize the holding tank either as a gas disengagement vessel or as a solid-liquid separator (e.g., settler, decanter), and finally (4) to allow efficient mixing of the electrolyte and hence to facilitate the sampling procedure.

The mass balance of the electroactive species inside a well-mixed holding tank is given by the differential equation:

$$V_T dC_{IN}/dt = (C_{OUT} - C_{IN})Q_v$$

On the other hand, we have seen previously that the molarity of the electroactive species for the electrochemical plug flow reactor is given at any time by the following equation:

$$C_{OUT}(t) = C_{IN}(t) \exp(\pm \varepsilon_I \nu_k a_e k_m \tau_R)$$

Hence, substituting equation of the molarity inside the mass balance equation we obtain the logarithmic first order differential equation:

$$dC_{IN}/dt = - C_{IN}(t) (Q_v/V_T)[1 - \exp(\pm \varepsilon_I \nu_k a_e k_m \tau_R)]$$

Introducing the residence time inside the holding tank: $\tau_T = (Q_v/V_T)$, we can rearrange the above differential equation:

$$dC_{IN}/C_{IN}(t) = - \{[1 - \exp(\pm \varepsilon_I \nu_k a_e k_m \tau_R)]/\tau_T\}dt$$

Therefore, integration yields the equation for the molarity of the electroactive species:

$$C_{IN}(t) = C_{IN}(t_o)\exp\{-[1 - \exp(\pm \varepsilon_I \nu_k a_e k_m \tau_R)](t/\tau_T)\}$$

Then, introducing the fractional conversion rate for a single pass ideal PFE, X_k^{PFE}, $[X_k^{PFE} = 1 - \exp(\pm \varepsilon_I \nu_k a_e k_m \tau_R)]$, we obtain the following equation:

$$C_{IN}(t) = C_{IN}(t_o)\exp\{- X_k^{PFE}(t/\tau_T)\}$$

10.1.5.5 Electrolysis at Limiting Current (Potentiostatic)

When the electrochemical reaction is performed at the maximum current density by fixing the electrode potential (i.e., potentiostatic mode), the limiting current is given by the following equation:

$$|I_L| = [zFQ_v C_{IN}(t)/(\pm \varepsilon_I \nu_k)][1 - \exp(\pm \varepsilon_I \nu_k a_e k_m \tau_R)] = [zFQ_v C_{IN}(t)/(\pm \varepsilon_I \nu_k)] X_k^{PFE}$$

Therefore, introducing the overall fractional conversion rate of the entire system, $X_k^T(t)$, which is defined as follows:

$$X_k^T(t) = [C_{IN}(t_o) - C_{IN}(t))/C_{IN}(t_o)] = 1 - [C_{IN}(t)/C_{IN}(t_o)]$$

Thus the overall fractional conversion rate of the system may be written as a direct function of the single pass fractional conversion rate of the PFE as indicated hereafter:

$$X_k^T(t) = 1 - \exp\{- X_k^{PFE}(t/\tau_T)\}$$

Then substituting the molarity of the electroactive species entering the PFE at a given time t, we obtain:

$$|I_L| = [zFQ_v C_{IN}(t_o)/(\pm \varepsilon_I \nu_k)] [1 - \exp(\pm \varepsilon_I \nu_k a_e k_m \tau_R)] \exp[- X_k^{PFE}(t/\tau_T)]$$

$$|I_L| = [zFQ_v C_{IN}(t_o)/(\pm \varepsilon_I \nu_k)] X_k^{PFE} \exp[- X_k^{PFE}(t/\tau_T)]$$

Therefore, the limiting current density is obtained by dividing the limiting current by the electrode surface area:

$$|j_L| = [zFQ_v\, C_{IN}(t_0)/(\pm\, \varepsilon_I\, \nu_k\, A_e)]\, X_k^{PFE} \exp[-\, X_k^{PFE}\, (t/\tau_T)]$$

As expected the instantaneous molarity of the electroactive species, the instantaneous fractional conversion rate and also the limiting current decrease exponentially with time.

The overall fractional conversion rate of the system, $X_k(t)$, after a given time usually expressed as a multiple (n) of the residence time inside the holding tank, τ_T, can be obtain from the single pass conversion rate, X_k^{PFE}, by means of the straightforward equation:

$$X_k^T(n) = [1 - \exp(-nX_k^{PFE})]$$

10.1.5.6 Cascade of Plug Flow Electrolyzers

Another mean is to use a cascade of several identical PFE connected in series (PFE-C), with the same electrode active surface area, A_e, and an individual volume V_R. This allows to achieve a high overall fractional conversion rate for a given volume flow rate of electrolyte.

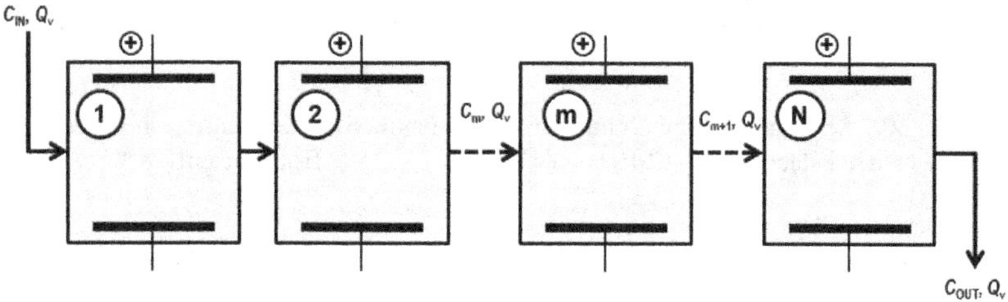

Figure 49 – Cascade of N cells of plug flow electrolyzer in series

Once the steady regime is established, all the residence times inside each electrochemical reactor are equals:

$$\tau_{R1} = \tau_{R2} = \tau_{R3} = \cdot\cdot = \tau_{Rl} = \quad = \tau_{RN} = V_R/Q_v$$

Therefore, the total residence time for the overall cascade is simply given by the sum of all the residence times, that is, the number of cells times the residence time of the first cell:

$$\tau_{cascade} = \Sigma_l \tau_{Rl} = N\tau_{R1}$$

For a single electrochemical reactor, l, in the cascade, the single fractional conversion rate between the outlet and the inlet, is given by:

$$X_{kl} = [1 - \exp(\pm\, \varepsilon_I\, \nu_k\, a_e\, \tau_R)]$$

The overall production rate of the entire cascade of electrochemical reactor is therefore the product of each single fractional conversion rate, thus:

$$X_k^{PFE\text{-}C} = \Pi_l X_{kl} = [1 - \exp(\pm\, \varepsilon_I\, \nu_k\, a_e\, \tau_R)]^N$$

10.1.6 Continuous Stirred Electrolyzer

In this type of reactor reactants are introduced and products withdrawn simultaneously in a continuous manner. The major feature of this reactor as indicated in Figure 7.10 is that the outlet concentration of the electroactive species is identical to that of the concentration inside the reactor, and it is uniform across the entire volume of the electrochemical reactor.

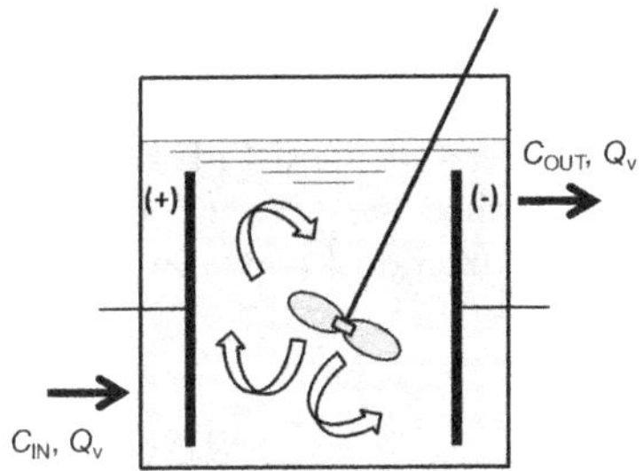

Figure 50 – Schematic of the continuous stirred electrolyzer (CSE)

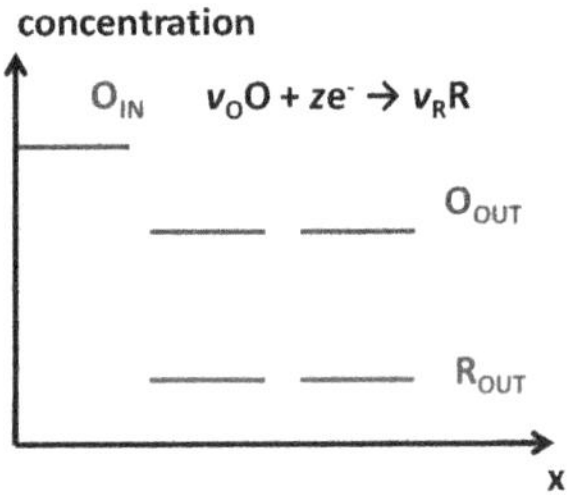

concentration

O_{IN} $\nu_O O + ze^- \rightarrow \nu_R R$

O_{OUT}

R_{OUT}

x

Figure 51 – Concentration vs. distance from the entrance

This class of electrochemical reactor finds extensive applications in large-scale plants for the purpose of reducing the operating cost and facilitating control of product quality. The CSE is a good for describing electrochemical refining and most electrowinning cells with a good stirring from the free convection induced by gradient of concentration of the electroactive species or forced convection induced by gas evolution.

The electrochemical reactor having a fixed volume, V_R, and for a given volume flow rate of electrolyte, Q_v, the condensed time dependent mass balance established previously is:

$$-dX_k/dt = X_k/\tau_R \pm \varepsilon_I\, \nu_k\, a_e\, |j|/zFC_{IN}$$

When the steady state conditions are reached, we have the simple equation:

$$X_k/\tau_R = (\pm\, \varepsilon_I\, \nu_k\, a_e)\, |j|/zFC_{IN}$$

Therefore the equations for the fractional conversion rate and the average residence time are respectively:

$$X_k = (\pm\, \varepsilon_I\, \nu_k\, a_e\, \tau_R) |j| / zFC_{IN}$$

$$\tau_R = zFC_{IN}X_k / (\pm\, \varepsilon_I\, \nu_k\, a_e) |j|$$

Again as mentioned previously for other reactor designs, the apparently straightforward mathematical form of the above equation hides the complexity related to the exact mathematical form of the current density.

10.1.6.1 Mass Transfer Limited Electrochemical Reaction

When the overall rate of the electrochemical reaction is controlled by the diffusion of the electroactive species, k, towards the working electrode, and assuming a narrow Nernst diffusion layer with a linear concentration profile, the absolute value of the current density of the electrochemical reaction at a given time, denoted $j(t)$, in A/m^2, can be express in a first approximation (see Section 7.10) as follows:

$$|j| = zFk_m\,(C - C_E)$$

Where

$\lvert j \rvert$	Absolute current density, in A/m^2,
k_m	mass transfer coefficient, in m/s,
z	number of electron exchanged,
F	Faraday constant, 96,485.309 C/mol,
C	molarity of the species in the bulk, mol/m^3.
C_E	molarity of the species at the electrode surface, mol/m^3.

10.1.6.2 Electrolysis at Limiting Current (Potentiostatic)

When the overall rate of the electrochemical reaction is controlled by the diffusion of the electroactive species towards the electrode, the absolute value of the current density of the electrochemical reaction can be express as a linear function of the concentration of the electroactive species in the bulk of the solution inside the reactor, C_{OUT}, which is by definition of the CSE time and spatially invariant therefore we have the following:

$$|j| = zFk_m(C_{OUT} - C_E)$$

If the electrolysis is performed at the limiting current by fixing the electrode potential (i.e., potentiostatic mode) so that the concentration of the electroactive species at the electrode surface is zero, then, the concentration gradient inside the diffusion layer reaches a maximum. Thus, the equation of the absolute value of the limiting current density, denoted j_L, in A/m^2, depends only to the concentration of the electroactive species in the bulk of the solution inside the reactor as follows:

$$|j_L| = zFk_m C_{OUT} = zFk_m C_{IN}(1 - X_k)$$

Therefore, substituting it in the fractional conversion rate equation we have:

$$X_k = (\pm \varepsilon_I \nu_k a_c \tau_R)|j_L|/zFC_{IN} = (\pm \varepsilon_I \nu_k a_c k_m \tau_R)(1 - X_k)$$

Rearranging the above equation, we obtain the fractional conversion rate and the average residence time for the CSE under a potentiostatic operation as a function of the mass transfer coefficient, the electrode surface area, and the volume flow rate as follow:

$$X_k^{CSE} = (\pm \varepsilon_I \nu_k a_c k_m \tau_R)/[1 + (\pm \varepsilon_I \nu_k a_c k_m \tau_R)] = 1 - 1/[1 + (\pm \varepsilon_I \nu_k a_c k_m \tau_R)]$$

$$X_k^{CSE} = 1 - 1/[1 + (\pm \varepsilon_I \nu_k A_c k_m/Q_V)]$$

Therefore, the outlet molarity of the electroactive species is simply:

$$C_{OUT} = C_{IN}/[1 + (\pm \varepsilon_I \nu_k A_c k_m/Q_V)]$$

And the limiting current density can be related to the inlet molarity of the electroactive species as:

$$|j_L| = zFk_m C_{IN}/[1 + (\pm \varepsilon_I \nu_k A_c k_m/Q_V)]$$

Comparing the above equations with those obtained previously for the plug flow electrolyzer, it is obvious that for a given value of k_m, A_c and Q_v being identical a lower fractional conversion rate can be achieved with the CSE. The major reason behind this is the lower performances because of the agitation and mixing conditions existing inside the continuously stirred tank reactor. Actually, in a PFE all the electroactive species entering the electrolyzer will flow quietly along the entire length of the reactor (i.e., over the entire surface of the electrodes) while on the CSE because of the mixing some electroactive species can eventually reach the exit without having seen the electrodes. This probability even small for bypassing the electrodes explains the differences in conversion rate between the two electrolyzer designs.

It is worth to mention that a faster rate of growth for the fractional conversion rate inside a PFE compared to that calculated inside a CSE. Moreover, the difference measured between the two fractional conversion rates for a given product is significant (i.e., above 2 percent) in the interval comprised between 0.3 and 30. Therefore, it is obvious that outside this range of product the CSE is approaching the fractional conversion rate of the PFE and because of the easier mathematical treatment this type can be used in first approximation for the solving industrial situation (e.g., electrowinning cells).

The only major advantage of the CSE is the positive impact of agitation and mixing that improve the overall mass transfer coefficient of the electroactive species at the electrode surface and hence helps to reduce significantly the size of the electrolyzer compared to that of the PFE that will be larger in order to be able to maintain the same mass transfer capabilities. One solution however is to utilize a PFE with turbulence promoters installed at the electrode surface or by using electrodes with corrugated surfaces and expanded metal meshes.

10.1.6.3 Continuous Stirred Electrolyzer with Recirculation

From the previous section describing the continuously stirred electrolyzer, for a given specific electrode surface area and residence time a maximum fractional conversion rate can be obtained.

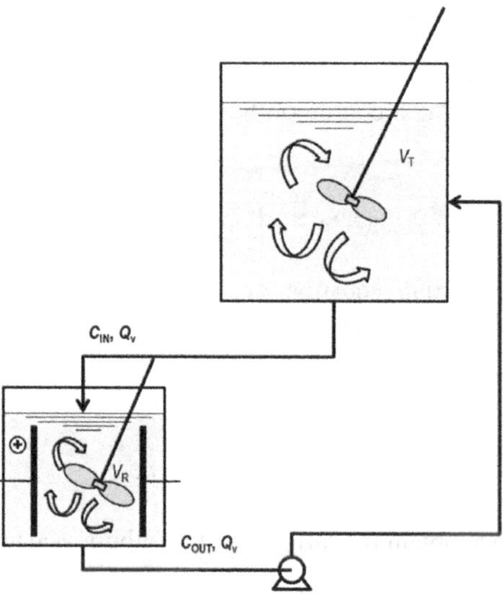

Figure 52 – Schematic of the continuously stirred electrolyzer with recirculation (CSE-R)

If it is necessary to increase the fractional conversion rate one option consists to connect the electrolyzer to a much larger holding tank with its volume, V_T, being much greater than the volume of the electrochemical reactor itself, V_R. Therefore, electrolyte is re-circulated in closed loop a fixed volume flow rate, Q_V, until the targeted conversion rate is reached.

The dimensionless ratio between the residence times, $\tau_R = (Q_v/V_R)$ and $\tau_T = (Q_v/V_T)$, inside the reactor and inside the holding tank respectively is equal to the ratio of their respective volume as follows:

$$\tau_T/\tau_R = (V_T/V_R)$$

Like in the case of the PFR operated in the recirculation mode, this option offers several advantages from an operation standpoint: (1) to keep the concentration of the electroactive species almost constant by replenishing periodically the reactants and hence allowing to operate the electrolyzer at under potentiostatic mode at the maximum current density, (2) to stabilize both the pH and ORP by adding reagents accordingly, (3) to utilize the holding tank either as a gas disengagement vessel or as a solid-liquid separator (e.g., settler, decanter), and finally (4) to allow efficient mixing of the electrolyte and hence to facilitate the sampling procedure.

The mass balance of the electroactive species inside a well-mixed holding tank is given by the differential equation:

$$V_T dC_{IN}/dt = (C_{OUT} - C_{IN})Q_v$$

On the other hand, we have seen previously that the molarity of the electroactive species exiting a continuously stirred electrolyzer is given at any time by the following equation:

$$C_{OUT}(t) = C_{IN}(t)/[1 + (\pm \varepsilon_I \nu_k A_e k_m/Q_V)]$$

Hence, substituting equation of the molarity inside the mass balance equation we obtain the logarithmic first order differential equation:

$$dC_{IN}/dt = C_{IN}(t)\{1/[1 + (\pm \varepsilon_I \nu_k A_e k_m/Q_V)] - 1\}(Q_v/V_T)$$

$$= C_{IN}(t)\{1/[1 + (\pm \varepsilon_I \nu_k A_e k_m/Q_V)] - 1\}/\tau_T$$

Therefore, we obtain the differential logarithmic equation:

$$dC_{IN}/C_{IN}(t) = \{1/[1 + (\pm \varepsilon_I \nu_k A_e k_m/Q_V)] - 1\}dt/\tau_T$$

Straightforward integration yields the integral solution:

$$C_{IN}(t) = C_{IN}(t_o)\exp\{-[1 - 1/[1 + (\pm \varepsilon_I \nu_k A_e k_m/Q_V)]](t/\tau_T)\}$$

Then, introducing the fractional conversion rate for a single pass ideal CSE, X_k^{CSE}, $[X_k^{CSE} = X_k = 1 - 1/[1 + (\pm \varepsilon_I \nu_k A_e k_m/Q_V)]]$, we obtain the following equation for the outlet molarity of the electroactive species after a given time of operation:

$$C_{IN}(t) = C_{IN}(t_o)\exp[-X_k^{CSE}(t/\tau_T)]$$

Therefore, we can introduce the dependent variable known as the overall fractional conversion rate of the system, $X_k^T(t)$, as a function of the fractional conversion rate per pass in the CSE:

$$X_k^T(t) = 1 - C_{IN}(t)/C_{IN}(t_o) = 1 - \exp[-X_k^{CSE}(t/\tau_T)]$$

As expected the instantaneous inlet molarity of the electroactive species, the instantaneous fractional conversion rate and also the limiting current decrease exponentially with time.

The overall fractional conversion rate of the system, $X_k(t)$, after a given time usually expressed as a multiple (n) of the residence time inside the holding tank, τ_T, can be obtain from the single pass conversion rate, X_k^{CSE}, by means of the straightforward equation:

$$X_k^T(n) = [1 - \exp(-nX_k^{CSE})]$$

10.1.6.4 Cascade of Continuous Stirred Electrolyzers

Another mean to improve the poor fractional conversion rate of a CSE compared to those obtained with a PFE is to connect several identical CSE reactors in series or arranged in cascades, with the same electrode active surface area, A_e, and individual volume V_R. This allows to achieve a high overall fractional conversion rate for a given volume flow rate of electrolyte.

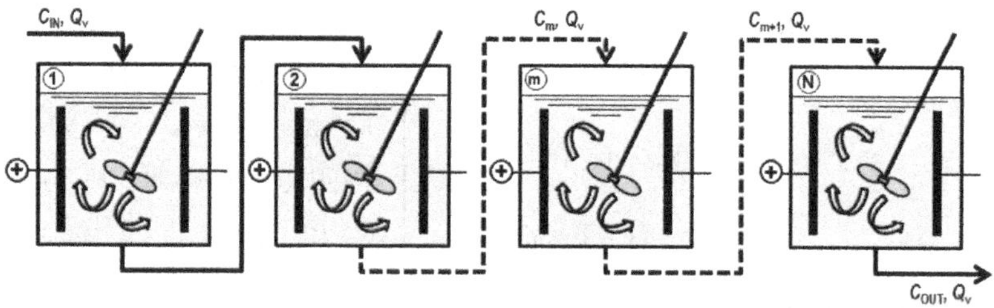

Figure 53 – Cascade of N continuously stirred electrolyzers in series

Once the steady regime is established, all the residence times inside each electrochemical reactor are equals:

$$\tau_{R1} = \tau_{R2} = \tau_{R3} = \cdots = \tau_{Rl} = \quad = \tau_{RN} = V_R/Q_v$$

Therefore, the total residence time for the overall cascade is simply given by the sum of all the residence times, that is, the number of cells times the residence time of the first cell:

$$\tau_{cascade} = \Sigma_l \tau_{Rl} = N\tau_{R1}$$

For a single electrochemical reactor, l, in the cascade, the single fractional conversion rate between the outlet and the inlet, is given by:

$$X_{kl} = (\pm \varepsilon_I \nu_k a_e \tau_R)/[1 + (\pm \varepsilon_I \nu_k a_e \tau_R)]$$

The overall production rate of the entire cascade of electrochemical reactor is therefore the product of each single fractional conversion rate, thus:

$$X_k^{CSE\text{-}C} = \Pi_l X_{kl} = \{(\pm \varepsilon_I \nu_k a_e \tau_R)/[1 + (\pm \varepsilon_I \nu_k A_e \tau_R)]\}^N$$

Finally, we have summarized in Table 40, the major equations for various type of electrochemical reactors described in this section.

Table 40 – Basic equations for various electrochemical reactors

Electrochemical reactor type	Basic equations	Electrolysis conducted at limiting current density (Potentiostatic operation)
Batch Stirred Electrolyzer (BSE)	$-dX_k/dt = \pm \varepsilon_I \nu_k a_e \lvert j\rvert/zFC_o$ $\tau_R = -zFC_o/(\pm \varepsilon_I \nu_k a_e) \int(dX_k/\lvert j\rvert)$ $X_k(t) = [(C_o - C)/C_o] = 1 - (C/C_o)$	$X_k(t) = [1 - \exp(\pm \varepsilon_I \nu_k a_e k_m t)]$ $C_k(t) = C_o \exp(\pm \varepsilon_I \nu_k a_e k_m t)$ $\tau_R = -[\pm 1/\varepsilon_I \nu_k a_e k_m] \ln(1 - X_k)$ $\lvert j_L\rvert = zFk_mC_o\exp(\pm \varepsilon_I \nu_k a_e k_m t)$
Plug Flow Electrolyzer (PFE)	$(dC_k/dt) = (dC_k/dV)Q_v \pm \varepsilon_I \nu_k a_e \lvert j\rvert/zF$ $V_R = [zFC_oQ_v/(\pm \varepsilon_I \nu_k a_e)]\int dX_k/\lvert j\rvert$ $\tau_R = [zFC_o/(\pm \varepsilon_I \nu_k a_e)]\int dX_k/\lvert j\rvert$ $X_k(t) = [(C_{IN} - C_{OUT})/C_{IN}] = 1 - (C_{OUT}/C_{IN})$	$V_R = -[Q_v/(\pm \varepsilon_I \nu_k a_e k_m)] \ln(1 - X_k)$ $A_e = -[Q_v/(\pm \varepsilon_I \nu_k k_m)] \ln(1 - X_k)$ $\tau_R = -[1/(\pm \varepsilon_I \nu_k a_e k_m)] \ln(1 - X_k)$ $X_k = [1 - \exp(\pm \varepsilon_I \nu_k a_e k_m \tau_R)]$ $C_{OUT} = C_{IN} \exp(\pm \varepsilon_I \nu_k a_e k_m \tau_R)$ $\lvert j_L\rvert = [zFQ_vC_o/(\pm \varepsilon_I \nu_k A_e)][1 - \exp(\pm \varepsilon_I \nu_k a_e k_m \tau_R)]$
Continuously Stirred Electrolyzer (CSE)	$-dX_k/dt = 0 = X_k/\tau_R \pm \varepsilon_I \nu_k a_e \lvert j\rvert/zFC_o$ $X_k = (\pm \varepsilon_I \nu_k a_e \tau_R) \lvert j\rvert/zFC_o$ $\tau_R = zFC_oX_k/(\pm \varepsilon_I \nu_k a_e) \lvert j\rvert$	$X_k = (\pm \varepsilon_I \nu_k a_e k_m \tau_R)/[1 + (\pm \varepsilon_I \nu_k a_e k_m \tau_R)]$ $C_{OUT} = C_{IN}[1 + (\pm \varepsilon_I \nu_k a_e k_m \tau_R)]$ $\tau_R = 1/[1 + (\pm \varepsilon_I \nu_k a_e k_m \tau_R)]$

10.1.7 Models for Describing the Electrowinning of Iron

The peculiar design of the divided electrolytic cell for performing the electrowinning of iron imposes to consider separately two distinct model approaches each applied to the cathode and the anode compartments.

A cascade of continuously stirred electrolyzers (CSE-C) is good model for describing the cathode compartment connected and arranged is series (i.e., banks).

The stirring inside rectangular polymer concrete tank acting as electrolyzer with the cathode hanging parallel is ensured by both forced convection due to manifolds installed at the bottom and gradient of concentration near the cathode surface.

The continuously stirred electrolyzer with recirculation (CSE-R) is a suitable model for describing the anode compartment connected to an anolyte holding tank acting as mixing vessel but also as an oxygen gas disengagement vessel. The stirring by forced convection inside the anode compartment where water is oxidized, and sulfuric acid is produced, is ensured from the strong oxygen gas evolution.

10.2 Mass and Energy Balances inside Electrolyzers

An important aspect to consider for all industrial electrolyzers is the mass, energy, and heat balances. Actually, considering the elevate currents circulating inside an electrochemical reactor, the amount of heat generated by Joule's heating ($P = iR^2$) due to various ohmic drops (e.g., electrode materials, electrolytes, separators, contacts) is usually significant, and if not addressed properly this could lead in certain to catastrophic thermal runaway.

Conversely, for certain electrochemical reactions that must be performed above ambient temperature by circulating huge volumes of electrolytes such as in the case of the electrowinning of iron, providing sufficient heat for compensating the heat losses through conduction, and evaporation of water, and entrainment of sulfuric acid mists from the anolyte must also be considered.

From the principle for the conservation of energy, the time variation of the energy of an electrochemical system is usually given as the sum of the electric power supplied to account for the irreversibility of the electrochemical process minus the power consumed by the increase in entropy minus the heat consumed by the electrochemical reaction.

Thus in the ***transient state***, the time variation of the energy stored is the system corresponds to the sum of the electric power supplied externally plus the enthalpy balance of the exiting and entering steams, and the production/consumption of the electroactive species times the enthalpy of the electrochemical reaction as follows:

$$\rho c_p(\partial T/\partial t) = U_{cell}I + (\rho_{out}Q_{v,out}h_{out} - \rho_{in}Q_{v,in}h_{in}) \pm (\varepsilon_I j A_e/E_q)\Delta h_R$$

For a divided electrolyser, we can write for each compartment the entering and leaving volume flow rates, Q_v, in m^3/s, and the mass concentrations c, in kg/m^3 of the electroactive species. However, because the mass is independent of a temperature change while volume changes with temperature, it is more accurate to use instead mass flow rates m, in kg/h, and the mass fractions, w, of the electroactive species each stream. The two latter physical quantities can be easily obtained afterwards using the simple equation involving the mass density of the stream k:

$$m_k = \rho_k Q_k$$

In Figure 54, we have depicted a schematic divided electrolyser such as the one used for electrowinning iron, and regenerating sulfuric acid and we summarized the flows of mass and energy related to both entering and living streams.

Inside the cathode compartment, the entering streams are on an hourly basis: (**1C**) the concentrated catholyte (<u>i</u>nlet) with a mass flow rate, $m_{ci} = \rho_{ci} Q_{ci}$, in kg/h, an initial mass fraction of ferrous sulfate, $w_{FS,i}$, and total iron, $w_{Fe,i}$, and a specific enthalpy, h_{ci}, in J/kg, plus (**2C**) the mass flow rate of make-up ferrous sulfate, $m_{FS} = \rho_{FS} Q_{FS}$, having a specific enthalpy, h_{FS}, in J/kg.

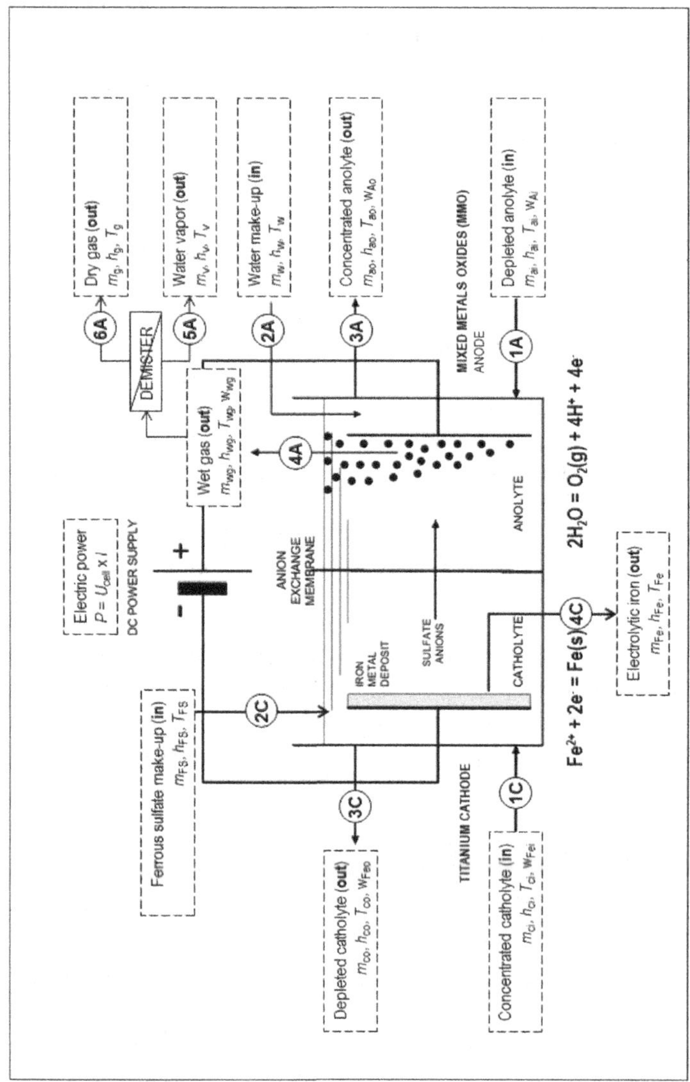

Figure 54 – Energy and mass flow rates inside a divided electrolyzer

The leaving streams are: (**3C**) the depleted catholyte (outlet) with a mass flow rate, $m_{co} = \rho_{co}Q_{co}$, in kg/h, a final mass fraction of ferrous sulfate $w_{FS,o}$, and total iron, $w_{Fe,O}$, and a specific enthalpy, h_{co}, in J/kg, plus (**4C**) the mass flow rate of electrolytic iron electrodeposited at the cathode, m_{Fe}, of active surface area, A_c, in m^2, by the electrochemical reaction conducted under a cathode current density, j_c, in A/m^2, and a Faradaic cathode current efficiency, ε_c, and E_q the gravimetric electrochemical equivalent for iron metal (960 Ah/kg). Moreover, the specific enthalpy of dissolution of the ferrous sulfate, Δh_{soln}, in J/kg, must also be accounted for. Therefore the mass and energy balances are as follows:

$$\Delta m_{catholyte} = (\rho_{co}Q_{co} - \rho_{ci}Q_{ci}) + \rho_{FS}Q_{FS} - (\varepsilon_c j_c A_c/E_q)[M_{FeSO4}/M_{Fe}]$$

$$\Delta m_{FeSO4} = (w_{FS,o}\rho_{co}Q_{co} - w_{FS,i}\rho_{ci}Q_{ci}) + \rho_{FS}Q_{FS} - (\varepsilon_c j_c A_c/E_q)[M_{FeSO4}/M_{Fe}]$$

$$\Delta m_{Fe} = (w_{Feo}\rho_{co}Q_{co} - w_{Fei}\rho_{ci}Q_{ci}) + w_{Fe}\rho_{FS}Q_{FS} - (\varepsilon_c j_c A_c/E_q)$$

$$\Delta h_{catholyte} = (\rho_{co}Q_{co}h_{co}\text{-}\rho_{ci}Q_{ci}h_{ci}) + \rho_{FS}Q_{FS}(h_{fs} + \Delta h_{soln}) + (\varepsilon_c j_c A_c/E_q)\Delta h_R$$

Similarly inside the anode compartment, the entering streams are on an hourly basis: (**1A**) the depleted anolyte (inlet) with a mass flow rate, $m_{ai} = \rho_{ai}Q_{ai}$, in kg/h, an initial mass fraction of sulfuric acid, w_{ai}, and specific enthalpy, h_{ai}, in J/kg, plus (**2A**) the mass flow rate of make-up water, $m_w = \rho_w Q_w$, having a specific enthalpy, h_w, in J/kg. The leaving streams are: (**3A**) the concentrated anolyte (outlet) with a mass flow rate, $m_{ao} = \rho_{ao}Q_{ao}$, in kg/h, a final mass fraction of sulfuric acid w_{ao}, and a specific enthalpy, h_{ao}, in J/kg, plus (**4A**) the wet oxygen gas evolving at the anode (+) with a mass flow rate, $m_{wg} = \rho_{wg}Q_{wg}$, in kg/h, mass fractions of water vapor, w_{wg}, and entrained sulfuric acid, w_{awg}, respectively and a specific enthalpy, h_{wg}, in J/kg, it is also necessary to consider the heat consumed by the evaporation of water and thus the latent enthalpy of vaporisation, Δh_{fg}, plus [**7A**] the amount of sulfuric acid co-produced by the electrochemical reaction conducted at anode of active surface area, A_a, in m^2, with an anode current density, j_a, in A/m^2, and a Faradaic anode current efficiency, ε_a, and with the gravimetric electrochemical equivalent for sulfuric acid (547 Ah/kg). Therefore the mass and energy balance inside the cathode compartment are:

$$\Delta m_{anolyte} = (\rho_{ao}Q_{ao} - \rho_{ai}Q_{ci}) + \rho_w Q_w - \rho_{wg}Q_{wg} + (\varepsilon_a j_a A_a/E_q)[M_{SO4}/M_{Fe}]$$

$$\Delta m_{acid} = (w_{ao}\rho_{ao}Q_{ao} - w_{ai}\rho_{ai}Q_{ci}) + w_{awg}\rho_{wg}Q_{wg} + (\varepsilon_a j_a A_a/E_q)[M_{H2SO4}/M_{Fe}]$$

$$\Delta h_{anolyte} = (\rho_{ao}Q_{ao}h_{ao}\text{-}\rho_{ai}Q_{ci}h_{ai}) + \rho_w Q_w h_w\text{-}\rho_{wg}Q_{wg}h_{wg}\text{-}w_{wg}\rho_{wg}Q_{wg}\Delta h_{fg} + (\varepsilon_a j_a A_a/E_q)\Delta h_R$$

Therefore, if we consider the electric power supplied, P, in W, which is equal to the overall cell voltage defined in previous Section 8.4, U_{cell}, V, times the total current, I, in A, we have the overall energy balance for the entire electrolyser:

$$U_{cell}I = (\rho_{co}Q_{co}h_{co}\text{-}\rho_{ci}Q_{ci}h_{ci}) + \rho_{FS}Q_{FS}(h_{fs} + \Delta h_{soln})\text{-}(\varepsilon_c j_c A_c/E_q)\Delta h_R + (\rho_{ao}Q_{ao}h_{ao}\text{-}\rho_{ai}Q_{ci}h_{ai}) + \rho_w Q_w h_w\text{-}\rho_{wg}Q_{wg}h_{wg}\text{-}w_{wg}\rho_{wg}Q_{wg}\Delta h_{fg} + (\varepsilon_a j_a A_a/E_q)\Delta h_R$$

Table 41 – Mass and energy balances for the iron electrowinning cell

Compartment	Cathode (-)	Anode (+)
Energy	$\Delta h_{catholyte} = (\rho_{co}Q_{co}h_{co}\text{-}\rho_{ci}Q_{ci}h_{ci}) +$	$\Delta h_{anolyte} = (\rho_{ao}Q_{ao}h_{ao}\text{-}\rho_{ai}Q_{ci}h_{ai}) + \rho_w Q_w h_w\text{-}\rho_{wg}Q_{wg}h_{wg}\text{-}$

balance	$\rho_{FS}Q_{FS}(h_{fs} + \Delta h_{soln}) + (\varepsilon_c j_c A_c/E_q)\Delta h_R$	$w_{wg}\rho_{wg}Q_{wg}\Delta h_{fg} + (\varepsilon_a j_a A_a/E_q)\Delta h_R$
Mass balance (Electrolyte)	$(\rho_{co}Q_{co} - \rho_{ci}Q_{ci}) + \rho_{FS}Q_{FS}$ - $(\varepsilon_c j_c A_c/E_q)[M_{FeSO4}/M_{Fe}]$	$(\rho_{ao}Q_{ao} - \rho_{ai}Q_{ci}) + \rho_w Q_w$ - $\rho_{wg}Q_{wg}$ + $(\varepsilon_a j_a A_a/E_q)[M_{H2O4}/M_{Fe}]$
Mass balance (electroactive species)	$\Delta m_{iron} = (w_{co}\rho_{co}Q_{co} - w_{ci}\rho_{ci}Q_{ci})$ + $\rho_{FS}Q_{FS}$ - $(\varepsilon_c j_c A_c/E_q)$	$\Delta m_{acid} = (w_{ao}\rho_{ao}Q_{ao} - w_{ai}\rho_{ai}Q_{ci})$ + $w_{awg}\rho_{wg}Q_{wg} + (\varepsilon_a j_a A_a/E_q)[M_{H2O4}/M_{Fe}]$

10.3 Heat Transfer Calculations

Between the two compartments of a divided electrolyzer, where both catholyte and anolyte circulate co- or counter currently, if there is a temperature difference, there is always a convective heat transfer taking place across the separator of geometric surface area, A, which is characterized by an ***overall heat transfer coefficient*** U, in W.m^{-2}.K^{-1}.

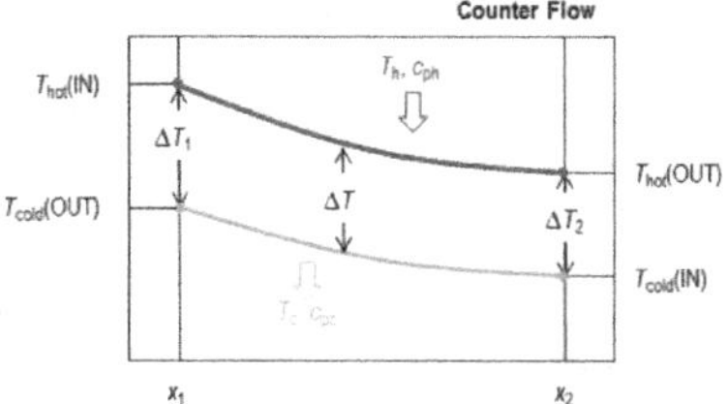

Figure 55 – Counter flow configuration

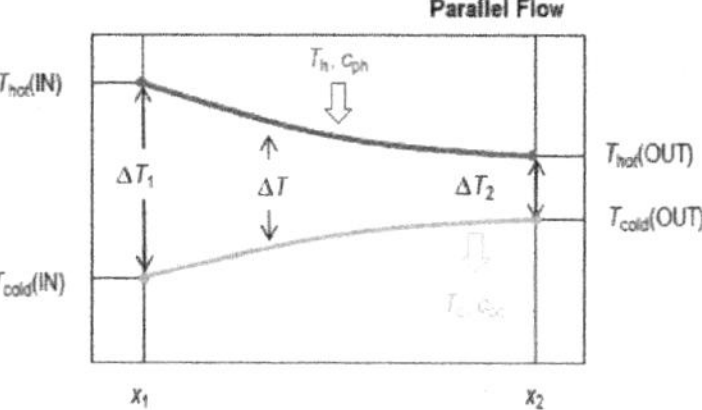

Figure 56 – Parallel flow configuration

In this particular case, the divided electrolytic cell acts as a cross flow heat exchanger, the heat flow rate being dictated by the temperature of each electrolyte using the ***logarithmic mean temperature difference***, denoted ΔT_{LMTD}, in K, depending on the two temperature approaches and configuration as follows:

$$q = FUA\Delta T_{LMTD}$$

Where

q heat rate in W (J/s),

U overall heat transfer coefficient in W.m^2.K^{-2},

A heat exchanger surface area in m^2,

F ***correction factor*** a function of parameters P and R, usually obtained graphically from correction factor charts available in the literature [96, 97].

[96] INCROPERA, F.P.; and DEWITT, D.P. (1996) *Introduction to heat transfer, Third Edition.* John Wiley and Sons, New York, NY, pp. 554-556

[97] HOLMAN, J.P. (1990) *Heat Transfer, Seventh edition.* McGraw-Hill Publishing Company, New York, NY.

These parameters are defined as follows:

$R = (T_1 - T_2)/(t_2 - t_1)$ and $P = (t_2 - t_1)/(T_1 - t_1)$

ΔT_{LMTD} Logarithmic mean temperature difference, in K.

The latter is defined below with ΔT_1 is the temperature difference between the two streams at end (1), and ΔT_2 is the temperature difference between the two streams at end (2).

$$\Delta T_{LMTD} = (\Delta T_2 - \Delta T_1)/(\ln\Delta T_2 - \ln\Delta T_1)$$

Table 42 – Counter and parallel crossflow HX

Configuration	Counter flow	Parallel-flow
Approach temperatures	$\Delta T_1 = T_{hot}$ (in) – T_{cold} (out) $\Delta T_2 = T_{hot}$ (out) – T_{cold} (in)	$\Delta T_1 = T_{hot}$ (in) – T_{cold} (in) $\Delta T_2 = T_{hot}$ (out) – T_{cold} (out)
Cross flow HX	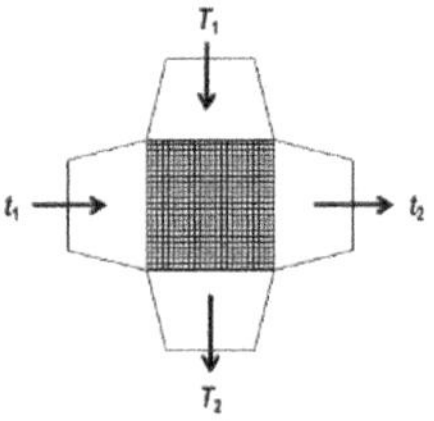 T_1, t_1, t_2, T_2	

11 Electrolytes

The chemical compositions of the electrolytes (i.e., catholyte and anolyte) are selected in order to satisfy the following technical requirements:

(i) they should allow to dissolve large amounts of the electroactive species (i.e., solute),

(ii) they must have a high ionic conductivity,

(iii) they must exhibit a low vapor pressure at the temperature required by the electrochemical process,

(iv) they must exhibit a low corrosiveness towards both electrode, membrane, piping, and cell materials.

11.1 Catholyte

The major occurrence of iron in sulfate effluents and in the pregnant leaching solutions from the nonferrous industries is in the form of iron (II) (i.e., ferrous) and/or iron (III) (i.e., ferric) sulfates usually in the hydrated form. Among them, iron (II) sulfate heptahydrate ($FeSO_4 \cdot 7H_2O$) also called ***copperas*** or ***green vitriol*** in the trade is the most common salt that can be obtained with a high purity by crystallization, and thus it will be the main raw material for preparing the catholyte. However, depending on the feed origin other non-electroactive cations might be present in significant amount (e.g., Li^+, Na^+, K^+, NH_4^+, Mg^{2+}, etc.). These cations do not represent an issue during electrowinning, and because they can even impart some beneficial effects, they will be discussed in the paragraph dealing with supporting electrolytes.

11.1.1 Solubility of Ferrous Sulfate and Density of Solutions

The solubility of ferrous sulfate in water along with the mass density of the saturated aqueous solutions obtained from experimental data available and collected from the scientific and technical literature [98, 99, 100, and 101] as a function of temperature are reported for convenience in Table 43.

---

[98] SEIDELL, A. (1919) *Solubilities of Inorganic and Organic Compounds. A Compilation of Quantitative Solubility Data from the Periodical Literature, Second Edition.* D. Van Nostrand Company, New York, NY, pp. 343-345.

[99] VOGEL, A.I. (1961) *A Textbook of Quantitative Inorganic Analysis, Third Edition.* Longman, London, U.K., Appendix A8, pages 1144-1445.

[100] BUDAVARI, S.(ed.)(1996) *The Merck Index, Twelfth Edition.* Merck & Co. Inc., Whitehouse Station, NJ, Miscellaneous Tables, Saturated Solutions, page MISC-62.

Table 43 – Solubility of $FeSO_4$ in water and mass density of solution vs. temperature

Temp.	Solubility in water					Satd. solution mass density (meas.) (kg/m^3)	Satd. solution mass density (calc.) (kg/m^3)	Hydrate at saturation	Water mass density (kg/m^3)	Solubity as concentration and molarity				
	$FeSO_4$ (wt.%)	Mass $FeSO_4$ per 100 kg H_2O	$FeSO_4.7H_2O$ (wt.%)	Mass copperas per 100 kg H_2O	Fe (wt.%)					g/L Fe	g/L $FeSO_4$	g/L copperas	mol/L Fe	eq/L Fe
0°C	13.57	15.70	24.84	33.05	4.99	1,118	1,133		999.972	57	152	278	1.012	2.025
1°C	13.80	16.00	25.25	33.78	5.07	1,140	1,136		999.898	58	157	288	1.031	2.063
10°C	17.11	20.65	31.32	45.60	6.29	1,178	1,174		999.699	74	202	369	1.322	2.644
20°C	20.95	26.51	38.35	62.21	7.70	1,220	1,220		998.204	94	256	468	1.683	3.366
21°C	21.32	27.10	39.02	63.99	7.84	1,233	1,225		997.992	96	263	481	1.719	3.437
25°C	22.99	29.86	42.08	72.65	8.45	1,255	1,246		997.045	105	289	528	1.886	3.772
30°C	24.76	32.91	45.32	82.88	9.10	1,283	1,269	**$FeSO_4.7H_2O$**	995.647	116	318	581	2.069	4.138
34°C	26.58	36.21	48.65	94.74	9.77	1,312	1,294		994.371	126	349	638	2.265	4.529
40°C	28.68	40.20	52.48	110.44	10.54	1,343	1,324		992.215	140	385	705	2.499	4.998
43°C	30.06	42.97	55.01	122.27	11.05	1,363	1,344		991.036	149	410	750	2.660	5.320
50°C	32.66	48.51	59.78	148.63	12.01	1,403	1,385		988.037	166	458	839	2.978	5.956
54°C	34.52	52.72	63.18	171.59	12.69	1,432	1,416		986.177	180	494	905	3.218	6.436
56.6°C	35.31	54.58	64.62	182.65	12.98	1,450	1,429		984.914	186	512	937	3.322	6.644
Temp.	$FeSO_4$ (wt.%)	Mass $FeSO_4$ per 100 kg H_2O	$FeSO_4.4H_2O$ (wt.%)	Mass tetrahydrate per 100 kg H_2O	Fe (wt.%)					g/L Fe	g/L $FeSO_4$		mol/L Fe	eq/L Fe
60°C	35.48	54.99	52.31	109.68	13.04	1,470	1,402	**$FeSO_4.4H_2O$**	983.200	183	522		3.273	6.547
64°C	35.73	55.61	52.69	111.36	13.14	1,450	1,405		981.970	185	518		3.304	6.609
Temp.	$FeSO_4$ (wt.%)	Mass $FeSO_4$ per 100 kg H_2O	$FeSO_4.2H_2O$ (wt.%)	Mass dihydrate per 100 kg H_2O	Fe (wt.%)									
70°C	32.78	48.77	48.34	93.56	12.05	1390	1,386		977.771	167	456		2.990	5.981
80°C	30.41	43.70	37.63	60.32	11.18	1,367	1,309	**$FeSO_4.2H_2O$**	971.799	146	416		2.620	5.241
90°C	27.23	37.42	33.69	50.81	10.01	1,270	1,256		965.321	126	346		2.251	4.503

[101] DEAN, J.A. (ed.) (1973) *Lange's Handbook of Chemistry, Eleventh Edition.* McGraw-Hill Book Company, New York, NY, Table 10.2: Solubility of inorganic compounds in water at various temperatures, page 10.8.

From these data, we can see clearly that ferrous sulfate heptahydrate exhibits a much greater solubility in hot water than most other metal sulfates. Actually, the solubility of ferrous sulfate heptahydrate (i.e., copperas) reaches a maximum at 56.6°C (130°F) with a mass percentage of 64.62 wt.% $FeSO_4.7H_2O$ (i.e., 35.31 wt.% $FeSO_4$) while above that temperature the solid phase in equilibrium with the saturated aqueous solution is the ferrous sulfate tetrahydrate ($FeSO_4.4H_2O$) with solubility reaching a maximum 35.73 wt.% $FeSO_4$ at 64°C (147.2°F). This pronounced behavior allows purifying copperas from other soluble metal sulfates (e.g., zinc and copper sulfates) by chilling and crystallization.

A practical empirical linear equation between the mass density of measured at 20°C and the mass percentage of ferrous sulfate with the two coefficients obtained from experiments is provided hereafter:

$$\rho(\text{kg/m}^3) = 14.629\, w_{FeSO4}(\text{wt.\%}) + 942.6$$

In practice, due to the unavoidable temperature changes that always occur during normal operation, and to prevent the unwanted blockages of piping lines, fittings, and valves, it is mandatory to operate at a concentration threshold well below the saturation in the temperature range 35°C to 60°C. Thus, arbitrarily the concentration was chosen safely at 75 percent of the maximum concentration of ferrous sulfate at the targeted operating temperature.

Therefore, by selecting a catholyte made of a concentrated aqueous solution of ferrous sulfate with a copperas concentration of 600 g/L and performing the electrolysis at an operating temperature of 60°C (140°F) seems a good and safe choice as it will allow to operate the electrowinning at a high cathode current density while preventing unwanted crystallization and also minimizing the water losses by evaporation. Actually, no crystallization should occur in the case the temperature drop -15°C (-27°F) below the maximum solubility temperature as the maximum solubility at 34°C is 638 g/L.

11.1.2 Electrical Conductivity of Ferrous Sulfate Solutions

The electrical conductivity of a saturated aqueous solution of ferrous sulfate vs. temperature at pH = 2.50 without a supporting electrolyte can be obtained from the practical equation below:

$$\kappa(\text{mS/cm}) = 1.201\, t(\text{C}^\circ) + 33.47$$

11.1.3 Specific Heat Capacity of Ferrous Sulfate Solutions

The ***specific heat capacity*** of an aqueous solution of ferrous sulfate with a mass fraction of $FeSO_4$, w_{FeSO4}, as a function of the absolute thermodynamic temperature, denoted $c_{psoln}(T)$, in J/kg/K, is simply given in a first approximation by the weighted average of the temperature dependent specific heat capacities of water and ferrous as follows:

$$c_{psoln}(T) = w_{FeSO4}\, c_{pFeSO4}(T) + (1 - w_{FeSO4})\, c_{pH2O}(T)$$

Each individual specific heat capacity can be calculated from practical equations where the three empirical coefficients were obtained from calorimetric experiments:

$$c_{pFeSO4}(T) = A_S + B_S T + C_S/T^2$$

$$c_{pH2O}(T) = A_w + B_w T + C_w/T^2$$

Therefore, the empirical equation for the specific heat capacity of the solution becomes simply:

$$c_{psoln}(T) = (w_{salt}\, A_S + w_{water}\, A_w) + (w_{salt}\, B_S + w_{water}\, B_w)T + (w_{salt}\, C_S + w_{water}\, C_w)/T^2$$

For convenience, we have calculated the specific heat capacity of solutions of ferrous sulfate vs. selected mass percentages, and temperatures, these are reported in Table 44.

Table 44 – Specific heat capacity of solutions of ferrous sulfate vs. temperature

Specific heat capacity of $FeSO_4$ solutions vs. mass percentage and temperature in J/(kg.K)								
Temp.	25°C	30°C	35°C	40°C	45°C	50°C	55°C	60°C
wt% $FeSO_4$	298.15 K	303.15 K	308.15 K	313.15 K	318.15 K	323.15 K	328.15 K	333.15 K
0	4,183	4,183	4,183	4,183	4,183	4,183	4,183	4,183
1	4,147	4,147	4,148	4,148	4,148	4,148	4,148	4,148
2	4,112	4,112	4,113	4,113	4,113	4,113	4,113	4,113
3	4,077	4,077	4,077	4,078	4,078	4,078	4,078	4,079
4	4,042	4,042	4,042	4,043	4,043	4,043	4,044	4,044
5	4,007	4,007	4,007	4,008	4,008	4,008	4,009	4,009
6	3,971	3,972	3,972	3,973	3,973	3,974	3,974	3,974
7	3,936	3,937	3,937	3,938	3,938	3,939	3,939	3,940
8	3,901	3,902	3,902	3,903	3,903	3,904	3,904	3,905
9	3,866	3,866	3,867	3,868	3,868	3,869	3,870	3,870
10	3,830	3,831	3,832	3,833	3,834	3,834	3,835	3,836
11	3,795	3,796	3,797	3,798	3,799	3,799	3,800	3,801
12	3,760	3,761	3,762	3,763	3,764	3,765	3,765	3,766
13	3,725	3,726	3,727	3,728	3,729	3,730	3,731	3,731
14	3,690	3,691	3,692	3,693	3,694	3,695	3,696	3,697
15	3,654	3,656	3,657	3,658	3,659	3,660	3,661	3,662
16	3,619	3,620	3,622	3,623	3,624	3,625	3,626	3,627
17	3,584	3,585	3,587	3,588	3,589	3,590	3,592	3,593
18	3,549	3,550	3,552	3,553	3,554	3,556	3,557	3,558
19	3,513	3,515	3,517	3,518	3,519	3,521	3,522	3,523
20	3,478	3,480	3,481	3,483	3,484	3,486	3,487	3,489
21	3,443	3,445	3,446	3,448	3,450	3,451	3,452	3,454
22	3,408	3,410	3,411	3,413	3,415	3,416	3,418	3,419
23	3,373	3,374	3,376	3,378	3,380	3,381	3,383	3,384
24	3,337	3,339	3,341	3,343	3,345	3,347	3,348	3,350
25	3,302	3,304	3,306	3,308	3,310	3,312	3,313	3,315
26	3,267	3,269	3,271	3,273	3,275	3,277	3,279	3,280
27	3,232	3,234	3,236	3,238	3,240	3,242	3,244	3,246
28	3,196	3,199	3,201	3,203	3,205	3,207	3,209	3,211
29	3,161	3,164	3,166	3,168	3,170	3,172	3,174	3,176
30	3,126	3,128	3,131	3,133	3,135	3,138	3,140	3,142
31	3,091	3,093	3,096	3,098	3,100	3,103	3,105	3,107
32	3,056	3,058	3,061	3,063	3,066	3,068	3,070	3,072
33	3,020	3,023	3,026	3,028	3,031	3,033	3,035	3,037
34	2,985	2,988	2,991	2,993	2,996	2,998	3,001	3,003
35	2,950	2,953	2,956	2,958	2,961	2,963	2,966	2,968

11.1.4 The Binary system: $FeSO_4-H_2O$

The exact hydrate composition with definite number of molecules of water can be determined from the examination of the solid-liquid phase diagram of the binary system: $FeSO_4-H_2O$ depicted in Figure 57.

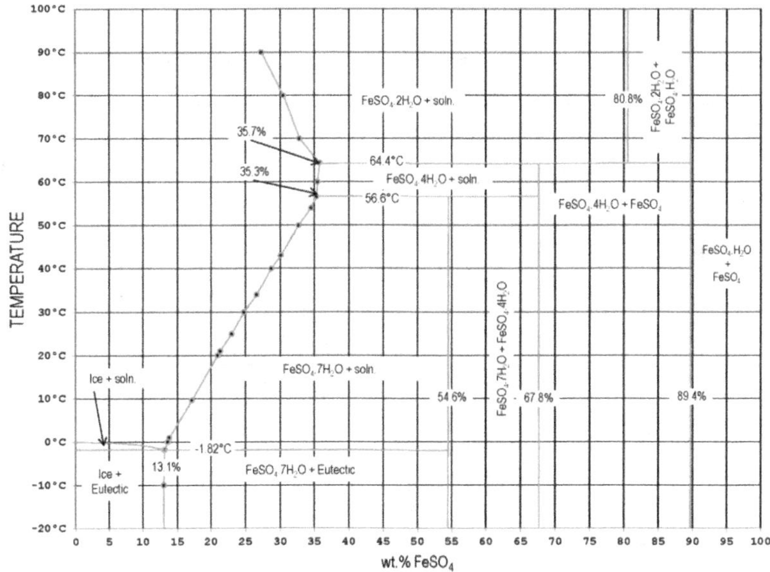

Figure 57 – Phase diagram of the binary $FeSO_4$–H_2O system

11.1.5 The Ternary System: $FeSO_4$–H_2SO_4–H_2O

The solubility of ferrous sulfate is strongly diminished by the presence of free sulfuric acid. Thus it is of paramount importance to know the phase diagram of the ternary system: H_2SO_4–$FeSO_4$–H_2O.

Historically, few comprehensive experimental studies and theoretical calculations were conducted, we can cite the pioneering work of Bullough et al. [102], who in 1952 determined the solubility of ferrous sulfate in aqueous solutions of sulfuric acid at temperatures ranging from 0°C to 100°C, and with sulfuric acid concentrations up to 50 wt.% H_2SO_4. These data allowed the authors to establish ternary phase diagrams. Later in 1992, the ternary system was revisited and modeled by Sippola [103]. Finally, more recently the ternary system was modeled by Kobylin et al. [104] who also included the ternary system H_2SO_4–$Fe_2(SO_4)_3$–H_2O. This was done in order to address the speciation of iron in acidic pregnant leach solutions originating from the hydrometallurgical

[102] BULLOUGH, W.; CANNING, T.A.; and STRAWBRIDGE, M.I. (1952) The solubility of ferrous sulphate in aqueous solutions of sulfuric acid. *Journal of Applied Electrochemistry* (JAE) **2**(12)(1952)703-707.

[103] SIPPOLA, H. (1992) *Solubility of Ferrous Sulfate in Sulfuric Acid: Thermodynamic Model* (in Finnish). Licentiate's Thesis. Helsinki University of Technology, Chemical Engineering Dept., Espoo, Finland.

[104] PETRI KOBYLIN, P.; KASKIALA, T., and SALMINEN, J. (2007) Modeling of H_2SO_4–$FeSO_4$–H_2O and H_2SO_4–$Fe_2(SO_4)_3$–H_2O systems for metallurgical applications. *Industrial & Engineering Chemical Research*, **46**(8)(2007)2601–2608.

processing of metallic ores with sulfuric acid or by sulfation. Hereafter, we have depicted in Figure 58, the schematic ternary phase diagram at 298.15K.

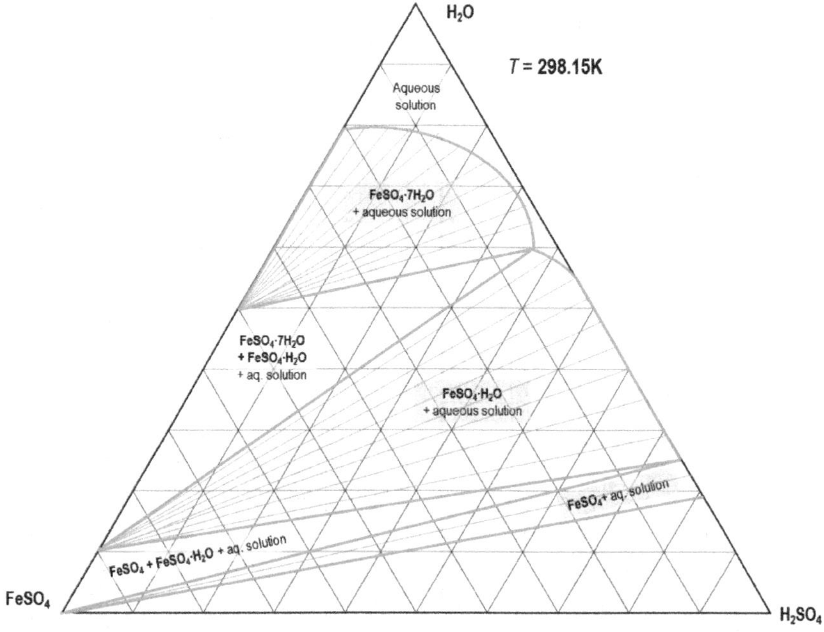

Figure 58 – Phase diagram of the ternary system: $FeSO_4-H_2SO_4-H_2O$

For certain acidic catholyte originating from pregnant leach solutions or spent pickling liquors containing both ferrous and ferric sulfates along with sulfuric acid, a thermodynamic model was developed recently by Yue et al. [105] regarding the speciation of the quaternary H_2SO_4-$Fe_2(SO_4)_3$-$FeSO_4$-H_2O system through a wide range of solution compositions and operating temperatures ranging from 25°C to 150°C.

[105] YUE, G.; Y. ZHAO, L.; OLVERA, O.; and ASSELIN, E. (2014) Speciation of the H_2SO_4-$Fe_2(SO_4)_3$-$FeSO_4$-H_2O system and development of an expression to predict the redox potential of the Fe^{3+}/Fe^{2+} couple up to 150°C. *Hydrometallurgy*. **147-148**(2014)196-209.

Table 45 – Solubility of ferrous sulfate vs. concentration of sulfuric acid

Absolute temperature	Temperature	H_2O (wt.%)	H_2SO_4 (wt.%)	$FeSO_4$ (wt.%)
273.15 K	0°C	59.23	38.05	2.72
273.15 K	0°C	56.00	41.20	2.80
273.15 K	0°C	55.18	41.96	2.86
273.15 K	0°C	54.47	43.21	2.32
273.15 K	0°C	52.66	45.83	1.51
273.15 K	0°C	41.60	57.30	1.10
273.15 K	0°C	46.92	53.04	0.04
298.15 K	25°C	66.04	21.11	12.85
298.15 K	25°C	50.60	38.40	11.00
298.15 K	25°C	59.65	30.05	10.30
298.15 K	25°C	59.58	31.37	9.05
298.15 K	25°C	58.50	34.45	7.05
298.15 K	25°C	57.39	37.80	4.81
298.15 K	25°C	54.74	42.28	2.98
298.15 K	25°C	51.24	47.47	1.29
318.15 K	45°C	63.45	13.70	22.85
318.15 K	45°C	63.09	15.90	21.01
318.15 K	45°C	62.50	19.75	17.75
318.15 K	45°C	62.35	22.00	15.65
318.15 K	45°C	61.60	25.75	12.65
328.15 K	55°C	65.10	1.50	33.40
328.15 K	55°C	65.30	3.40	31.30
328.15 K	55°C	65.25	4.35	30.40
328.15 K	55°C	65.55	4.75	29.70
328.15 K	55°C	65.05	9.10	25.85
328.15 K	55°C	65.05	11.05	23.90
328.15 K	55°C	62.85	21.80	15.35
328.15 K	55°C	60.85	30.80	8.35
328.15 K	55°C	53.78	42.76	3.46
333.15 K	60°C	66.35	1.35	32.30
333.15 K	60°C	66.33	1.97	31.70
333.15 K	60°C	66.55	2.35	31.10
333.15 K	60°C	66.40	4.85	28.75
333.15 K	60°C	66.75	6.05	27.20
333.15 K	60°C	66.20	8.40	25.40
333.15 K	60°C	66.10	10.38	23.52
333.15 K	60°C	64.28	17.60	18.12
333.15 K	60°C	63.03	21.95	15.02
333.15 K	60°C	61.98	25.50	12.52
333.15 K	60°C	59.53	32.87	7.60
333.15 K	60°C	56.48	38.96	4.56
333.15 K	60°C	51.40	46.63	1.97
333.15 K	60°C	44.77	54.58	0.65
353.15 K	80°C	71.80	1.60	26.60
353.15 K	80°C	71.82	2.00	26.18
353.15 K	80°C	71.95	2.45	25.60
353.15 K	80°C	71.65	3.75	24.60
353.15 K	80°C	71.60	4.50	23.90
353.15 K	80°C	71.02	6.88	22.10
353.15 K	80°C	70.52	8.08	21.40
353.15 K	80°C	67.62	13.88	18.50
353.15 K	80°C	64.70	20.30	15.00
353.15 K	80°C	62.12	26.40	11.48
353.15 K	80°C	60.59	30.66	8.75
353.15 K	80°C	56.90	37.75	5.35
353.15 K	80°C	52.44	44.83	2.73
353.15 K	80°C	47.30	51.57	1.13
353.15 K	80°C	43.35	56.00	0.65
373.15 K	100°C	78.33	2.97	18.70
373.15 K	100°C	76.23	5.79	17.98
373.15 K	100°C	74.14	8.24	17.62
373.15 K	100°C	71.68	11.04	17.28
373.15 K	100°C	69.94	13.28	16.78
373.15 K	100°C	67.94	16.08	15.98
373.15 K	100°C	66.10	19.10	14.80
373.15 K	100°C	64.83	21.17	14.00
373.15 K	100°C	61.67	28.38	9.95
373.15 K	100°C	57.46	35.94	6.60
373.15 K	100°C	53.98	42.19	3.83
373.15 K	100°C	52.04	44.97	2.99
373.15 K	100°C	47.53	50.85	1.62
373.15 K	100°C	42.77	56.31	0.92

11.1.6 Solubility of Metal Sulfates

The dimensionless ***solubility***, denoted S_A, of several metals sulfates reported in grams of anhydrous or hydrated salt per 100 grams of pure water as a function of temperature gathered from experimental data in the existing literature [106, 107, 108] is reported Table 46.

---

[106] VOGEL, A.I. (1961) *A Textbook of Quantitative Inorganic Analysis, Third Edition*. Longman, London, UK. In Appendix A8, pages 1144-1445.

[107] BUDAVARI, S. (ed.)(1996) *The Merck Index, 12th Edition*. Merck & Co., Whitehouse Station, NJ, Miscellaneous Tables pages MISC-62.

[108] RAHMAN, F; and SKYLLAS-KAZACOS, M. Solubility of vanadyl sulfate in concentrated sulfuric acid solutions. *Journal Power Sources*, **72**(1998)104-110.

Table 46 – Solubility of metal sulfates vs. temperature

Solubility (S_A) of anhydrous and hydrated metal sulfates in grams per 100 grams of pure water												
Substance	Formula	0°C	10°C	15°C	20°C	30°C	40°C	50°C	60°C	70°C	80°C	90°C
Aluminium sulfate	Al2(SO4)3	31.2	33.5		36.4	40.4	45.8	52.2	59.2	66.2	73.0	80.8
Aluminum ammonium sulfate	$NH_4Al(SO_4)_2.12H_2O$	2.6	4.5		6.6	9.0	12.4	15.9	21.1	26.9	35.2	50.3
Aluminum potassium sulfate	$KAl(SO_4)_2.12H_2O$	3.0	4.0		5.9	7.9	11.7	17.0	25.0	40.0	71.0	109.0
Aluminum sodium sulfate	$NaAl(SO_4)_2.12H_2O$	56.2	60.5		61.5	66.7						
Ammonium sulfate	(NH4)2SO4	70.6	73.0		75.4	78.1	81.2	84.3	87.4		94.1	
Cadmium sulfate	$CdSO_4$	75.4	76.0	76.6		78.5		81.8		66.7	63.1	60.8
Chromium(III) sulfate	Cr2(SO4)3.18H2O			220.0								
Cobalt(II) sulfate	$CoSO_4$	25.5	30.5	36.1	42.0	48.8		55.0		53.8	45.3	38.9
Copper(II) sulfate	CuSO4.5H2O	23.1	27.5	32.0	37.8	44.6		61.8		83.8		114.0
Ferrous ammonium sulfate	(NH4)2Fe(SO4)2.6H2O			26.9						73.0		
Iron(II) sulfate	$FeSO_4$			28.8		40.0	48.0	60.0	73.3		101.0	79.9
Iron(III) sulfate	Fe2(SO4)3.9H2O											
Lithium sulfate	Li_2SO_4	36.1	35.5	34.8	34.2	33.7		32.6		31.4	30.9	
Magnesium sulfate	$MgSO_4$	25.5	30.4	35.1	39.7	44.7	50.4	54.8	59.2	54.8	52.9	50.2
Manganese(II) sulfate	$MnSO_4$	52.9	59.7	62.9	62.9	60.0		53.6		45.6	40.9	35.3
Nickel(II) sulfate	NiSO4.6H2O	28.1	33.0		44.4	46.6	49.2	55.6		64.5	70.1	76.7
Potassium sulfate	K_2SO_4	7.4	9.3	11.1	13.0	14.8		18.2		21.4	22.9	24.1
Sodium sulfate	Na_2SO_4	4.9	9.1	19.5	40.8	48.8		45.3		43.7	42.7	42.5
Zinc sulfate	$ZnSO_4$	41.6	47.2	53.8	61.3	70.5		75.4		71.1		60.5

The relationship between the mass percentage of a solute A, denoted w_A, in mass percent, and the solubility described above can be calculated using the simple equation:

$$w_A = 1/(1 + 100/S_A)$$

Similarly the relationship between the molality of a solute A (i.e., the number of moles of solute per one kilogram of water), denote b_A, in mol/kg, and the dimensionless solubility defined above can be calculated knowing the molar mass in kg/mol, using the simple equation:

$$b_A = S_A/(10M_A)$$

11.1.7 Dissociation Constants of Metal Sulfates

Let's consider a metal sulfate of a multivalent metal cation M^{z+} with the chemical formula, $M_2(SO_4)_z$, dissolved into water, the reaction of dissociation is written as follows:

$$M_2(SO_4)_z = 2M^{z+} + zSO_4^{2-}$$

If we introduce the dimensionless ***degree of ionization***, denoted α, defined as the activity of the metal cation (resp. sulfate anions) over the initial molarity (activity) of the salt denoted C_{salt}, in mol/L upon dissociation, the molarity of the undissolved metal sulfate is $C_{salt}(1 - \alpha)$ while the molarities of the metal cations, and sulfate anions are as follows:

$$(M^{z+}) = 2\alpha C_{salt} \quad \text{and} \quad (SO_4^{2-}) = z\alpha C_{salt}$$

The ***dissociation constant*** of the salt denoted K_d, is given by:

$$K_d = (M^{z+})^2(SO_4^{2-})^z/(M_2(SO_4)_z)$$

Replacing the activities of the cations and anions by the equations involving the degree of dissociation we obtain the general ***Ostwald equation***:

$$K_d = (2\alpha C_{salt})^2(z\,\alpha C_{salt})^z/[C_{salt}(1 - \alpha)] = 2^2z^z\ \alpha^{(2+z)}C_{salt}^{(2+z-1)}/(1 - \alpha)$$

For a symmetric 2-2 metal sulfate MSO_4, the above equation becomes:

$$K_d(MSO_4) = \alpha^2C_{salt}^2/(1 - \alpha)$$

The resolution of the above quadratic equation allows calculating the degree of dissociation. In the particular case of diluted aqueous solutions, the degree of dissociation is usually much smaller than unity, thus the degree of dissociation is simply the square root of the ratio of the dissociation constant and molarity of the salt:

$$\alpha \approx [K_d(MSO_4)/C_{salt}]^{0.5} \text{ (diluted electrolyte)}$$

Table 47 – Dissociation constant and degree of dissociation of metal sulfates

$pK_{dissociation} = \text{colg}_{10}(M^{z+})^2(SO_4^{2-})^z$			C_{salt} = 1.0 M	
Metal sulfate	Formula	$pK_{dissociation}$	$K_{dissociation}$	α
Ammonium sulfate	$NH_4SO_4^-$	1.1	0.0794	28%
Cadmium sulfate	$CdSO_4$	2.31	0.0049	7%
Chromium (II) sulfate	CrSO4	1.30	0.0501	22%
Cobalt(II) sulfate	$CoSO_4$	2.25	0.0056	7%
Copper(II) sulfate	CuSO4	2.30	0.0050	7%
Iron(II) sulfate	$FeSO_4$	0.00	1.0000	100%
Lithium sulfate	$LiSO_4^-$	0.60	0.2512	50%
Magnesium sulfate	$MgSO_4$	2.30	0.0050	7%
Manganese(II) sulfate	$MnSO_4$	2.30	0.0050	7%
Nickel(II) sulfate	NiSO4	2.39	0.0041	6%
Potassium sulfate	KSO_4^-	1.00	0.1000	32%
Sodium sulfate	$NaSO_4^-$	0.70	0.1995	45%
Vanadyl sulfate	VOSO4	1.80	0.0158	13%
Zinc sulfate	$ZnSO_4$	2.28	0.0052	7%

11.1.8 Electrical Conductivity of Metal Sulfates

The electrical conductivities of aqueous solutions in S/m of the single metal sulfates (i.e., $FeSO_4$, $VOSO_4$, $NiSO_4$, $MnSO_4$) as a function of the concentration of salts found in the technical literature are reported for convenience in Table 48.

Table 48 – Electrical conductivity of solutions metal sulfates in S/m at 20°C

Mass percent of $M_x(SO_4)_y$	3.65	5.0	7.15	10.40	13.4	17.5	19.0
$(NH_4)_2SO_4$		5.52	7.38	10.20	n.a.	n.a.	17.50
$CuSO_4$	1.46	1.89	2.45	3.20	3.89	4.58	-
$FeSO_4$	1.54	1.95	2.58	3.27	3.90	4.42	4.61
K_2SO_4	n.a.	4.58	6.19	8.63	-	-	-
Li_2SO_4	n.a.	4.00	4.84	6.12	-	-	-
$MgSO_4$	n.a.	2.63	3.23	4.15	4.59	4.78	4.70
$MnSO_4$	n.a.	1.90	2.62	3.72	3.83	3.95	5.03
Na_2SO_4	n.a.	4.09	5.21	6.90	8.22	-	-
$NiSO_4$	1.54	1.92	2.53	3.22	3.85	4.34	4.52
Zn_2SO_4	n.a.	1.91	2.47	3.29	3.84	4.31	4.48

As for the supporting electrolyte, we expect that the overall electrical conductivity is obtained from the contribution of all ionic species as all ions participate positively by either electro-migration or/and diffusion to the overall electrical conductivity of the electrolyte unless some association between ionic species occurs.

11.1.9 Influence of the pH and Precipitation

The pH dependence of the solubility of metal hydroxides, with the general chemical formula $M(OH)_z$ is of paramount importance and the pH of the catholyte must be controlled accurately. The precipitation pH for several metal hydroxides gathered from the literature [109, 110,] are reported in Table 49.

The ***solubility product*** for a given metal hydroxide, denoted K_s, is described by the following chemical equilibrium for the precipitation reaction as follows:

$$M^{z+} + zOH^- = M(OH)_z(s)$$

[109] POURBAIX, M. (1966) *Atlas of electrochemical equilibria in aqueous solutions.* CEBELCOR, Brussels, Belgium, pp. .

[110] CHARLOT, G. (1963) *L'analyse qualitative et les reactions en solutions, cinquième edition.* Masson & Cie, Paris, France, pp. .

As $M(OH)_z(s)$ is a solid, its activity is equal to unity, the ***Gulden-Waage law of mass action*** can thus be written simply as follows:

$$K_s = (M^{z+})(OH^-)^z$$

The solubility of the metal hydroxide denoted s, in mol/m^3, can be calculated using the molarity of the metal cation and the hydroxyl anions:

$$s = (M^{z+}) \qquad \text{or} \qquad s = (OH^-)/z$$

By substituting the ion activities by the above equivalences, we can calculate the solubility as a function of the solubility product: $K_s = z^z s^{z+1}$. Thus the solubility is simply: $s = [K_s/z^z]^{1/z+1}$.

On the other hand, we can rearrange the solubility product as follows leaving the activity of hydroxyl anion unchanged:

$$s = K_s/(OH^-)^z$$

If we introduce the auto-protolysis constant for pure water defined as:

$$K_w = (H^+)(OH^-) = 10^{-14} \qquad \text{STP (298.15 K, 101.325 kPa)}$$

Then, after replacing the activity of hydroxyl anions, the solubility can be rewritten as follows:

$$s = K_s/[K_w/(H^+)]^z$$

Taking the Briggs logarithm of the above equation, and based on the three usual definitions: $pK_w = \text{colog}_{10}K_w$, $pK_s = \text{colog}_{10}K_s$, and $pH = \text{colog}_{10}(H^+)$, we finally obtain the pH dependence equation of the solubility product:

$$\log_{10}s = z\,pK_w - pK_s - z\,pH$$

Moreover, for some amphoteric metal cations (e.g., Al^{3+}, Zn^{2+}) forming soluble hydroxo-complexes at high pH, these equilibria must be taken into account. However, because the electrowinning of iron is always performed at pH below 4.0 the behavior of metal hydroxides for alkaline pH is of no concern. If the reader is interested to know more, we recommend on the subject the textbook from Charlot [111] along with the didactic review article by Scholz and Kahlert [112].

---

[111] CHARLOT, G. (1963) *L'analyse qualitative et les reactions en solutions, cinquième edition. Chapite X: Solubilité et Acidité.* Masson & Cie, Paris, France, pp. 90-95.

[112] SCHOLZ, F.; and KAHLERT, H. (2015) The calculation of the solubility of metal hydroxides, oxide-hydroxides, and oxides, and their visualisation in logarithmic diagrams. *ChemTexts* (2015)1-7.

Table 49 – Precipitation pH of selected metal hydroxides

Metal cation	Precipitation reaction (Hydrolysis)	pH (*) (Start)	pH (**) (End)	Precipitate color	Solubility constant (pK_S)
Titanium (IV)	$TiO^{2+} + H_2O = TiO(OH)_2 + 2H^+$	0.5	w/o	White	29.00
Manganese (IV)	$Mn^{4+} + 2H_2O = MnO_2 + 4H^+$	0.5	13	White	32.89
Tin (II)	$Sn^{2+} + 2OH^- = Sn(OH)_2$	0.5	9.0	White	26.26
Vanadium (V)	$2VO_2^+ + OH^- = V_2O_5 + H^+$	1.8	3.0	Reddish brown	14.70
Iron (III)	$Fe^{3+} + 3OH^- = Fe(OH)_3$	2.0	w/o	Reddish brown	38.80
Titanium (III)	$Ti^{3+} + 3OH^- = Ti(OH)_3$	3.0	w/0	Violet	37.50
Aluminum (III)	$Al^{3+} + 3OH^- = Al(OH)_3$	3.9	12.0	White	32.89
Vanadium (IV)	$2VO^{2+} + 2H_2O = VO(OH)_2 + 4H^+$	4.0	8.5	Gray brown	22.13
Vanadium (III)	$V^{3+} + 3OH^- = V(OH)_3$	4.5	12.0	Green	2.90
Chromium (III)	$Cr^{3+} + 3OH^- = Cr(OH)_3$	5.0	12.5	Gray	30.20
Copper (II)	$Cu^{2+} + 2OH^- = Cu(OH)_2$	5.2	w/o	Bluish	19.32
Zinc (II)	$Zn^{2+} + 2OH^- = \beta\text{-}Zn(OH)_2$	6.5	14.0	White	16.20
Nickel (II)	$Ni^{2+} + 2OH^- = Ni(OH)_2$	7.0	16.2	Pale green	15.26
Cobalt (II)	$Co^{2+} + 2OH^- = Co(OH)_2$	7.5	17.0	Pink	14.90
Lead (II)	$Pb^{2+} + 2OH^- = Pb(OH)_2$	7.5	13.0	White	15.30
Iron (II)	$Fe^{2+} + 2OH^- = Fe(OH)_2$	7.5	w/o	Pale green	16.31
Cadmium (II)	$Cd^{2+} + 2OH^- = \beta\text{-}Cd(OH)_2$	8.0	w/o	White	14.35
Manganese (II)	$Mn^{2+} + 2OH^- = Mn(OH)_2$	8.5	17.0	Pink	12.80

Notes: (*) pH for the beginning of precipitation for a solution with a molarity of 0.01M; (**) alkaline pH for the re-dissolution of amphoteric species.

From the above table, we can see clearly that the pH of the catholyte at least of the beginning must be maintained below 1.5. This precaution is mandatory especially for aerated catholyte, in in order to avoid the precipitation of Fe^{3+}. By contrast, for fully reduced solutions of ferrous sulfate, the pH can be much higher because ferrous hydroxide does not precipitate below pH 5.5

On the other hand, because the cathode potential for the hydrogen evolution reaction decreases as $(RT\ln 10/F)\log_{10}(H^+)$ or $-(RT\ln 10/F)$pH (i.e., -59.1 mV/pH at 25°C) it is necessary to keep the highest pH possible which is compatible with the chemistry of metal cations present, and ideally approaching 3.5. This implies to adjust constantly the acidity of the catholyte accordingly by adding sulfuric acid, ammonium hydroxide, sodium hydroxide, or magnesia.

11.1.10 Supporting Electrolytes

The utilization of a ***supporting electrolyte*** also called ***base electrolyte*** or ***indifferent electrolyte*** is extremely important because it allows: (i) to increase the ionic conductivity (i.e., to reduce ohmic drop) of the electrolyte solution despite the depletion of electroactive species, (ii) to neglect the mass transfer by electromigration of electroactive species because their transference number become zero, and all the electric current is carried by electro-inactive ions, (iii) to stabilize the diffusion coefficients of electroactive species, and finally (iv) to fix the ionic strength of the electrolyte solution allowing to use molarities in spite of thermodynamic activities.

The proper selection of a supporting electrolyte requires choosing the solute with strong inorganic salts because they are totally ionized and they provide a solution with a high ionic conductivity. In order to obtain the wider electrochemical span, careful selection of constituting cations and anions must be conducted. On the anode side, most electronegative elements with anions difficult to oxidize (e.g., SO_4^{2-}) are desired while on the cathodic side, most electropositive elements such as alkali-metals (e.g., Li^+, Na^+, K^+) having cations not easily reduced or ammoniums (NH_4^+) represent a good choice. The minimum molarity should be at least 0.1 mol/L.

A catholyte made of copperas in water "as is" with a fixed pH around 2.5 has an ionic conductivity around 51.5 mS/m at 20°C therefore the addition of a supporting electrolyte can be beneficial to increase the conductivity and thus reduce the ohmic drop inside the cathode compartment. Actually, most of the current will be carried by the electromigration of the alkali-metal cation instead of the electroactive species.

At this point, it is worth to mention that depending on the origin of iron sulfate(s) several non-electroactive cations (e.g., Li^+, Na^+, K^+, NH_4^+, Mg^{2+}, Al^{3+}, etc.) might be present in significant amount and their presence improve the electrical conductivity. However, if upon recirculation a build-up of such cations occurs in the solution, it will be necessary to perform a bleed periodically and recover the copperas by fractional crystallization.

11.1.10.1 Ammonium Sulfate

Ammonium sulfate represents an excellent supporting electrolyte as the double salt of ammonium iron (II) sulfate hexahydrate with CAS No. [7783-85-9], also called ***Mohr's salt***, with the chemical formula $(NH_4)_2Fe(SO_4)_2(H_2O)_6$ readily dissolves into water to yield the stable octahedral aquo-complex $[Fe(H_2O)_6]^{2+}$. The graph of the solubility in water at 30°C of ferrous sulfate in the presence of ammonium sulfate is depicted in Figure 59.

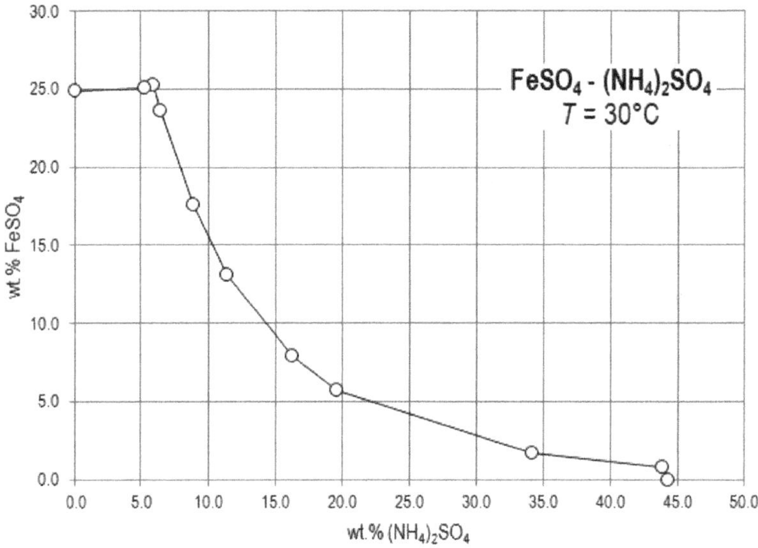

Figure 59 – Solubility of $FeSO_4$ in water vs. $(NH_4)_2SO_4$

The plot shows that up to a 6 mass percent of ammonium sulfate in the solution does not affect the solubility of ferrous sulfate that remains almost identical to that of a pure solution of copperas. Therefore, it is advantageous to use ammonium sulfate as supporting electrolyte where the electrowinning plant location permits. This is especially true if there is proximity with an ammonia plant or a fertilizer plant. In the former cases gaseous ammonia can be injected directly into the catholyte while in the latter case ammonium sulfate can be used instead.

It is worth mentioned however that we did observed that when electrowinning is performed at elevated cathode current density some ammonium cations can be reduced at the cathode yielding hydrazine, NH_2-NH_2. For such operating conditions, it is suitable to use an alkali-metal cation instead.

11.1.10.2 Sodium Sulfate

Because often the pH adjustment of pregnant leach solutions, weak acids and liquid effluents uses sodium hydroxide lye in the metallurgical industries, sodium sulfate, Na_2SO_4, is a ubiquitous alkali-metal sulfate often found by default. Recently, the trials regarding the sulfuric acid leaching or the sulfuric acid digestion sulfation of bauxite residues discussed in Section 2.4.1 will co-produce along with the iron sulfate(s) large amounts of sodium sulfate. Moreover, sodium sulfate is also a cheap chemical ($110/tonne) and it is largely available commercially that also explains it is widely used as supporting electrolyte. However, the solubility curve for sodium sulfate shows a step increase with temperature thus this could lead to the crystallization of sodium sulfate decahydrate, $Na_2SO_4.10H_2O$ (i.e., Glaubert's salt) especially in warm concentrated solutions of ferrous sulfate can cause unwanted blockages of piping and pumps and it must be addressed carefully.

11.1.10.3 Potassium Sulfate

Potassium sulfate, K_2SO_4, is more expensive than its counterpart sodium sulfate ($400/tonne) but it exhibits a slower increase of its solubility with temperature, and it does not form hydrates that could crystalize upon cooling or due to salting out effects. When compared to sodium sulfate, potassium sulfate brings a beneficial effect as supporting electrolyte as it increases the cathode current efficiency, and the morphology of the iron electrodeposit.

11.1.10.4 Magnesium Sulfate

Magnesium sulfate heptahydrate (i.e., Epsom's salt) with the chemical formula $MgSO_4.7H_2O$ not only exhibits the same crystal structure as copperas but also exhibits a high solubility in water.

11.1.10.5 Aluminum Sulfate

Aluminum sulfate is a ubiquitous metal sulfate presents in pregnant leach solutions produced from the sulfuric acid digestion of bauxite for the production of aluminum sulfate and alum. When added in minute amount to the catholyte, it improves the cathode current efficiency especially at low pH.

11.1.10.6 Lithium Sulfate

As for ammonium sulfate minute additions of lithium sulfate to a concentrated aqueous solution of ferrous sulfate does not affect the solubility of the latter up to 3.5 mass percent (see Figure 60).

However, lithium sulfate, Li_2SO_4, is not a common sulfate due to its scarcity and elevates cost ($7,500/tonne). This having been said, it is found in pregnant leach solutions that are produced commercially in the lithium industry from the sulfuric acid roasting of spodumene concentrates using the ***acid-roast***

process invented by Ellestad and Leute [113]. At present, all the iron contaminant is removed by neutralization with limestone, and precipitated as hydroxide along with gypsum. But in the future, the electrowinning iron and regeneration of sulfuric acid value could represent a solution to avoid neutralization and disposal costs.

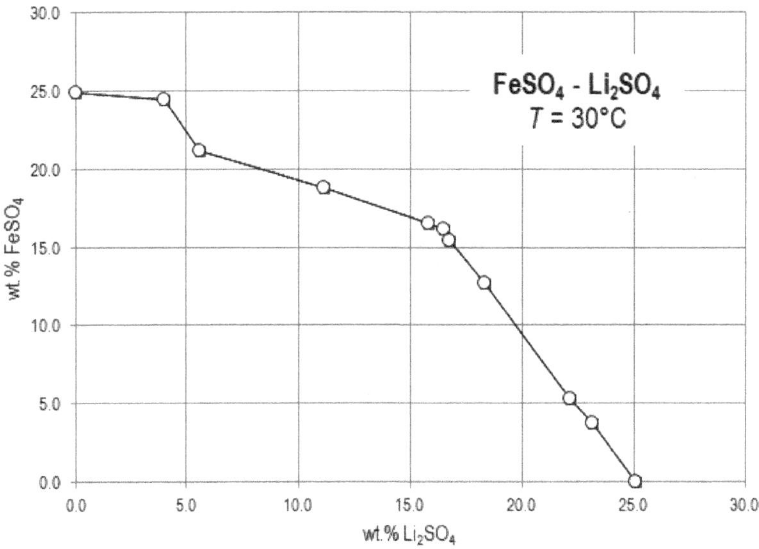

Figure 60 – Solubility of $FeSO_4$ in water vs. Li_2SO_4

11.1.11 Additives

11.1.11.1 Buffering Agents

Because the pH among other parameters is critical for obtaining an excellent cathode current efficiency, we have assessed the effect of buffering agents on the cathode current efficiency and the characteristics of the iron metal deposit thus obtained.

Actually, buffers are commonly used in electroplating baths in order to keep the pH constant. The role of buffers is especially relevant as at the cathode surface the pH raises due to the unavoidable hydrogen evolution that consumes hydrogen cations, and creates locally a much higher pH than in the bulk of the catholyte. For instance, this alkaline thin layer can reach a pH up to 6.0 while the catholyte still exhibits a pH of 2.0. At such elevate pH the ferrous cations in the catholyte is prone to fast air oxidation into Fe(III) that will precipitate as greenish-

[113] ELLESTAD, R.B.; and LEUTE, K.M. (1950) *Method of Extracting Lithium Values from Spodumene Ores.* U.S. Patent Application 2,516,109 (Metalloy Corporation), July 25th, 1950.

brown flocks of ferrous-ferric hydroxide $Fe(OH)_2$-FeOOH and contaminate the deposited iron metal.

In electrowinning the utilization of buffers is usually less pronounced as they introduce additional chemicals and the treatment of the spent liquors can pose environmental issues. In the particular case of the electrowinning of iron one possible buffering agent that was tested successfully is boric acid, H_3BO_3 however when using anion exchange membrane boric acid tends to contaminate the anolyte.

11.1.11.2 Surfactants

Surfactants such as sodium dodecylbenzenesulfonate, sodium lauryl sulfate, saponins, or proprietary formulations such as Dowfax® and Tergitol® (Trademarks of *Dow*), can be used as protective foam blankets as they provide a viable mean for reducing mists, and to prevent the air oxidation of the catholyte.

11.1.11.3 Levelling and Brightening Agents

Brighteners such as sodium lauryl sulfate or thiourea $(NH_2)_2CS$, improve the morphology of electrolytic iron.

11.1.11.4 Complexing Agents

Because ammonium cations form relatively stable complexes with Fe(II) they exhibit the effect of suppressing the precipitation of iron hydroxide. Similarly EDTA is a strong complexing agent preventing the precipitation of metal hydroxides.

A concise list of additives, complexing, and buffering agents are reported in Table 50 hereafter.

Table 50 – Proposed buffering agents and additives to improve deposition

Buffering agent	Benefits
Aluminum (III) cations	Increases the cathode current efficiency at low pH
Ammonium sulfate	Form relatively stable and soluble complexes with Fe(II)
Boric acid	Buffer and extends bath service life
Citric acid	Cracks reducer
EDTA	Complexing agent preventing the precipitation of metal hydroxides
Glycine	Smooth metal deposits
Sodium dodecylbenzenesulfonate	Surfactant
Sodium lauryl sulfate	Brightener
Urea	Prevents the precipitation of metal hydroxides

11.1.12 Electroactive Impurities

Finally, in the catholyte, the presence of reducible metals as impurities also affects the cathode current efficiency. Some metallic impurities are simply reduced to a lower oxidation state [e.g., Fe(III), V(IV, V), Ti(IV)] thus consuming a fraction of the circulating current. Others are reduced even further down to the metallic element [e.g., Cu(II), Cr(III), Ni(II), Zn(II), Mn(II)].

In the latter case, the foreign electrodeposited metal can promote the hydrogen gas evolution (e.g., Ni) and thus postpones the deposition of metallic iron or conversely it can form a co-deposit with iron forming an ***iron-rich alloy*** [e.g., Cr(III), Ni(II), Zn(II), Mn(II)].

The list of these reducible metallic impurities often encountered in iron-rich effluents, pregnant leach solutions (PLS), and spent pickling liquors (SPLs) ordered by half-redox reaction potentials are reported in Table 51.

Table 51 – Half electrochemical reactions related to impurities

$VO_2^+ + 2H^+ + e^- = VO^{2+} + H_2O$
$Fe^{3+} + e^- = Fe^{2+}$
$Cu^{2+} + 2e^- = Cu(s)$
$VO^{2+} + 2H^+ + e^- = V^{3+} + H_2O$
$TiO^{2+} + 2H^+ + e^- = Ti^{3+} + H_2O$
$V^{3+} + e^- = V^{2+}$
$Ni^{2+} + 2e^- = Ni(s)$
$Cr^{3+} + 3e^- = Cr(s)$
$Zn^{2+} + 2e^- = Zn(s)$
$Ti^{3+} + e^- = Ti^{2+}$
$V^{2+} + 2e^- = V(s)$
$Mn^{2+} + 2e^- = Mn(s)$

11.1.13 Practical Catholyte Composition and Properties

From experiments and technical considerations, the suitable catholyte consists of a warm aqueous solution of ferrous sulfate.

Actually, in order to electrowin iron at the maximum cathode current density, it is important to operate with the highest concentration of ferrous sulfate in the catholyte to maintain the highest limiting current possible.

Therefore, operating at concentration of ferrous sulfate near the saturation concentration will meet these requirements. However, in order to avoid blockage issues by crystallization during temperature drops, it was decided arbitrarily to use a saturated solution of ferrous sulfate at room temperature that correspond to the under saturated solution at the operating temperature.

The initial catholyte is usually prepared above 30°C and it must contain a maximum of 26.6 mass percent of $FeSO_4$ (i.e., 326 g/L $FeSO_4$) or when expressed as total ferrous iron 116 g/L Fe(II) or nearly 2.2 M. If needed a maximum of 5 wt.% $(NH_4)_2SO_4$ can be added to be used as both complexing agent and supporting electrolyte, along with minor amounts of additives as already discussed in Section 11.1.11. The suitable pH should be at least 2.5 with an operating temperature ranging between 50 and 60°C.

The composition, physical and chemical properties of the catholyte vs. the operating temperature are reported in Table 52 assuming that the reducible metals have a maximum concentration of 1 mg/L (i.e., 1 ppm w/v).

Table 52 – Composition and selected properties of the catholyte vs. temperature

4_CATHOLYTE PROPERTIES	25°C	30°C	40°C	50°C	54°C	60°C	70°C	80°C	90°C
Maximum solubility of copperas (wt.%)	42.1	45.3	52.5	59.8	63.2				
Maximum solubility of ferrous sulfate (wt.%)	23.0	24.8	28.7	32.7	35.3	35.5	32.8	30.4	27.2
Maximum solubility of ferrous cations (wt.%)	8.5	9.1	10.5	12.0	13.0	13.0	12.1	11.2	10.0
Mass density of saturated solution (ρ_{std}/kg.m^{-3})	1.255	1.283	1.343	1.403	1.432	1.470	1.390	1.367	1.270
Maximum concentration of copperas (g/L)	528	581	705	839	905				
Maximum concentration of ferrous sulfate (g/L)	289	318	385	458	506	522	456	416	346
Maximum concentration of ferrous cations (g/L)	106	117	142	168	186	192	168	153	127
Mass percentage of copperas (wt.%)	36.3	39.1	45.3	51.6	55.8	56.0	51.8	48.0	43.0
Mass percentage of ferrous sulfate anhydrous (wt.%)	**17.2**	**18.6**	**21.5**	**24.5**	**26.5**	**26.6**	**24.6**	**22.8**	**20.4**
Mass percentage of iron (wt.%)	6.3	6.8	7.9	9.0	9.7	9.8	9.0	8.4	7.5
Concentration of ferrous sulfate anhydrous (g/L)	185	203	246	293	324	334	292	266	221
Concentration of ferrous iron (Fe^{2+}) (g/L)	**68**	**75**	**91**	**108**	**119**	**123**	**107**	**98**	**81**
Mass density of catholyte (ρ_{CA}/kg.m^{-3})	1,176	1,196	1,239	1,283	1,312	1,313	1,284	1,258	1,223
SUPPORTING ELECTROLYTE									
Mass percentage of ammonium sulfate (anhydrous)	5.0	5.0	5.0	5.0	5.0	5.0	5.0	5.0	5.0
Concentration of ammonium (g/L)	59	60	62	64	66	66	64	63	61
Operating pH (min)	2.50	2.50	2.50	2.50	2.50	2.50	2.50	2.50	2.50
ORP (V/MSSA) with (Fe^{3+})/(Fe^{2+}) = 10^{-6}	-1.109	-1.108	-1.106	-1.104	-1.103	-1.103	-1.105	-1.106	-1.109
ORP (V/AgCl) with (Fe^{3+})/(Fe^{2+}) = 10^{-6}	-0.679	-0.679	-0.678	-0.676	-0.674	-0.674	-0.675	-0.676	-0.677
Catholyte electrical conductivity (κ_{ca}/S.m^{-1})	5.1	5.7	6.9	8.1	8.6	9.3	10.5	11.7	12.9
Catholyte electrical conductivity (κ_{an}/S.m^{-1})[pH = 2.5]	7.0	7.7	9.5	10.9	11.4	12.3	13.7	15.1	16.5
Catholyte specific heat capacity (c_P/J.K^{-1}.kg^{-1})	3,575	3,530	3,430	3,329	3,262	3,259	3,332	3,397	3,481
Catholyte mass density (ρ_{ca}/kg.m^{-3})	1,250	1,247	1,239	1,226	**1,211**	1,193	1,170	1,142	1,110
Catholyte dynamic viscosity (η_{ca}/mPa.s)	1.50	1.20	1.00	0.82	0.77	0.70	0.61	0.53	0.47
Catholyte kinematic viscosity (ν_{ca}/m^2.s^{-1})	1.20E-06	9.62E-07	8.09E-07	6.72E-07	6.37E-07	5.90E-07	5.21E-07	4.68E-07	4.28E-07
Diffusion coefficient of Fe^{2+} (D/m^2.s^{-1})	7.19E-10	9.12E-10	1.12E-09	1.39E-09	1.49E-09	1.64E-09	1.91E-09	2.18E-09	2.46E-09
H_2O vapor pressure above solution (π/mmHg)	21.68	27.98	48.68	81.76	92.22	131.26	206.27	312.78	462.79
Partial pressure of hydrogen gas (p_{H2}/mmHg)	738.32	732.02	711.32	678.24	667.78	628.74	553.73	447.22	297.21
Molarity of Fe^{2+}(/mol.m^{-3})	1216	1339	1622	1931	2130	2197	1920	1752	1457
Molarity of SO_4^{2-}(/mol.m^{-3})	1222	1345	1629	1937	2137	2204	1926	1758	1463
Molarity of H^+(/mol.m^{-3})	3.16	3.2	3.2	3.2	3.2	3.2	3.2	3.2	3.2
Coefficient activity of Fe^{2+}	1.000	1.000	1.000	1.000	1.000	1.000	1.000	1.000	1.000
Coefficient activity of SO_4^{2-}	1.000	1.000	1.000	1.000	1.000	1.000	1.000	1.000	1.000
Coefficient activity of H^+	1.000	1.000	1.000	1.000	1.000	1.000	1.000	1.000	1.000
Activity of Fe^{2+}(/mol.m^{-3})	1215.7	1338.5	1622.5	1930.7	2130.2	2197.2	1919.9	1751.6	1457.1
Activity of SO_4^{2-}(/mol.m^{-3})	1222.0	1344.9	1628.8	1937.1	2136.5	2203.5	1926.2	1757.9	1463.4
Activity of H^+(/mol.m^{-3})	3.2	3.2	3.2	3.2	3.2	3.2	3.2	3.2	3.2
Osmolarity (/mol.m^{-3})	4,879	5,370	6,506	7,739	8,537	8,805	7,695	7,022	5,844
Ionic strength (I/mol.m^{-3})	4,877	5,368	6,504	7,737	8,535	8,803	7,694	7,020	5,843

11.1.14 Reducing and Dummying the Catholyte

For obtaining the best iron deposits from pure copperas, and for the reasons explained previously in Section 11.1.9, it is good practice to perform the electrowinning of iron from a fully reduced catholyte, that is, with no detectable traces of ferric iron cations (i.e., [Fe(III)]/[Fe(II)] below 10^{-4}). In this case, the electrowinning of iron can be performed safely until pH 6.0 at room temperature.

Actually, when traces of ferric actions are present colloidal particles of the reddish brown ferric hydroxide, $Fe(OH)_3$, starts to precipitate at pH 2.5 forming flocs resulting in a voluminous sludge while if all the iron is only present as Fe^{2+}, the greenish ferrous hydroxide, $Fe(OH)_2$, precipitates at pH above 6.0. Conversely, if both iron species are present, the ferroso-ferric precipitate precipitates at pH 3.5. The presence of ferric hydroxide is also impacting the quality of the electrolytic iron deposit as tiny inclusions of embedded particles inside the iron metal yield dark-colored electrodeposits. Note that even clean aqueous solutions of copperas originating from the titanium pigment industry may contain ferric cations if the pH of the solution is not enough acidic to prevent the rapid air oxidation. Moreover, when operating at higher bath temperature, the formation of sludge due to air oxidation becomes a serious issue limiting the maximum operating temperature of 60°C. Moreover, spent pickling liquors, and most pregnant leach solutions contains both ferric and ferrous iron along with vanadium, titanium, and in a lesser extent some manganese and traces of chromium as metal sulfates that could precipitate.

This means that if the catholyte is slightly oxidized, by instance by air oxidation or due to long period of storage, conducting electrolysis above pH 3.0 will require appropriate conditioning. This is usually performed by adding ammonia, magnesia or soda ash directly to the catholyte to raise the pH in order to trigger the precipitation of $Fe(OH)_3$ which is removed continuously by filtration or centrifugation, this procedure is called "***dummying***" the bath.

Therefore, in order to ensure that all the iron is present as Fe(II) prior electrowinning and without consuming too many chemicals, it is often better to fully reduce the ferric cations into ferrous cations by performing either the chemical or the electrochemical reduction of the catholyte. The latter technique is privileged when combined with electrowinning as similar equipment are used.

11.1.14.1 Chemical Reduction

The chemical reduction is often performed in the titanium pigment industry by using metallic iron in various form (e.g., scrap iron, powder, granules, flakes, turnings, etc.) or by injecting sulfur dioxide gas or in certain cases where aluminum, magnesium species are not objectionable and deleterious for the electrowinning, it is also possible to perform the chemical reduction utilizing either aluminum or magnesium metal in various forms achieving the same results.

The potentiometric control of the advancement of the reduction by measuring the oxidation-reduction potential (ORP) was first patented [114] and used industrially in the 1960s by the titanium dioxide pigment producer *Titan GmbH* (now *Kronos*) at its TiO_2-plant located in Leverkusen, Germany. The targeted oxidation redox potential indicating the completion of the reduction of all ferric iron ranges from -50 mV down to -100 mV/AgCl. The specific consumptions of common industrial agents for reducing Fe(III) into Fe(II) are reported in Table 53.

Table 53 – Specific consumption of reducing agents

Reducing agent	Chemical reaction	Specific consumption (kg/tonne Fe^{3+})
Sulfur dioxide (SO_2)	$SO_2(g) + 2H_2O + 2Fe^{3+} = SO_4^{2-} + 4H^+ + 2Fe^{2+}$	573
Iron (Fe)	$Fe(s) + 2Fe^{3+} = 3Fe^{2+}$	500
Magnesium (Mg)	$Mg(s) + 2Fe^{3+} = Mg^{2+} + 2Fe^{2+}$	217
Aluminum (Al)	$Al(s) + 3Fe^{3+} = Al^{3+} + 3Fe^{2+}$	161

11.1.14.2 Electrochemical Reduction and Pre-electrolysis

By contrast with the chemical reduction, the electrochemical method despite not being widely used industrially is the most efficient as the only reductant is the electron that is simply supplied by the cathode, and thus the production rate being directly linked to the electric current.

It is worth to mention that the electrochemical reduction is not new as it was first utilized in the early 1980s by the titanium dioxide producer *Thann et Mulhouse S.A.* (now *Tronox*) at its plant located in Thann, France [115]. The electrolysis was conducted using a divided electrolyzer with either a porous ceramic diaphragm or an anion exchange membrane as separators. The catholyte consisted of a digestion liquor from the sulfation of ilmenite with the intent to reduce all the Fe(III) and produces some traces of Ti(III), the latter being required to prevent the air oxidation. However, instead of sulfuric acid, and in order to reduce drastically the overall cell voltage, and minimizing the specific energy consumption, the anolyte consisted of an acidic solution of ferrous sulfate from recycled copperas.

---

[114] STEINHAUSEN, H. (1967) *Process for automatically regulating the reduction of the iron and titanium values in a digestion liquor.* U.S. Patent 3,486,847, December 30th, 1969.

[115] RIVORY, M.X (1980) *Process for the production of pigmentary titanium dioxide by the sulphric acid method.* U.S. Patent 4,206,021, June 3rd, 1980.

Simultaneously in Italy, a similar electrolytic process invented by Traini et al. and was patented by *Oronzio de Nora Impianti Elettrochimici S.p.A.* [116]. The process was implemented and used commercially by *Millennium Inorganic Chemicals SA* at its plant located in Scarlino, Tuscany, Italy.

In 1982, the Japanese membrane producer *Asahi Glass Co Ltd.* patented also the electrochemical reduction of ferric iron [117] using their own Selemion® (Trademark of *Asahi Glass Co. Ltd.*) brand as anion exchange membranes.

In the 1990, the chemical company *Rhone-Poulenc Chimie* (later *Millennium Inorganic Chemicals SA*, today *Tronox*), Courbevois, France patented also a similar electrochemical process [118] but using a cation exchange membrane instead as separator.

In all cases, the electrochemical reduction is performed in order to reduce all the ferric back to ferrous. During the electrochemical reduction, the pH is maintained always below 1.0. Actually, strongly acidic conditions do not only prevent the precipitation of metal hydroxides but also impede the electrodeposition of metallic iron, and other reducible metals at the cathode. It also promotes to some extent the discharge of protons with evolution of nascent hydrogen gas acting as a reducing agent, and providing a reducing protective blanket.

As for the chemical reduction, the targeted oxidation-reduction potential (ORP) indicating the completion of the reduction usually ranges from -50 mV/AgCl down to -500 mV/AgCl. The theoretical volumetric electric charge required to prepare a fully reduced pregnant solution depends on the pH, the total concentrations of Fe(III), and other reducible metal cations, and their specific electrochemical equivalents that are reported in Table 38.

During the testing at the pilot scale, the electrochemical reduction was performed by using a high flow rate divided electrolyzer of the plate and frame type with two compartments such as the FLOWPRO series manufactured by *Electrochem Technologies & Materials Inc.* (Montreal, QC) (see Figure 98). The solution to be reduced (i.e., catholyte) is circulated inside the cathode compartment. The separator is either a diaphragm (e.g., microporous polypropylene) or more preferably an anion exchange membrane. The schematic flow diagram for the integrated process is depicted in Figure 61.

The suitable electrolyzer configuration comprised a mixed metals oxides (MMO) coated-titanium anode of the type Ti/Ta_2O_5-IrO_2 for evolving oxygen

---

[116] TRAINI, C.; BIANCHI, G.; and PELLEGRI, A. (1980) *Electrolytic process for treating ilmenite leach solutions.* U.S. Patent 4,230,542 (Oronzio de Nora Impianti Elettrochimici S.p.A.), October 28th, 1980.

[117] KAWAHARA, T.; and HAMANO, T. (1982) *Method for reducing iron salt.* Japanese patent JP S591688A (Asahi Glass Co Ltd.), 1982.

[118] BACHOT, J.; and LE ROUX, O. (1990) *Electrolytic cell/process for the reduction of titanium/iron solutions.* U.S. Patent 4,919,772 A, (Rhone-Poulenc Chimie) April, 24th, 1990.

($MMO-O_2$) and for regenerating sulfuric acid. The cathode is made of various materials including mild steel 1010, pure electrolytic copper C110, chemical lead, C.P. titanium, and zirconium. Moreover, in order to increase significantly the actual cathode surface area and to promote the mass transfer, the cathode compartment was packed with metallic wool, meshes of expanded metal and plastic.

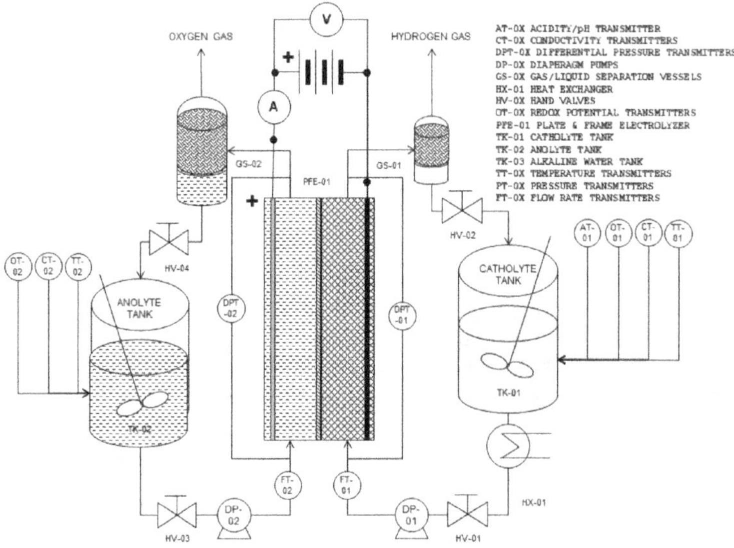

Figure 61 – Schematic P&ID diagram for the electrochemical reduction

The narrow electrode-membrane, and the inter-electrode gaps ensure a high fluid velocity and a turbulent regime. Each compartment was connected to the related catholyte (resp. anolyte) storage tank with a capacity up to 279 US gallons (ca. 1.056 m^3) through piping and tubing and the circulation of the catholyte (resp. anolyte) is ensured by air operated diaphragm pumps depending on the volume flow rate ranging from 3 gal/min (11.4 L/min) to 20 gal/min (75.7 L/min).

The electrolysis was performed under a batch mode with recirculation under a galvanostatic mode. When performing the electrolysis at high current, the Joule's heating of the electrolytes is controlled by installing either a plate and frame heat exchanger or by using a coiled heat exchanger inside the storage tank.

Several operating parameters were recorded as a function of time such as the current intensity, the overall cell voltage, the cathode potential vs. a reference electrode usually the mercury-mercurous sulfate-sulfuric acid, the pH, the oxidation-reduction potential, the electrical conductivity, the temperature, the electric charge circulated, and the volume flow rate.

Among them the oxidation-reduction potential was the most critical parameter as it indicates the progression of the electrochemical reduction. The experimental plot of the ORP vs. the specific charge circulated shows a typical sigma-shape of redox titration plots with the ORP dropping in a matter of minutes at the end point prior completion from +230 mV down to -230 mV/AgCl.

The theoretical specific (resp. volumetric) electric charge required for completing the reduction was calculated based on the initial concentrations of Fe(III), and in lesser extent the concentration of other reducible contaminants, and the faradaic current efficiency was simply calculated as the ratio of the theoretical charge required to the actual charge consumed. Because of the acidic conditions imposed to prevent the precipitation of metal hydroxides, and the electrodeposition of reducible metals, the faradaic cathode current efficiency obtained ranged from 50 percent up to 90 percent depending on the type of cathode material used.

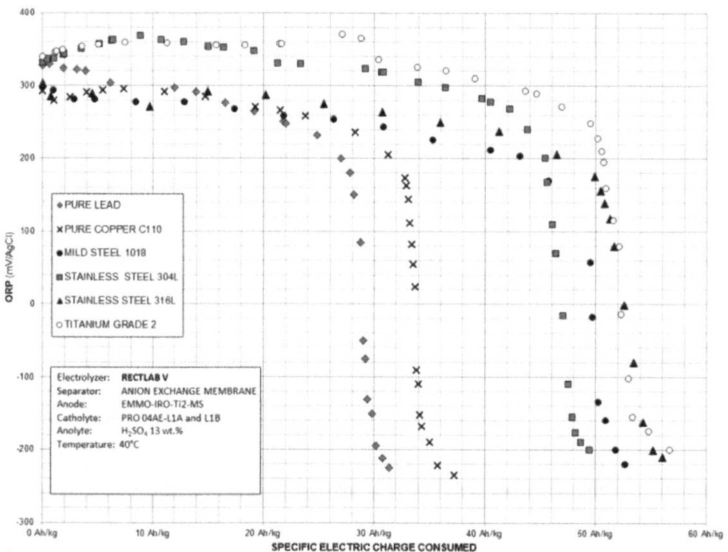

Figure 62 – Electrochemical reduction plots with various cathode materials

The Figure 62 shows several experimental plots recorded of the oxidation-reduction potential vs. specific charge measured inside the cathode compartment of a prototype electrolyzer for various cathode materials

From the above plots, it is clear that chemical lead is the most effective cathode for performing the electrochemical reduction in sulfate electrolytes due to its high hydrogen overvoltage, corrosion resistance, and low cost. The plot depicted in Figure 63 was recorded during the electrochemical reduction of a large batch of an actual pregnant solution obtained from sulfation experiments.

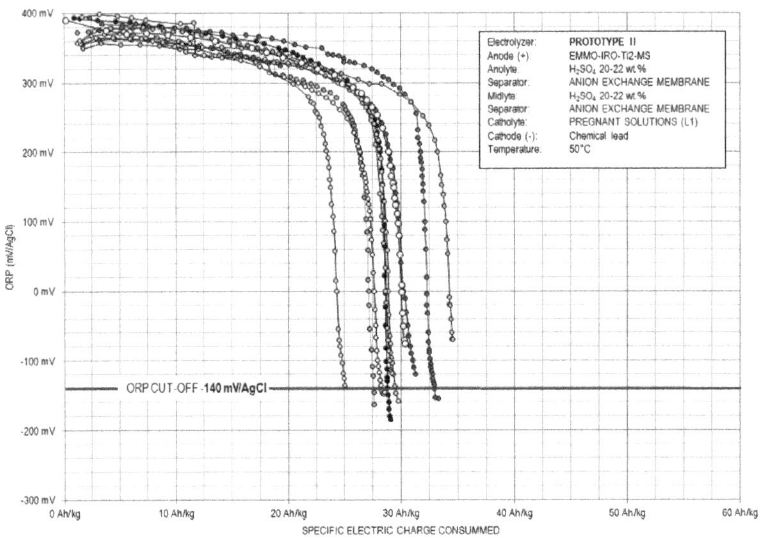

Figure 63 – Electrochemical reduction of a pregnant leach solution

11.2 Anolyte

The anolyte consists of an aqueous solution of sulfuric acid with a mass percentage ranging from 5 to 30 wt.% H_2SO_4. The three relevant physical properties of the anolyte for conducting the electrochemical calculations are the mass density, ρ, in kg/m^3, the dynamic viscosity, η, in mPa.s, the specific heat capacity, c_p, in J/K/kg, and electrical conductivity, κ, in mS/cm. We have decided to summarize these properties in the following paragraphs. More details regarding the physical properties of sulfuric acid were described in details by Cardarelli [119].

11.2.1 Mass Density

The mass density of pure aqueous solution of sulfuric acid at a given temperature is an important property that allows the accurate determination of the mass percentage of acid. The most accurate and internationally adopted values for the mass density of aqueous solutions of sulfuric acid at atmospheric pressure, denoted by the Greek letter ρ_A, and expressed in kg/m^3, as a function of the mass percentage of sulfuric acid in wt.% H_2SO_4, ranging from 1 wt.% up to 31 wt.% and for several temperatures ranging from 15°C and 80°C are reported in Table **54**.

[119] CARDARELLI, F. (2022) *Sulfuric Acid Digestion, Sulfuric Acid Baking, and Sulfation Roasting in Mineral and Chemical Processing, and Extractive Metallurgy*. Electrochem Technologies & Materials Inc., Montreal, QC, Canada, pages 5

Table 54 – Mass density of sulfuric acid solutions

wt.%	15°C	20°C	25°C	30°C	40°C	50°C	60°C	80°C
1	1,006.0	1,005.1	1,003.8	1,002.2	998.6	994.4	989.5	977.9
2	1,012.9	1,011.8	1,010.4	1,008.7	1,005.0	1,000.6	995.6	983.9
3	1,019.7	1,018.4	1,016.9	1,015.2	1,011.3	1,006.7	1,001.7	990.0
4	1,026.4	1,025.0	1,023.4	1,021.6	1,017.6	1,012.9	1,007.8	996.1
5	1,033.2	1,031.7	1,030.0	1,028.1	1,024.0	1,019.2	1,014.0	1,002.2
6	1,040.0	1,038.5	1,036.7	1,034.7	1,030.5	1,025.6	1,020.3	1,008.4
7	1,046.9	1,045.3	1,043.4	1,041.4	1,037.1	1,032.1	1,026.6	1,014.6
8	1,053.9	1,052.2	1,050.2	1,048.1	1,043.7	1,038.6	1,033.0	1,020.9
9	1,061.0	1,059.1	1,057.1	1,054.9	1,050.3	1,045.1	1,039.5	1,027.3
10	1,068.1	1,066.1	1,064.0	1,061.7	1,057.0	1,051.7	1,046.0	1,033.8
11	1,075.3	1,073.1	1,071.0	1,068.6	1,063.7	1,058.4	1,052.6	1,040.3
12	1,082.5	1,080.2	1,078.0	1,075.6	1,070.5	1,065.1	1,059.3	1,046.9
13	1,089.8	1,087.4	1,085.1	1,082.6	1,077.4	1,071.9	1,066.1	1,053.6
14	1,097.1	1,094.7	1,092.2	1,089.7	1,084.4	1,078.8	1,072.9	1,060.3
15	1,104.5	1,102.0	1,099.4	1,096.8	1,091.4	1,085.7	1,079.8	1,067.1
16	1,112.0	1,109.4	1,106.7	1,104.0	1,098.5	1,092.7	1,086.8	1,074.0
17	1,119.5	1,116.8	1,114.1	1,111.3	1,105.7	1,099.8	1,093.8	1,080.9
18	1,127.1	1,124.3	1,121.5	1,118.7	1,112.9	1,107.0	1,100.9	1,087.9
19	1,134.7	1,131.8	1,129.0	1,126.1	1,120.2	1,114.2	1,108.1	1,095.0
20	1,142.4	1,139.4	1,136.5	1,133.5	1,127.5	1,121.5	1,115.3	1,102.1
21	1,150.1	1,147.1	1,144.1	1,141.0	1,134.9	1,128.8	1,122.6	1,109.3
22	1,157.9	1,154.8	1,151.7	1,148.6	1,142.4	1,136.2	1,129.9	1,116.6
23	1,165.7	1,162.6	1,159.4	1,156.3	1,150.0	1,143.7	1,137.3	1,123.9
24	1,173.6	1,170.4	1,167.2	1,164.0	1,157.6	1,151.2	1,144.8	1,131.3
25	1,181.6	1,178.3	1,175.0	1,171.8	1,165.3	1,158.8	1,152.3	1,138.8
26	1,189.6	1,186.2	1,182.9	1,179.6	1,173.0	1,166.5	1,159.9	1,146.3
27	1,197.6	1,194.2	1,190.9	1,187.5	1,180.8	1,174.2	1,167.6	1,153.9
28	1,205.7	1,202.3	1,198.9	1,195.5	1,188.7	1,182.0	1,175.3	1,161.6
29	1,213.8	1,210.4	1,206.9	1,203.5	1,196.6	1,189.8	1,183.1	1,169.3
30	1,222.0	1,218.5	1,215.0	1,211.5	1,204.6	1,197.7	1,190.9	1,177.1
31	1,230.2	1,226.7	1,223.2	1,219.6	1,212.6	1,205.7	1,198.8	1,184.9

11.2.2 Dynamic Viscosity

The ***dynamic viscosity*** (i.e., absolute viscosity) of a fluid (e.g., gas, liquid) denoted η or μ and expressed in mPa.s (1 cP = 1mPa.s), is defined as the proportional factor between the shear stress and the velocity gradient as follows:

$$\tau = \eta \, (du/dy)_x$$

On the other hand, the ***kinematic viscosity*** of a fluid (e.g., gas, liquid) denoted ν and expressed in $m^2.s^{-1}$, is defined as the ratio of dynamic viscosity amd mass density of the fluid:

$$\nu = \eta / \rho$$

For instance, the dynamic viscosities of aqueous solutions of sulfuric acid vs. the mass percentage of acid at 25°C from the experimental data obtained by Rhodes and Barbour [120]are reported in Table **55**.

Table 55 – Dynamic viscosity of sulfuric acid solutions

Mass percentage (wt.% H_2SO_4)	Dynamic viscosity (mPa.s)
5.00	1.01
9.39	1.11
13.42	1.22
17.42	1.34
20.34	1.41
24.10	1.58
29.80	1.88
39.70	2.46

11.2.3 Specific Heat Capacity

The specific heat capacity of an aqueous solution of sulfuric acid, with a mass fraction of sulfuric acic, w_A, as a function of the thermodynamic temperature, denoted $c_{psoln}(T)$, in J/kg/K, is simply the weighted average of the temperature dependent specific heat capacities of water, and sulfuric acid as follows:

$$c_{psoln}(T) = w_A \, c_{pA}(T) + (1 - w_A) \, c_{pwater}(T)$$

[120] RHODES; F.H.; and BARBOUR, C.B. (1923) The viscosities of mixtures of sulfuric acid and water. *Industrial and Engineering Chemistry* **15**(8)850-852.

Each individual specific heat capacity can be calculated from practical equations where the three empirical coefficients were obtained from calorimetric experiments:

$$c_{pA}(T) = A_A + B_A T + C_A/T^2$$

$$c_{pwater}(T) = A_w + B_w T + C_w/T^2$$

Therefore, the empirical equation for the specific heat capacity of the solution becomes simply:

$$c_{psoln}(T) = (w_A\, A_A + w_{water}\, A_w) + (w_A\, B_A + w_{water}\, B_w)T + (w_A\, C_A + w_{water}\, C_w)/T^2$$

For convenience, we have calculated the specific heat capacity of solutions of sulfuric acid vs. selected mass percentages, and temperatures, these are reported in Table 56. The variation of the specific heat capacity of aqueous solutions of sulfuric acid vs. the mass percentage decreases linearly with increasing concentration of sulfuric acid up to 30 wt.% H_2SO_4.

Table 56 – Specific heat capacity of sulfuric acid vs. mass percentage and temperature

Specific heat of sulfuric acid vs. mass percentage and temperature in J/(kg.K)								
Temp.	25°C	30°C	35°C	40°C	45°C	50°C	55°C	60°C
wt% H_2SO_4	298.15 K	303.15 K	308.15 K	313.15 K	318.15 K	323.15 K	328.15 K	333.15 K
0	4,183	4,183	4,183	4,183	4,183	4,183	4,183	4,183
1	4,155	4,155	4,155	4,155	4,155	4,155	4,156	4,156
2	4,127	4,128	4,128	4,128	4,128	4,128	4,128	4,129
3	4,100	4,100	4,100	4,101	4,101	4,101	4,101	4,102
4	4,072	4,072	4,073	4,073	4,074	4,074	4,074	4,075
5	4,044	4,045	4,045	4,046	4,046	4,047	4,047	4,048
6	4,017	4,017	4,018	4,018	4,019	4,020	4,020	4,021
7	3,989	3,990	3,990	3,991	3,992	3,992	3,993	3,993
8	3,961	3,962	3,963	3,964	3,964	3,965	3,966	3,966
9	3,934	3,935	3,936	3,936	3,937	3,938	3,939	3,939
10	3,906	3,907	3,908	3,909	3,910	3,911	3,912	3,912
11	3,878	3,880	3,881	3,882	3,883	3,884	3,885	3,885
12	3,851	3,852	3,853	3,854	3,855	3,856	3,857	3,858
13	3,823	3,824	3,826	3,827	3,828	3,829	3,830	3,831
14	3,795	3,797	3,798	3,800	3,801	3,802	3,803	3,804
15	3,768	3,769	3,771	3,772	3,774	3,775	3,776	3,777
16	3,740	3,742	3,743	3,745	3,746	3,748	3,749	3,750
17	3,712	3,714	3,716	3,717	3,719	3,721	3,722	3,723
18	3,685	3,687	3,688	3,690	3,692	3,693	3,695	3,696
19	3,657	3,659	3,661	3,663	3,664	3,666	3,668	3,669
20	3,629	3,632	3,634	3,635	3,637	3,639	3,641	3,642
21	3,602	3,604	3,606	3,608	3,610	3,612	3,614	3,615
22	3,574	3,576	3,579	3,581	3,583	3,585	3,586	3,588
23	3,547	3,549	3,551	3,553	3,555	3,557	3,559	3,561
24	3,519	3,521	3,524	3,526	3,528	3,530	3,532	3,534
25	3,491	3,494	3,496	3,499	3,501	3,503	3,505	3,507
26	3,464	3,466	3,469	3,471	3,474	3,476	3,478	3,480
27	3,436	3,439	3,441	3,444	3,446	3,449	3,451	3,453
28	3,408	3,411	3,414	3,417	3,419	3,421	3,424	3,426
29	3,381	3,384	3,386	3,389	3,392	3,394	3,397	3,399
30	3,353	3,356	3,359	3,362	3,365	3,367	3,370	3,372
31	3,325	3,328	3,332	3,334	3,337	3,340	3,343	3,345
32	3,298	3,301	3,304	3,307	3,310	3,313	3,315	3,318
33	3,270	3,273	3,277	3,280	3,283	3,286	3,288	3,291
34	3,242	3,246	3,249	3,252	3,255	3,258	3,261	3,264
35	3,215	3,218	3,222	3,225	3,228	3,231	3,234	3,237
36	3,187	3,191	3,194	3,198	3,201	3,204	3,207	3,210
37	3,159	3,163	3,167	3,170	3,174	3,177	3,180	3,183
38	3,132	3,136	3,139	3,143	3,146	3,150	3,153	3,156
39	3,104	3,108	3,112	3,116	3,119	3,122	3,126	3,129
40	3,076	3,080	3,084	3,088	3,092	3,095	3,099	3,102

11.2.4 Electrical Conductivity

Because of the strong acidity due to the high dissociation constant of the first hydrogen, the ***electrical conductivity*** of solutions of sulfuric acid, κ, in S/m, is extremely high, and solutions of sulfuric acid are among the most electrically conductive aqueous electrolytes. The electrical conductivity of solutions of sulfuric acid in S/m is reported in Table **57**.

Table 57 – Electrical conductivity of sulfuric acid vs. percentage and temperature

wt.%	15°C	20°C	25°C	30°C	40°C	50°C	60°C	70°C	80°C	90°C
5	19.66	21.02	22.32	23.51	24.65	26.76	28.53	30.07	31.18	32.50
10	37.70	40.55	43.35	44.55	49.48	53.90	56.85	60.00	62.37	65.13
15	52.00	56.25	60.45	62.20	69.40	75.78	80.15	85.45	88.93	93.13
20	62.65	68.05	73.15	75.70	85.30	91.90	99.80	107.10	111.80	117.68
25	68.80	74.80	80.80	83.73	95.23	105.93	113.30	122.15	128.43	135.78
30	**70.75**	**77.20**	**83.85**	**87.05**	99.73	111.93	120.55	130.90	138.98	147.73
34	69.55	76.40	83.25	86.63	**99.85**	**112.83**	**122.00**	**133.50**	141.78	151.95
35	68.98	75.85	82.70	86.10	99.43	112.52	121.80	133.50	**141.93**	152.30
36	68.15	75.15	82.00	85.37	98.80	111.98	121.35	133.25	141.87	**152.43**
40	64.24	71.10	77.85	81.27	94.65	108.03	117.55	130.15	139.43	150.52
Conversion factor: 1 S/m = 10 mS/cm (E) = 10 mmho/cm (E)										

From the above table, we can see that the highest electrical conductivity when measured at a room temperature of 20°C is 77 S/m (770 mS/cm) correspond to 30 mass percent while shifting to higher values with increasing temperature up to the maximum of 152 S/m (1520 mS/cm) for 36 mass percent at 90°C. These maxima for each temperature are depicted in the Figure 64.

It is interesting to note that this high ionic conductivity of aqueous solutions of sulfuric acid combined with their extremely low freezing points ranging from -40°C (-40°F) for 30 wt.% and even down to -63°C (-81.4°F) for a strength of 35 wt.%, explains their widely adopted utilization, for more than a century and a half, in electrochemistry as acidic electrolytes in the lead acid batteries invented in 1859 by the French physicist Gaston Planté.

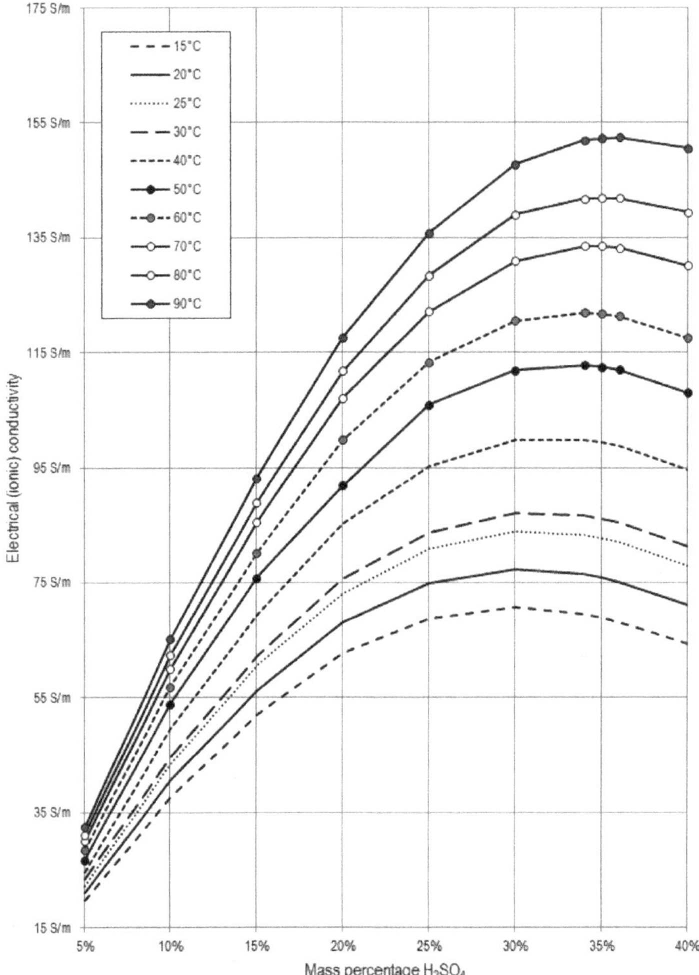

Figure 64 – Electrical conductivity vs. mass percentage of sulfuric acid

11.2.5 Final Concentration of Sulfuric Acid

During electrowinning, the sulfate anions in the catholyte diffuses across the anion exchange membrane towards the anode compartment where they combine with the protons left behind from the oxygen evolution reaction to yield sulfuric acid. Therefore, the concentration of sulfuric acid increases constantly until reaching a maximum threshold dictated by the concentration of ferrous sulfate in the catholyte and the initial concentration of sulfuric acid in the anolyte.

We will present hereafter the calculations for obtaining this information as a function of operating parameters such as the initial concentrations of copperas and sulfuric acid in the catholyte and anolyte respectively.

The electrochemical reaction involving anhydrous ferrous sulfate is:

$$FeSO_4(s) + H_2O = Fe(s) + H_2SO_4 + 0.5O_2(g)$$

In the particular case, where the starting material is copperas, we have:

$$FeSO_4\cdot 7H_2O = [Fe(s) + 6H_2O] + H_2SO_4 + 0.5O_2(g)$$

However, in practice, the electrowinning of iron is always performed with a catholyte consisting of an aqueous solution of $FeSO_4$ with a mass percentage ranging from 2 wt.% up to saturation, (i.e., 26.58 wt.% at 34°C) or even up to 35.48 wt.% $FeSO_4$ at 60°C. This catholyte composition allows electrowinning iron metal at the highest cathode current density.

On the other hand, because the anolyte must be electrically conductive the anolyte entering the anode compartment is never pure water but always an aqueous solution of sulfuric acid. Therefore, the concentration of sulfuric acid increases constantly until reaching a maximum threshold dictated by the initial concentration of sulfuric acid in the anolyte. This behavior has a strong impact on the operation, and it is also critical from an economic standpoint. Actually, beside the recovery of metallic iron, the second most important goal during the electrowinning of iron is to reach the highest concentration of sulfuric acid obtainable in order to reduce the need to concentrate further the acid by an energy demanding process (e.g., thermal vacuum evaporation).

Therefore, it is important to modify the previous electrochemical reaction scheme accordingly by taking into account the amount of water imposed by the dilution of the copperas in the catholyte, and the pre-existing amount of sulfuric acid present in the anolyte prior electrolysis.

Thus by introducing, the dimensionless stoichiometric coefficients x, y, and z corresponding to the moles of water in the catholyte, and anolyte respectively, and the moles of sulfuric acid in the anolyte, the overall chemical reaction scheme becomes:

Prior electrolysis:	$FeSO_4\cdot 7H_2O + xH_2O$ Catholyte (in)	+	$(1+y)H_2O + zH_2SO_4$ Anolyte (in)		=
After electrolysis:	$[Fe(s) + (7 + x)H_2O]$ Catholyte (out)	+	$yH_2O + (1+ z)H_2SO_4$ Anolyte (out)	$+ 0.5O_2(g)$	

Therefore, from the first member of the above equation, we can now calculate the initial mass fractions of copperas, w_C^0, in the catholyte, and that of sulfuric acid, w_A^o, in the anolyte prior electrolysis using the relative molar masses of copperas, M_C, water, M_{H2O}, and sulfuric acid, M_{H2SO4} respectively:

$$w_C^o = 1/[1 + x(M_{H2O}/M_C)]$$

$$w_A^o = 1/[1 + (M_{H2O}/M_{H2SO4})(1+y)/z]$$

Conversely, it is also very useful to calculate the related stoichiometric coefficients x and z from the initial mass fractions of copperas in the catholyte and the sulfuric acid in the anolyte as follows:

$$x = (1/w_C^o - 1)(M_C/M_{H2O})$$

$$z = [(1+y)/(1/w_A^o - 1)](M_{H2O}/M_{H2SO4})$$

On the other hand, if we impose that before the electrolysis begins the masses of catholyte and anolyte on each side of the anion exchange membrane are equal, this leads to the following simple mass balance equation:

$$M_C + xM_{H2O} = (1+y)M_{H2O} + zM_{H2SO4}$$

Afterwards replacing z in the above equation, then we obtain a direct relationship between the two stoichiometric coefficients x and y:

$$M_C + xM_{H2O} = (1+y)M_{H2O}\ [1 + 1/(1/w_A^o - 1)]$$

$$y = (1 - w_A^o)[(M_C/M_{H2O}) + x] - 1$$

After electrolysis, knowing the three coefficients x, y, and z, the final mass percentage of sulfuric acid that can be obtained theoretically, w_A^F, is given by:

$$w_A^F = 1/[1 + (M_{H2O}/M_{H2SO4})y/(1 + z)]$$

Based on these equations, we can calculate the maximum percentage of sulfuric acid that can be obtained in the anolyte at the end of electrolysis as a function of initial anolyte and catholyte compositions. To avoid tedious computations, selected figures were calculated and reported in Table 58. It is worth to mention that because all the calculated figures are mass fractions, they are valid at any temperatures.

Table 58 – Mass percentage of sulfuric acid vs. anolyte and catholyte compositions

$(FeSO_4{\cdot}7H_2O + \mathbf{x}H_2O) + [(1+\mathbf{y})H_2O + \mathbf{z}H_2SO_4] = Fe(s) + (7+\mathbf{x})H_2O + [(1+\mathbf{z})H_2SO_4 + \mathbf{y}H_2O] + 0.5O_2$										
Catholyte: mass percentages			$m_{catholyte} = m_{anolyte}$		**Anolyte**: initial mass percentage of sulfuric acid					
$FeSO_4.7H_2O$	$FeSO_4$	Fe(total)	x ↓	w_{AN}(in) →	**5%**	**10%**	**15%**	**20%**	**25%**	**30%**
2%	1.09%	0.40%	756.178	z →	7.086	14.173	21.259	28.346	35.432	42.519
				y →	732.030	693.449	654.869	616.288	577.708	539.127
				w_{AN}(end) →	5.7%	10.6%	15.6%	20.6%	25.6%	**30.5%**
5%	2.73%	1.00%	293.212	z →	2.835	5.669	8.504	11.338	14.173	17.008
				y →	292.212	276.780	261.348	245.915	230.483	215.051
				w_{AN}(end) →	6.7%	11.6%	16.5%	21.5%	26.4%	**31.3%**
10%	5.46%	2.01%	138.890	z →	1.417	2.835	4.252	5.669	7.086	8.504
				y →	145.606	137.890	130.174	122.458	114.742	107.025
				w_{AN}(end) →	8.3%	13.1%	18.0%	22.9%	27.7%	**32.6%**
15%	8.20%	3.01%	87.449	z →	0.945	1.890	2.835	3.779	4.724	5.669
				y →	96.737	91.593	86.449	81.305	76.161	71.017
				w_{AN}(end) →	9.9%	14.7%	19.5%	24.2%	29.0%	**33.8%**
20%	10.93%	4.02%	61.729	z →	0.709	1.417	2.126	2.835	3.543	4.252
				y →	72.303	68.445	64.587	60.729	56.871	53.013
				w_{AN}(end) →	11.4%	16.1%	20.9%	25.6%	30.3%	**35.0%**
25%	13.66%	5.02%	46.297	z →	0.567	1.134	1.701	2.268	2.835	3.402
				y →	57.642	54.556	51.470	48.383	45.297	42.210
				w_{AN}(end) →	12.9%	17.6%	22.2%	26.9%	**31.5%**	**36.2%**
30%	16.39%	6.03%	36.008	z →	0.472	0.945	1.417	1.890	2.362	2.835
				y →	47.869	45.297	42.725	40.153	37.581	35.008
				w_{AN}(end) →	14.3%	18.9%	23.5%	28.2%	**32.8%**	**37.4%**
35%	19.12%	7.03%	28.660	z →	0.405	0.810	1.215	1.620	2.025	2.430
				y →	40.887	38.683	36.478	34.274	32.069	29.864
				w_{AN}(end) →	15.8%	20.3%	24.8%	29.4%	**33.9%**	**38.5%**
40%	21.86%	8.03%	23.148	z →	0.354	0.709	1.063	1.417	1.772	2.126
				y →	35.651	33.722	31.793	29.864	27.935	26.006
				w_{AN}(end) →	17.1%	21.6%	26.1%	**30.6%**	**35.1%**	**39.6%**
45%	24.59%	9.04%	18.862	z →	0.315	0.630	0.945	1.260	1.575	1.890
				y →	31.579	29.864	28.150	26.435	24.720	23.006
				w_{AN}(end) →	18.5%	22.9%	27.3%	**31.8%**	**36.2%**	**40.6%**
50%	27.32%	10.04%	15.432	z →	0.283	0.567	0.850	1.134	1.417	1.701
				y →	28.321	26.778	25.235	23.692	22.148	20.605
				w_{AN}(end) →	19.8%	24.2%	28.5%	**32.9%**	**37.3%**	**41.6%**
55%	30.05%	11.05%	12.626	z →	0.258	0.515	0.773	1.031	1.288	1.546
				y →	25.656	24.253	22.850	21.447	20.044	18.641
				w_{AN}(end) →	21.1%	25.4%	29.7%	**34.0%**	**38.3%**	**42.6%**
60%	32.78%	12.05%	10.288	z →	0.236	0.472	0.709	0.945	1.181	1.417
				y →	23.434	22.148	20.862	19.576	18.290	17.004
				w_{AN}(end) →	22.3%	26.6%	**30.8%**	**35.1%**	**39.4%**	**43.6%**
65%	35.52%	13.06%	8.310	z →	0.218	0.436	0.654	0.872	1.090	1.308
				y →	21.555	20.368	19.181	17.993	16.806	15.619
				w_{AN}(end) →	23.5%	27.7%	**32.0%**	**36.2%**	**40.4%**	**44.6%**
$M_{copperas}$ 278.01556			M_{H2SO4}		98.07948	M_{water} 18.01528				

11.2.6 Selection of Construction Materials

In order to handle safely hot sulfuric acid in the anode compartment, it is mandatory to select suitable corrosion, and heat resistant materials with good dielectric properties to ensure proper electrical insulation.

Therefore, essentially polymers are suitable for this demanding application. Thermoplastics are selected for piping and fittings along with solid pieces with structural application (e.g., frames, turbulence promoters) while soft elastomers are required for gaskets (e.g., O-ring, flat gaskets).

The chemical compatibility of some commercial thermoplastics and thermosetting plastics, and elastomers for handling warm sulfuric acid up to 30 wt.% are provided in Table 59.

Table 59 – Plastics compatibility with cold and hot sulfuric acid (30 wt.% H_2SO_4)

Plastics (Brand name)	Maximum service temperature	Chemical resistance ratings	
		Cold (20°C)	Hot (60°C)
ABS (Duraplus®)	20°C (70°F)	C-Fair	X-Unsuitable
CPVC (Corzan®)	82°C (180°F)	A-Excellent	A-Excellent
EPDM	60°C (140°F)	B-Good	C-Fair
Epoxy resin (Novalac®)	100°C (210°F)	A-Excellent	B-Good
HDPE	38°C (100°F)	A-Excellent	X-Unsuitable
Neoprene®	60°C (140°F)	B-Good	C-Fair
PC (Lexan®)	88°C (190°F)	A-Excellent	B-Good
PFA	180°C (350°F)	A-Excellent	A-Excellent
PMMA (Plexiglas®)	40°C (104°F)	B-Good	B-Good
PP	60°C (140°F)	A-Excellent	B-Good
PPO (Noryl®)	100°C (210°F)	A-Excellent	B-Good
PSU	180°C (350°F)	A-Excellent	A-Excellent
PTFCE (Kel-F®)	180°C (350°F)	A-Excellent	A-Excellent
PTFE (Teflon®)	180°C (350°F)	A-Excellent	A-Excellent
PVC (Corzan®)	60°C (140°F)	A-Excellent	B-Good
PVDC (Halar®)	100°C (210°F)	A-Excellent	A-Excellent
PVDF (Kynar®)	120°C (250°F)	A-Excellent	A-Excellent
PVHF (Viton®)	100°C (210°F)	A-Excellent	A-Excellent
Notes: Duraplus® (Trademark of *IPEX Branding Inc.*); Plexiglas® (Trademark of *Röhm GmbH*); Kynar®(Trademark of *Total*); Lexan® (Trademark of *Sabic Global Technologies B.V.*); Teflon® (Trademark of *Chemours*); Novolac® (Trademark of *Olin Corporation*); Corzan® (Trademark of *Lubrizol*); Halar® (Trademark of *Solvay Solexis Inc.*); Kynar® (Trademark of *Arkema, Inc.*); Kel-F® (Trademark of *3M Company*); Neoprene® (Trademark of *E.I. Dupont de Nemours*); Viton® (Trademark of *Chemours Company*); Noryl® (Trademark of *Shpp Global Technologies B.V.*).			

A selection of the most suitable materials in each class ordered by increasing thermal and chemical resistance is listed in Table 60.

Table 60 – Recommended plastics and elastomers for piping and gaskets

Polymer materials	Thermoplastics (e.g., frame, piping) maximum operating temperature	Elastomers (e.g., gaskets)
Type (Brand names)	PVC (60°C) CPVC (80°C) Polycarbonate (80°C) PTFE (260°C)	EPDM (60°C) PVHF (Viton®)(80°C)

11.2.7 Practical Anolyte Composition and Properties

Usually, the anolyte consists of an aqueous solution of sulfuric acid originating either as by-product from the main process itself or from an acid recovery unit used to separate the iron and other metal sulfates from the free acid. From an economic standpoint, and beside the recovery of pure metallic iron, the second most important goal for electrowinning iron with the FerWIN® process is to reach the highest concentration of sulfuric acid obtainable in the anolyte in order to reduce the need to concentrate further the acid by an energy demanding process (e.g., thermal vacuum evaporation). Therefore determining the optimum lower and upper thresholds for the concentration of sulfuric acid was of paramount importance.

From previous Section 11.2.3, the electrical conductivity of aqueous solutions of sulfuric acid reaches a maximum at each operating temperature above which it decreases again. For instance at 60°C, this conductivity is 121 S/m for a mass percentage of 30 wt.% H_2SO_4. Moreover, the increasing corrosiveness of sulfuric acid towards the anode and membrane materials with increasing concentration and temperature also limits the upper threshold. Even if some less common anode materials substrates (e.g., Nb, Ta) and some anion exchange membranes can withstand concentrations of sulfuric acid up to 45 mass percent in some particular instances, in practice, a maximum and safe mass percentage of 30 wt.% H_2SO_4 is recommended. Because both practical maxima are close, it was then decided from an operating standpoint that the maximum concentration of sulfuric acid allowed in the anode compartment must be maintained below 30 mass percent at all times.

On the other hand, we have adopted the lower threshold for the concentration of sulfuric acid as 10 mass percent H_2SO_4 in order to maintain a sufficient electrical conductivity as such anolyte solution exhibits an electrical conductivity of 57 S/m. Therefore, based on these lower and upper concentration thresholds, a maximum concentration span of 20 mass percent of sulfuric acid is expected during operation. In order to simplify the electrochemical calculations in the next sections, we have selected a mass percentage of 20 mass percent H_2SO_4 for the anolyte composition. The selected properties of the above anolyte as a function of the operating temperature are reported in Table 61.

Table 61 – Selected properties of anolyte vs. temperature

3_ANOLYTE PROPERTIES	25°C	30°C	40°C	50°C	54°C	60°C	70°C	80°C	90°C
Sulfuric acid mass percentage (wt.% H_2SO_4)	20%	20%	20%	20%	20%	20%	20%	20%	20%
Sulfuric acid mass concentration (g/L)	227.3	226.6	225.4	224.2	223.7	222.9	221.7	220.4	219.2
Anolyte electrical conductivity (κ_{an}/S.m^{-1})	72.6	76.3	83.6	91.0	93.9	98.4	105.7	113.1	120.4
Anolyte specific heat capacity (c_P/J.K^{-1}.kg^{-1})	3,629	3,632	3,635	3,639	3,640	3,642	3,645	3,648	3,651
Anolyte dynamic viscosity (η_{an}/mPa.s)	1.37	1.23	1.01	0.86	0.81	0.75	0.67	0.62	0.59
Anolyte mass density (ρ_{an}/kg.m^{-3})	1,136	1,133	1,127	1,121	1,118	1,115	1,108	1,102	1,096
Anolyte kinematic viscosity (ν_{an}/m^2.s^{-1})	1.20E-06	1.08E-06	8.95E-07	7.64E-07	7.22E-07	6.70E-07	6.05E-07	5.62E-07	5.35E-07
Diffusion coefficient of SO_4^{2-} (/m^2.s^{-1})	1.05E-09	1.19E-09	1.49E-09	1.82E-09	1.95E-09	2.15E-09	2.46E-09	2.75E-09	2.98E-09
H_2O vapor pressure above solution (π/mmHg)	21.68	27.98	48.68	81.76	92.22	131.26	206.27	312.78	462.79
SO_3 vapor pressure above solution (π/mmHg)	0.00	0.00	0.00	0.00	0.00	0.00	0.00	0.00	0.00
H_2SO_4 vapor pressure above solution (π/mmHg)	0.00	0.00	0.00	0.00	0.00	0.00	0.00	0.00	0.00
Total vapor pressure above solution (π/mmHg)	21.68	27.98	48.68	81.76	92.22	131.26	206.27	312.78	462.79
Partial pressure of oxygen gas (p_{O2}/mmHg)	738.32	732.02	711.32	678.24	667.78	628.74	553.73	447.22	297.21
Coefficient activity of H^+(/mol.m^{-3})	0.170	0.159	0.138	0.121	0.114	0.106	0.095	0.086	0.076
Coefficient activity of SO_4^{2-}(/mol.m^{-3})	0.170	0.159	0.138	0.121	0.114	0.106	0.095	0.086	0.076
Molarity of H^+(/mol.m^{-3})	4,634	4,622	4,596	4,571	4,561	4,545	4,520	4,495	4,469
Molarity of SO_4^{2-}(/mol.m^{-3})	2,317	2,311	2,298	2,285	2,280	2,273	2,260	2,247	2,235
Activity of H^+(/mol.m^{-3})	788	735	634	553	518	482	429	387	340
Activity of SO_4^{2-}(/mol.m^{-3})	394	367	317	277	259	241	215	193	170
Osmolarity (/mol.m^{-3})	13,903	13,865	13,789	13,712	13,682	13,636	13,560	13,484	13,408
pH (molarity)	-0.67	-0.66	-0.66	-0.66	-0.66	-0.66	-0.66	-0.65	-0.65
pH (activity)	0.10	0.13	0.20	0.26	0.29	0.32	0.37	0.41	0.47
Ionic strength (I/mol.m^{-3})	6,951	6,932	6,894	6,856	6,841	6,818	6,780	6,742	6,704

12 Electrodes

12.1 Selection Criteria

The industrial success of an electrowinning process relies mainly on the proper selection of suitable electrode materials. Several scientific and technical criteria must be considered when the practicing electrochemical engineer is selecting an appropriate electrode material. As a general rule, electrode materials must exhibit the following requirements:

- High exchange current density (j_0), and a large electron transfer coefficient (α or β) for the selected electrochemical reaction to decrease the activation overpotential,
- Good electronic conductivity to decrease the ohmic drop, and related Joule heating,
- Good corrosion resistance to both chemical and electrochemical reactions, combined with no passivating and blistering behavior, leading to abnormal electrode degradation and consumption,
- A good set of mechanical properties suited for industrial use (i.e., low density, high tensile strength, stiffness), and other suitable physical properties such as a good thermal conductivity,
- Ease of fabrication (i.e., machining, joining, and cleaning) allowing obtaining clean and intricate shapes,
- Finally, and most importantly a cost affordable price is also required in order to keep a low operating cost.

12.2 Cathodes

For the cathode, the material selection is easier compared to the anode because the operating conditions are less demanding. Usually a cathode material required must exhibit both a good corrosion resistance in sulfate media, a high overpotential for hydrogen evolution, and a poor adherence for the electrolytic iron deposit rendering the stripping of the plate easy. Nowadays, a plethora of metal and alloys are available commercially in a wide variety of mill products and shapes.

However, for selecting the most appropriate electrode material, it is important to consider its selectivity towards to the kinetic of the desired electrochemical reaction. Thus for electrowinning of iron metal from ferrous sulfate electrolytes, the most important electrochemical properties is the overpotential for the deleterious hydrogen gas evolution reaction (HER) resulting from the discharge of protons.

12.2.1 Cathode Materials

Based on the previous criteria, the best candidates that were selected and tested for electrowinning iron are listed hereafter in Table 62 these are in decreasing order: Zircadyne® 702 (Trademark of *ATI-Wah Chang*, Albany, OR), C.P. titanium ASTM grade 2, aluminum AA 1100, austenitic stainless steel AISI 304L, mild steel AISI 1018, and high-silicon cast iron such as Duriron® (Trademark of the *Duriron Chemical Company* Inc., Dayton, OH).

Note that most of the metal and alloys are used with a surface finish in the "*as received*" condition except for some materials such as aluminum or mild steel that are often covered with a passivation layer for the former or mill scale for the latter that required to conduct a surface pre-treatment prior to the perform the electrowinning of iron.

Table 62 – Industrial cathode materials

Group	Metal or alloy	Advantages	Drawbacks	Surface finish and pre-treatment
Low hydrogen overvoltage	Stainless steel 316	Lower overpotential than 304, good corrosion resistance in slightly acidic solutions	Highest electrical resistivity, higher price than 304 due to its Mo	Bright mill finish (annealed), solvent degreasing
	Stainless steel 304	Good dimensional stability in these solutions.	Highest electrical resistivity of the selected cathode materials	Bright mill finish (annealed), solvent degreasing
Medium hydrogen overvoltage	Copper C110	Highest electrical conductivity of all candidates	Contamination of the electrolyte by Cu(II), high cost, poor mechanical strength when annealed	Mirror finish (annealed), solvent degreasing.
	Mild steel 1010	Good electrical and mechanical properties Cheapest substrate, no bath contamination. Perfect as starter sheet	Corrodes in slightly acidic media. Poor dimensional stability if not polarized as cathode during shutdown	Mill scale finish, sandblasting, solvent degreasing, hot acid pickling in hot sulfuric acid, citrate rinsing
	Aluminum 1011	Cheapest substrate with steel, high strength-to-weight ratio, excellent thermal and electrical conductivity	Corrosion in acidic electrolytes, release of Al(III), surface finish difficult to maintain	Bright mill finish, solvent degreasing
High hydrogen overvoltage	Titanium Grade 2	High H_2 overvoltage, density 60% that of steel, outstanding corrosion resistance, excellent dimensional stability (blank cathode)	High electrical resistivity but lower than that of stainless steels. Medium cost	Bright mill finish, solvent degreasing
	Zircadyne® 702	Highest H_2 overvoltage, density 80% that of steel, outstanding corrosion resistance	Very expensive. Restrictions due to its nuclear applications. 705 more expensive than 702 due to its Nb	Bright mill finish, solvent degreasing
	Zircadyne®705			Bright mill finish, solvent degreasing

12.2.2 Cathode Materials Physical Properties

Some relevant properties of the selected cathode materials are reported in the following in Table 63.

Table 63 – Mass density and electrical resistivity of selected cathode materials

Cathode metal or alloy and grade	Mass density (ρ/kg.m^{-3})	Electrical resistivity (ρ/$\mu\Omega$.cm)	Resistivity temperature coefficient (K^{-1})
Aluminum AA 1100	2,700	4.0	+0.00450
Copper C110	8,960	1.71	+0.00438
Graphite (R9710)	2,260	1,375	-0.00050
Lead (Chemical)	11,350	20.6	+0.00428
Mild steel AISI 1010	7,890	15.9	+0.00651
Niobium (99.95 Nb)	8,570	15.2	+0.00263
Stainless steel AISI 304	8,000	72.0	+0.00105
Stainless steel AISI 316	8,000	74.0	+0.00092
Tantalum (99.95 wt.%)	16,656	12.5	+0.00382
Titanium Grade 2	4,512	56.2	+0.00540
Zirconium 702	6,510	39.7	+0.00440

12.2.3 Hydrogen Overvoltage

The main property of the cathode material in order to control the hydrogen gas evolution reaction (HER) is the cathode activation overpotential or simply cathode overpotential. As previously defined in Section 7.3, the cathode overvoltage, denoted η_c, expressed in volts, is the difference between the cathode potential denoted $E_c(j)$, in V/SHE for a given cathode current density, denoted j_c, in A/m^2, and the Nernst electrode potential for the reduction (i.e., discharge) of the protons, E_{H2}, when no current is circulating inside the electrolyzer ($j_c = 0$) as follows:

$$\eta_c = E_c(j) - E_{H2}$$

The practical measurement of the hydrogen overvoltage at a given cathode current density, is performed by recording the polarization curve, that is, the cathode potential vs. the cathode current density (E_c, j_c) for a given pH or acid concentration, and fixed operating temperature.

12.2.4 Cathode Tafel's Coefficients

During the reduction, and in a first approximation, the cathode potential is sufficiently negative to neglect the anode term in the Butler-Volmer equation for the current density as a function of the electrode overpotential (see Section 7.11.1). By performing the logarithmic transform, the mathematical expression for the cathode overpotential as a function of the Briggs logarithm of the absolute value of cathode current density is:

$$\eta_c = E_c(j) - E_{H2} = (RT\ln 10/\beta nF)[\log_{10}|j_0| - \log_{10}|j|]$$

With R the ideal gas constant, 8.3145 J.mol^{-1}.K^{-1}, T the absolute thermodynamic temperature in K, n the number of electrons exchanged, F the Faraday constant, 96,485.309 C/mol, β the electron transfer coefficient for the cathode reaction, and finally, j_0 the absolute value of the anode exchange current density in A/m^2.

In industrial practice, the two Tafel's coefficients (b_c, a_c) are preferred and used by industrial electrochemists. These are simply related to the previous parameters by the straightforward practical linear equation:

$$\eta_c = E_c(j) - E_{H2} = a_c - b_c \log_{10}|j|$$

With the two anode Tafel's coefficients being defined as follows: (i) the ***cathode Tafel's slope*** being $b_c = -(RT\ln 10/\beta nF)$ and (ii) the ***Tafel's intercept*** being: $a_c = b_c \log_{10}|j_0| = (RT\ln 10/\beta nF) \log_{10}|j_0|$.

In addition, at very low cathode current densities, in practice below -25 A/m^2, the polarization curves exhibits a linear region where it is possible to approximate directly the relationship between the anode overpotential and the anode current density by a linear transform as follows:

$$\eta_c = E_c(j) - E_{H2} = (RT/\beta nFj_0)\, j$$

By comparison of the above equation with the generalized Ohm's law, it is possible to define a new electrochemical quantity called the ***activation resistance of polarization***, denoted R_p, and expressed in Ω.m^2.

The two Tafel's coefficients are obtained from the linear portion of the semi-logarithmic Horiuti diagrams (see Section 7.11.3.2) representing the cathode overpotential vs. the logarithm of the absolute value of the cathode current density (η_c, $\log_{10}|j_c|$). It is important to mention that the semi-log plots obtained exhibits always two distinct linear regions depending on the type of current regime. The first linear portion is valid for low cathode current densities ranging from -100 A/m^2 to -1,000 A/m^2 while the second portion for a high cathode current densities ranging from -1,000 A/m² to -10,000 A/m². In both cases, the two straight lines satisfy the empirical Tafel's equation.

The numerical values of Tafel's coefficients are scarce in the scientific and technical literature especially for industrial electrodes. The numerical values provided in this monograph were measured from laboratory and prototype experiments with cathode surface area ranging from 250 cm² up to 929 cm². When the temperature dependence of Tafel's coefficients was not available, the coefficients established at room temperature were used at any temperature.

In order to illustrate the influence of the operating parameters on the overpotential for the hydrogen gas evolution reaction (HER) for various commercial cathode materials, we will provide hereafter, the measures obtained at under forced circulation of the catholyte and using a mercury-mercurous sulfate reference electrode.

12.2.4.1 Hydrogen Overpotential for Diluted Sulfuric Acid

The first scenario addresses the cathode polarization for the hydrogen evolution at 20°C in 1N sulfuric acid. The plot of the cathode polarization vs. the cathode current density is depicted in Figure 65,

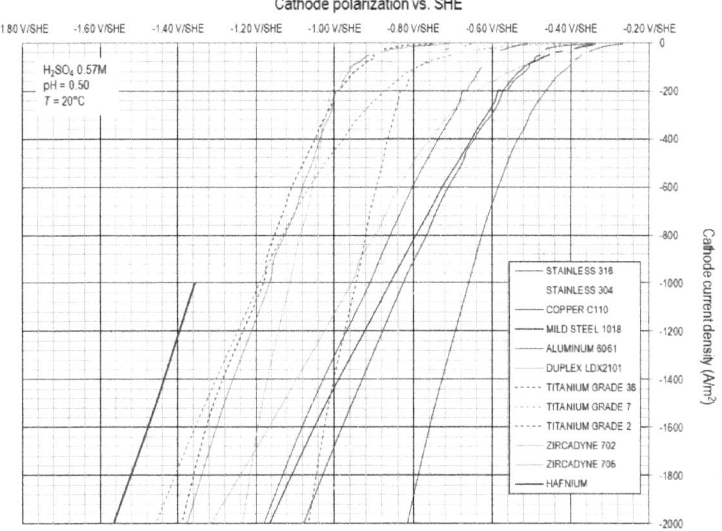

Figure 65 – Cathode polarization vs. current density for 1 N H_2SO_4

This plot will allow establishing a baseline for the behavior of the various cathode materials in the absence of electroactive metal cations (e.g., ferrous cations), and it will serve as a reference for comparison with the polarization of cathode in ferrous sulfate solutions. Afterwards, the measured overpotentials vs. the cathode current density are reported in Table 64 hereafter.

Table 64 – Cathode overpotential for H_2 evolution in 1 N sulfuric acid at 20°C

H_2SO_4 1N 20°C	CATHODE OVERPOTENTIAL ($\eta_{H2} = E - E_{H2}$) in volts								
CATHODE MATERIAL	**-5** A/m²	**-25** A/m²	**-50** A/m²	**-100** A/m²	**-250** A/m²	**-500** A/m²	**-1000** A/m²	**-1500** A/m²	**-2000** A/m²
TUNGSTEN ALLOY (DENSIMET)	0.300	0.272	0.265	0.247	0.211	0.184	0.117	0.059	-0.010
ALUMINUM AA 2024	0.229	0.139	0.100	0.057	-0.090	-0.167	-0.291	-0.372	-0.446
MOLYBDENUM	0.022	-0.015	-0.035	-0.074	-0.126	-0.203	-0.340	-0.455	-0.582
HASTELLOY B2	-0.046	-0.149	-0.216	-0.256	-0.343	-0.433	-0.575	-0.696	-0.812
CARPENTER 20Cb-3	-0.085	-0.184	-0.234	-0.279	-0.367	-0.457	-0.591	-0.704	-0.816
HASTELLOY HX	-0.122	-0.192	-0.235	-0.282	-0.372	-0.470	-0.632	-0.763	-0.883
HASTELLOY C-276	-0.148	-0.222	-0.250	-0.291	-0.385	-0.482	-0.610	-0.729	-0.843
INCOLOY 825	-0.077	-0.160	-0.201	-0.265	-0.368	-0.483	-0.650	-0.799	-0.943
MONEL 400	-0.235	-0.262	-0.310	-0.357	-0.440	-0.492	-0.657	-0.773	-0.876
NAVAL BRASS C464	-0.234	-0.328	-0.381	-0.424	-0.496	-0.576	-0.703	-0.810	-0.918
PHOSPHOR BRONZE C510	-0.257	-0.336	-0.387	-0.438	-0.504	-0.590	-0.702	-0.803	-0.914
STAINLESS AISI 316L	-0.299	-0.367	-0.405	-0.437	-0.517	-0.592	-0.691	-0.775	-0.847
STAINLESS AISI 304	-0.349	-0.417		-0.485	-0.555	-0.659	-0.817	-0.947	-1.064
NICKEL 200	-0.216	-0.334	-0.395	-0.461	-0.564	-0.688	-0.892	-1.059	-1.250
COPPER C110	-0.378	-0.498	-0.512	-0.540	-0.618	-0.710	-0.860	-0.990	-1.112
MILD STEEL AISI 1018	-0.370	-0.424	-0.486	-0.549	-0.627	-0.721	-0.891	-1.053	-1.198
ZINC	-0.646	-0.652	-0.661	-0.673	-0.713	-0.774	-0.900	-1.026	-1.156
ALUMINUM AA 6061 T6	-0.540	-0.597		-0.658	-0.716	-0.801	-0.942	-1.087	-1.212
TITANIUM Grade 26	-0.233	-0.304	-0.416	-0.508	-0.672	-0.824	-1.030	-1.118	-1.198
NIOBIUM	-0.524	-0.609	-0.621	-0.641	-0.727	-0.827	-0.972	-1.072	-1.171
DUPLEX LDX2101	-0.434	-0.501	-0.514	-0.575	-0.729	-0.849	-1.004	-1.179	-1.363
TITANIUM Grade 36	-0.683	-0.741	-0.782	-0.821	-0.869	-0.908	-0.975	-1.043	-1.095
TANTALUM	-0.527	-0.617	-0.666	-0.754	-0.905	-1.007	-1.132	-1.155	-1.235
TITANIUM Grade 7	-0.457	-0.657	-0.737	-0.820	-0.938	-1.054	-1.223	-1.361	-1.488
ZIRCADYNE 702	-0.776	-0.874	-0.940	-0.991	-1.045	-1.076	-1.143	-1.216	-1.266
ZIRCADYNE 705	-0.739	-0.880	-0.943	-0.985	-1.032	-1.085	-1.195	-1.311	-1.405
TITANIUM Grade 2	-0.782	-0.904	-0.934	-0.965	-1.036	-1.108	-1.212	-1.339	-1.420
HAFNIUM	-0.462	-0.568	-0.635	-0.892	-1.067	-1.217	-1.387	-1.487	-1.597
PURE LEAD	-0.320	-0.483	-0.803	-1.193	-1.502	-1.990	-2.910	-3.970	-4.950

From the above tabulated data, it is then possible to calculate the cathode Tafel's coefficients for both low and high current density regimes these are reported in Table 65.

Table 65 – Cathode Tafel's coefficients in 1 N sulfuric acid at 20°C

H_2SO_4 1N 20°C	CATHODE TAFEL'S COEFFICIENTS [$\eta_{H2} = a + b \log_{10} \lvert J\,(A/m^2) \rvert$] LOW CURRENTS: -100 to -500 A/m²				HIGH CURRENTS: -500 to -2000 A/m²		
CATHODE MATERIAL	b (V/decade)	a (V)	$\log_{10} j_o$ (A/m²)	R_p (µΩ.m²)	b (V/decade)	a(V)	$\log_{10} j_o$ (A/m²)
TUNGSTEN ALLOY (DENSIMET)	-0.090	0.428	4.744	1,400	-0.310	1.032	3.327
ALUMINUM AA 2024	-0.323	0.697	2.159	4,500	-0.456	1.070	2.345
MOLYBDENUM	-0.182	0.296	1.629	1,850	-0.610	1.461	2.397
HASTELLOY B2	-0.251	0.251	0.997	5,150	-0.616	1.245	2.022
CARPENTER 20Cb-3	-0.253	0.231	0.912	4,950	-0.582	1.129	1.941
HASTELLOY HX	-0.267	0.256	0.961	3,500	-0.648	1.291	1.992
HASTELLOY C-276	-0.271	0.256	0.943	3,700	-0.586	1.117	1.907
INCOLOY 825	-0.309	0.359	1.162	4,150	-0.746	1.553	2.081
MONEL 400	-0.193	0.028	0.143	1,350	-0.629	1.217	1.933
NAVAL BRASS C464	-0.216	0.011	0.052	4,700	-0.554	0.933	1.686
PHOSPHOR BRONZE C510	-0.215	-0.003	-0.012	3,950	-0.521	0.833	1.599
STAINLESS AISI 316L	-0.221	0.038	0.171	3,320	-0.417	0.575	1.378
STAINLESS AISI 304	-0.245	0.043	0.174	3,240	-0.661	1.169	1.769
NICKEL 200	-0.321	0.189	0.589	5,900	-0.902	1.773	1.966
COPPER C110	-0.241	-0.019	-0.080	5,780	-0.654	1.106	1.692
MILD STEEL AISI 1018	-0.243	-0.024	-0.100	2,820	-0.777	1.432	1.843
ZINC	-0.142	-0.384	-2.698	300	-0.616	0.910	1.478
ALUMINUM AA 6061 T6	-0.202	-0.217	-1.078	2,740	-0.671	1.063	1.584
TITANIUM Grade 26	-0.450	0.397	0.881	3,550	-0.616	0.831	1.350
NIOBIUM	-0.217	-0.227	-1.046	4,250	-0.559	0.693	1.238
DUPLEX LDX2101	-0.392	0.256	0.654	3,240	-0.826	1.462	1.770
TITANIUM Grade 36	-0.124	-0.543	-4.370	2,937	-0.308	-0.039	-0.128
TANTALUM	-0.363	-0.030	-0.082	4,500	-0.355	-0.051	-0.142
TITANIUM Grade 7	-0.333	-0.119	-0.358	9,340	-0.707	0.903	1.276
ZIRCADYNE 702	-0.122	-0.718	-5.868	4,903	-0.315	-0.187	-0.594
ZIRCADYNE 705	-0.142	-0.670	-4.724	7,140	-0.524	0.376	0.718
TITANIUM Grade 2	-0.203	-0.526	-2.586	5,640	-0.519	0.340	0.655
HAFNIUM	-0.464	0.039	0.083	5,300	-0.615	0.452	0.734
PURE LEAD	-1.121	1.135	1.012	7,340	-4.801	11.203	2.334

12.2.4.2 Hydrogen Overpotential for Concentrated Sulfuric Acid

The second scenario addresses the cathode polarization for the hydrogen evolution at 20°C in 32 wt.% sulfuric acid. The plot of the cathode polarization vs. the cathode current density is depicted in Figure 66.

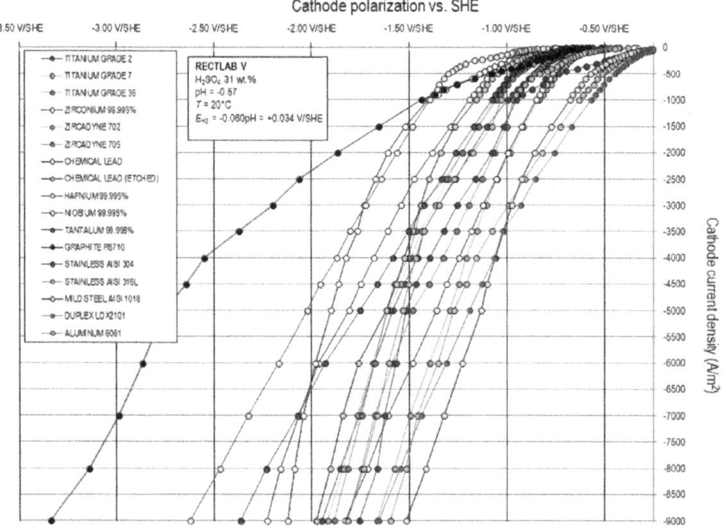

Figure 66 – Cathode overpotential vs. current density in 31 wt.% H_2SO_4

As previously, the measured cathode overpotentials vs. the cathode current density are reported in Table 66 hereafter.

Table 66 – Cathode overpotential for H_2 evolution in 31 wt.% sulfuric acid at 20°C

H_2SO_4 31 wt.% 20°C	CATHODE OVERPOTENTIAL ($\eta_{H2} = E - E_{H2}$) in volts													
CATHODE MATERIAL	-5 A/m²	-25 A/m²	-50 A/m²	-100 A/m²	-250 A/m²	-500 A/m²	-1000 A/m²	-1500 A/m²	-2000 A/m²	-3000 A/m²	-4000 A/m²	-5000 A/m²	-7000 A/m²	-9000 A/m²
MILD STEEL 1010	-0.158	-0.213	-0.266	-0.335	-0.439	-0.535	-0.641	-0.740	-0.823	-0.940	-1.026	-1.100	-1.287	-1.481
DUPLEX LDX 2101	-0.204	-0.236	-0.246	-0.277	-0.335	-0.416	-0.531	-0.634	-0.724	-0.895	-1.029	-1.157	-1.401	-1.621
STAINLESS 316L	-0.124	-0.200	-0.229	-0.296	-0.397	-0.477	-0.594	-0.691	-0.784	-0.959	-1.124	-1.237	-1.421	-1.561
TITANIUM Grade 7	-0.390	-0.528	-0.559	-0.589	-0.644	-0.705	-0.801	-0.881	-0.951	-1.071	-1.173	-1.259	-1.461	-1.631
NIOBIUM	-0.437	-0.555	-0.595	-0.636	-0.677	-0.732	-0.816	-0.889	-0.961	-1.089	-1.210	-1.327	-1.573	-1.793
TITANIUM Grade 36	-0.560	-0.645	-0.664	-0.701	-0.756	-0.826	-0.932	-0.965	-1.031	-1.161	-1.293	-1.449	-1.643	-1.781
STAINLESS 304	-0.128	-0.213	-0.259	-0.319	-0.465	-0.701	-0.915	-0.986	-1.043	-1.222	-1.361	-1.481	-1.591	-1.721
ALUMINUM 6061 T6	-0.345	-0.462	-0.510	-0.571	-0.666	-0.798	-0.996	-1.045	-1.141	-1.313	-1.431	-1.501	-1.631	-1.781
TITANIUM Grade 2	-0.547	-0.614	-0.632	-0.670	-0.737	-0.824	-0.961	-1.070	-1.153	-1.315	-1.421	-1.551	-1.721	-1.911
ZIRCADYNE 702	-0.529	-0.600	-0.657	-0.684	-0.809	-0.917	-1.029	-1.116	-1.194	-1.331	-1.451	-1.571	-1.731	-1.881
ZIRCADYNE 705	-0.628	-0.699	-0.736	-0.779	-0.852	-0.917	-1.019	-1.110	-1.196	-1.401	-1.471	-1.581	-1.711	-1.851
TANTALUM	-0.582	-0.660	-0.691	-0.748	-0.858	-0.937	-1.042	-1.136	-1.229	-1.388	-1.551	-1.720	-2.039	-2.329
ZIRCONIUM	-0.631	-0.735	-0.823	-0.867	-0.945	-1.039	-1.158	-1.253	-1.349	-1.509	-1.646	-1.775	-2.032	-2.194
LEAD	-0.301	-0.649	-0.715	-0.783	-0.955	-1.105	-1.400	-1.485	-1.573	-1.696	-1.790	-1.866	-2.011	-2.089
HAFNIUM	-0.635	-0.809	-0.874	-0.943	-1.131	-1.267	-1.359	-1.447	-1.528	-1.687	-1.838	-1.990	-2.293	-2.590
GRAPHITE	-0.477	-0.620	-0.667	-0.696	-0.815	-1.047	-1.400	-1.621	-1.833	-2.165	-2.516	-2.717	-2.954	-3.306

From the above tabulated data, it is then possible to calculate the cathode Tafel's coefficients for both low and high current density regimes these are reported in **Error! Not a valid bookmark self-reference.**.

Table 67 – Cathode Tafel's coefficients in 31 wt.% sulfuric acid at 20°C

H_2SO_4 31 wt.%	CATHODE TAFEL'S COEFFICIENTS [$\eta_{H2} = a + b \log_{10}\lvert J(A/m^2)\rvert$]						
20°C	LOW CURRENTS: -100 to -100 A/m²				HIGH CURRENTS: -1000 to -9000 A/m²		
CATHODE MATERIAL	b (V/decade)	a (V)	$\log_{10} j_o$ (A/m²)	R_p (μΩ.m²)	b (V/decade)	a(V)	$\log_{10} j_o$ (A/m²)
MILD STEEL 1010	-0.285	0.238	0.835	2,960	-0.848	1.947	2.296
DUPLEX LDX 2101	-0.196	0.121	0.619	1,700	-1.127	2.925	2.594
STAINLESS 316L	-0.259	0.222	0.859	3,660	-1.028	2.543	2.473
TITANIUM Grade 7	-0.165	-0.257	-1.560	6,700	-0.850	1.805	2.124
NIOBIUM	-0.136	-0.361	-2.661	5,840	-1.001	2.267	2.265
TITANIUM Grade 36	-0.177	-0.343	-1.939	4,060	-0.908	1.868	2.058
STAINLESS 304	-0.537	0.776	1.445	4,340	-0.879	1.778	2.022
ALUMINUM 6061 T6	-0.320	0.080	0.248	5,700	-0.831	1.545	1.859
TITANIUM Grade 2	-0.218	-0.229	-1.051	3,040	-0.992	2.066	2.083
ZIRCADYNE 702	-0.332	-0.017	-0.051	3,540	-0.897	1.711	1.907
ZIRCADYNE 705	-0.197	-0.384	-1.951	3,460	-0.883	1.670	1.890
TANTALUM	-0.271	-0.207	-0.765	3,760	-1.321	3.030	2.293
ZIRCONIUM	-0.243	-0.374	-1.537	4,880	-1.077	2.140	1.986
LEAD	-0.459	0.139	0.302	20,120	-0.753	0.905	1.201
HAFNIUM	-0.464	-0.016	-0.034	8,260	-1.260	2.531	2.008
GRAPHITE	-0.492	0.310	0.632	6,800	-2.025	4.752	2.346

12.2.5 Electro-crystallization Overvoltage

It was first observed experimentally by Foersted et al. [121] that during the electrodeposition of metallic iron at the cathode, and as for other metals of the iron group VIIIA (i.e., Fe, Co, Ni) a significant overvoltage exists during the cathode process. It is estimated on average at 20°C to be about -0.128 V. This behavior contrasts with well-known electrodeposition of nonferrous metals such as copper or zinc that exhibits almost no measurable electro-crystallization overvoltage.

The values for the various overpotentials for each electrode material as a function of the operating temperature are reported in Table 68 and Table 107.

[121] FOERSTER, F.; HEROLD, V.;and MUSTAD, O. The electrochemical properties of iron. *Abhand. Deutsch. Bunsen Geschichte*, **2**(1909)59-81.

Table 68 – Electrode kinetics data for anode and cathode electrode reactions

2_KINETICS DATA	25°C	30°C	40°C	50°C	54°C	60°C	70°C	80°C	90°C
O_2 evolution overpotential (η_{O2}/V)	0.3856	0.3856	0.3856	0.3856	0.3856	0.3856	0.3856	0.3856	0.3856
Fe deposition overpotential (η_{Fe}/V)	-0.128	-0.121	-0.106	-0.091	-0.086	-0.077	-0.062	-0.048	-0.033
H_2 evolution overpotential (η_{H2}/V)	-1.2171	-1.2171	-1.2171	-1.2171	-1.2171	-1.2171	-1.2171	-1.2171	-1.2171
$O_2/2H_2O$ overvoltage (U/V vs. SHE)	1.6108	1.6046	1.5918	1.5790	1.5735	1.5657	1.5524	1.5386	1.5223
Fe^{2+}/Fe^0 overvoltage (U/V vs. SHE)	-0.6591	-0.6503	-0.6325	-0.6148	-0.6072	-0.5974	-0.5838	-0.5695	-0.5567
$2H^+/H_2$ overvoltage (U/V vs. SHE)	-1.3650	-1.3675	-1.3725	-1.3774	-1.3794	-1.3824	-1.3874	-1.3923	-1.3973
Overpotential contribution (η/V)	**0.514**	**0.506**	**0.492**	**0.477**	**0.471**	**0.462**	**0.448**	**0.433**	**0.419**
Cell overvoltage (U/V)	**2.270**	**2.255**	**2.224**	**2.194**	**2.181**	**2.163**	**2.136**	**2.108**	**2.079**

12.2.6 Cathode Polarization vs. Materials

Theoretically, it is expected that neither the anode material nor the anion exchange membrane should have a direct impact, under normal operating conditions (i.e., no proton leaks), on the electrochemical reactions occurring at the cathode. However in practice due to the leakage of protons across the membrane there is some acidification of the catholyte overtime if not addressed by adjusting the pH.

Therefore, the screening tests for cathode materials were performed by measuring simply the polarization curves and cathode current efficiency for the electrodeposition of iron using an parallepipedic undivided electrolyzer with a saturated aqueous solution of ferrous sulfate as electrolyte, and a soluble sacrificial anode made of mild steel grade AISI 1010 or better of pure ARMCO®(Trademark of *Armco Steel Corporation*) iron. In this case and above pH 1.0, the major electrochemical reactions at the electrodes are:

Soluble iron anode (+): $Fe(s) = Fe^{2+} + 2e^-$

Cathode (-): $Fe^{2+} + 2e^- = Fe(s)$

This decision was taken for two major reasons: (i) in order to focus only the electrochemical reactions occurring at the cathode without any interferences such as the mass transfer of sulfate anions across the membrane, (ii) the acidification of the catholyte due to leakage of protons as mentioned earlier, and (iii) in order to keep constant the high concentration of ferrous cations during the entire duration of the tests ensuring that the limiting current density is far greater than the cathode current density used during the measures.

The latter was kept almost constant by using a saturated aqueous solution of ferrous sulfate, and relying on a soluble mild steel anode supplying ferrous cations upon its anodic dissolution at the same feed rate since anode and cathode had the same effective immersed surface areas.

Before recording the polarization curves, the freshly prepared electrolyte was either pre-reduced chemically with pure electrolytic iron powder for several hours under inert atmosphere or pre-electrolyzed with a mild steel 1010 cathode at -1000 A/m^2 during 30 minutes in order to reduce the concentration of ferric cations down to trace levels.

The recorded plots of the cathode polarization of selected cathode materials vs. the cathode current density down to -1500 A/m^2 at 22°C in the above electrolyte at pH 1.0 and 2.0 respectively are depicted in Figure 67 and in Figure 68.

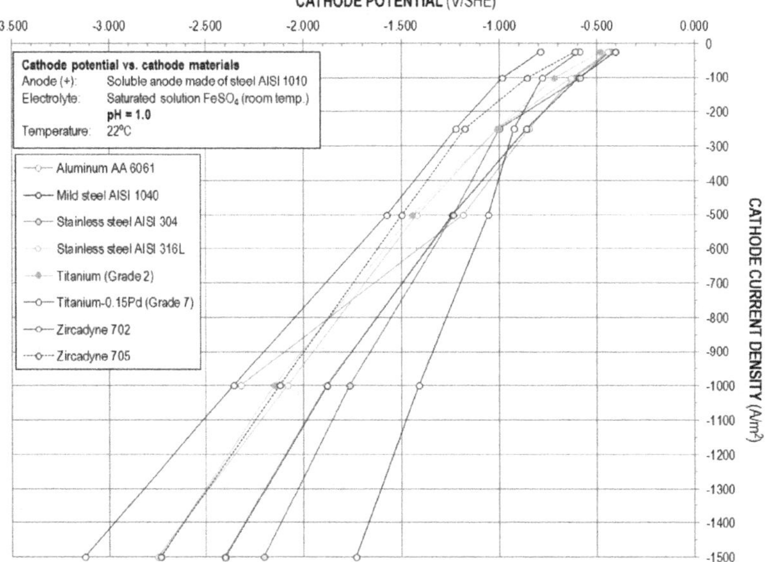

Figure 67 – Cathode potential vs. cathode current density in $FeSO_4$ (pH = 1.0)

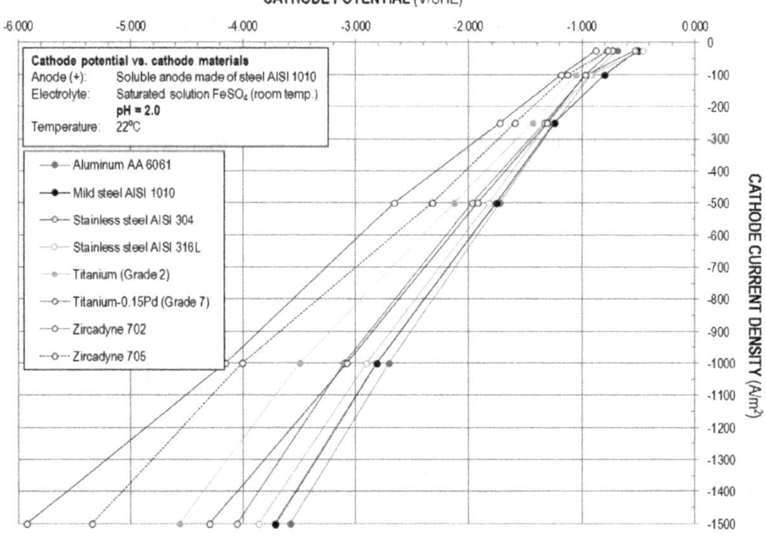

Figure 68 – Cathode potential vs. cathode current density in $FeSO_4$ (pH = 2.0)

The cathode polarization vs. cathode current density, and cathode materials was also recorded at 54°C and pH 2.0 with a saturated solution of ferrous sulfate at 54°C while the second solution was saturated at room temperature, and then raised to the operating temperature; these experimental data are summarized in Table 69 and in Table 70 respectivelly.

Table 69 – Cathode polarization vs. cathode current density (saturated)

Cathode current densities (A/m^2)	Ti Gr.2	Ti-0.15Pd	Zr-702	Al-6061	Steel 1010	SS-304	SS-316
-25	-0.225	-0.335	-0.321	-0.352	-0.183	-0.118	-0.050
-100	-0.404	-0.380	-0.429	-0.478	-0.519	-0.506	-0.343
-250	-0.637	-0.594	-0.639	-0.682	-0.759	-0.750	-0.554
-500	-1.007	-0.965	-0.985	-1.096	-1.144	-1.133	-0.902
-1000	-1.758	-1.734	-1.689	-1.877	-1.901	-1.896	-1.583
-1500	-2.475	-2.490	-2.391	-2.676	-2.614	-2.664	-2.216
Experimental conditions: Anode material (+): soluble anode made of mild steel AISI 1010; Electrolyte: saturated solution of $FeSO_4$ at operating temperature (i.e., excess copperas crystals at bottom of electrolyzer) with pH = 2.0 and temperature: 54°C.							

Table 70 – Cathode polarization vs. cathode current density (concentrated)

Cathode current densities (A/m^2)	Ti Gr.2	Ti-0.15Pd	Zr-702	Zr-705	Al 6061	Steel 1010	SS 304	SS 316	Cu C110
-25	-0.393	-0.373	-0.132	-0.423	-0.400	-0.179	-0.136	-0.112	-0.406
-100	-0.546	-0.561	-0.391	-0.608	-0.590	-0.504	-0.534	-0.503	-0.567
-250	-0.857	-0.832	-0.676	-0.900	-0.833	-0.857	-0.835	-0.808	-0.840
-500	-1.390	-1.253	-1.140	-1.320	-1.331	-1.382	-1.343	-1.374	-1.360
Experimental conditions: Anode material (+): soluble anode made of mild steel AISI 1010; Electrolyte: saturated solution of $FeSO_4$ prepared at room temperature (1,264 kg/m^3) with pH 2.0 and Temperature: 54°C.									

From these data, we can see clearly that using cathodes made of chemically pure titanium and zirconium metals exhibit the highest cathode polarization but mild steel exhibits also a satisfactory cathode polarization when measured in such saturated solution of ferrous sulfate. This explains why chemically pure titanium (e.g., ASTM grade 2) can be used as a blank cathode and mild steel grade AISI 1010 can be used satisfactorily as a starter sheet cathode.

12.2.7 Cathode Polarization vs. Temperature

The cathode polarization vs. cathode materials was also recorded at 25°C and 54°C and pH 2.0 with a solution of $FeSO_4$ saturated at room temperature, the experimental data are summarized in Table 71.

Table 71 – Cathode polarization vs. temperature

Temp.	Ti	Ti-0.15Pd	Zr-702	Zr-705	Al 6061	Steel 1010	SS 304	SS 316	Cu C110
25°C	-1.946	-1.850	-2.000	-1.990	-2.000	-2.196	-1.970	-1.900	-2.000
54°C	-1.390	-1.253	-1.140	-1.320	-1.331	-1.382	-1.343	-1.374	-1.360
Experimental conditions: Anode material (+): soluble anode made of mild steel AISI 1010; Electrolyte: saturated solution of $FeSO_4$ prepared at room temperature (1,264 kg/m^3) with pH = 2.00; Cathode current density (CCD): -500A/m^2.									

12.2.8 Cathode Polarization vs. Concentration

The cathode polarization vs. the concentration of $FeSO_4$ in the catholyte at pH 2.0 was recorded, and the experimental data are summarized in Table 72.

Table 72 – Cathode polarization vs. catholyte saturation

$FeSO_4$ percent	Ti Gr. 2	Ti-0.15Pd	Zr-702	Zr-705	Al 6061	Steel 1010	SS 304	SS 316	Cu C110
34 wt.% (54°C)	-1.007	-0.965	-0.985	-1.010	-1.096	-1.144	-1.133	-0.902	n.a.
21 wt.% (21°C)	-1.390	-1.253	-1.140	-1.320	-1.331	-1.382	-1.343	-1.374	-1.360
Experimental conditions: Anode material (+): soluble anode made of mild steel AISI 1010; pH = 2.00; Cathode current density (CCD): -500A/m^2.									

12.2.9 Cathode Polarization vs. pH

The cathode polarization vs. the pH of the catholyte was recorded, and the experimental data are summarized in Table 73.

Table 73 – Cathode Polarization vs. pH

pH	Ti	Ti-0.15Pd	Zr-702	Zr-705	Al 6061	Steel 1010	SS 304	SS 316	Cu C110
1.00 (25°C)	-2.022	-1.876	-2.100	-2.050	-2.102	-2.100	-1.990	-1.954	-1.915
2.00 (25°C)	-1.946	-1.700	-1.980	-1.950	-1.853	-2.196	-1.950	-1.900	-1.867
2.50 (54°C)	-0.947	-0.902	-0.928	-0.910	-1.043	-1.076	-1.071	-0.842	-0.980
Experimental conditions: Anode material (+): soluble anode of mild steel AISI 1010; Electrolyte: saturated solution of $FeSO_4$ prepared at room temperature (1,264 kg/m^3); Cathode current density (CCD): -500A/m^2.									

12.2.10 Cathode Polarization vs. Surface Treatment

The influence of various surface treatment currently performed during metal finishing operations have an impact on the cathode polarization and the adherence of the electrodeposited iron. Because each metal and alloys may be subject to various surface finishing treatments, we have summarized the most usual surface treatments performed during prototype, and pilot testing, and aimed for a commercial operation.

Table 74 – Selected surface finishing techniques

Cathode material	Surface as received	Surface treatment
C.P. Titanium (ASTM grade 2)	Smooth mill finish	Chemical etching
Titanium-0.15Pd (ASTM grade 7)	Smooth mill finish	Chemical etching
Aluminum AA 2024	Smooth mill finish	Passivation
Zircadyne® 702	Smooth mill finish	Chemical polishing (Mirror finish)
Zircadyne® 705	Smooth mill finish	Chemical polishing (Mirror finish)
Pure copper C110	Bright mill finish	Electrochemical polishing
Pure nickel 201	Smooth mill finish	Electrochemical polishing
Mild steel AISI 1010	Magnetite mill scale	Chemical pickling
Austenitic stainless steel AISI 304	Bright mill finish	Electrochemical polishing
Austenitic stainless steel AISI 316	Bright mill finish	Electrochemical polishing

12.2.11 Cathode Overvoltage vs. Materials, and pH

Based on all the experimental data collected during the last 14 years of laboratory and prototype testing especially regarding the polarization for various cathode materials as a function of temperature, pH, cathode current density, and concentration of iron, we were finally able to established a set of practical charts for each metallic substrate showing the cathode polarization required for the electrodeposition of metallic iron vs. the potential for evolving hydrogen at a fixed cathode current density, and for a given, pH, iron concentration, and operating temperature. We will exemplify the use of such charts in the following three examples.

For instance, the Table 75 lists the polarization conditions for electrowinning iron at -500 A/m², from a catholyte at pH 1.0 with a total concentration of iron equal to 50 g/L Fe(II), the latter mimics some spent pickling liquors. In this case, we can see that, if we use a mild steel cathode at 54°C, the difference between the electrodeposition of iron and the evolution of hydrogen is only 119 mV while if we use instead a titanium cathode, the potential difference becomes much larger 514 mV allowing to reach a much better current efficiency.

Table 75 – Potentials for iron deposition and hydrogen evolution (pH 1.0, -500 A/m²)

OPERATING TEMPERATURE		25°C	30°C	40°C	50°C	54°C	60°C	70°C	80°C	90°C
Absolute thermodynamic temperature		298.15 K	303.15 K	313.15 K	323.15 K	327.15 K	333.15 K	343.15 K	353.15 K	363.15 K
		-500 A/m²		pH 1.0		Fe(II)	50.0 g/L			
$2H^+/H_2$ std. electrode potential (E^0/V vs. SHE)		0.000	0.000	0.000	0.000	0.000	0.000	0.000	0.000	0.000
$2H^+/H_2$ electrode potential (E/V vs. SHE) at pH		-0.059	-0.060	-0.062	-0.064	-0.065	-0.066	-0.068	-0.070	-0.072
Fe^{2+}/Fe std. electrode potential (E^0/V vs. SHE)		-0.447	-0.445	-0.442	-0.439	-0.437	-0.435	-0.431	-0.428	-0.424
Fe^{2+}/Fe electrode potential (E/V vs. SHE)		-0.448	-0.447	-0.443	-0.440	-0.439	-0.437	-0.433	-0.429	-0.426
Fe deposition overpotential (η_{Fe}/V)[Temp. non comp]	IRON	-0.343	-0.343	-0.343	-0.343	-0.343	-0.343	-0.343	-0.343	-0.343
Fe deposition overpotential (η_{Fe}/V) [compensated]	IRON	-0.293	-0.272	-0.231	-0.189	-0.173	-0.148	-0.107	-0.066	-0.025
H_2 evolution overpotential (η_{H2}/V)	STAINLESS 304	-0.615	-0.615	-0.615	-0.615	-0.615	-0.615	-0.615	-0.615	-0.615
H_2 evolution overpotential (η_{H2}/V)	COPPER C110	-0.658	-0.658	-0.658	-0.658	-0.658	-0.658	-0.658	-0.658	-0.658
H_2 evolution overpotential (η_{H2}/V)	MILD STEEL 1010	-0.666	-0.666	-0.666	-0.666	-0.666	-0.666	-0.666	-0.666	-0.666
H_2 evolution overpotential (η_{H2}/V)	ALUMINUM 1001	-0.748	-0.748	-0.748	-0.748	-0.748	-0.748	-0.748	-0.748	-0.748
H_2 evolution overpotential (η_{H2}/V)	TITANIUM GR. 2	-1.061	-1.061	-1.061	-1.061	-1.061	-1.061	-1.061	-1.061	-1.061
STAINLESS STEEL 304										
Fe^{2+}/Fe^0 polarization onto iron (U/V vs. SHE)		-0.741	-0.719	-0.674	-0.630	-0.612	-0.585	-0.540	-0.495	-0.450
$2H^+/H_2$ polarization onto slainless (U/V vs. SHE)		-0.674	-0.675	-0.677	-0.679	-0.680	-0.681	-0.683	-0.685	-0.687
Fe^{2+}/Fe^0 polarization onto iron (U/V vs. MSSA)		-1.395	-1.373	-1.328	-1.284	**-1.266**	-1.239	-1.194	-1.149	-1.104
$2H^+/H_2$ polarization onto stainless (U/V vs. MSSA)		-1.328	-1.329	-1.331	-1.333	-1.334	-1.335	-1.337	-1.339	-1.341
COPPER C110	ΔE (H_2 vs. Fe)	0.067	0.044	-0.003	-0.049	-0.068	-0.096	-0.143	-0.190	-0.237
Fe^{2+}/Fe^0 polarization onto iron (U/V vs. SHE)		-0.741	-0.719	-0.674	-0.630	-0.612	-0.585	-0.540	-0.495	-0.450
$2H^+/H_2$ polarization onto copper (U/V vs. SHE)		-0.718	-0.719	-0.721	-0.723	-0.723	-0.725	-0.727	-0.728	-0.730
Fe^{2+}/Fe^0 polarization onto iron (U/V vs. MSSA)		-1.395	-1.373	-1.328	-1.284	**-1.266**	-1.239	-1.194	-1.149	-1.104
$2H^+/H_2$ polarization onto copper (U/V vs. MSSA)		-1.372	-1.373	-1.375	-1.377	-1.377	-1.379	-1.381	-1.382	-1.384
MILD STEEL 1010	ΔE (H_2 vs. Fe)	0.023	0.000	-0.046	-0.093	-0.112	-0.140	-0.187	-0.233	-0.280
Fe^{2+}/Fe^0 polarization onto iron (U/V vs. SHE)		-0.741	-0.719	-0.674	-0.630	-0.612	-0.585	-0.540	-0.495	-0.450
$2H^+/H_2$ polarization onto mild steel (U/V vs. SHE)		-0.725	-0.726	-0.728	-0.730	-0.730	-0.732	-0.734	-0.736	-0.738
Fe^{2+}/Fe^0 polarization onto iron (U/V vs. MSSA)		-1.395	-1.373	-1.328	-1.284	**-1.266**	-1.239	-1.194	-1.149	-1.104
$2H^+/H_2$ polarization onto mild steel (U/V vs. MSSA)		-1.379	-1.380	-1.382	-1.384	-1.384	-1.386	-1.388	-1.390	-1.392
ALUMINUM 1001	ΔE (H_2 vs. Fe)	0.016	-0.007	-0.054	-0.100	-0.119	-0.147	-0.194	-0.240	-0.287
Fe^{2+}/Fe^0 polarization onto iron (U/V vs. SHE)		-0.741	-0.719	-0.674	-0.630	-0.612	-0.585	-0.540	-0.495	-0.450
$2H^+/H_2$ polarization onto aluminum (U/V vs. SHE)		-0.807	-0.808	-0.810	-0.812	-0.813	-0.814	-0.816	-0.818	-0.820
Fe^{2+}/Fe^0 polarization onto iron (U/V vs. MSSA)		-1.395	-1.373	-1.328	-1.284	**-1.266**	-1.239	-1.194	-1.149	-1.104
$2H^+/H_2$ polarization onto aluminum (U/V vs. MSSA)		-1.461	-1.462	-1.464	-1.466	-1.467	-1.468	-1.470	-1.472	-1.474
TITANIUM GR. 2	ΔE (H_2 vs. Fe)	-0.066	-0.089	-0.136	-0.183	-0.201	-0.229	-0.276	-0.323	-0.370
Fe^{2+}/Fe^0 polarization onto iron (U/V vs. SHE)		-0.741	-0.719	-0.674	-0.630	-0.612	-0.585	-0.540	-0.495	-0.450
$2H^+/H_2$ polarization onto titanium (U/V vs. SHE)		-1.120	-1.121	-1.123	-1.125	-1.126	-1.127	-1.129	-1.131	-1.133
Fe^{2+}/Fe^0 polarization onto iron (U/V vs. MSSA)		-1.395	-1.373	-1.328	-1.284	**-1.266**	-1.239	-1.194	-1.149	-1.104
$2H^+/H_2$ polarization onto titanium (U/V vs. MSSA)		-1.774	-1.775	-1.777	-1.779	-1.780	-1.781	-1.783	-1.785	-1.787
	DELTA	-0.379	-0.402	-0.449	-0.495	-0.514	-0.542	-0.589	-0.636	-0.683

Now, if we operate with the same catholyte composition as described previously but electrowinning at a much higher cathode current density of -1500 A/m² as reported in Table 76. In this case, we can see that, if even if we use a mild steel cathode at 54°C, the difference between the electrodeposition of iron and the evolution of hydrogen is 467 mV that becomes sufficient to ensure a better current efficiency. This corroborates the observations made by previous researchers that are summarized in Section 3.3. In short higher is the acidity higher the cathode current density must be to enhance the overpotential for the hydrogen gas evolution reaction.

Table 76 – Potentials for iron deposition and hydrogen evolution (pH 1.0, -1500 A/m²)

OPERATING TEMPERATURE		25°C	30°C	40°C	50°C	54°C	60°C	70°C	80°C	90°C
Absolute thermodynamic temperature		298.15 K	303.15 K	313.15 K	323.15 K	327.15 K	333.15 K	343.15 K	353.15 K	363.15 K
		-1500 A/m²		pH 1.0		Fe(II)	50.0 g/L			
$2H^+/H_2$ std. electrode potential (E^0/V vs. SHE)		0.000	0.000	0.000	0.000	0.000	0.000	0.000	0.000	0.000
$2H^+/H_2$ electrode potential (E/V vs. SHE) at pH		-0.059	-0.060	-0.062	-0.064	-0.065	-0.066	-0.068	-0.070	-0.072
Fe^{2+}/Fe std. electrode potential (E^0/V vs. SHE)		-0.447	-0.445	-0.442	-0.439	-0.437	-0.435	-0.431	-0.428	-0.424
Fe^{2+}/Fe electrode potential (E/V vs. SHE)		-0.448	-0.447	-0.443	-0.440	-0.439	-0.437	-0.433	-0.429	-0.426
Fe deposition overpotential (η_{Fe}/V)[Temp. non comp]	IRON	-0.380	-0.380	-0.380	-0.380	-0.380	-0.380	-0.380	-0.380	-0.380
Fe deposition overpotential (η_{Fe}/V) [compensated]	IRON	-0.329	-0.306	-0.260	-0.214	-0.196	-0.168	-0.122	-0.076	-0.030
H_2 evolution overpotential (η_{H2}/V)	STAINLESS 304	-0.930	-0.930	-0.930	-0.930	-0.930	-0.930	-0.930	-0.930	-0.930
H_2 evolution overpotential (η_{H2}/V)	COPPER C110	-0.970	-0.970	-0.970	-0.970	-0.970	-0.970	-0.970	-0.970	-0.970
H_2 evolution overpotential (η_{H2}/V)	MILD STEEL 1010	-1.036	-1.036	-1.036	-1.036	-1.036	-1.036	-1.036	-1.036	-1.036
H_2 evolution overpotential (η_{H2}/V)	ALUMINUM 1001	-1.068	-1.068	-1.068	-1.068	-1.068	-1.068	-1.068	-1.068	-1.068
H_2 evolution overpotential (η_{H2}/V)	TITANIUM GR. 2	-1.308	-1.308	-1.308	-1.308	-1.308	-1.308	-1.308	-1.308	-1.308
STAINLESS STEEL 304										
Fe^{2+}/Fe^0 polarization onto iron (U/V vs. SHE)		-0.777	-0.753	-0.703	-0.654	-0.634	-0.605	-0.555	-0.506	-0.456
$2H^+/H_2$ polarization onto slainless (U/V vs. SHE)		-0.989	-0.990	-0.992	-0.994	-0.995	-0.996	-0.998	-1.000	-1.002
Fe^{2+}/Fe^0 polarization onto iron (U/V vs. MSSA)		-1.431	-1.407	-1.357	-1.308	**-1.288**	-1.259	-1.209	-1.160	-1.110
$2H^+/H_2$ polarization onto stainless (U/V vs. MSSA)		-1.643	-1.644	-1.646	-1.648	-1.649	-1.650	-1.652	-1.654	-1.656
COPPER C110	ΔE (H_2 vs. Fe)	-0.212	-0.238	-0.289	-0.340	-0.361	-0.392	-0.443	-0.495	-0.546
Fe^{2+}/Fe^0 polarization onto iron (U/V vs. SHE)		-0.777	-0.753	-0.703	-0.654	-0.634	-0.605	-0.555	-0.506	-0.456
$2H^+/H_2$ polarization onto copper (U/V vs. SHE)		-1.030	-1.030	-1.032	-1.034	-1.035	-1.036	-1.038	-1.040	-1.042
Fe^{2+}/Fe^0 polarization onto iron (U/V vs. MSSA)		-1.431	-1.407	-1.357	-1.308	**-1.288**	-1.259	-1.209	-1.160	-1.110
$2H^+/H_2$ polarization onto copper (U/V vs. MSSA)		-1.684	-1.684	-1.686	-1.688	-1.689	-1.690	-1.692	-1.694	-1.696
MILD STEEL 1010	ΔE (H_2 vs. Fe)	-0.252	-0.278	-0.329	-0.380	-0.401	-0.432	-0.483	-0.535	-0.587
Fe^{2+}/Fe^0 polarization onto iron (U/V vs. SHE)		-0.777	-0.753	-0.703	-0.654	-0.634	-0.605	-0.555	-0.506	-0.456
$2H^+/H_2$ polarization onto mild steel (U/V vs. SHE)		-1.096	-1.097	-1.099	-1.101	-1.101	-1.103	-1.104	-1.106	-1.108
Fe^{2+}/Fe^0 polarization onto iron (U/V vs. MSSA)		-1.431	-1.407	-1.357	-1.308	**-1.288**	-1.259	-1.209	-1.160	-1.110
$2H^+/H_2$ polarization onto mild steel (U/V vs. MSSA)		-1.750	-1.751	-1.753	-1.755	-1.755	-1.757	-1.758	-1.760	-1.762
ALUMINUM 1001	ΔE (H_2 vs. Fe)	-0.318	-0.344	-0.395	-0.446	-0.467	-0.498	-0.549	-0.601	-0.653
Fe^{2+}/Fe^0 polarization onto iron (U/V vs. SHE)		-0.777	-0.753	-0.703	-0.654	-0.634	-0.605	-0.555	-0.506	-0.456
$2H^+/H_2$ polarization onto aluminum (U/V vs. SHE)		-1.127	-1.128	-1.130	-1.132	-1.133	-1.134	-1.136	-1.138	-1.140
Fe^{2+}/Fe^0 polarization onto iron (U/V vs. MSSA)		-1.431	-1.407	-1.357	-1.308	**-1.288**	-1.259	-1.209	-1.160	-1.110
$2H^+/H_2$ polarization onto aluminum (U/V vs. MSSA)		-1.781	-1.782	-1.784	-1.786	-1.787	-1.788	-1.790	-1.792	-1.794
TITANIUM GR. 2	ΔE (H_2 vs. Fe)	-0.350	-0.376	-0.427	-0.478	-0.499	-0.530	-0.581	-0.633	-0.684
Fe^{2+}/Fe^0 polarization onto iron (U/V vs. SHE)		-0.777	-0.753	-0.703	-0.654	-0.634	-0.605	-0.555	-0.506	-0.456
$2H^+/H_2$ polarization onto titanium (U/V vs. SHE)		-1.367	-1.368	-1.370	-1.372	-1.373	-1.374	-1.376	-1.378	-1.380
Fe^{2+}/Fe^0 polarization onto iron (U/V vs. MSSA)		-1.431	-1.407	-1.357	-1.308	**-1.288**	-1.259	-1.209	-1.160	-1.110
$2H^+/H_2$ polarization onto titanium (U/V vs. MSSA)		-2.021	-2.022	-2.024	-2.026	-2.027	-2.028	-2.030	-2.032	-2.034
	DELTA	-0.590	-0.616	-0.667	-0.718	-0.739	-0.770	-0.821	-0.873	-0.924

In another instance, the Table 77 lists the polarization conditions for electrowinning iron at -750 A/m², from a catholyte at pH 2.5 with a total concentration of iron equal to 80 g/L Fe(II). In this case, we can see that, even if we use a stainless steel 304 cathode at 54°C, the difference between the electrodeposition of iron and the evolution of hydrogen is 312 mV that will ensure the electrodeposition of an iron deposit of good quality.

Table 77 – Potentials for iron deposition and hydrogen evolution (pH 3.0, -750 A/m^2)

OPERATING TEMPERATURE		25°C	30°C	40°C	50°C	54°C	60°C	70°C	80°C	90°C
Absolute thermodynamic temperature		298.15 K	303.15 K	313.15 K	323.15 K	327.15 K	333.15 K	343.15 K	353.15 K	363.15 K
		-750 A/m^2		pH 3.0		Fe(II)	80.0 g/L			
$2H^+/H_2$ std. electrode potential (E^0/V vs. SHE)		0.000	0.000	0.000	0.000	0.000	0.000	0.000	0.000	0.000
$2H^+/H_2$ electrode potential (E/V vs. SHE) at pH		-0.177	-0.180	-0.186	-0.192	-0.195	-0.198	-0.204	-0.210	-0.216
Fe^{2+}/Fe std. electrode potential (E^0/V vs. SHE)		-0.447	-0.445	-0.442	-0.439	-0.437	-0.435	-0.431	-0.428	-0.424
Fe^{2+}/Fe electrode potential (E/V vs. SHE)		-0.442	-0.441	-0.437	-0.434	-0.432	-0.430	-0.426	-0.422	-0.418
Fe deposition overpotential (η_{Fe}/V)[Temp. non comp]	IRON	-0.356	-0.356	-0.356	-0.356	-0.356	-0.356	-0.356	-0.356	-0.356
Fe deposition overpotential (η_{Fe}/V) [compensated]	IRON	-0.306	-0.284	-0.241	-0.198	-0.181	-0.156	-0.113	-0.070	-0.027
H_2 evolution overpotential (η_{H2}/V)	STAINLESS 304	-0.731	-0.731	-0.731	-0.731	-0.731	-0.731	-0.731	-0.731	-0.731
H_2 evolution overpotential (η_{H2}/V)	COPPER C110	-0.774	-0.774	-0.774	-0.774	-0.774	-0.774	-0.774	-0.774	-0.774
H_2 evolution overpotential (η_{H2}/V)	MILD STEEL 1010	-0.802	-0.802	-0.802	-0.802	-0.802	-0.802	-0.802	-0.802	-0.802
H_2 evolution overpotential (η_{H2}/V)	ALUMINUM 1001	-0.866	-0.866	-0.866	-0.866	-0.866	-0.866	-0.866	-0.866	-0.866
H_2 evolution overpotential (η_{H2}/V)	TITANIUM GR. 2	-1.152	-1.152	-1.152	-1.152	-1.152	-1.152	-1.152	-1.152	-1.152
STAINLESS STEEL 304										
Fe^{2+}/Fe^0 polarization onto iron (U/V vs. SHE)		-0.748	-0.725	-0.679	-0.632	-0.613	-0.585	-0.539	-0.492	-0.445
$2H^+/H_2$ polarization onto slainless (U/V vs. SHE)		-0.909	-0.912	-0.917	-0.923	-0.926	-0.929	-0.935	-0.941	-0.947
Fe^{2+}/Fe^0 polarization onto iron (U/V vs. MSSA)		-1.402	-1.379	-1.333	-1.286	**-1.267**	-1.239	-1.193	-1.146	-1.099
$2H^+/H_2$ polarization onto stainless (U/V vs. MSSA)		-1.563	-1.566	-1.571	-1.577	-1.580	-1.583	-1.589	-1.595	-1.601
COPPER C110	ΔE (H_2 vs. Fe)	-0.160	-0.186	-0.239	-0.291	-0.312	-0.344	-0.397	-0.449	-0.502
Fe^{2+}/Fe^0 polarization onto iron (U/V vs. SHE)		-0.748	-0.725	-0.679	-0.632	-0.613	-0.585	-0.539	-0.492	-0.445
$2H^+/H_2$ polarization onto copper (U/V vs. SHE)		-0.951	-0.954	-0.960	-0.966	-0.968	-0.972	-0.978	-0.984	-0.990
Fe^{2+}/Fe^0 polarization onto iron (U/V vs. MSSA)		-1.402	-1.379	-1.333	-1.286	**-1.267**	-1.239	-1.193	-1.146	-1.099
$2H^+/H_2$ polarization onto copper (U/V vs. MSSA)		-1.605	-1.608	-1.614	-1.620	-1.622	-1.626	-1.632	-1.638	-1.644
MILD STEEL 1010	ΔE (H_2 vs. Fe)	-0.203	-0.229	-0.281	-0.334	-0.355	-0.386	-0.439	-0.492	-0.545
Fe^{2+}/Fe^0 polarization onto iron (U/V vs. SHE)		-0.748	-0.725	-0.679	-0.632	-0.613	-0.585	-0.539	-0.492	-0.445
$2H^+/H_2$ polarization onto mild steel (U/V vs. SHE)		-0.980	-0.983	-0.989	-0.995	-0.997	-1.001	-1.007	-1.013	-1.019
Fe^{2+}/Fe^0 polarization onto iron (U/V vs. MSSA)		-1.402	-1.379	-1.333	-1.286	**-1.267**	-1.239	-1.193	-1.146	-1.099
$2H^+/H_2$ polarization onto mild steel (U/V vs. MSSA)		-1.634	-1.637	-1.643	-1.649	-1.651	-1.655	-1.661	-1.667	-1.673
ALUMINUM 1001	ΔE (H_2 vs. Fe)	-0.232	-0.258	-0.310	-0.363	-0.384	-0.415	-0.468	-0.521	-0.574
Fe^{2+}/Fe^0 polarization onto iron (U/V vs. SHE)		-0.748	-0.725	-0.679	-0.632	-0.613	-0.585	-0.539	-0.492	-0.445
$2H^+/H_2$ polarization onto aluminum (U/V vs. SHE)		-1.044	-1.047	-1.053	-1.059	-1.061	-1.064	-1.070	-1.076	-1.082
Fe^{2+}/Fe^0 polarization onto iron (U/V vs. MSSA)		-1.402	-1.379	-1.333	-1.286	**-1.267**	-1.239	-1.193	-1.146	-1.099
$2H^+/H_2$ polarization onto aluminum (U/V vs. MSSA)		-1.698	-1.701	-1.707	-1.713	-1.715	-1.718	-1.724	-1.730	-1.736
TITANIUM GR. 2	ΔE (H_2 vs. Fe)	-0.295	-0.322	-0.374	-0.426	-0.448	-0.479	-0.532	-0.585	-0.637
Fe^{2+}/Fe^0 polarization onto iron (U/V vs. SHE)		-0.748	-0.725	-0.679	-0.632	-0.613	-0.585	-0.539	-0.492	-0.445
$2H^+/H_2$ polarization onto titanium (U/V vs. SHE)		-1.330	-1.333	-1.338	-1.344	-1.347	-1.350	-1.356	-1.362	-1.368
Fe^{2+}/Fe^0 polarization onto iron (U/V vs. MSSA)		-1.402	-1.379	-1.333	-1.286	**-1.267**	-1.239	-1.193	-1.146	-1.099
$2H^+/H_2$ polarization onto titanium (U/V vs. MSSA)		-1.984	-1.987	-1.992	-1.998	-2.001	-2.004	-2.010	-2.016	-2.022
	DELTA	-0.581	-0.607	-0.660	-0.712	-0.733	-0.765	-0.818	-0.870	-0.923

12.2.12 Current Efficiency vs. Materials and Temperature

The cathode current efficiency vs. the cathode material and temperature for a catholyte at pH 2.0 and a cathode current density of -500 A/m^2 is reported in in Table 78.

Table 78 – Cathode current efficiency vs. materials and temperature

Temp.	Ti	Ti-0.15Pd	Zr-702	Zr-705	Al 6061	Steel 1010	SS 304	SS 316	Cu C110
25°C	95.2	90.0	95.0	93.0	97.7	93.8	47.6	50.0	85.0
54°C	98.0	94.2	99.0	94.2	90.9	88.1	90.2	90.9	94.2
Experimental conditions: Anode material (+): soluble anode made of two rectangular plates made of carbon steel AISI 1010; Electrolyte: $FeSO_4$ saturated solution prepared at room temperature (1,264 kg/m^3) with imposed pH = 2.00 and j_c = -500 A/m^2.									

12.2.13 Cathode Current Efficiency vs. Initial pH and Time

When electrowinning metallic iron from a catholyte made of a warm concentrated solution of ferrous sulfate (350 g/L $FeSO_4$) and using a divided electrolyzer with an anolyte made of 10 wt.% H_2SO_4 at a constant temperature of 50°C, and with an initial pH of 2.5, under a cathode current density of -500 A/m^2, the cathode current efficiency (CCE) measured after one hour of electrolysis is 98 percent.

However, if no pH adjustments are made regularly after certain duration of electrolysis because the sulfuric acid concentration build-ups inside the anode compartment, the proton rejection capability of the anion exchange membrane becomes insufficient to prevent the driving force for the diffusion of protons across the membrane, and thus the acidification of the catholyte occurs.

By performing several experiments by increasing the duration of electrowinning for the same volume of catholyte with a recirculation from a holding tank, we did observe that the final pH gradually decreased after each run. Actually, for the last run after 8 hours of continuous operation it reached 1.5 with a cathode current efficiency of only 70 percent as depicted in Figure 69.

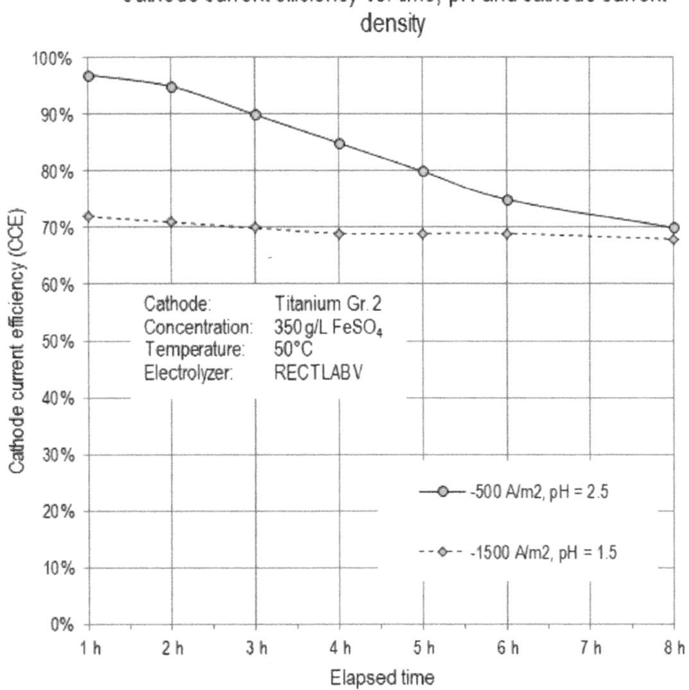

Figure 69 – Cathode current efficiency vs. cathode current density, pH and duration

Conversely, performing the electrowinning at a much higher cathode current density of -1500 A/m^2 with the same volume of catholyte but with an initial acidic pH of 1.5, the cathode current efficiency after one hour was 72 percent. Surprisingly, the cathode current efficiency after each run decreased only slightly and after 8 hours, the cathode current efficiency was still 68 percent. This latter behavior can be attributed to the high cathode current density that leads to equilibrium between the reaction rate for the reduction (i.e., consumption) of protons and the diffusion of protons (i.e., leakage) across the membrane.

From these results, it is therefore of paramount importance to kept the pH above 2.5 to ensure proper electrodeposition of metallic iron for instance by circulating the catholyte through a pH adjustment tank where it will be in contact with mill scale, iron (II) carbonate or a neutralizing agent that will neutralize the excess protons.

The initial concentration of sulfuric acid in the anolyte also has an impact as when reaching 30 wt.% the transport number of sulfate anions decreases with an increase in temperature while the transport number of protons increases.

12.2.14 Cathode Current Efficiency vs. pH and $FeSO_4$

The relationship between the cathode current efficiency (CCE) for the electrodeposition of electrolytic iron metal vs. the pH and the concentration of ferrous sulfate in the catholyte was investigated for pH ranging from 0.5 to 4.0 and for two cathode current density of -500 and -1500 A/m^2 respectively at an operating temperature of 50°C. The plotted experimental results obtained are depicted in Figure 70.

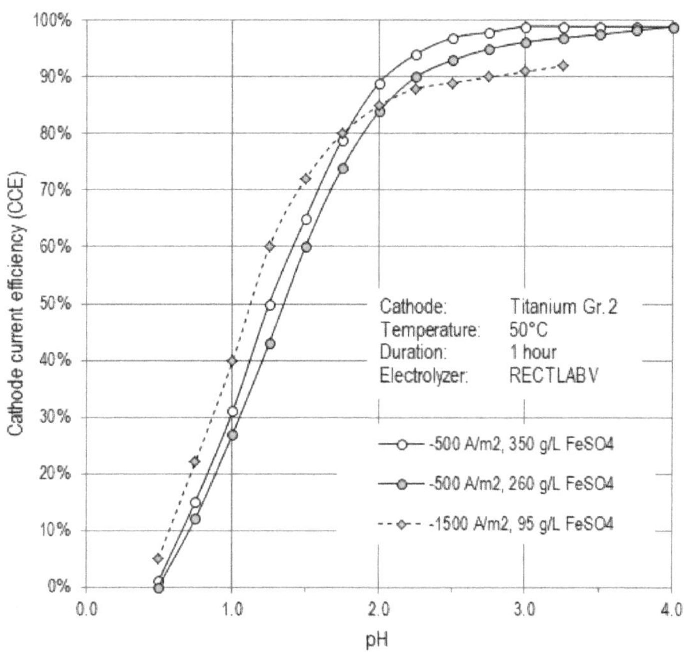

Figure 70 – Cathode current efficiency vs. pH and concentration of $FeSO_4$

From the plots, we can see clearly that in the pH range 0.5 up to 2.0, the cathode current efficiency increases almost linearly. In all cases, the cathode current efficiency is almost zero for pH below 0.5 but it is worth to note that at pH 0.5 it is 5 percent when operating under a high cathode current density of -1500 A/m^2.

When the pH increases from 0.5 to 1.5 the cathode current efficiency reaches 60 percent at -500 A/m^2 for a catholyte containing 260 g/L $FeSO_4$ and even 65 percent for concentrated solution with 350 g/L. Interestingly, when electrolyzing a catholyte with a lower iron concentration of 95 g/L $FeSO_4$, that is, similar to the concentration found is some pregnant leach solutions, and spent pickling liquors, at a much higher cathode current density of -1500 A/m^2, the cathode current efficiency measured for that acidic range of pH is always 3-5 percent higher up reaching 40 percent at pH 1.0 and 72 percent at pH 1.5.

Above pH 1.75, the cathode current efficiency increases less rapidly following a parabolic trend to reach 95 percent at pH 2.5 and nearly 99 percent at pH 3.0 with a catholyte containing 350 g/L $FeSO_4$. However, electrolyzing under high current density above that pH threshold does not bring any benefits except a higher production rate of iron as the cathode current efficiency ranges from 90-92 percent.

There was very little difference in the cathode current efficiency for plating metallic iron for concentration of ferrous sulfate ranging from 260 to 350 g/L above pH 2.5.

Above pH 3.0, at a cathode current density of -500 A/m^2, the cathode current efficiency reaches a plateau of nearly 99.5 percent from 3.5 to 4.0. However at such elevate pH, the ferrous cations in the catholyte are prone to rapid air oxidation into Fe(III) that will precipitate as greenish-brown flocks of ferrous-ferric hydroxide $Fe(OH)_2FeOOH$ and thus contaminate the electrodeposited iron metal. Therefore in practice, for preventing these issues, it will be necessary to perform from time to time the dummying of the catholyte with a constant cross flow filtration of the bath.

Alternatively, it is possible for certain plant locations near an ammonia facility to inject gaseous ammonia or ammonium hydroxide (i.e., aqueous ammonia) directly into the anode compartment to neutralize the excess of sulfuric acid formed. This option avoids the acidification of the catholyte. The ammonium sulfate brine co-produced is removed, and it can be used to crystallize ammonium sulfate to be used as fertilizer.

Another possibility consists to use a three-compartment electrolyzer with a central compartment containing a dilute aqueous solution of sulfuric acid acting as a buffer while concentrated sulfuric acid is produced at the anode.

12.2.15 Cathode Current Efficiency at pH below 1.35

The tests consisted to measure the cathode current efficiency with a CP titanium cathode at low pH below the threshold of 1.35 using the RECTLAB V cell with a batch recirculation mode. Actually, as many ferrous sulfate solutions and spent pickling liquors contain free sulfuric acid and hence are usually acidic it was interesting to determine the best cathode current efficiency obtainable under these harsh conditions for electrowinning iron.

Table 79 – Cathode current efficiencies at pH below 1.4 vs. cathode current densities

Temp.	28°C	37°C	25°C	34°C	42°C	29°C	37°C
pH (20°C)	1.2	1.2	1.1	1.2	1.3	1.4	1.3
j_c (A/m^2)	-500	-1500	-1200	-1200	-1000	-1500	-2000
CCE (%)	66.9	56	47	35.2	44.3	83.2	83.1
Experimental conditions: Anode material (+): Ti/Ta_2O_5-IrO_2; Anion exchange membrane; Anolyte: H_2SO_4 5.0 to 6.0 wt.%; Catholyte: $FeSO_4$ saturated aqueous solution prepared at room temperature, Cathode (-): C.P. titanium grade 2.							

In all the cases, the final rest or open circuit potential (OCV) at the end of each electrowinning experiment was equal to the Nernst electrode potential of an iron metal electrode in equilibrium with a saturated solution of ferrous sulfate at 25°C, that is -0.398 V/SHE, with slight departure from this value mainly attributed to an increase in temperature and variation in the actual concentration of ferrous cations. This indicated clearly that the cathode was totally coated by iron metal and behaves as an electrode of the first king of the pure metal.

From the above tabulated data, we can observe several relevant points, listed hereafter:

It is remarkable that higher the cathode current density together with a lower temperature yields a much greater cathode current efficiency. This can be explained as in such acidic solution pure iron metal is electrochemically active. In other words, the iron corrodes readily. Actually, once the electrolysis is stopped and the cathode is not polarized anymore, a steady stream of hydrogen gas evolution immediately occurs. This means that there is a competition between the iron deposition rate and the corrosion rate of the iron metal electrodeposited. Based on practical figures for the iron metal corrosion rate at pH 1.0, counteracting it requires at least a cathode current density of -250 A/m^2 at room temperature. Moreover, increasing the temperature also accelerates the corrosion rate following the Arrhenius law.

Therefore, we can conclude that poor yield and current efficiencies of 50 percent and less can be expected when performing the electrowinning at acidic pH below 1.35 if the cathode current density is lower than -500 A/m^2 as part of the current is only consumed to protect the newly form iron metal deposit instead of plating.

However, by maintaining the catholyte temperature below 30°C and conducting the electrowinning under elevate cathode current densities below -1000 A/m^2, it is possible to obtain bright and smooth iron metal plates with a cathode current efficiency above 80 percent. Moreover, as indicated during corrosion studies of mild steel during pickling, an increasing concentration of ferrous sulfate also decreases the corrosion rate significantly acting to some extent as a corrosion inhibitor.

12.2.16 Cathode Current Efficiency vs. pH and Current Density

We have measured the cathode current efficiency for electrowinning iron during 60 minutes at cathode current densities ranging from of $-250/m^2$ down to $-1500\ A/m^2$ at an operating temperature of 50°C with a catholyte containing 260 g/L $FeSO_4$.

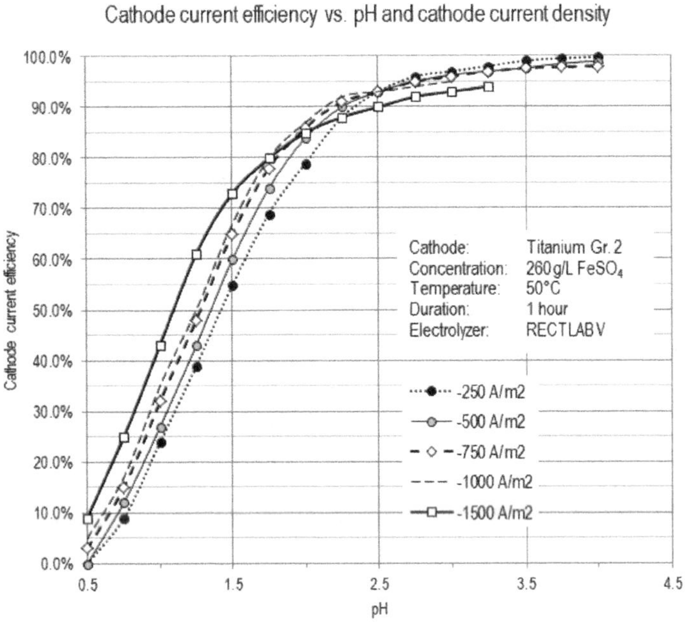

Figure 71 – Cathode current efficiency vs. pH and cathode current density

As already mentioned in Section 12.2.14, for an acidic pH ranging from 0.5 to 1.5 higher the cathode current density higher is the cathode current efficiency. However, above pH 2.0, the situation reverses and the lower cathode current densities yield better current efficiencies, along with smoother and brighter electrolytic iron deposits.

12.2.17 Cathode Current Efficiency vs. pH and Catholyte

The direct and indirect utilization of a supporting electrolyte during the electrowinning of iron was worth to be investigated as several sulfates were used or recommended in the prior art.

For that purpose, we have added intentionally to a warm catholyte containing 360 g/L of ferrous sulfate at a given pH either ammonium sulfate $(NH_4)_2SO_4$, or sodium sulfate, Na_2SO_4, or potassium sulfate, K_2SO_4, or magnesium sulfate, $MgSO_4$ targeting a concentration of 50 g/L.

The plot of the cathode current efficiencies vs. the pH and the cathode current densities for a pH ranging from 1.75 to 3.5 are depicted in Figure 72.

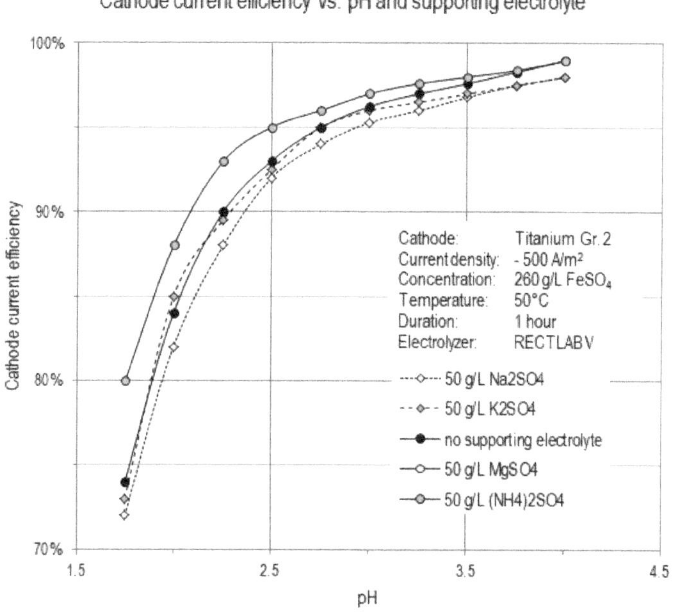

Figure 72 – Cathode current efficiency vs. supporting electrolyte, pH and CCD

From the above results, we can observe that for a pH below 2.75 and at given cathode current density the cathode current efficiency obtained increases from sodium, potassium, magnesium and ammonium, but only magnesium and ammonium offer a benefit compared to the catholyte without supporting salt. However, when the pH is raised above 3.5, the effect is less pronounced as all the current efficiencies are above 99.5% irrespective of the presence or not of supporting electrolyte.

12.2.18 Purity of Electrodeposited Iron

12.2.18.1 Electrolytic Iron Metal

As a general rule, by using pure copperas as feed with tight chemical specifications especially regarding deleterious metals such as zinc, titanium, nickel, chromium, manganese and copper, below detection limits, always results in the highest purity of electrolytic iron. For instance, the elemental chemical analysis of an electrolytic iron metal deposit obtained from the electrowinning of crude copperas originating from the sulfation of ilmenite is reported in Table 80. Note that the highest contaminant was zinc. The latter impurities were linked by the titanium plant owner to the utilization during the chemical reduction process of poor quality scrap iron that was contaminated with galvanized steel.

Table 80 – Chemical composition of an electrolytic iron deposit from copperas

Fe	**99.64** wt.%
Cr	28 ppm wt.
Mn	41 ppm wt.
V	5 ppm wt.
Ti	40 ppm wt.
Ni	164 ppm wt.
Co	166 ppm wt.
Zn	**1647** ppm wt.
Cu	31 ppm wt.
Al	327 ppm wt.
Na	297 ppm wt.
K	164 ppm wt.

Regarding, non-metallic impurities, oxygen is the most abundant impurity element in electrodeposited iron. Therefore, the effects of the pH of catholyte, the cathode current density, the electrolysis time, and operating temperature must be well controlled during electrowinning. We found that usually, the oxygen content decreases with the electrolysis temperature but increases with the bath pH as for pH above 3.5 the oxygen contamination originates from co-deposition/absorption of precipitated ferrous-ferric hydroxide $Fe(OH)_2FeO(OH)$ with a dark green color.

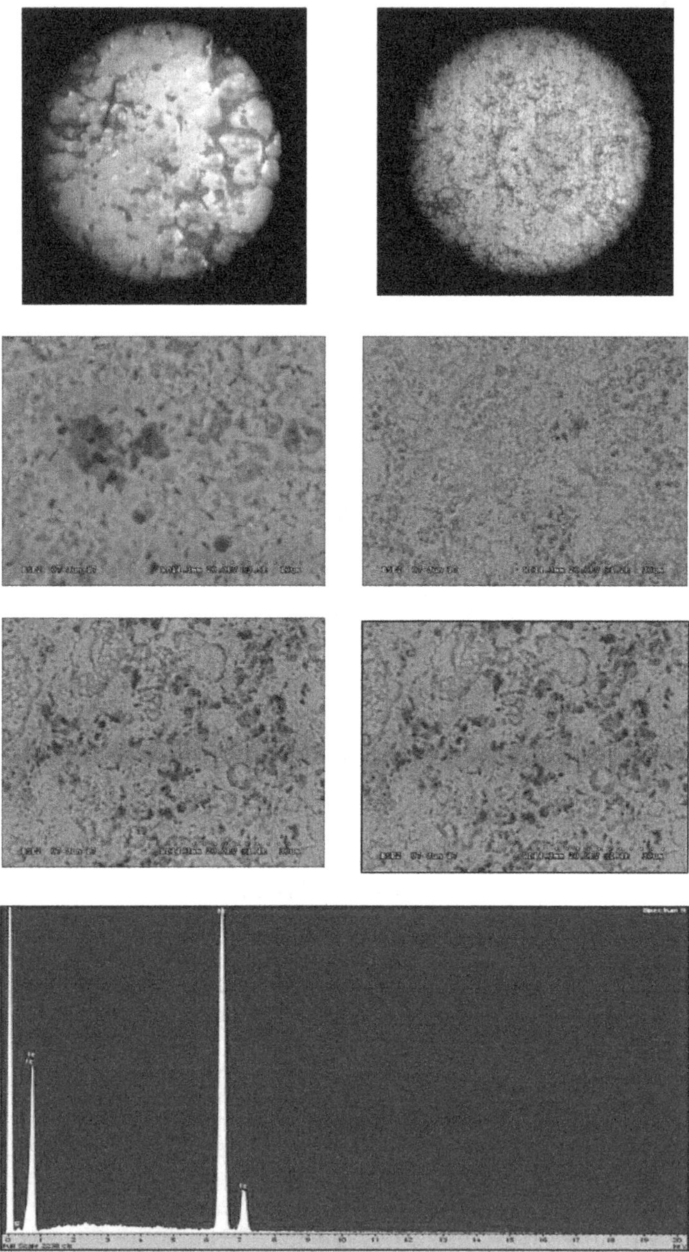

Figure 73 – Microphotographs and EPMA of electrolytic alpha-iron deposits

Actually, at the cathode surface due to the discharge of some protons there is a much higher pH than in the bulk of the catholyte. This alkaline thin diffusion layer can reach locally a pH up to 6.0 even in the case the catholyte exhibits a pH of 2.0. However, in the presence of ammonium cations that form relatively stable complexes with Fe(II), they have the effect of delaying/suppressing the precipitation of iron hydroxide.

In the particular cases, where additives are added to the catholyte such as organic brighteners and leveling agents (e.g., sodium lauryl sulfate), and surfactants such as sodium dodecyl-benzenesulfonate some trace amounts of sulfur and carbon can be detected and can contaminate the electrodeposited iron if no particular precautions are taken.

12.2.18.2 Iron-rich Alloys

Often actual pregnant leach solutions, spent pickling liquors, effluents and copperas, contains other metallic impurities, there is a possibility to electrodeposit concurrently with iron other reducible metal cations.

These metals once deposited will yield: either (1) a layered metallic structure if the reduction potentials are far apart leading to successive deposition steps or (2) an iron-rich alloy when the electrode potentials overlap leading to the simultaneous reduction of metallic cations, or eventually (3) forming embedded inclusions such as oxides, and hydroxides if the deposition pH favors the chemical precipitation.

The major reducible metals that can be encountered in these solutions are but not restricted to manganese, chromium, nickel, copper, zinc, cadmium, and tin. From the calculated electrode potentials for the reduction of each cations (see Table 94), it is clear that nobler metals such as copper and nickel will be deposited first onto the cathode while more active metals such as chromium, zinc, and manganese will be deposited after iron began to deposit or will be electrodeposited simultaneously. These metals contaminates the iron electrodeposit due to co-deposition and underpotential behavior forming an iron-rich alloy with sometimes a higher commercial value than pure iron itself especially when alloyed with high value metals such as chromium, nickel, and manganese.

Table 81 – Macro- and micro-photographs of iron and iron-rich alloys

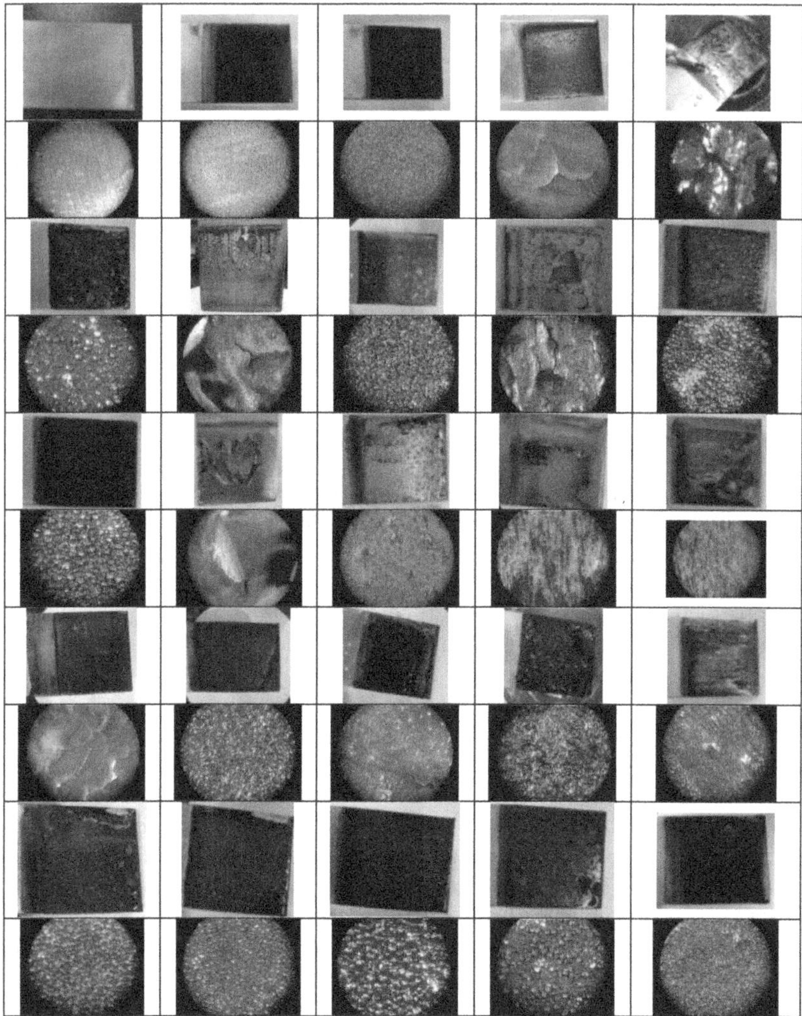

For instance, the elemental chemical composition of such iron-rich alloys obtained after electrowinning spent pickling liquors (SPLs) supplied from a stainless steel descaling line are reported in Table 82.

Table 82 – Composition of electrodeposited iron-rich alloys from pickling liquors

Fe	Cr	Ni	Mn	Si
66.3%	30.1%	1.5%	1.3%	0.8%
68.0%	27.7%	1.5%	1.8%	1.0%
56.5%	38.5%	1.8%	2.0%	1.2%
72.9%	24.5%	0.7%	1.6%	0.3%
70.6%	26.0%	0.6%	2.3%	0.5%
69.1%	28.1%	0.7%	1.8%	0.3%
69.6%	27.8%	0.8%	1.4%	0.4%
69.9%	27.5%	0.5%	1.4%	0.7%

Fe	Cr	Ni	Mn	Si
83.8%	15.3%	0.0%	0.7%	0.2%
83.1%	15.9%	0.0%	0.7%	0.3%
74.0%	24.6%	0.0%	1.2%	0.3%
74.2%	24.6%	0.0%	1.5%	0.0%
70.8%	27.3%	0.8%	1.2%	0.0%
88.0%	8.4%	2.5%	0.7%	0.4%
70.6%	26.3%	1.3%	1.5%	0.4%
74.6%	24.2%	0.0%	1.2%	0.0%
73.6%	25.0%	0.3%	1.1%	0.0%
76.3%	22.2%	0.0%	1.5%	0.0%

12.3 Anodes

Although the selection of a suitable material for an anode follows the same pattern as for cathode materials, this step is still a critical issue in the final design of an industrial electrolyzer because of the peculiar operating conditions that anodes must withstand. Historically, the failure of the anode has often led to the abandonment of several industrial processes. For instance, in aqueous solutions, as major problem arises because the anode is the electrode where the electrochemical oxidation occurs; hence, the anode material must withstand harsh conditions due to both the elevated positive potential, and the high acidity of the electrolyte. Moreover, traces of impurities in the electrolyte might be an additional source of corrosion and deactivation in some cases. Therefore, the material selection process must always be based on strong knowledge and clear understanding of the properties of the materials involved.

12.3.1 Anode Materials

On the anode side, lead anodes that were first historically used for electrowinning various metals since the 1930s can be chosen as satisfactory anode material, especially the cold-rolled lead-silver anodes if low anode current density is used.

However, in order to significantly decrease the overpotential for the anodic evolution of nascent oxygen gas, a dimensionally stable anode especially optimized for oxygen evolution is strongly recommended as it is a long lasting anode material. This composite anode material first discovered by H.B. BEER in 1963[122] has demonstrated a greater service life and has permitted to reduce drastically production costs since its first commercial introduction in the 1970s. For that purpose, mixed metals oxides (MMO) coated-titanium anodes with an electro-catalyst coating made of IrO_2-Ta_2O_5 is nowadays the best candidate despite its price is strongly impacted by the escalating prices of iridium (see Section 19.6).

When harsher conditions due to elevate sulfuric acid concentration, and anode current density are encountered, the titanium substrate must be replaced by Ti-0.25Pd, and for higher anode current densities well above +2,000 A/m^2, such as those used for the production of iron powder, more expensive refractory metal substrates are used such as niobium, tantalum or their alloys could also be used to ensure an extended service life.

Table 83 – Selected anode materials and suppliers

Anode material	Main suppliers
Ti(Grade 1)/Ta_2O_5-IrO_2	De Nora Elettrodi, Tianode Ltd., Permascand AB., Evoqua Technologies, Electrochem Technologies & Materials Inc.
Ti(Grade 2)/Ta_2O_5-IrO_2	
Ti-0.15Pd(Grade 7)/Ta_2O_5-IrO_2	
Nb/Ta_2O_5-IrO_2	
Ta/Ta_2O_5-IrO_2	
Pb-0.5Ag/PbO_2	Glencore, Le Plomb Francais
Pb-6Sb/PbO_2	
Pb-Ca-Sn/PbO_2	

12.3.2 Oxygen Overvoltage

The main property of the anode material in order to control the oxygen gas evolution reaction (OER) is the anode activation overpotential or simply anode

[122] BEER, H.B. (1963) *Noble metal coated electrode and method of making the same.* U.S. Patent 3,096,272, July 2th, 1963.

overvoltage. As previously defined in Section 7.3, the anode overpotential for the OER, denoted η_{O2}, expressed in volts, is defined as the difference between the anode potential denoted $E_a(j)$, in V/SHE for a given anode current density, denoted j_a, in A/m^2, and the Nernst electrode potential for the oxidation of water, E_{O2}, when no current is circulating inside the electrolyzer ($j_a = 0$) as follows:

$$\eta_{O2} = E_a(j) - E_{O2}$$

In this case the thermodynamic electrode potential chosen is the Nernst electrode potential for the oxygen gas evolution reaction with an activity of protons equal to unity is $E_{th} = E_{O2} = +1.229$ V/SHE but for accurate calculations the actual potential values based on the temperature, and the pH must be used (See Section 5.6).

The practical measurement of the oxygen overvoltage at a given current density, is performed by recording the polarization curve, that is, the anode potential vs. the anode current density (E_a, j_a) for a given pH, and operating temperature.

Table 84 – Oxygen evolution overpotentials for various MMO anodes

	Conditions		ANODE OVERPOTENTIAL ($\eta_{O2} = E - E_{O2}$) in volts										
ANODE MATERIAL	**ANOLYTE**	**TEMP**	**+10 A/m²**	**+20 A/m²**	**+50 A/m²**	**+100 A/m²**	**+250 A/m²**	**+500 A/m²**	**+1000 A/m²**	**+1600 A/m²**	**+2000 A/m²**	**+3000 A/m²**	**+4000 A/m²**
Ti (Gr.2)/IrO_2-Ta_2O_5 (Electrochem)	H_2SO_4 10 wt.%	20°C	0.301	0.317	0.341	0.365	0.408	0.453	0.518	0.576	0.611	0.690	0.763
Nb/IrO_2 (B)	H_2SO_4 10 wt.%	20°C	0.275	0.292	0.316	0.344	0.390	0.441	0.535	0.630	0.686	0.829	0.961
Ti-0.15Pd (Gr.7)/IrO_2-Ta_2O_5 (A)	H_2SO_4 10 wt.%	20°C	0.316	0.337	0.368	0.396	0.446	0.499	0.576	0.656	0.701	0.808	0.901
Ti (Gr.1)/IrO_2-Ta_2O_5 (A)	H_2SO_4 10 wt.%	20°C	0.306	0.318	0.343	0.367	0.416	0.471	0.562	0.654	0.711	0.849	0.982
Ti-0.15Pd (Gr.7)/IrO_2-Ta_2O_5 (B)	H_2SO_4 10 wt.%	20°C	0.317	0.345	0.368	0.394	0.446	0.496	0.580	0.657	0.711	0.819	0.919
Ta/IrO_2 (Electrochem)	H_2SO_4 10 wt.%	20°C	0.296	0.311	0.338	0.366	0.413	0.469	0.564	0.662	0.720	0.869	0.997
Ti (Gr.2)/IrO_2-Ta_2O_5 (B)	H_2SO_4 10 wt.%	20°C	0.326	0.341	0.370	0.404	0.458	0.519	0.612	0.700	0.754	0.857	0.956
Nb/IrO_2 (B)	H_2SO_4 30 wt.%	80°C	0.311	0.326	0.350	0.378	0.411	0.449	0.500	0.550	0.581	0.654	0.720
Ti (Gr.2)/IrO_2-Ta_2O_5 (Electrochem)	H_2SO_4 30 wt.%	80°C	0.337	0.341	0.367	0.391	0.428	0.467	0.522	0.573	0.604	0.667	0.724
Ti (Gr.1)/IrO_2-Ta_2O_5 (A)	H_2SO_4 30 wt.%	80°C	0.343	0.359	0.380	0.405	0.444	0.484	0.541	0.596	0.634	0.708	0.773
Ta/IrO_2 (Electrochem)	H_2SO_4 30 wt.%	80°C	0.335	0.351	0.387	0.409	0.450	0.496	0.551	0.612	0.646	0.726	0.790
Ti-0.15Pd (Gr.7)/IrO_2-Ta_2O_5 (B)	H_2SO_4 30 wt.%	80°C	0.354	0.372	0.393	0.425	0.466	0.510	0.576	0.632	0.669	0.740	0.807
Ti (Gr.2)/IrO_2-Ta_2O_5 (B)	H_2SO_4 30 wt.%	80°C	0.306	0.318	0.418	0.450	0.493	0.545	0.562	0.654	0.713	0.792	0.862
Ti-0.15Pd (Gr.7)/IrO_2-Ta_2O_5 (B)	H_2SO_4 30 wt.%	80°C	0.351	0.365	0.399	0.426	0.476	0.530	0.602	0.672	0.717	0.806	0.886

12.3.3 Impact of Sulfuric Acid Concentration

Because the mass percentage of sulfuric acid in the anolyte increases continuously during the electrowinning of iron, it is important to measure the polarizations for various anode materials covering a large span of concentration and temperature. Therefore, the plot of oxygen overpotential vs. the anode current density [$\eta_{O2} = f(j_a)$] was recorded for several cathode materials in 10 wt.% and 30 wt.% sulfuric respectively. For instance, the polarization plots of a commercial mixed metals oxides (MMO) coated-titanium anodes, measured in 30 mass percent sulfuric acid at 60°C, is depicted in Figure 74.

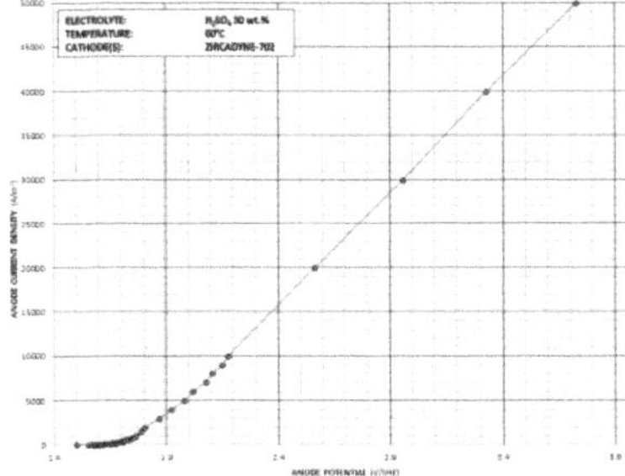

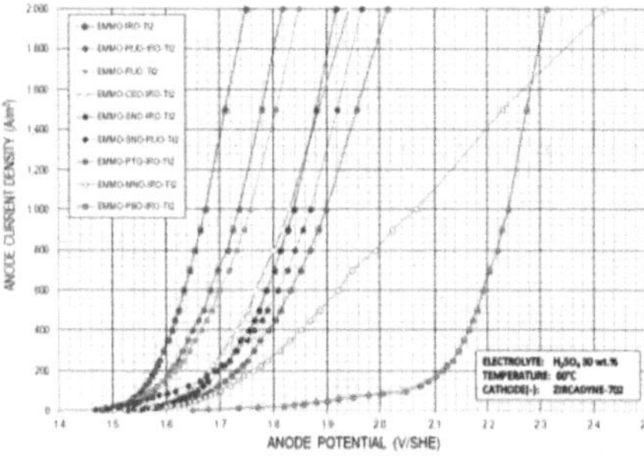

Figure 74 – Polarization of MMO anode in 30 percent sulfuric acid

Figure 75 – Polarization of MMO anodes with various catalysts coatings

12.3.4 Impact of Catalyst Coating

Close examination of the plotted data in Figure 75 shows that the among all the commercial mixed metals oxides (MMO) coated anode materials, the formulation Ti/Ta_2O_5-IrO_2 exhibits the lowest polarization at +500 A/m^2 in 30 wt.% H_2SO_4 the with an average polarization of +1.630 V/SHE that corresponds to an overpotential for the oxygen gas evolution of only +0.400 V.

12.3.5 Anode Tafel's Coefficients

From the previous anode polarization plots, we can calculate the practical electrode kinetics parameters for each selected anode materials, namely the Tafel's slope and exchange current densities along with the activation resistance of polarization.

The Tafel's coefficients are usually obtained from the linear portion of the semi-logarithmic transform of polarization plot starting from positive electrode potentials but below the diffusion regime.

During the oxidation, and in a first approximation, the anode potential is sufficiently positive to neglect the cathode term of the Butler-Volmer equation for the current density as a function of the anode overpotential. By performing the logarithmic transform, the mathematical expression for the anode overpotential as a function of the Briggs logarithm of the absolute value of anode current density is:

$$\eta_a = E_a - E_{O2} = (RT\ln 10/\alpha nF)[\log_{10}|j| - \log_{10}|j_0|]$$

With R the ideal gas constant, 8.3145 J/mol/K, T the thermodynamic temperature in K, n the number of electrons exchanged, F the Faraday constant, 96,485.309 C/mol, α the electron transfer coefficient for the anode reaction, and finally, j_0 the absolute value of the anode exchange current density in A/m^2.

In industrial practice, the two Tafel's coefficients (b_a, a_a) are preferred and used by industrial electrochemists. These are simply related to the previous parameters by the straightforward practical linear equation:

$$\eta_a = E_a - E_{th} = a_a + b_a \log_{10} j$$

With the two anode Tafel's coefficients being defined as follows: (i) the ***anode Tafel's slope*** being $b_a = +(RT\ln 10/\alpha nF)$, and (ii) the ***anode Tafel's intercept*** being: $a_a = b_a \log_{10}|j_0| = (RT\ln 10/\alpha nF) \log_{10}|j_0|$.

The two Tafel's coefficients are obtained from the linear portion of the semi-logarithmic Horiuti diagrams (see Section 7.11.3.2) representing the anode overpotential vs. the logarithm of the absolute value of the anode current density (η_a, $\log_{10}|j_a|$). It is important to mention that the semi-log plots obtained exhibits always two distinct linear regions depending on the type of current regime. The first linear portion is valid for low anode current densities ranging from +100 A/m^2 to +1,000 A/m^2 while the second portion for a high anode current densities ranging from +1,000 A/m^2 to +10,000 A/m^2. In both cases, the two straight lines satisfy the empirical Tafel's equation.

In addition, at very low anode current densities, in practice below +25 A/m^2, the polarization curves exhibits a linear region where it is possible to approximate directly the relationship between the anode overpotential and the anode current density by a linear transform as follows:

$$\eta_a = E_a - E_{O2} = (RT/\alpha nFj_0)\, j$$

By comparison of the above equation with the generalized Ohm's law, it is possible to define a new electrochemical quantity called the ***activation resistance of polarization***, denoted R_p, and expressed in $\Omega.m^2$.

The numerical values of Tafel's coefficients are scarce in the scientific and technical literature especially for industrial anodes. The numerical values provided in this monograph were measured from laboratory and prototype experiments. When the temperature dependence of Tafel's coefficients was not available, the coefficients established at room temperature were used at any temperature.

Hereafter in Table 85 are reported the Tafel's coefficients for the oxygen gas evolution reaction (OER) for several commercial anodes with an anolyte containing 10 wt.% and 30 wt.% sulfuric acid under forced circulation.

Table 85 – Tafel's coefficients for anode materials in 10 and 30 wt.% H_2SO_4

	CATHODE TAFEL'S COEFFICIENTS [$\eta_{O2} = a + b \log_{10} J$ (A/m²)]						
	LOW CURRENTS: +100 to +500 A/m²				HIGH CURRENTS: +500 to +2000 A/m²		
ANODE MATERIAL	ANOLYTE	TEMP	$\log_{10} j_o$ (A/m²)	R_p (μΩ.m²)	b (V/decade)	a(V)	$\log_{10} j_o$ (A/m²)
Ti (Gr.2)/IrO_2-Ta_2O_5 (Electrochem)	H_2SO_4 10 wt.%	20°C	0.031	950	0.399	-0.689	1.727
Nb/IrO_2 (B)	H_2SO_4 10 wt.%	20°C	0.626	990	0.693	-1.565	2.258
Ti-0.15Pd (Gr.7)/IrO_2-Ta_2O_5 (A)	H_2SO_4 10 wt.%	20°C	0.185	1,240	0.531	-1.031	1.940
Ti (Gr.1)/IrO_2-Ta_2O_5 (A)	H_2SO_4 10 wt.%	20°C	0.550	910	0.681	-1.502	2.206
Ti-0.15Pd (Gr.7)/IrO_2-Ta_2O_5 (B)	H_2SO_4 10 wt.%	20°C	0.317	1,180	0.552	-1.090	1.974
Ta/IrO_2 (Electrochem)	H_2SO_4 10 wt.%	20°C	0.632	1,040	0.708	-1.579	2.232
Ti (Gr.2)/IrO_2-Ta_2O_5 (B)	H_2SO_4 10 wt.%	20°C	0.473	1,080	0.560	-1.078	1.926
Nb/IrO_2 (B)	H_2SO_4 30 wt.%	80°C	-0.727	980	0.359	-0.586	1.633
Ti (Gr.2)/IrO_2-Ta_2O_5 (Electrochem)	H_2SO_4 30 wt.%	80°C	-0.514	800	0.330	-0.474	1.438
Ti (Gr.1)/IrO_2-Ta_2O_5 (A)	H_2SO_4 30 wt.%	80°C	-0.507	860	0.379	-0.605	1.595
Ta/IrO_2 (Electrochem)	H_2SO_4 30 wt.%	80°C	-0.473	1,260	0.393	-0.636	1.619
Ti-0.15Pd (Gr.7)/IrO_2-Ta_2O_5 (B)	H_2SO_4 30 wt.%	80°C	-0.360	940	0.376	-0.560	1.490
Ti (Gr.2)/IrO_2-Ta_2O_5 (B)	H_2SO_4 30 wt.%	80°C	-0.280	1,470	0.405	-0.611	1.506
Ti-0.15Pd (Gr.7)/IrO_2-Ta_2O_5 (B)	H_2SO_4 30 wt.%	80°C	-0.051	1,230	0.464	-0.799	1.723

12.3.6 Anode Current Efficiency vs. Sulfuric Acid in Catholyte

When the sulfuric acid concentration is increased in the catholyte the increase of free sulfuric acid on the cathode side strongly affects the anode current efficiency. Actually, under acidic conditions such as those existing in spent pickling liquors, and acidic pregnant leach solutions, with a low pH ranging from 0.5 to 1.5, the sulfate anions become the minor species while the hydrogen sulfate (i.e., bisulfate) anions HSO_4^- predominate representing between 80-88 percent of all the sulfate species [123].

Actually, as under strongly acidic conditions, the proportion of bisulfate anions (HSO_4^-) predominates over sulfate anions (SO_4^{2-}) in the catholyte. Actually, as the current across the anion exchange membrane is transported by the anions, under strongly acidic conditions for one Faraday circulated two moles of bisulfate anions are transported and diffuses through the membrane towards the anode and unite with two protons to form two moles sulfuric acid according to:

$$2HSO_4^- + 2H^+ = 2H_2SO_4$$

The above reaction enhanced the production of sulfuric acid in the anolyte and also explains why the anode current efficiency is always close to unity.

---

[123] CARDARELLI, F. (2022) *Sulfuric Acid Digestion, Sulfuric Acid Baking, and Sulfation Roasting in Mineral and Chemical Processing, and Extractive Metallurgy*. Electrochem Technologies & Materials Inc., Montreal, QC, Canada, *Chapter 2: Physical and Chemical Properties of Pure Sulfuric Acid*, pages 10-11.

By comparison when electrolyzing a catholyte having a pH above 1.5, sulfate anions are the predominant species and after circulating a total electric charge of two Faraday only one mole of sulfate anion migrates and diffuse through the anion exchange membrane to unite with two protons, forming only one mole sulfuric acid at the anode according to:

$$SO_4^- + 2H^+ = H_2SO_4.$$

12.3.7 Anode Current Efficiency vs. Impurities

Among all the deleterious inorganic impurities, fluoride anions are by far the most detrimental for mixed metal oxides MMO coated-titanium anodes. On the other hand, multivalent transition metal cations especially those of ferric iron (Fe^{3+}), peroxovanadium (VO_2^+), and cupric cations (Cu^{2+}) all ensure that the passivity of the underlying titanium substrate is maintained and protect the anode.

12.4 Recommended Electrodes

Based on the previous information, the recommended electrodes materials for performing the electrowinning of iron are listed in Table 86.

Table 86 – Recommended electrode materials

Range of current densities	Anode (+)	Cathode (-)
Low current density ($\|j\| < +500$ A/m^2)	Ti/TiO_2-IrO_2 Chemical lead Cold rolled Pb-Ag anodes	Titanium (ASTM grade 2) Aluminum AA 1000-series Mild steel AISI 1010 Stainless steel AISI 304 High-silicon cast iron
High current density (+500 A/m^2 < $\|j\|$ < +2,000 A/m^2)	Ti/TiO_2-IrO_2 Ti-0.25Pd/TiO_2-IrO_2	Titanium (ASTM grade 2) Mild steel AISI 1010 Stainless steel AISI 316 High-silicon cast iron
Very high current density (+2,000 A/m^2 < $\|j\|$)	Nb/Nb_2O_5-IrO_2 Ta/Ta_2O_5-IrO_2	Titanium (ASTM grade 2) Zirconium 702 Mild steel AISI 1010 High-silicon cast iron

13 Separators

In order to succeed for electrowinning iron the separation of product streams must be performed without affecting the electrolyzer performances, for that reason at least one separator is required eventually two depending on the type of electrolyzer design adopted. In the particular case of the electrolysis of ferrous sulfate, the major requirements for the separator are as follows:

- Good physical barrier between anolyte and catholyte,
- Electronic insulator to avoid bipolar polarization,
- Impervious to neutral species including solvent (i.e., water),
- Low pore size to minimize oxygen gas bubble transfer,
- Good mechanical strength (i.e., high burst pressure) to withstand high pressure differential due to strong oxygen gas evolution at the anode,
- Low thickness and homogeneous to reduce ohmic drop (*iR*) even at high current densities up to 10,000 A/m^2,
- Chemical inertness at low pH and in hot sulfuric acid with traces of oxidizing species such as ferric cations,
- Excellent permselectivity to sulfate anions while impeding other anions and all cations to cross the barrier. Actually without separator Fe^{2+} and Fe^{3+} cations can move freely between the anode and cathode compartment, reversibly changing oxidation state as Fe(II) could be oxidized to Fe(III) at the anode, and then by-passing most of the current,
- Excellent protons rejection capabilities to avoid the acidification of the catholyte,
- Thermally and creep resistant at the operating temperature,
- Low cost and commercial availability.

13.1 Diaphragms

Historically, asbestos diaphragms were first used followed by non-woven cloths made of polypropylene (see Section 3.2.1).

13.2 Anion Exchange Membranes (AEM)

The best separator materials that meet all these requirements are ion-exchange membranes which act similarly to ion-exchange resins. Because the displacement of cations must impeded, anion-exchange membrane (AEM) permeable to sulfate anions while non-permeable to cations such as H^+, Na^+, Ca^{2+} are required for this electrochemical application. These membranes are divided into two categories: ***heterogeneous ion exchange membranes***, that are obtained by mixing beads of an ion exchange resin with a thermoplastic polymer, and ***homogeneous membranes*** with an ion exchange groups chemically bonded to a cross-linked polymer backbone.

13.3 Commercial Brands

Several commercial anion exchange membranes are available among which the brands: Neosepta® (Trademark of *Tokuyama Co. Ltd.*), Excellion® (Trademark of *SnowPure LLC*), Ultrex® (Trademark of *Membranes International*), Fumasep® (Trademark of *Fuma-Tech GmbH.*) and Selemion® (Trademark of *Asahi Glass Co. Ltd.*) along with some cation exchange membranes such as Nafion® (Trademark of *Chemours*)were tested at *Electrochem Technologies & Materials Inc.* Selected technical specifications from manufacturers are reported in Table 88.

Table 87 – Measured dry density, thickness, and swelling

Trade name and grade	Thicknesses (measured)	Surface mass density (g/m²)	Mass density (kg/m³)	Swelling ($\Delta A/A$)
EXCELLION® **I-200**	343 µm	372	1,086	9.7%
NEOSEPTA® **ACM**	102 µm	123	1,210	7.9%
NEOSEPTA® **AMH**	203 µm	200	983	1.8%
NEOSEPTA® **AHA**	191 µm	204	1,072	5.7%
ULTREX® **AMI-7001**	495 µm	552	1,115	3.6%
SELEMION® **CMD**	343 µm	433	1,262	1.5%
SELEMION® **AMD**	330 µm	416	1,260	1.0%
SELEMION® **AMT**	203 µm	224	1,104	5.7%
SELEMION® **AMV**	114 µm	135	1,179	12.2%
SELEMION® **AAV**	102 µm	126	1,238	15.3%
FUMASEP® **FAA-3-PK-130**	140 µm	134	957	0.0%
FUMASEP® **FAB-PK-130**	127 µm	106	835	0.0%
FUMASEP® **FAD-PET-100**	102 µm	124	1,220	9.7%
FUMASEP® **FAN-PET-100**	102 µm	139	1,369	0.0%
FUMASEP® **FAP-PK-4130**	127 µm	112	883	0.0%
FUMASEP® **FAS-PET-130**	127 µm	132	1,041	0.0%

Prior installation and utilization each dry membrane must be immersed in the anolyte (H_2SO_4 30 wt.%) during 48 hours at 60°C in order to reach its final dimensions. The immersion stabilizes the swelling of the polymeric material and avoids any offset between installed and final dimensions.

Table 88 – Specifications and physical properties of anion-exchange membranes

Trade name and grade	Manufacturer	Color	Description	Thickness range (µm)	Exchange capacity (mEq/g)	ASI (ohm cm²)	Transport number (t_a)	Max. temp	Mullen's burst pressure	Proton transfer µM/cm²/min	YS (MPa)	UTS (MPa)
EXCELLION® **I-200**	Snowpure LLC	Milky white	Translucent thick fabric	320-340	1.3	5.0-10.0	0.99	80°C	0.28-0.30	n.a.	n.a.	n.a.
NEOSEPTA® **ACM**	Tokoyama Soda Co. Ltd.	Golden	Thin fabric	110-130	1.4-1.7	4.0-5.0	0.98	60°C	0.20-0.30	n.a.	n.a.	n.a.
NEOSEPTA® **AMH**	Tokoyama Soda Co. Ltd.	Yellowish brown	Thick fabric	260-280	1.3-1.5	11.0-13.0	0.98	60°C	1.18	n.a.	n.a.	n.a.
NEOSEPTA® **AHA**	Tokoyama Soda Co. Ltd.	Pinkish yellow	Translucent, flexible fabric	180-240	1.2	3.0-5.0	0.98	60°C		n.a.	n.a.	n.a.
ULTREX® **AMI-7001**	Membranes International	Yellow straw	Thick and heavy fabric	482-533	1.3	40.0	0.99	90°C	0.55	n.a.	n.a.	n.a.
SELEMION® **CMD**	Asahi Glass Co. Ltd.	Dark purple	Opaque thick fabric	340-420		17	0.06	80°C	0.98-1.96	n.a.	n.a.	n.a.
SELEMION® **AMD**	Asahi Glass Co. Ltd.	Black	Opaque thick fabric	340-420		8.0-10.0	0.95	80°C	0.98-1.96	n.a.	n.a.	n.a.
SELEMION® **AMT**	Asahi Glass Co. Ltd.	White	Strong thick fabric	220		6.0	0.96	80°C	0.70	n.a.	n.a.	n.a.
SELEMION® **AMV**	Asahi Glass Co. Ltd.	Light straw	Thin membrane, translucent	130		1.5-3.0	0.96	80°C	0.20	n.a.	n.a.	n.a.
SELEMION® **AAV**	Asahi Glass Co. Ltd.	Golden	Thin membrane, translucent	130		17.5	0.95	80°C	0.30	n.a.	n.a.	n.a.
FUMASEP® **FAA-3-PK-130**	Fuma-Tech GmbH	Yellow	Thin and flexible fabric	100-130	1.4-1.6	1.9-2.5	0.95	40°C		800-2500	20-30	40-80
FUMASEP® **FAB-PK-130**	Fuma-Tech GmbH	Pinkish yellow	Thin and flexible fabric	110-140	0.7-1.0	10-20	0.96	50°C		60-400	20-30	40-80
FUMASEP® **FAD-PET-100**	Fuma-Tech GmbH	Brownish white	Brittle when dry	60-100		1.2	0.95	40°C		500-2000	15	50
FUMASEP® **FAN-PET-100**	Fuma-Tech GmbH	Golden yellow	Thin and flexible fabric	100				40°C		n.a.	n.a.	n.a.
FUMASEP® **FAP-PK-4130**	Fuma-Tech GmbH	White	Thin fabric	130-160	1.1-1.3	0.45-0.65		40°C		1500	n.a.	30-50
FUMASEP® **FAS-PET-130**	Fuma-Tech GmbH	Brownish yellow	Thin and flexible fabric	75-130	1.0-1.4	4-7	0.95	40°C		1200-1900	25-30	50-60

13.4 Ohmic Drop

The ionic resistance of ion exchange membranes is often reported as the ***area specific impedance***, denoted *ASI*, and expressed in $\Omega.m^2$. Actually, this electrical quantity is useful for predicting the performance of the membrane as it is the ratio of the membrane's thickness to the ionic electrical conductivity of the membrane. The relationships between the ASI, the ohmic drop and the current density are provided hereafter:

$$U = RI = (x_m/\kappa)j = ASI \times j$$

Thus knowing the *ASI* and the current density, we can calculate directly the ohmic drop without using the thickness of the membrane. The experimental setup for measuring the ohmic drop is depicted in Figure 76.

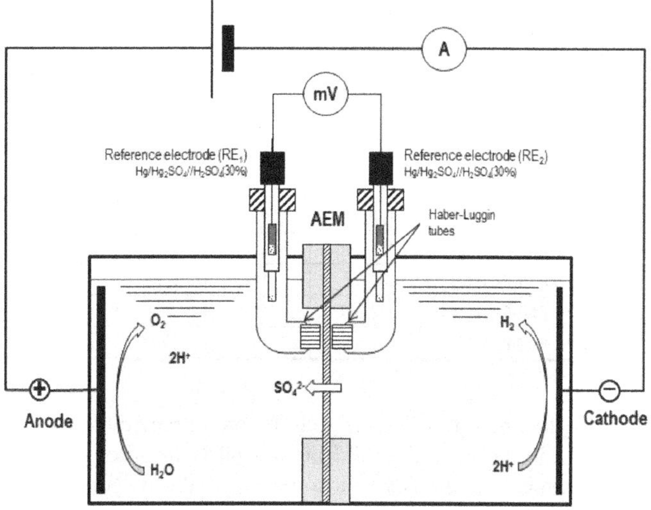

Figure 76 – Experimental setup for measuring of the ohmic drop across a membrane

13.4.1 Low Current Density

The plot of the ohmic drop across several anion exchange membrane vs. membrane cathode densities below 3500 A/m^2 is depicted in Figure 77. The related *ASI* for each membrane at that low current density range are reported in Table 90.

13.4.2 High Current Density

The plot of the ohmic drop of anion exchange membranes vs. membrane cathode densities up to 8,000 A/m^2 is depicted in Figure 78. The reason behind these measurements was for the supporting the production of electrolytic iron powder that utilizes very high current densities inside plate and frame or tubular electrolyzers. The related *ASI* for each membrane for that high current density range is reported in Table 90.

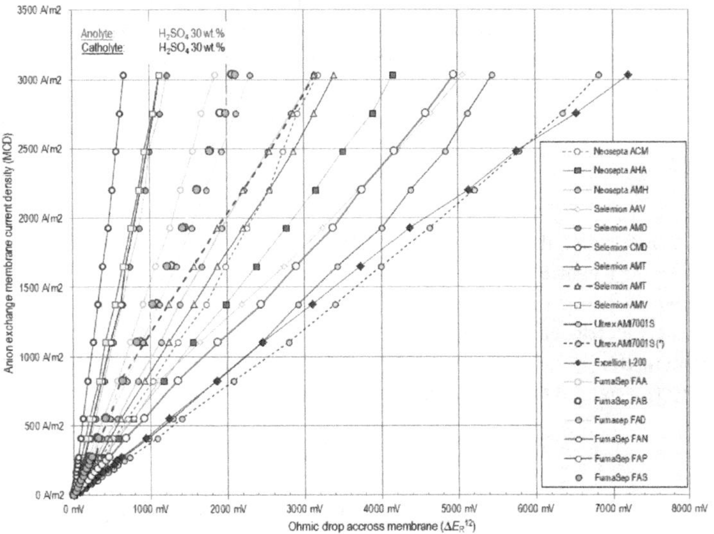

Figure 77 – Ohmic drop vs. membrane current density below 3500 A/m²

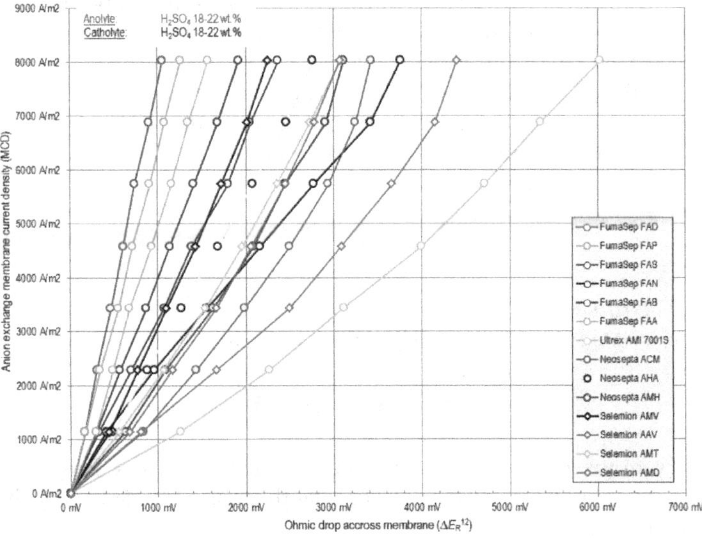

Figure 78 – Ohmic drop vs. membrane current density up to 8000 A/m²

13.5 Transference Numbers

Upon polarization of the electrodes in an open electrolyzer, the protons from the anode compartment tends to electro-migrate towards the cathode negatively charged. Therefore, the ***apparent proton transference*** or transport number, denoted t_{H+}, corresponds to the dimensionless ratio of the electric current carried by the protons to the overall electric current circulating inside the cell.

$$t_{H+} = j_{H+}/j_{total}$$

Conversely, the sulfate anions from the cathode compartment tends to electro-migrate towards the anode positively charged, the apparent sulfate anions transference or transport number, denoted t_{SO4}, corresponds to the dimensionless ratio of the electric current transported by the sulfate anions from the cathode compartment that cross the membrane by electro-migration, diffusion, and electro-osmosis to the overall current circulating in the cell.

$$t_{SO4^{2-}} = j_{SO4^{2-}}/j_{total}$$

The sum of the transference numbers involved is always equal to unity:

$$t_{H+} + t_{SO4} = 1$$

Under pure electro-migration conditions, that is, no supporting electrolyte is present, the velocity of an ion k, denoted v_k, in m/s, is directly proportional to the electrical field strength existing between the anode and the cathode and hence to the electric potential gradient. As already discussed in Section 6.2, the proportional physical quantity, is the ***microscopic electrical mobility*** of the ion u_k, in $m^2.s^{-1}.V^{-1}$. The relation between the ion velocity and the electric field strength is given by the following equation:

$$\mathbf{v}_k = u_k\boldsymbol{E} = -u_k\nabla\mathbf{V}$$

The ***molar flux density*** of an ion denoted J_k and expressed in $mol.m^{-2}.s^{-1}$ is simply calculated from the molarity of the ion, C_k, in mol/m^3:

$$\boldsymbol{J}_k = C_k\mathbf{v_k} = -C_k u_k\nabla\mathbf{V}$$

From the above equation, the electro-migration current density of an ion, denoted j_m, in A/m^2 is obtained by multiplying the molar flux density by the molar charge of the ion and it is given by:

$$\boldsymbol{j}_m = Z_k F C_k\mathbf{v_k} = -Z_k F C_k u_k\nabla\mathbf{V}$$

When both the anolyte and catholyte consist of diluted sulfuric acid, only protons and sulfate anions are involved. The current density carried by each individual ion is as follows:

$$\boldsymbol{j}_{H+} = -Z_{H+}F[H^+]u_{H+}\nabla\mathbf{V} = -F[H^+]u_{H+}\nabla\mathbf{V}$$

$$j_{SO4} = -Z_{SO4}F[SO_4^{2-}]u_{SO4}\nabla\mathbf{V} = -2F[SO_4^{2-}]u_{SO4}\nabla\mathbf{V}$$

By definition of the previous transference numbers, we obtain:

$$t_{H+} = j_{H+}/(j_{H+} + j_{SO4}) = u_{H+}[H^+]/\{u_{H+}[H^+] + 2u_{SO4}[SO_4^{2-}]\}$$

$$t_{SO4} = j_{SO4}/(j_{H+} + j_{SO4}) = 2u_{SO4}[SO_4^{2-}]/\{u_{H+}[H^+] + 2u_{SO4}[SO_4^{2-}]\}$$

Because sulfuric acid of molarity C_A is a strong electrolyte and entirely ionized, the mass balance imposes: $C_A = [SO_4^{2-}] = [H^+]/2$

Thus, the equations for the transference numbers are as follows:

$$t_{H+} = j_{H+}/(j_{H+} + j_{SO4}) = u_{H+}/[u_{H+} + u_{SO4}] = l_{H+}/[l_{H+} + l_{SO4}]$$

$$t_{SO4} = j_{SO4}/(j_{H+} + j_{SO4}) = u_{SO4}/[u_{H+} + u_{SO4}] = l_{H+}/[l_{H+} + l_{SO4}]$$

From tabulated data, the limiting equivalent conductivities of protons and sulfate anions are 35 and 8 $mS.m^2.eq^{-1}$ respectively. Thus, the transport numbers are close to 81% for H^+, and 19% for SO_4^{2-} inside an open electrolyzer.

When installing a separator, especially an ion exchange membrane, that divides the electrolyzer into two compartments, this affects the electro-migration of all ions. Actually, during electrolysis, the discharge or protons with the evolution of hydrogen gas at the cathode releases sulfate anions that migrate toward the anode and cross selectively the anion exchange membrane hence depleting the cathode compartment.

On the other hand, at the anode water is oxidized with the evolution of oxygen gas while generating protons that are repelled to some extent by the anion exchange membrane thus combining with sulfate anions thus increasing the sulfuric acid concentration at the anode. Unfortunately, the selectivity of anion exchange membranes towards protons is never fulfilled as some protons reach the cathode.

The equations for calculating the transference number inside a divided electrolyser are reported in Table 89.

Table 89 – Ions transport equations inside the membrane electrolyzer

Cell compartment	Cathode compartment (-)	Anode compartment (+)
Electrode reaction	$2H^+ + 2e^- \rightarrow H_2(g)$	$H_2O \rightarrow O_2(g) + 2H^+$
Initial conditions	$n_{H+}(IN) = 2C_{CA}(IN)V_{CA}(IN)$ $n_{SO4}(IN) = C_{CA}(IN)V_{CA}(IN)$	$n_{H+}(IN) = 2C_{AN}(IN)V_{AN}(IN)$ $n_{SO4}(IN) = C_{AN}(IN)V_{AN}(IN)$
Final conditions (protons)	$n_{H+}(END) = 2C_{CA}(IN)V_{CA}(IN) - I\Delta t/2F + t_{H+}(I\Delta t/2F)$ $n_{H+}(END) = 2C_{CA}(END)V_{CA}(END)$	$n_{H+}(END) = 2C_{AN}(IN)V_{AN}(IN) + I\Delta t/2F - t_{H+}(I\Delta t/2F)$ $n_{H+}(END) = 2C_{AN}(END)V_{AN}(END)$
Final conditions (sulfates)	$n_{SO4}(END) = C_{CA}(IN)V_{CA}(IN) - t_{SO4}(I\Delta t/2F)$ $n_{SO4}(END) = C_{CA}(END)V_{CA}(END)$	$n_{SO4}(END) = C_{AN}(IN)V_{AN}(IN) + t_{SO4}(I\Delta t/2F)$ $n_{SO4}(END) = C_{AN}(END)V_{AN}(END)$
Molar variations (protons)	$\Delta n_{H+} = (t_{H+}-1)(I\Delta t/2F)$ $\Delta n_{H+} = 2[C_{CA}(END)V_{CA}(END) - C_{CA}(IN)V_{CA}(IN)]$	$\Delta n_{H+} = (1 - t_{H+})(I\Delta t/2F)$ $\Delta n_{H+} = 2[C_{AN}(END)V_{AN}(END) - C_{AN}(IN)V_{AN}(IN)]$
Molar variations (sulfates)	$\Delta n_{SO4} = -t_{SO4}(I\Delta t/2F)$ $\Delta n_{SO4} = [C_{CA}(END)V_{CA}(END) - C_{CA}(IN)V_{CA}(IN)]$	$\Delta n_{SO4} = +t_{SO4}(I\Delta t/2F)$ $\Delta n_{SO4} = [C_{AN}(END)V_{AN}(END) - C_{AN}(IN)V_{AN}(IN)]$
Transference numbers	$t_{H+} = 1 + 2[C_{CA}(END)V_{CA}(END) - C_{CA}(IN)V_{CA}(IN)](2F/I\Delta t)$ $t_{SO4} = [C_{CA}(IN)V_{CA}(IN) - C_{CA}(END)V_{CA}(END)](2F/I\Delta t)$ $t_{H+} + t_{SO4} = 1$	$t_{H+} = 1 - 2[C_{AN}(END)V_{AN}(END) - C_{CA}(IN)V_{CA}(IN)](2F/I\Delta t)$ $t_{SO4} = [C_{AN}(END)V_{AN}(END) - C_{AN}(IN)V_{AN}(IN)](2F/I\Delta t)$ $t_{H+} + t_{SO4} = 1$

Notes: $C_{AN}(IN)$, $C_{AN}(END)$, $C_{CA}(IN)$, and $C_{CA}(END)$ are the initial and final anolyte and catholyte molarities in mol/L; $V_{AN}(IN)$, $V_{AN}(END)$, $V_{CA}(IN)$, and $V_{CA}(END)$ the initial and final volumes of anolyte and catholyte in L; I is the average current in A; Δt the electrolysis duration in s, and finally F the Faraday constant in C/mol.

The experimental results that were obtained are presented in Table 90 hereafter.

Table 90 – Measured ASI, and ohmic drop of anion exchange membranes

Trade name and grade	Max. current density (A/m^2)	Ionic conductivity (mS/cm)		ASI (mohm m^2)		Ohmic drop (V)	ACE	CCE
	[when $\Delta E < 2V$]	LCD: 1000 - 3000	HCD: 1000 - 9000 A/m^2	LCD	HCD	1.1 kA/m^2	5.0 kA/m^2	
EXCELLION® **I-200**	889	1.46	4.64	2.341	0.739	2.46		
NEOSEPTA® **ACM**	1,676	0.94	2.63	1.090	0.386	1.36	8%	41%
NEOSEPTA® **AMH**	1,998	2.00	5.46	1.018	0.372	1.14	10%	52%
NEOSEPTA® **AHA**	1,394	1.36	5.65	1.400	0.337	1.55	24%	35%
ULTREX® **AMI-7001**	815	2.16	7.20	2.298	0.688	2.79	30%	30%
SELEMION® **CMD**	**3,031**	9.06		0.379		0.48		
SELEMION® **AMD**	**3,031**	8.12	9.48	0.407	0.348	0.52		
SELEMION® **AMT**	1,653	1.79	5.57	1.137	0.365	1.24		
SELEMION® **AMV**	**3,031**	3.02	4.30	0.379	0.266	0.42	10%	58%
SELEMION® **AAV**	1,009	0.55	1.93	1.859	1.930	2.18	50%	56%
FUMASEP® **FAA-3-PK-130**	**3,031**	2.26	7.42	0.617	0.188	0.74	34%	56%
FUMASEP® **FAB-PK-130**	**2,883**	1.78	4.27	0.712	0.297	0.88	30%	15%
FUMASEP® **FAD-PET-100**	**2,590**	1.33	7.87	0.766	0.129	0.90	12%	30%
FUMASEP® **FAN-PET-100**	1,164	0.61	2.01	1.678	0.504	1.87	33%	16%
FUMASEP® **FAP-PK-4130**	**3,031**	5.59	7.97	0.227	0.159	0.27	19%	26%
FUMASEP® **FAS-PET-130**	**2,791**	1.80	5.35	0.706	0.238	0.83	22%	29%

13.6 Membranes Protons Leakage and Rejection

For all electrowinning processes implying ion exchange membranes, the selectivity of ion transport across the membrane is of paramount importance in order to reach a process efficiency which is compatible with technical-economic criteria.

Because, ion-exchange membranes are swollen polymeric ion exchangers, and, due to the presence of adsorbed water, anion exchange membranes become proton conductors. The proton exhibits unusual behavior. Actually, the proton electro-migrates by a mechanism which is fundamentally different from that of other cations, indicated by an abnormally high ionic mobility.

The proton transfer across AEM occurs through two mechanisms when AEMs are submitted to an electrical field: first by the ***Grotthus mechanism*** according to which the proton migrates from one water molecule to another, and secondly by the classical co-ion leakage when proton migrates like another adsorbed cation. This phenomenon of ***proton leakage*** or poor ***proton rejection*** is the main problem encountered during the concentration of sulfuric acid in the anode compartment.

The experimental determination of proton leakage through the membranes was measured using a modified two-compartment RECTLAB V cell with the cathode compartment separated from the anode compartment of both identical volumes by the membrane to be tested. The anode consisted of a mixed metals oxides (MMO) coated-titanium anode while the cathode was made of pure zirconium metal. The anodic chamber contained 200 mL of dilute aqueous solution of sulfuric acid H_2SO_4. The cathode cell compartment was filled with 0.1M H_2SO_4 as catholyte and equipped with a pH probe in order to measure the pH accurately. The applied current density was 500 A/m^2 and the duration of electrolysis was 30 min.

After, electrolysis, the proton concentration in both chambers was determined by both mass density and refractive index measurement for the anolyte and by acid-base titration for the catholyte. All measurements were carried out at room temperature, and the determinations were repeated twice for each set of experimental conditions.

The transported proton or apparent transport number corresponds to the ratio of the ionic current transported by the protons from the anode chamber that cross the membrane by electro-migration, diffusion, and electro-osmosis to the overall current circulating in the cell. It is simply calculated using the following equation:

$$t_{H+}(\text{leakage})(\%) = 100\{[V_{cath(END)}10^{-pH(END)} - V_{cath(IN)}10^{-pH(IN)}]F/3600\}/I\Delta t$$

with

pH(IN)	initial pH of the catholyte,
pH(END)	final pH of the catholyte,
$V_{cath(IN)}$	initial volume of catholyte in L,
$V_{cath(END)}$	final volume of catholyte in L
I	the average current in A,
Δt	the electrolysis duration in s,
F	the Faraday constant, 96,485.309 C/mol.

13.7 Membranes Service Life

During the electrowinning of iron, the anion exchange membranes are impacted by factors such as the passage of electric current, the Joule's heating, the hydrodynamic flow of the anolyte and catholyte, the fouling by colloidal particles, the pressure differential, the exposure to strong acidity on the anolyte side, and to strong concentration of ferrous sulfate in the catholyte.

Because of the difference in density between catholyte and anolyte, and the inner pressure inside the anode compartment due to forced circulation and oxygen gas evolution, the electrowinning is conducted with a level of catholyte slightly higher than that of the anolyte, this create a ***pressure differential*** impeding a flow of anolyte across the membrane.

These factors can cause the premature degradation of the functions ensuring the active ion exchange, and the destruction of the supporting polymer matrix. The immediate consequences are the decrease of the performances, a steep decrease of proton rejection, and in the worst case the loss of the physical barrier all necessitating the immediate replacement of the membrane with associated shut down of the electrowinning.

The determination of the service life of several commercial anion exchange membrane under actual electrowinning conditions was conducted both at the laboratory, prototype, and pilot scale.

The impact of operating parameters that were the membrane current density, the temperature, the total charge circulated per unit surface area of membrane, the acidity and oxidation-reduction potential of the anolyte, the presence of colloidal particles suspended in the catholyte (e.g., silica, titanium dioxide, carbon, sulfur), and the volume flow rate of the anolyte inside the anode compartment.

Usually, the accelerated service life tests were conducted at 60°C under a membrane current density of 2000 A/m^2 lasting from few weeks up to several months some even reaching a total charge per unit surface area of 4 MAh/m^2

before the test was stopped in some instances. The most important parameters that were recorded regularly were the overall cell voltage, the ohmic drop across the membrane, the visual aspcct and color, and the proton rejection.

Some samples of end-of-life anion and cation exchange membranes that were tested using the RECTLAB V cell and the PROTOTYPE II for several weeks are depicted in Figure 79.

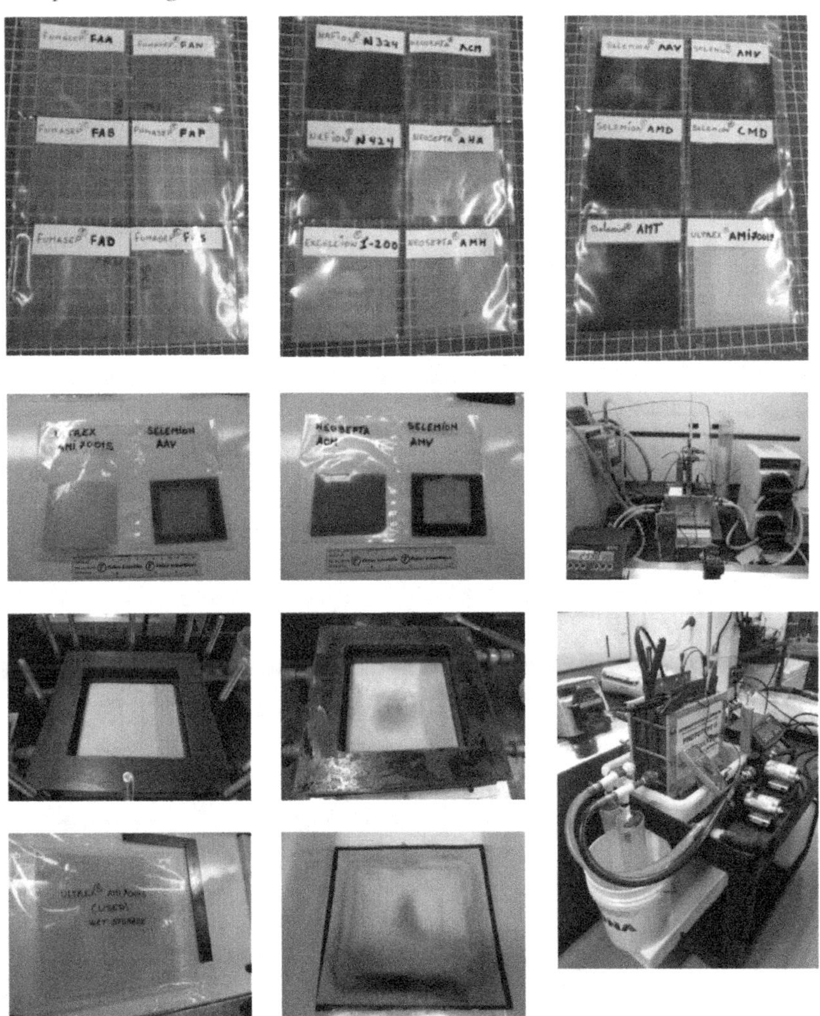

Figure 79 – Anion exchange membranes after accelerated service life testing

14 Electrochemical Calculations

In this chapter, based on the equations and quantities defined and described in the previous sections along with the properties and characteristics of the electrolytes, electrodes, and separators we will perform the step by step calculations for a set of electrodes and membranes having commercial dimensions.

14.1 Electrochemical Performances

In an electrochemical process, electricity is usually a crucial and most costly input. Therefore, industrial electrolyzers are always: (i) engineered to minimize the ***specific energy consumption*** per unit mass of chemical produced, i.e., the actual electrical energy required to produce a given mass of chemical, denoted by the symbol e_m or the acronym *SEC*, and expressed in the SI in J/kg (kWh/kg), and (ii) maximizing the ***space-time yield***, i.e., the mass of product produced per unit electrode area and per unit time denoted by the symbol Y_m, or the acronym *STY*, and expressed in the SI in $kg.m^{-2}.h^{-1}$.

14.1.1 Minimizing the Specific Energy Consumption

For decreasing the specific energy consumption the two options available consist: (i) to increase the ***Faradaic current efficiency***, *CE*, and (ii) to decrease the ***overall cell voltage***, denoted U_{cell}, and expressed in volts.

Actually, when an ***electric current***, I in A, circulates inside the electrolyzer, the overall cell voltage,denoted U_{cell}, in V, is equal to the summation of several contributions, and it is usually expressed by the following general equation [124]:

$$U_{cell} = [E_{th(an.)} - E_{th(cath.)}] + [\Sigma_k (\eta_{an, k} - \eta_{cath, k})] + j \Sigma_k R_k A_k + \Delta E_J + \Delta U_t$$

Where

U_{cell} overall cell voltage, in V,

$E_{th(an.)}$, $E_{th(cath.)}$ Nernstian electrode potentials, in V,

[124] CARDARELLI, F. (2018) *Materials Handbook: A Concise Desktop Reference, Third Edition*. Springer, Cham, Switzerland, pp. 830-832.

$\eta_{an, k}$, $\eta_{cath, k}$	anodic and cathodic overpotentials, in V,
j	electric current density, in $A.m^{-2}$,
ΔE_J	liquid junction potential, in V,
R_k	electrical resistance of the medium k, in Ω,
A_k	cross sectional area of the medium k, in m^2,
ΔU_t	cell potential drift in V.

That can be written in a condensed form as follows:

$$U_{cell} = \Delta U_{th} + \Sigma\eta + IR_T + \Delta E_J + \Delta U_t$$

The first term ΔU_{th} represents the ***reversible cell voltage*** also called the ***thermodynamic cell voltage***, the second term $\Sigma\eta$ is the contribution of both anode and cathode ***overpotentials*** (i.e., concentration, activation, and passivation), the third term, iR_T, is the sum of all the ***ohmic drops*** (i.e., electrolytes, electrodes, separator, contacts, and bus bars), the ***liquid junction potential*** due to the separator, ΔE_J, and the finally fourth term ΔU_t, is the ***cell potential drift*** which is a time-dependent variable related to the aging of electrodes, and separator materials.

Therefore, for a targeted electrochemical reaction, which is taking place at the working electrode (i.e., cathode in the case of iron electrowinning), the reversible cell voltage can be minimized by carefully selecting a proper electrochemical reactions occurring at the counter electrode (i.e., anode).

The ***activation overpotential*** can be reduced by selecting appropriate electrode materials with enhanced catalytic properties while the **concentration overpotential** can be minimized enhancing the mass transfer at the electrode by forced circulation, and by using turbulent promoters.

The ***ohmic drop*** is reduced: (1) by using highly conductive electrolytes compatible with the chemistry of the process, (2) by designing the narrowest ***inter electrode gap*** or ***membrane-electrode gaps*** while keeping proper fluid flow, allowing the harvest of the deposit at the cathode, and the escape of oxygen gas at the anode, (3) by using separators with high ionic conductivity, and low thicknesses, and finally (4) by using bus bars and current collectors with few electrical contacts.

Finally, the ***potential drift*** can be reduced using long lasting electrodes, and separator materials with slow degradation rates.

14.1.2 Increasing the Space Time Yield

Regarding the ***space-time yield***, it is important to operate at the highest current density allowed by the electrochemical reactions compatible with a long service life of electrode materials, and separators. It is also of paramount importance to operate with the highest ***Faradaic current efficiency***, *CE*.

Therefore in the following paragraphs, we will detail the calculations using a step-by-step approach to address each single contribution to the overall cell voltage namely the reversible cell voltage, the anode, and cathode overpotentials, the ohmic drop, the liquid junction potential, and the aging potential based on the main electrochemical reactions taking place at each electrodes along with the unwanted side reactions occurring inside each compartment.

14.2 Electrochemical Reactions

The patented FerWIN® iron electrowinning process depicted schematically in Figure 80 consists to electrolyze a warm aqueous solution of iron (II) sulfate inside a divided electrolyzer by means of an anion exchange membrane (AEM). The anion exchange membrane is acting as a physical separator to prevent the mixing of both anolyte and catholyte while allowing the crossing of sulfate anions from the catholyte towards the anode compartment.

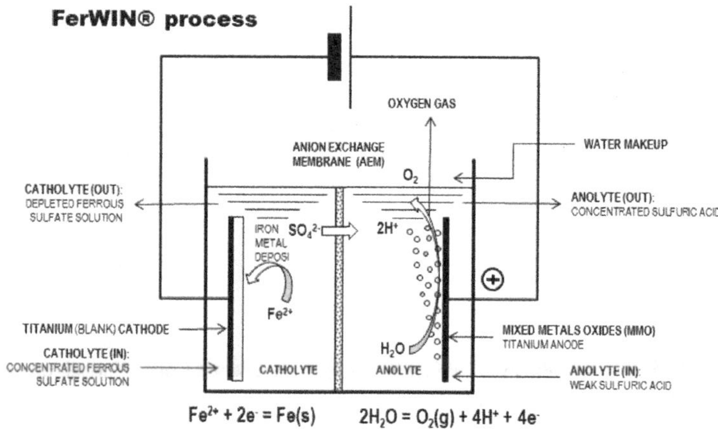

Figure 80 – Schematic of the electrolyzer with electrochemical reactions

At the cathode ferrous cations are reduced producing electrolytic iron metal. At the anode, the sulfate anions crossing the membrane combine with the protons left behind from the oxygen gas evolution reaction (OER) to form sulfuric acid. Therefore, the strength of sulfuric acid increases constantly until reaching a maximum threshold dictated by the initial strength in the anolyte (Section 11.2.5).

14.2.1 Main Electrochemical Reactions

The description of major (i.e., desired) and competitive (i.e., side or unwanted) electrochemical reactions occurring in each compartment along with the overall electrochemical reaction are listed for convenience in Table 91.

Table 91 – Main, side, and overall electrochemical reactions

Electrode	Anode (+)	Cathode (-)
Major (desired) reactions	$2H_2O = O_2(g) + 4H^+ + 4e^-$	$Fe^{2+} + 2e^- = Fe(s)$
Competitive (side) reactions	$Fe^{2+} = Fe^{3+} + e^-$ $2SO_4^{2-} = S_2O_8^{2-} + 2e^-$	$2H^+ + 2e^- = H_2(g)$ $Fe^{3+} + e^- = Fe^{2+}$ $Fe^{3+} + 3e^- = Fe(s)$
Overall electrochemical reaction	$FeSO_4 \cdot 7H_2O$(copperas) $+ H_2O = Fe(s) + H_2SO_4 + 7H_2O + 0.5O_2(g)$	

The major electrochemical reactions occurring are at the cathode the reduction of ferrous cations into metallic iron while at the anode the oxidation of water with the evolution of nascent oxygen gas.

The combination of the two major half-reactions corresponds to the electrolysis of ferrous sulfate depositing metallic iron at the cathode, and producing concentrated free sulfuric acid together with oxygen gas at the anode according to the overall electrochemical reaction involving theoretically anhydrous ferrous sulfate:

$$FeSO_4(s) + H_2O = Fe(s) + H_2SO_4 + 0.5O_2(g)$$

Because the anodic oxidation of ferrous cations back into ferric cations at the anode, and the reduction of nascent oxygen at the cathode, the electrolyzer must be divided into two compartments by at least a separator (i.e., barrier) such as a diaphragm or better by an anion exchange membrane. The latter impedes ferrous cations to diffuse towards the anode while allowing the sulfate anions to reach the anode. Thus preventing the loop for the reduction/oxidation of iron, that consumes inefficiently the current.

14.2.2 Side Electrochemical Reactions

The well-known major competitive reaction that can occur at the cathode is the reduction of the hydronium cations (i.e., protons) with the evolution of nascent hydrogen gas. If it is not addressed properly by adjusting the pH of the catholyte but remaining low enough to avoid precipitation of metal hydroxides, and by selecting a suitable cathode material, this side reaction will consumed most of the current, and thus affects the cathode current efficiency for depositing of metallic iron.

$$2H^+ + 2e^- = H_2(g)$$

On the other hand, on the anode side, there is always a possibility especially at high current densities to oxidize the sulfate anions into peroxodisulfate (i.e., persulfate) anions, $S_2O_8^{2-}$ as follows:

$$2SO_4^{2-} = S_2O_8^{2-} + 2e^-$$

This side reaction must be taken seriously into account especially when operating at elevate anode current densities above +2,000 A/m^2 and for temperatures colder than 30°C which could be case when performing the electrowinning of metallic iron powder under high current density both at the anode and cathode. Fortunately, during the electrowinning of metallic iron, the operating temperature always ranges between 40°C and 60°C thus impeding this side reaction as the thermal decomposition rate of persulfate is faster than the production rate by electrolysis. Thus it will be omitted in the following calculations.

It is also worth to mention that ubiquitous traces of ferrous cations always present in some impure sulfuric acid used as anolyte can be oxidized back into ferric cations.

$$Fe^{3+} = Fe^{2+} + e^-$$

This latter scenario is particularly relevant when electrowinning iron and recycling sulfuric acid from spent pickling solution (SPLs) as the iron-depleted catholyte can be recirculated in the anolyte compartment to strengthen its concentration sulfuric acid, and thus refurbishes its original pickling capabilities.

14.2.3 Electrochemical Reactions Related to Impurities

Often in practice, especially when dealing with impure copperas, pregnant leach solutions (PLS), and spent pickling liquors (SPL), in the catholyte beside ferrous cations, and water (H_2O) as main electroactive species other reducible metal cations and/or electroactive species can be present simultaneously. These ubiquitous electroactive species are namely: iron (Fe^{3+}), titanium (TiO^{2+}, Ti^{3+}, Ti^{2+}), vanadium (VO_2^+, VO^{2+}, V^{3+}, V^{2+}, V), chromium (Cr^{3+}, Cr^{2+}, Cr), manganese (Mn^{2+}, Mn), nickel (Ni^{2+}, Ni), copper (Cu^{2+}, Cu), and zinc (Zn^{2+}, Zn).

14.3 Theoretical (Reversible) Cell Voltage

In order to be able to calculate the theoretical (reversible) cell voltage, it is of paramount importance to calculate first the standard electrode potential of each redox couples for both major (i.e., desired reactions) and competitive (i.e., side and unwanted reactions) electrochemical reactions that can simultaneously take place at each electrode (i.e., cathode and anode) during electrowinning along with their temperature, and pH dependences.

14.3.1 Standard Electrode Potentials

In the particular case of electrowinning iron from an aqueous solution of ferrous sulfate, the most probable electrochemical reactions with their standard electrode potentials (298.15K, and 101.325 kPa) are summarized in Table 92.

Table 92 – Standard electrode potentials at 298.15 K and 101.325 kPa

Electrode	Anode (+)	Cathode (-)
Major (desired) reactions	$2H_2O = O_2(g) + 4H^+ + 4e^-$ $E^0_{298.15K}(O_2/2H_2O) = +1.229$ V/SHE	$Fe^{2+} + 2e^- = Fe(s)$ $E^0_{298.15K}(Fe^{2+}/Fe^0) = -0.447$ V/SHE
Competitive (side) reactions	$Fe^{2+} = Fe^{3+} + e^-$ $E^0_{298.15K}(Fe^{3+}/Fe^{2+}) = +0.771$ V/SHE	$2H^+ + 2e^- = H_2(g)$ $E^0_{298.15K}(2H^+/H_2) = +0.000$ V/SHE $Fe^{3+} + e^- = Fe^{2+}$ $E^0_{298.15K}(Fe^{3+}/Fe^{2+}) = +0.771$ V/SHE $Fe^{3+} + 3e^- = Fe(s)$ $E^0_{298.15K}(Fe^{3+}/Fe) = -0.041$ V/SHE

In addition, we have provided in Table 93, the standard electrode potential for the half electrochemical reactions involving reducible metal impurities.

Table 93 – Standard electrode potentials of reducible metallic impurities

Half-electrochemical reaction	Standard electrode potentials
$VO_2^+ + 2H^+ + e^- = VO^{2+} + H_2O$	$E^0_{298.15K}(VO_2^+/VO^{2+}) = +0.999$ V/SHE
$Fe^{3+} + e^- = Fe^{2+}$	$E^0_{298.15K}(Fe^{3+}/Fe^{2+}) = +0.771$ V/SHE
$Cu^{2+} + 2e^- = Cu(s)$	$E^0_{298.15K}(Cu^{2+}/Cu) = +0.342$ V/SHE
$VO^{2+} + 2H^+ + e^- = V^{3+} + H_2O$	$E^0_{298.15K}(VO^{2+}/V^{3+}) = +0.338$ V/SHE
$TiO^{2+} + 2H^+ + e^- = Ti^{3+} + H_2O$	$E^0_{298.15K}(TiO^{2+}/Ti^{3+}) = +0.099$ V/SHE
$V^{3+} + e^- = V^{2+}$	$E^0_{298.15K}(V^{3+}/V^{2+}) = -0.255$ V/SHE
$Ni^{2+} + 2e^- = Ni(s)$	$E^0_{298.15K}(Ni^{2+}/Ni) = -0.257$ V/SHE
$Cr^{3+} + e^- = Cr^{2+}$	$E^0_{298.15K}(Cr^{3+}/Cr^{2+}) = -0.424$ V/SHE
$Cr^{3+} + 3e^- = Cr(s)$	$E^0_{298.15K}(Cr^{3+}/Cr) = -0.744$ V/SHE
$Zn^{2+} + 2e^- = Zn(s)$	$E^0_{298.15K}(Zn^{2+}/Zn) = -0.762$ V/SHE
$Ti^{3+} + e^- = Ti^{2+}$	$E^0_{298.15K}(Ti^{3+}/Ti^{2+}) = -0.900$ V/SHE
$V^{2+} + 2e^- = V(s)$	$E^0_{298.15K}(V^{2+}/V) = -1.175$ V/SHE

$Mn^{2+} + 2e^- = Mn(s)$	$E^0_{298.15K}(Mn^{2+}/Mn)$ = -1.185 V/SHE

14.3.2 Standard Electrode Potentials vs. Temperature

It is well known that conducting the electrowinning at temperature above ambient exhibits several advantages: (i) it increases greatly the reaction kinetics such as the charge transfer across electrode-electrolyte interface, (ii) it improves the mass transfer owing to the usually lower viscosity of electrolytes, and greater diffusion coefficient of electroactive species, (iii) it allows to dissolve more ferrous sulfate inside the catholyte allowing a higher limiting cathode current density, and finally (iv) it diminishes the ohmic drop owing to enhanced ionic conductivities.

Hence, it is important to perform the electrowinning at the highest allowed temperature which is compatible with other practical considerations (e.g., electrode materials, corrosion of cell materials, and evaporation rate of solutions).

Based on the thermodynamic equations established in Section 5 for calculating the standard electrode potential for a given half-electrochemical reaction as a function of temperature, the values of the standard electrode potentials of selected electroactive species at an operating temperature ranging from 25°C (298.15 K) up to 90°C (363.15K) are reported in Table 94.

Table 94 – Standard electrode potentials vs. temperature

Practical temperature		25°C	30°C	40°C	50°C	54°C	60°C	70°C	80°C	90°C
Absolute thermodynamic temperature	pH	298.15 K	303.15 K	313.15 K	323.15 K	327.15 K	333.15 K	343.15 K	353.15 K	363.15 K
Redox half-cell		Standard electrode potentials (E^0/V vs.SHE)								
$O_2/2H_2O$	**0.00**	**1.229**	**1.225**	**1.216**	**1.208**	**1.205**	**1.200**	**1.191**	**1.183**	**1.175**
VO_2^+/VO^{2+}	0.00	0.999	1.003	1.009	1.015	1.017	1.021	1.028	1.034	1.040
Fe^{3+}/Fe^{2+}		0.771	0.796	0.847	0.897	0.917	0.948	0.998	1.049	1.100
Cu^{2+}/Cu		0.342	0.344	0.348	0.353	0.354	0.357	0.362	0.366	0.371
VO^{2+}/V^{3+}	0.00	0.338	0.325	0.300	0.275	0.265	0.249	0.224	0.199	0.173
TiO^{2+}/Ti^{3+}	0.00	0.099	0.089	0.068	0.047	0.038	0.026	0.005	-0.016	-0.037
$2H^+/H_2$	**0.00**	**0.000**	**0.000**	**0.000**	**0.000**	**0.000**	**0.000**	**0.000**	**0.000**	**0.000**
V^{3+}/V^{2+}		-0.255	-0.253	-0.249	-0.245	-0.243	-0.241	-0.236	-0.232	-0.227
Ni^{2+}/Ni		-0.257	-0.255	-0.250	-0.245	-0.243	-0.241	-0.236	-0.231	-0.226
Fe^{2+}/Fe		**-0.447**	**-0.445**	**-0.442**	**-0.439**	**-0.437**	**-0.435**	**-0.431**	**-0.428**	**-0.424**
Cr^{3+}/Cr		-0.744	-0.742	-0.737	-0.733	-0.731	-0.728	-0.723	-0.719	-0.714
Zn^{2+}/Zn		-0.762	-0.760	-0.756	-0.752	-0.751	-0.749	-0.745	-0.741	-0.737
Ti^{3+}/Ti^{2+}		-0.900	-0.892	-0.876	-0.859	-0.852	-0.841	-0.823	-0.805	-0.786
V^{2+}/V		-1.175	-1.174	-1.172	-1.171	-1.170	-1.169	-1.166	-1.164	-1.162
Mn^{2+}/Mn		-1.185	-1.185	-1.195	-1.219	-1.233	-1.258	-1.311	-1.378	-1.459

14.3.3 Standard Reversible Cell Voltage

From the standard electrode potentials, it is then possible to calculate the ***standard reversible cell voltage***, denoted ΔE^0, in V, for the main electrochemical reaction occurring during the electrowinning of iron. It consists simply to the algebraic difference between the standard electrode potentials of oxidation reaction occurring at the anode (+), that is, the oxygen gas evolution reaction (OER), and the reduction of ferrous cations into metallic iron at the cathode (-) with all species involved having an activity or fugacity equal to unity. For instance for a thermodynamic temperature, T, in K, the standard reversible cell voltage is given by:

$$\Delta E^0(T) = [E^0_T(O_2/2H_2O) - E^0_T(Fe^{2+}/Fe^0)]$$

Based on the numerical values of standard electrode potentials for the main and side electrochemical reactions, the values of the standard reversible cell voltages from 40°C (313.15 K) to 60°C (333.15K) are listed in Table 95.

Table 95 – Main standard reversible cell voltage vs. temperature

Electrode	Anode (+)	Cathode (-)
Major desired reactions	$2H_2O = O_2(g) + 4H^+ + 4e^-$ $E^0_{40°C}(O_2/2H_2O) = +1.216$ V/SHE $E^0_{50°C}(O_2/2H_2O) = +1.208$ V/SHE $E^0_{60°C}(O_2/2H_2O) = +1.200$ V/SHE	$Fe^{2+} + 2e^- = Fe(s)$ $E^0_{40°C}(Fe^{2+}/Fe) = -0.442$ V/SHE $E^0_{50°C}(Fe^{2+}/Fe) = -0.439$ V/SHE $E^0_{60°C}(Fe^{2+}/Fe) = -0.435$ V/SHE
Standard reversible cell voltages	$\Delta E^0_{40°C} = [E^0_{40°C}(O_2/2H_2O) - E^0_{40°C}(Fe^{2+}/Fe)] = 1.658$ V $\Delta E^0_{50°C} = [E^0_{50°C}(O_2/2H_2O) - E^0_{50°C}(Fe^{2+}/Fe)] = 1.647$ V $\Delta E^0_{60°C} = [E^0_{60°C}(O_2/2H_2O) - E^0_{60°C}(Fe^{2+}/Fe)] = 1.635$ V	

Similarly based on the definition of the ***standard thermoneutral electrode potential*** for each electrode reaction (Section 5.11), the corresponding figures are listed in Table 96.

Table 96 – Main standard thermoneutral cell voltage vs. temperature

Electrode	Anode (+)	Cathode (-)
Major desired reactions	$2H_2O = O_2(g) + 4H^+ + 4e^-$ $E^{TN}_{40°C}(O_2/2H_2O) = +1.479$ V/SHE $E^{TN}_{50°C}(O_2/2H_2O) = +1.478$ V/SHE $E^{TN}_{60°C}(O_2/2H_2O) = +1.476$ V/SHE	$Fe^{2+} + 2e^- = Fe(s)$ $E^{TN}_{40°C}(Fe^{2+}/Fe) = -0.583$ V/SHE $E^{TN}_{50°C}(Fe^{2+}/Fe) = -0.611$ V/SHE $E^{TN}_{60°C}(Fe^{2+}/Fe) = -0.638$ V/SHE
Standard thermoneutral cell voltages	$\Delta E^{TN}_{40°C} = [E^0_{40°C}(O_2/2H_2O) - E^0_{40°C}(Fe^{2+}/Fe)] = 2.062$ V $\Delta E^{TN}_{50°C} = [E^0_{50°C}(O_2/2H_2O) - E^0_{50°C}(Fe^{2+}/Fe)] = 2.088$ V $\Delta E^{TN}_{60°C} = [E^0_{60°C}(O_2/2H_2O) - E^0_{60°C}(Fe^{2+}/Fe)] = 2.115$ V	

In case the reader wants to have standard electrode potentials for a wider temperature range these are reported in Table 97. For convenience we have also plotted the tabulated data to show in Figure 81 the wide span for the electrode potentials of various cathode reactions vs. the temperature.

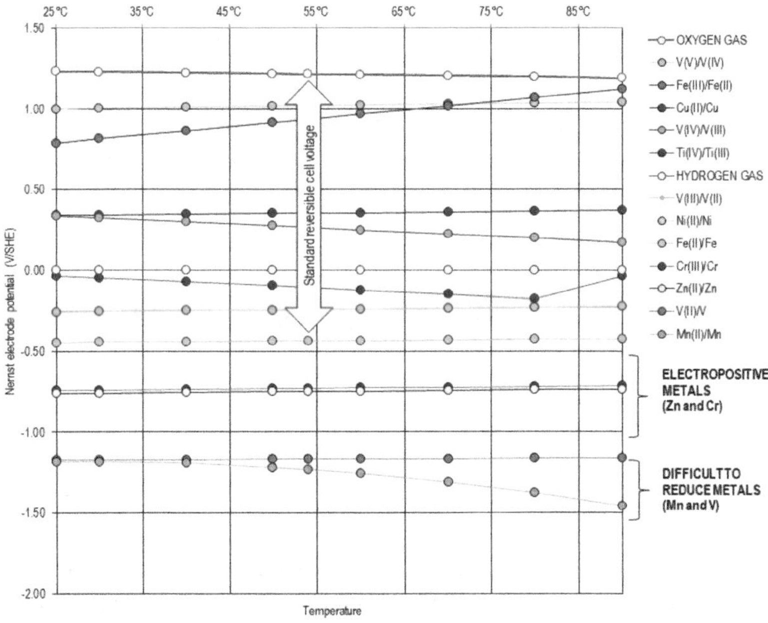

Figure 81 – Standard electrode potential of various redox couples vs. temperature

Close examination of both tabulated and plotted data of the standard electrode potentials vs. temperature indicates clearly that conducting the electrowinning of iron well above room temperature is always thermodynamically favorable.

Table 97 – Standard potential, reversible, and thermoneutral voltage vs. temperature

OPERATING TEMPERATURE	25°C	30°C	40°C	50°C	54°C	60°C	70°C	80°C	90°C
Absolute thermodynamic temperature	298.15 K	303.15 K	313.15 K	323.15 K	327.15 K	333.15 K	343.15 K	353.15 K	363.15 K
1_THERMODYNAMIC DATA									
$O_2/2H_2O$ std. electrode potential (E^0/V vs. SHE)	**1.229**	**1.225**	**1.216**	**1.208**	**1.205**	**1.200**	**1.191**	**1.183**	**1.175**
VO_2^+/VO^{2+} std. electrode potential (E_0/V vs. SHE)	0.999	1.003	1.009	1.015	1.017	1.021	1.028	1.034	1.040
Fe^{3+}/Fe^{2+} std. electrode potential (E^0/V vs. SHE)	0.771	0.796	0.847	0.897	0.917	0.948	0.998	1.049	1.100
$Cu^{2+}/Cu(s)$ std. electrode potential (E^0/V vs. SHE)	0.342	0.344	0.348	0.353	0.354	0.357	0.362	0.366	0.371
VO^{2+}/V^{3+} std. electrode potential (E^0/V vs. SHE)	0.338	0.325	0.300	0.275	0.265	0.249	0.224	0.199	0.173
TiO^{2+}/Ti^{3+} std. electrode potential (E^0/V vs. SHE)	0.099	0.089	0.068	0.047	0.038	0.026	0.005	-0.016	-0.037
$2H^+/H_2$ std. electrode potential (E^0/V vs. SHE)	**0.000**	**0.000**	**0.000**	**0.000**	**0.000**	**0.000**	**0.000**	**0.000**	**0.000**
V^{3+}/V^{2+} std. electrode potential (E^0/V vs. SHE)	-0.255	-0.253	-0.249	-0.245	-0.243	-0.241	-0.236	-0.232	-0.227
$Ni^{2+}/Ni(s)$ std. electrode potential (E^0/V vs. SHE)	-0.257	-0.255	-0.250	-0.246	-0.243	-0.241	-0.236	-0.231	-0.226
Fe^{2+}/Fe std. electrode potential (E^0/V vs. SHE)	**-0.447**	**-0.445**	**-0.442**	**-0.439**	**-0.437**	**-0.435**	**-0.431**	**-0.428**	**-0.424**
Cr^{3+}/Cr^{2+} std. electrode potential (E^0/V vs. SHE)	-0.424	-0.424	-0.424	-0.424	-0.424	-0.424	-0.424	-0.424	-0.424
$Cr^{3+}/Cr(s)$ std. electrode potential (E^0/V vs. SHE)	-0.744	-0.742	-0.737	-0.733	-0.731	-0.728	-0.723	-0.719	-0.714
$Zn^{2+}/Zn(s)$ std. electrode potential (E^0/V vs. SHE)	-0.762	-0.760	-0.756	-0.752	-0.751	-0.749	-0.745	-0.741	-0.737
Ti^{3+}/Ti^{2+} std. electroda potential (E^0/V vs. SHE)	-0.900	-0.892	-0.876	-0.869	-0.852	-0.841	-0.823	-0.805	-0.786
$V^{2+}/V(s)$ std. electrode potential (E^0/V vs. SHE)	-1.175	-1.174	-1.172	-1.171	-1.170	-1.169	-1.166	-1.164	-1.162
$Mn^{2+}/Mn(s)$ std. electrode potential (E^0/V vs. SHE)	-1.185	-1.185	-1.195	-1.219	-1.233	-1.258	-1.311	-1.378	-1.459
STANDARD REVERSIBLE CELL VOLTAGE (ΔE^0)	**1.676**	**1.670**	**1.658**	**1.646**	**1.642**	**1.635**	**1.623**	**1.611**	**1.599**
$O_2/2H_2O$ std. thermoneutral potential (E_{TN}/V vs. SHE)	1.481	1.481	1.479	1.478	1.477	1.476	1.475	1.473	1.472
Fe^{2+}/Fe std. thermoneutral potential (E_{TN}/V vs. SHE)	-0.541	-0.555	-0.583	-0.611	-0.622	-0.638	-0.666	-0.694	-0.722
STANDARD THERMONEUTRAL CELL VOLTAGE (ΔE_{TN})	**2.023**	**2.036**	**2.062**	**2.088**	**2.099**	**2.115**	**2.141**	**2.167**	**2.194**

14.3.4 Nernst Electrode Potentials

Since the temperature dependence of standard electrode potentials are known, it is now possible to calculate the Nernstian electrode potentials at a given absolute temperature T, in K, taking into account the thermodynamic activity, and fugacity of involved electroactive species using the Nernst equation:

Anode (+) reactions:

$$E_{O2}(T) = E^0_T(O_2/2H_2O) + (RT/4F)\ln(f_{O2}a_{H+}{}^4)$$

$$E_{S2O8}(T) = E^0_T(S_2O_8{}^{2-}/2SO_4{}^{2-}) + (RT/2F)\ln[(S_2O_8{}^{2-})/(SO_4{}^{2-})^2]$$

Cathode (-) reactions:

$$E_{Fe(II)}(T) = E^0_T(Fe^{2+}/Fe^0) + (RT/2F)\ln(a_{Fe2+})$$

$$E_{Fe(III)}(T) = E^0_T(Fe^{3+}/Fe^{2+}) + (RT/F)\ln(a_{Fe3+}/a_{Fe2+})$$

$$E_{H2}(T) = E^0_T(2H^+/H_2) + (RT/2F)\ln(a_{H+}{}^2/f_{H2})$$

Unless otherwise required, the electrowinning will be conducted under atmospheric pressure (p_0 = 101.325 kPa), and for simplicity the fugacity of gases are assumed to be equal to the partial pressure of each gases (i.e., $f_{O2} \cong p_{O2}$; and $f_{H2} \cong p_{H2}$), and the activities of all the species in solid or liquid state are assumed to be equal to unity. In addition, if the hydrogen potential function pH = colog$_{10}a_{H+}$ is introduced, the Nernst's equations become:

Anodic (+) reactions:

$E_{O2}(T) = E^0{}_T(O_2/2O^{2-}) - (RT\ln 10/F)\,pH + (RT\ln 10/4F)\log_{10}(p_{O2})$

$E_{S2O8}(T) = E^0{}_T(S_2O_8{}^{2-}/2SO_4{}^{2-}) + (RT/2F)\ln[(S_2O_8{}^{2-})/(SO_4{}^{2-})^2]$

Cathodic (-) reactions:

$E_{Fe(II)}(T) = E^0{}_T(Fe^{2+}/Fe^0) + (RT\ln 10/2F)\log_{10}(a_{Fe2+})$

$E_{Fe(III)}(T) = E^0{}_T(Fe^{3+}/Fe^{2+}) + (RT\ln 10/F)\log_{10}(a_{Fe3+}/a_{Fe2+})$

$E_{H2}(T) = E^0{}_T(2H^+/H_2) - (RT\ln 10/F)\,pH - (RT\ln 10/2F)\log_{10}(p_{H2})$

Note that the partial pressure of each gas must be corrected from the contribution of the vapor pressure of the electrolyte at each temperature, for instance, by using the numerical data extracted from literature such as those provided by the ***Dühring plot***[125] for the electrolyte.

$p_{O2} \cong (P_{atm} - \pi_{anolyte})$

$p_{H2} \cong (P_{atm} - \pi_{catholyte})$ with $\pi_{catholyte} = \pi_{soln}$

For the anolyte, by definition the vapor pressure over the aqueous solution of sulfuric acid is theoretically the sum of the vapor pressure of sulfuric acid (H_2SO_4) plus that of sulfur trioxide (SO_3), and water vapor (H_2O). However, in practice for aqueous solutions of sulfuric acid with a mass percentage below 30 wt.% H_2SO_4 the vapor pressures of H_2SO_4, and SO_3 are negligible. Thus, assuming that the ***Raoult's law*** applies satisfactorily, the vapor pressure of the anolyte is equal to the mole fraction of the vapor pressure of pure water at the same temperature:

$\pi_{anolyte} = x_{water}\,\pi_{water}$

Where

$\pi_{anolyte}$ vapor pressure of the anolyte solution in Pa,

x_{water} dimensionless mole fraction of water,

π_{water} saturated vapor pressure of water in Pa.

The latter physical quantity is a function of temperature according to the empirical ***Antoine's equation***:

$\log_{10}\pi_{water} = A_{water} - B_{water}/T$

Where

[125] CARDARELLI, F. (2022) *Sulfuric Acid Digestion, Sulfuric Acid Baking, and Sulfation Roasting in Mineral and Chemical Processing, and Extractive Metallurgy*. Electrochem Technologies & Materials Inc., Montreal, Canada, Section 5.7, pp. 46-48

π_{water} vapor pressure of a single component k in Pa,

T absolute temperature in K,

A_w, B_w empirical constants.

From tabulated data [126], the vapor pressure of water expressed in Pascal (Pa) is calculated using the following empirical equation with the temperature in K:

$$\log_{10}\pi_{water}\ (Pa) = 73.649 - 7258.2/T - 7.3037\ \ln T - 4.1653 \times 10^{-6}\ T^2$$

Similarly for the catholyte, due to lack of experimental data, we assumed that the Raoult's law applies, and hence the vapor pressure over the catholyte solution consists to the partial vapor pressure of water at the same temperature

$$\pi_{anolyte} = x_{water}\ \pi_{water}$$

Where

$\pi_{catholyte}$ vapor pressure of the catholyte solution in Pa,

x_{water} dimensionless mole fraction of water,

π_{water} saturated vapor pressure of water in Pa.

14.3.5 Nernst Electrode Potentials vs. Temperature

The Nernst electrode potentials are reported in Table 100. Close examination clearly indicates that the reduction of protons remains the competitive side-reaction at the cathode. Therefore the proper selection of the electrode material will allow solving this key issue and will be discussed in the next section.

Table 98 – Nernst potential, reversible, and thermoneutral voltage vs. temperature

OPERATING TEMPERATURE Absolute thermodynamic temperature	25°C 298.15 K	30°C 303.15 K	40°C 313.15 K	50°C 323.15 K	54°C 327.15 K	60°C 333.15 K	70°C 343.15 K	80°C 353.15 K	90°C 363.15 K
$O_2/2H_2O$ electrode potential (E/V vs. SHE)	**1.223**	**1.216**	**1.204**	**1.191**	**1.185**	**1.177**	**1.164**	**1.150**	**1.134**
VO_2^+/VO^{2+} electrode potential (E_0/V vs. SHE) at pH(catholyte)	0.704	0.702	0.698	0.694	0.693	0.691	0.687	0.684	0.680
Fe^{3+}/Fe^{2+} electrode potential (E^0/V vs. SHE)	0.485	0.503	0.538	0.574	0.588	0.611	0.656	0.699	0.746
Cu^{2+}/Cu electrode potential (E^0/V vs. SHE)	0.200	0.200	0.199	0.199	0.199	0.198	0.198	0.198	0.198
VO^{2+}/V^{3+} electrode potential (E/V vs. SHE) at pH(catholyte)	0.042	0.024	-0.011	-0.046	-0.060	-0.081	-0.116	-0.152	-0.187
TiO^{2+}/Ti^{3+} electrode potential (E/V vs. SHE) at pH(catholyte)	-0.196	-0.212	-0.243	-0.274	-0.286	-0.305	-0.336	-0.366	-0.397
$2H^+/H_2$ electrode potential (E/V vs. SHE) at pH(catholyte)	**-0.148**	**-0.150**	**-0.155**	**-0.160**	**-0.162**	**-0.165**	**-0.170**	**-0.175**	**-0.180**
V^{3+}/V^{2+} electrode potential (E/V vs. SHE)	-0.256	-0.253	-0.249	-0.245	-0.243	-0.241	-0.236	-0.232	-0.227
Ni^{2+}/Ni electrode potential (E/V vs. SHE)	-0.398	-0.398	-0.398	-0.398	-0.398	-0.398	-0.398	-0.398	-0.398
Ti^{3+}/Ti^{2+} electrode potential (E/V vs. SHE)	-0.900	-0.892	-0.876	-0.859	-0.852	-0.841	-0.823	-0.805	-0.786
Fe^{2+}/Fe electrode potential (E/V vs. SHE)	**-0.444**	**-0.442**	**-0.435**	**-0.429**	**-0.426**	**-0.424**	**-0.422**	**-0.419**	**-0.418**
Cr^{3+}/Cr^{2+} electrode potential (E/V vs. SHE)	-0.424	-0.424	-0.424	-0.424	-0.424	-0.424	-0.424	-0.424	-0.424
Cr^{3+}/Cr electrode potential (E/V vs. SHE)	-0.837	-0.836	-0.836	-0.833	-0.833	-0.832	-0.830	-0.829	-0.827
Zn^{2+}/Zn electrode potential (E/V vs. SHE)	-0.904	-0.905	-0.906	-0.907	-0.907	-0.908	-0.909	-0.909	-0.910
V^{2+}/V electrode potential (E/V vs. SHE)	-1.314	-1.316	-1.319	-1.321	-1.323	-1.324	-1.327	-1.329	-1.331
Mn^{2+}/Mn electrode potential (E/V vs. SHE)	-1.325	-1.327	-1.342	-1.371	-1.387	-1.415	-1.472	-1.544	-1.630
THERMODYNAMIC CELL VOLTAGE (U_{th}/V)	**1.667**	**1.658**	**1.639**	**1.620**	**1.612**	**1.601**	**1.586**	**1.569**	**1.552**
$O_2/2H_2O$ thermoneutral electrode potential (E_{TN}/V vs. SHE)	1.475	1.472	1.466	1.460	1.458	1.454	1.448	1.440	1.431
Fe^{2+}/Fe thermoneutral electrode potential (E_{TN}/V vs. SHE)	-0.539	-0.552	-0.576	-0.602	-0.611	-0.627	-0.656	-0.686	-0.716
THERMONEUTRAL CELL VOLTAGE (U_{TN}/V)	**2.014**	**2.024**	**2.043**	**2.062**	**2.069**	**2.081**	**2.104**	**2.126**	**2.147**

[126] PERRY, R.H.; and GREEN, D.W. (1998) *Perry's Chemical Engineers' Handbook, Seventh Edition.* McGraw-Hill Book Company, New York; NY, pp. 2-76

14.3.6 Nernst Electrode Potentials vs. Temperature and pH

Because some half-electrochemical reactions described in the previous paragraphs involve acid-base equilibrium in addition to the exchange of electrons, the Nernst electrode potential is also dependent on the pH.

This is well known for the reduction of protons leading to the hydrogen gas evolution reaction (HER), and the oxidation of water leading to the oxygen gas evolution reaction (OER). In both cases, the Nernst electrode potential decrease linearly with an increase of pH with a negative slope of -59 mV per decade under standard temperature and pressure conditions. This means that for an increase of one unit in pH the Nernst electrode potential decreases by 59 mV.

In addition, the Nernst electrode of several oxygenated metal cations such as VO_2^+, VO^{2+}, and TiO^{2+}, also exhibits such behavior while the other redox couples involving Fe, Cr, Mn, Ni, Cu, and Zn arc not affected by the pH. 'The Nernst electrode potential for selected half-electrochemical reactions vs. the temperature and PH are reported in Table 99 hereafter.

Table 99 – Nernst electrode potentials vs. temperature and pH

Practical temperature		25°C	30°C	40°C	50°C	54°C	60°C	70°C	80°C	90°C
Absolute thermodynamic temperature	pH	298.15 K	303.15 K	313.15 K	323.15 K	327.15 K	333.15 K	343.15 K	353.15 K	363.15 K
Redox half-cell		Nernst electrode potentials (E^0/V vs.SHE)								
$O_2/2H_2O$	**0.00**	**1.2290**	**1.2248**	**1.2163**	**1.2079**	**1.2046**	**1.1996**	**1.1913**	**1.1830**	**1.1748**
$O_2/2H_2O$	-0.15	1.2297	1.2257	1.2175	1.2094	1.2062	1.2014	1.1934	1.1854	1.1775
$O_2/2H_2O$	-0.25	1.2302	1.2263	1.2183	1.2104	1.2073	1.2026	1.1948	1.1870	1.1793
$O_2/2H_2O$	-0.50	1.2315	1.2277	1.2203	1.2129	1.2100	1.2056	1.1982	1.1910	1.1838
$O_2/2H_2O$	-1.00	1.2340	1.2307	1.2243	1.2179	1.2153	1.2115	1.2052	1.1989	1.1927
VO_2^+/VO^{2+}	0.80	0.806	0.806	0.806	0.805	0.805	0.805	0.805	0.805	0.805
VO_2^+/VO^{2+}	1.00	0.782	0.782	0.781	0.780	0.779	0.779	0.778	0.777	0.776
VO_2^+/VO^{2+}	1.50	0.723	0.722	0.719	0.716	0.714	0.713	0.710	0.707	0.704
VO_2^+/VO^{2+}	2.00	0.664	0.661	0.656	0.651	0.649	0.646	0.642	0.637	0.632
VO_2^+/VO^{2+}	2.25	0.634	0.631	0.625	0.619	0.617	0.613	0.608	0.602	0.596
VO_2^+/VO^{2+}	2.50	0.605	0.601	0.594	0.587	0.585	0.580	0.573	0.567	0.560
Fe^{3+}/Fe^{2+}		0.787	0.813	0.864	0.915	0.935	0.966	1.017	1.068	1.120
Cu^{2+}/Cu		0.214	0.214	0.214	0.214	0.214	0.214	0.214	0.215	0.215
VO^{2+}/V^{3+}	0.80	0.144	0.128	0.097	0.065	0.052	0.033	0.001	-0.030	-0.062
VO^{2+}/V^{3+}	1.00	0.120	0.104	0.072	0.039	0.026	0.007	-0.026	-0.058	-0.091
VO^{2+}/V^{3+}	1.50	0.061	0.044	0.010	-0.025	-0.039	-0.059	-0.094	-0.129	-0.163
VO^{2+}/V^{3+}	2.00	0.002	-0.016	-0.052	-0.089	-0.104	-0.125	-0.162	-0.199	-0.235
VO^{2+}/V^{3+}	2.25	-0.027	-0.046	-0.084	-0.121	-0.136	-0.158	-0.196	-0.234	-0.271
VO^{2+}/V^{3+}	2.50	-0.057	-0.076	-0.115	-0.153	-0.168	-0.192	-0.230	-0.269	-0.307
$2H^+/H_2$	**0.00**	**0.000**	**0.000**	**0.000**	**0.000**	**0.000**	**0.000**	**0.000**	**0.000**	**0.000**
$2H^+/H_2$	0.50	-0.030	-0.030	-0.031	-0.032	-0.032	-0.033	-0.034	-0.035	-0.036
$2H^+/H_2$	0.66	-0.039	-0.040	-0.041	-0.042	-0.043	-0.044	-0.045	-0.046	-0.048
$2H^+/H_2$	0.80	-0.047	-0.048	-0.050	-0.051	-0.052	-0.053	-0.054	-0.056	-0.058
$2H^+/H_2$	1.00	-0.059	-0.060	-0.062	-0.064	-0.065	-0.066	-0.068	-0.070	-0.072
$2H^+/H_2$	1.50	-0.089	-0.090	-0.093	-0.096	-0.097	-0.099	-0.102	-0.105	-0.108
$2H^+/H_2$	2.00	-0.118	-0.120	-0.124	-0.128	-0.130	-0.132	-0.136	-0.140	-0.144
$2H^+/H_2$	2.25	-0.133	-0.135	-0.140	-0.144	-0.146	-0.149	-0.153	-0.158	-0.162
$2H^+/H_2$	2.50	-0.148	-0.150	-0.155	-0.160	-0.162	-0.165	-0.170	-0.175	-0.180
TiO^{2+}/Ti^{3+}	0.80	-0.033	-0.048	-0.073	-0.096	-0.107	-0.124	-0.149	-0.175	-0.037
TiO^{2+}/Ti^{3+}	1.00	-0.057	-0.073	-0.099	-0.122	-0.134	-0.151	-0.177	-0.203	-0.037
TiO^{2+}/Ti^{3+}	1.50	-0.117	-0.135	-0.163	-0.187	-0.200	-0.219	-0.247	-0.276	-0.037
TiO^{2+}/Ti^{3+}	2.00	-0.177	-0.197	-0.227	-0.252	-0.266	-0.287	-0.318	-0.348	-0.037
TiO^{2+}/Ti^{3+}	2.25	-0.207	-0.228	-0.259	-0.284	-0.299	-0.322	-0.353	-0.384	-0.037
TiO^{2+}/Ti^{3+}	2.50	-0.237	-0.259	-0.291	-0.317	-0.332	-0.356	-0.388	-0.420	-0.037
V^{3+}/V^{2+}		-0.354	-0.354	-0.353	-0.352	-0.352	-0.351	-0.350	-0.349	-0.348
Ni^{2+}/Ni		-0.354	-0.353	-0.351	-0.350	-0.349	-0.348	-0.347	-0.345	-0.344
Fe^{2+}/Fe		**-0.439**	**-0.437**	**-0.433**	**-0.430**	**-0.428**	**-0.426**	**-0.422**	**-0.418**	**-0.414**
Cr^{3+}/Cr		-0.795	-0.793	-0.790	-0.788	-0.786	-0.785	-0.782	-0.779	-0.776
Zn^{2+}/Zn		-0.846	-0.845	-0.844	-0.843	-0.843	-0.842	-0.841	-0.840	-0.839
V^{2+}/V		**-1.224**	**-1.224**	**-1.224**	**-1.224**	**-1.224**	**-1.224**	**-1.223**	**-1.223**	**-1.222**
Mn^{2+}/Mn		-1.257	-1.257	-1.270	-1.297	-1.312	-1.338	-1.393	-1.463	-1.546

14.3.7 Thermodynamic (Decomposition) Cell Voltage

From the Nernst electrode potentials, it is then possible to calculate the ***thermodynamic reversible cell voltage***, also called the ***decomposition cell voltage*** and denoted U_{th}, in V, for the main electrochemical reaction occurring during the electrowinning of iron.

The thermodynamic reversible cell voltage is the algebraic difference between the Nernst electrode potential of the half-reaction occurring at the anode (+), that is, the oxygen gas evolution reaction, minus the electrode potential for the reduction of ferrous cations in metallic iron at the cathode (-) as follows:

$$U_{th}(T) = [E_T(O_2/2H_2O) - E_T(Fe^{2+}/Fe)]$$

Replacing in the equation, the Nernst electrode potentials, we obtain:

$$U_{th}(T) = [E^0_T(O_2/2H_2O) - E^0_T(Fe^{2+}/Fe)] + (RT/4F)\ln(f_{O2}a_{H+}^4) + (RT/2F)\ln(a_{Fe2+})$$

Introducing the standard reversible cell voltage defined previously, we obtain the condensed equation for the decomposition cell voltage as a function of temperature, pH of the anolyte, and activity of ferrous cations in the catholyte:

$$U_{th}(T) = \Delta E^0(T) + (RT/2F)\,[0.5\ln(f_{O2}a_{H+}^4) + \ln(a_{Fe2+})]$$

The calculated decomposition cell voltages from 40°C (313.15 K) to 60°C (333.15K) with an anolyte having a pH = 0, and a catholyte containing $[Fe^{2+}]$ = 1.423 mol/dm³ are reported in Table 100 hereafter.

Table 100 – Thermodynamic and thermoneutral cell voltage vs. temperature

Electrode	Anode (+)	Cathode (-)
Major desired reactions	$2H_2O = O_2(g) + 4H^+ + 4e^-$ $E_{40°C}(O_2/2H_2O)$ = +1.204 V/SHE $E_{50°C}(O_2/2H_2O)$ = +1.191 V/SHE $E_{60°C}(O_2/2H_2O)$ = +1.177 V/SHE	$Fe^{2+} + 2e^- = Fe(s)$ $E_{40°C}(Fe^{2+}/Fe)$ = -0.435 V/SHE $E_{50°C}(Fe^{2+}/Fe)$ = -0.429 V/SHE $E_{60°C}(Fe^{2+}/Fe)$ = -0.424 V/SHE
Thermodynamic (decomposition) cell voltage	U_{th}(40°C) = +1.639 V U_{th}(50°C) = +1.620 V U_{th}(60°C) = +1.601 V	
Thermoneutral cell voltage	U_{TN}(40°C) = + 2.043 V U_{TN}(50°C) = + 2.062 V U_{TN}(60°C) = + 2.081V	

14.4 Electrochemical Cell

For these calculations, we have arbitrarily used the design of a single tall rectangular cell similar to the one to be used industrially, and that will be described later in Section 16.8. It consists of a divided electrolyzer with an enclosed anode compartment with a hanging cathode plate facing the separator. The size and dimensions are listed in Table 101 hereafter. This design and dimensions allow a good current distribution, excellent mass transport conditions when forced circulation is used, ease of harvesting the iron metal plate, and a favorable space-time yield.

Table 101 – Electrolyzer single cell size and dimensions

anode surface area (A_A)	2400 in^2	15484 cm^2
anode compartment volume (V_A)	600 in^3	9832 cm^3
anode active heigth (h_A)	60.000 in	152.40 cm
anode active width (w_A)	40.000 in	101.60 cm
anode plate thickness (x_A)	0.125 in	0.32 cm
anode-membrane gap (x_{AM})	0.250 in	0.64 cm
anode hydrodynamic diameter (D_h)	0.498 in	1.26 cm
L/D_h ratio	98.388	98.388
anolyte volume flow rate (Q_{vA})	**75.0** gal/min	283.9 dm^3/min
anode face surface velocity (u_A)	1.60 ft/s	0.49 m/s
anode current density (J_A)	**46.4** ASF	**500** A.m^{-2}
membrane width	60.000 in	152.400 cm
membrane height	40.000 in	101.600 cm
membrane surface area (A_M)	2400 in^2	15483.84 cm^2
membrane thickness (x_M)	0.005 in	0.0130 cm
membrane current density (J_m)	**46.4** ASF	**500** A.m^{-2}
cathode surface area (A_C)	2400 in^2	15484 cm^2
cathode compartment volume (V_C)	2400 in^3	39329 cm^3
cathode specific surface area ($a_e = A_C/V_{Catholyte}$)	190.335 in^{-1}	0.787 cm^{-1}
cathode active heigth (h_C)	60.000 in	152.40 cm
cathode active width (w_C)	40.000 in	101.60 cm
cathode plate thickness (x_C)	0.125 in	0.32 cm
cathode-membrane gap (x_{CM})	1.000 in	2.54 cm
cathode hydrodynamic diameter (D_h)	1.960 in	4.98 cm
L/Dh ratio	24.995	24.995
catholyte volume flow rate (Q_C)	**0.8** gal/min	2.839 dm^3/min
	0.045 gal/hour	0.170 m^3/h
cathode face surface velocity (u_C)	0.072 in/s	0.0018 m/s
	0.36 ft/hour	0.110 m/h
cathode current density (J_C)	**-46.4** ASF	**-500** A.m^{-2}
Number of electric contacts	4.00	**4.00**
Inter-electrodes gap (x_{AC})	1.255 in	3.188 cm
Total current intensity (I)	774.00 A	**774.0** A

14.5 Mass Transfer Coefficients

Before to calculate the electrodes overpotentials for mass diffusion controlled electrochemical reactions, it is of paramount importance to calculate the mass transfer coefficients for both the anode and cathode for a given electrolyzer design, sizes, and dimensions, the physical properties of the catholyte (Section 11.1.13) and of the anolyte (Section 11.2.7), and the hydrodynamic conditions (i.e., laminar, turbulent). It will also be important to distinguish between the flow occurring inside the enclosed anode compartment, and the flow around the hanging cathodes. For these calculations, we have adopted a single cell as pilot electrolyzer with characteristics reported in Table 101.

Based on these dimensions and the fluid properties of the electrolytes, it is then possible to calculate the mass transfer coefficients for the hydrodynamic conditions specific to each compartment.

On the anode side, because the anode compartment is a totally enclosed (see Section 16.8.4), the hydrodynamic conditions existing inside the narrow channel with mesh anodes acting as turbulent promoters and combined with a strong evolution of oxygen gas enhancing the turbulences even further, the best way for describing the flow conditions is a forced convection with turbulent flow.

On the cathode side, the flow around the hanging cathodes immersed inside a rectangular tank with circulation of the catholyte by a manifold installed at the bottom of the tank, it can be best approximated by a laminar flow taking place between the cathode plate and the separator (i.e., the membrane).

14.5.1 Forced Convection and Turbulent Flow

Now if we consider the forced circulation of the anolyte inside the anode compartment with a turbulent flow regime, after calculating the hydraulic diameter, along with the dimensionless ***Reynolds*** and ***Schmidt*** numbers, we can use the following empirical correlation providing the ***Sherwood number*** that can be written as follows:

$$Sh = k_m D_h / D = 5.57\ Re^{0.4} Sc^{1/3}$$

Hence, introducing the actual constant and the three empirical exponents, the mass transfer coefficient can be finally expressed numerically as follows:

$$k_m = 5.57\ D_{Fe}\ (Re^{0.4} Sc^{1/3}) / D_h$$

14.5.2 Laminar Flow between Cathode and Separator

Now if we consider the circulation of the catholyte around the cathodes and between the hanging cathode plate, and the opposite membrane from the anode compartment assuming a the laminar flow regime seems natural. Thus after calculating the hydraulic diameter, along with the dimensionless ***Reynolds***, ***Schmidt***, and ***Grashof*** numbers, we can use the following empirical correlation (see Table 37) to calculate the Sherwood number that can be written as follows:

$$Sh = k_m D_h / D = 0.0225\ (Sc Gr)^{0.85} (x/h)^2$$

Hence, the mass transfer coefficient can be finally expressed numerically as follows:

$$k_m = 0.0225\ D_{Fe}\ (Sc Gr)^{0.85} (x/h)^2 / D_h$$

It is important to mention, that at the cathode surface at pH below 2.0 some hydrogen gas evolution always occurs, this gas evolution creates tiny bubbles that sweep the surface of the cathode upward disturbing the diffusion layer, and has a strong influence on the mass transfer of ferrous cations due to the additional forced convection effects inside the parallel plate arrangement. This certainly increases the mass transfer coefficient significantly. The relevant physical properties of the anolyte and catholyte, and sizes of anode and cathode compartment for estimating the mass transfer coefficients are presented in Table 102 hereafter.

Table 102 – Mass transfer coefficients for the anode and cathode at 60°C

Electrode	Anode (+)	Cathode (-)
Flow regime	Turbulent	Laminar
Electrolyte properties (60°C)	$\rho_{anolyte}$ = 1,115 kg/m³ $\nu_{anolyte} = 0.67 \times 10^{-6}$ m².s⁻¹ $D_{SO_4^{2-}} = 2.15 \times 10^{-9}$ m².s⁻¹ $[SO_4^{2-}]$ = 2,273 mol.m⁻³	$\rho_{catholyte}$ = 1,193 kg/m³ $\nu_{catholyte} = 0.59 \times 10^{-6}$ m².s⁻¹ $D_{Fe2+} = 1.64 \times 10^{-9}$ m².s⁻¹ $[Fe^{2+}]$ = 2,197 mol.m⁻³
Compartment characteristic dimensions	e_{AM} = ¼ in = 6.35 mm h_A = 60 in = 1.524 m w_A = 40 in = 1160 mm D_h = 1.26 cm	e_{CM} = 1 in = 25.4 mm h_C = 60 in = 1.524 m w_C = 40 in = 1160 mm D_h = 4.98 cm
Mass transfer coefficient	$k_{SO4} = 2.474 \times 10^{-4}$ m.s⁻¹	$k_{Fe} = 6.145 \times 10^{-5}$ m.s⁻¹

The cathode mass transfer coefficients based on the best estimated physical properties of the catholyte, and the cathode compartment size and dimensions, are presented in Table 103 hereafter.

Table 103 – Mass transfer coefficients for the cathode vs. temperature

OPERATING TEMPERATURE	25°C	30°C	40°C	50°C	54°C	60°C
Absolute thermodynamic temperature	298.15 K	303.15 K	313.15 K	323.15 K	327.15 K	333.15 K
Reynold number ($Re = uD_h/\nu$)	76	95	113	136	143	155
Schmidt number ($Sc = \nu/D$)	1,669	1,055	722	483	429	361
Grashoff number [$Gr = g_n h^3(1 - \rho_0/\rho)/\nu^2$]	2.99E+06	4.62E+06	6.36E+06	8.79E+06	9.23E+06	1.00E+07
Membrane-cathode gap/cathe height (x/h)	2.50E-02	2.50E-02	2.50E-02	2.50E-02	2.50E-02	2.50E-02
Schmidt × Grashoff ($Sc \times Gr$)	4.99E+09	4.87E+09	4.59E+09	4.25E+09	3.96E+09	3.61E+09
Natural convection (Laminar)						
Sherwood number ($Sh = aRe^a Sc^b Gr^c$)	175	174	172	168	166	162
Cathode mass transfer coefficient (k_{ca}/m.s⁻¹)	2.53E-06	3.193E-06	3.865E-06	4.709E-06	4.940E-06	5.314E-06
Thickness of diffusion layer (δ/µm)	284 µm	286 µm	290 µm	295 µm	301 µm	308 µm
Cathode limiting current density (J_{max}/A.m⁻²)	**-594**	**-825**	**-1,210**	**-1,754**	**-2,031**	**-2,253**
Forced convection (Turbulent)						
Sherwood number ($Sh = aRe^a Sc^b Gr^c$)	71	70	69	68	67	67
Cathode mass transfer coefficient (k_{ca}/m.s⁻¹)	1.02E-06	1.280E-06	1.546E-06	1.887E-06	2.002E-06	2.185E-06
Thickness of diffusion layer (δ/µm)	703 µm	712 µm	725 µm	737 µm	742 µm	748 µm
Cathode limiting current density (J_{max}/A.m⁻²)	**-240**	**-331**	**-484**	**-703**	**-823**	**-926**
Laminar flow between cathode plate and separator						
Sherwood number ($Sh = aRe^a Sc^b Gr^c$)	2465	2412	2295	2148	2025	1871
Cathode mass transfer coefficient (k_{ca}/m.s⁻¹)	3.560E-05	4.419E-05	5.162E-05	6.003E-05	6.040E-05	6.145E-05
Thickness of diffusion layer (δ/µm)	20 µm	21 µm	22 µm	23 µm	25 µm	27 µm
Cathode limiting current density (J_{max}/A.m⁻²)	**-8,351**	**-11,413**	**-16,162**	**-22,364**	**-24,827**	**-26,053**

The anode mass transfer coefficients based on the best estimated physical properties of the anolyte, and the anode compartment size and dimensions, are presented in Table 104 hereafter.

Table 104 – Mass transfer coefficients for the anode vs. temperature

OPERATING TEMPERATURE Absolute thermodynamic temperature	25°C 298.15 K	30°C 303.15 K	40°C 313.15 K	50°C 323.15 K	54°C 327.15 K	60°C 333.15 K
Reynold number (**Re** = uD_h/ν)	5,137	5,713	6,906	8,099	8,561	9,225
Schmidt number (**Sc** = ν/D)	1,147	909	599	420	370	312
Grashoff number (**Gr** = $g_n h^3(1 - \rho_0/\rho)/\nu^2$)	2.87E+12	3.48E+12	4.88E+12	6.41E+12	7.04E+12	7.94E+12
Sherwood number (**Sh** = a$Re^a Sc^b Gr^c$)[Laminar]	888	879	862	847	841	833
Anode mass transfer coefficient (k_{an}/m.s^{-1})[Laminar]	7.375E-05	8.278E-05	1.019E-04	1.218E-04	1.30E-04	1.414E-04
Thickness of diffusion layer (δ/μm)[Laminar]	14 μm	14 μm	15 μm	15 μm	15 μm	15 μm
Anode limiting current density (J_{max}/A.m^{-2})[Laminar]	**32,978**	**36,912**	**45,191**	**53,706**	**57,081**	**62,020**
Sherwood number (**Sh** = a$Re^a Sc^b Gr^c$)[Turbulent]	1778	1717	1612	1526	1496	1456
Anode mass transfer coefficient (k_{an}/m.s^{-1})[Turbulent]	1.476E-04	1.617E-04	1.905E-04	2.195E-04	2.308E-04	2.474E-04
Thickness of diffusion layer (δ/μm)[Turbulent]	7 μm	7 μm	8 μm	8 μm	8 μm	9 μm
Anode limiting current density (J_{max}/A.m^{-2})[Turbulent]	**66,002**	**72,090**	**84,494**	**96,800**	**101,579**	**108,487**

14.6 Electrode Reactions Overpotentials

14.6.1 Anode Overpotential

The anode is where the oxidation of water takes place with the oxygen gas evolution reaction (OER). Thus the oxygen overpotential according to the definition of Gerischer (see Section 7.3) expressed in V, is simply the difference between the anode potential, $E_A(j)$ in V/SHE, measured at a given anode current density and the Nernst electrode potential for the oxygen gas evolution reaction denoted E_{O2}, in V/SHE:

$$\eta_{O2} = E_A(j) - E_{O2}$$

Because the electrochemical oxidation at the anode is essentially controlled by the electron transfer, thus the overpotential for the evolution of oxygen gas is obtained from the practical Tafel's equation (Section 7.11.3.1) established for a given regime (i.e., low and high current densities):

$$\eta_{O2} = a + b \log_{10} j_a$$

With the two empirical Tafel's coefficients for the above equation obtained from experiments. In this case, as we use a commercial mixed metals oxides (MMO) coated-titanium anode EMMO-IRO-TI2-MS of the type Ti/IrO_2-Ta_2O_5, we can use the coefficients that were provided in Section 12.3.5 for low cathode current density below -1000 A/m^2 as follows:

$$\eta_{O2}\,(V) = 0.130 + 0.102 \log_{10} j_a(A/m^2)$$

14.6.2 Cathode Overpotentials

In practice, for the electrodeposition of metallic iron at the cathode, there are several overpotentials to consider, namely the overpotential due to the electro crystallization of metallic iron, the concentration overpotential, and finally the overpotential for the reduction of protons with the evolution of nascent hydrogen gas at the cathode.

14.6.2.1 Electrodeposition of Metallic Iron

In a first approximation, the overpotential for the electro-crystallization of metallic iron is almost constant. The adopted value for iron the electro-crystallization overpotential in these calculations is -0.128 V when measured at 25°C and it decreases with an increase of temperature with a given temperature coefficient, $(\partial\eta_{Fe}/\partial t)$, of few mV/K (mV/°C).

$$\eta_{Fe}\,(V) = -0.128 + (\partial\eta_{Fe}/\partial t)\; t\,(°C)$$

14.6.2.2 Iron Concentration Overpotential

As already explained in details in Section 7.4.1, in presence of mass diffusion alone controlling the electrode kinetics assuming a linearized Nernstian diffusion layer, concentration overpotential arises because of these gradients of concentration. Practical expressions for estimating the concentration overpotential for a binary electrolyte such as $FeSO_4$ when a supporting electrolyte is present for instance ammonium sulfate, the mass transfer coefficient at the cathode can be approximated by the following equation:

$$\eta(j) = (RT/2F)\ln(1 - j_c/j_{c,\,max}) = (RT\ln 10/2F)\log_{10}(1 - j_c/j_{c,\,max})$$

The limiting (i.e., maximum) cathode current density for the reduction of ferrous iron in the above equation is related to the mass transfer coefficient k_m which itself depends on the diffusion coefficient and the hydrodynamic conditions existing at the cathode surface, and it was calculated Section 14.4. Thus the limiting cathode current density is calculated as follows:

$$j_{c,\,max} = 2Fk_m\,[Fe(II)]$$

Note that when operating at less than ninety percent of the limiting cathode current density, the order of magnitude for the concentration overpotential is relatively small in the order of only few millivolts.

14.6.2.3 Hydrogen Gas Evolution Reaction

Even if under the best operating conditions used for electrowinning metallic iron from ferrous sulfates, the reduction of the protons with evolution of nascent hydrogen gas is the main side reaction occurring at the cathode. Therefore, it is important to calculate the overpotential for a given cathode material.

Thus the hydrogen overpotential for the hydrogen gas evolution reaction (HER) according to the definition of Gerischer (see Section 7.3) expressed in V, is simply the difference between the cathode potential, $E_C(j)$ in V/SHE, measured at a given cathode current density and the Nernst electrode potential for the hydrogen gas evolution reaction denoted E_{H2}, in V/SHE:

$$\eta_{H2} = E_C(j) - E_{H2}$$

As the electrochemical reduction of protons at the cathode is controlled by the transfer of electrons, thus the overpotential for the evolution of hydrogen gas is obtained from the practical Tafel's equation (Section 7.11.3.2) established for a given regime (i.e., low and high current densities):

$$\eta_{H2} = a + b \log_{10} j_c$$

With the two empirical Tafel's coefficients for the above equation obtained from experiments. In this case, as we use a cathode made of chemically pure titanium grade 2 as blank cathode, we can use the coefficients that were provided in Section 12.2.4.1 for low cathode current density below -1000 A/m^2 as follows:

$$\eta_{H2}\,(V) = 0.340 - 0.519 \log_{10} j_a(A/m^2)$$

We have summarized the above anode and cathode overpotentials at 60°C in the following Table 105.

Table 105 – Electrode overpotentials at 500 A/m^2 and 60°C

Electrode	Anode (+)	Cathode (-)
Current densities	J_a = +500 A.m^{-2}	J_c = -500 A.m^{-2}
Selected electrode material	MMO-O_2 made of Ti/Ta_2O_5-IrO_2	C.P. Titanium (ASTM grade 2) balnk cathode
Practical overpotential equations (Tafel, etc.)	η_{O2} (V) = 0.130 + 0.102 $\log_{10} j$	$\eta_{crystal}$ = -0.128 V $+ a\, t$ (Nucleation) η_{diff} = -0.030 $\log_{10}(1 - j/j_{max})$ (Diffusion) η_{H2} = 0.340 - 0.519 $\log_{10} j$ (Gas evolution)
Overpotentials	η_{O2} = +0.407 V/SHE	η_{cryst} = -0.077 V/SHE η_{diff} = - 0.004 V/SHE η_{H2} = -1.060 V/SHE

For more data, we have summarized the overvoltage and overpotentials for the charge (electron) transfer, diffusion, and electro-crystallization vs. temperature in Table 106.

Table 106 – Overpotentials for activation, diffusion and crystallization vs. temperature

2 KINETICS DATA	25°C	30°C	40°C	50°C	54°C	60°C	70°C
O_2 evolution overpotential (η_{O2}/V)	0.4070	0.4070	0.4070	0.4070	0.4070	0.4070	0.4070
Fe diffusion overpotential (η_{Fe}/V)	-0.024	-0.012	-0.007	-0.005	-0.004	-0.004	-0.004
Fe electrocrystalization overpotential (η_{Fe}/V)	-0.128	-0.121	-0.106	-0.091	-0.086	-0.077	-0.062
H_2 evolution overpotential (η_{H2}/V)	-1.0606	-1.0606	-1.0606	-1.0606	-1.0606	-1.0606	-1.0606
$O_2/2H_2O$ overvoltage (U/V vs. SHE)	1.6297	1.6235	1.6106	1.5977	1.5921	1.5843	1.5710
Fe^{2+}/Fe^0 overvoltage (U/V vs. SHE)	-0.5960	-0.5621	-0.5415	-0.5208	-0.5121	-0.5005	-0.4840
$2H^+/H_2$ overvoltage (U/V vs. SHE)	-1.2085	-1.2110	-1.2160	-1.2209	-1.2229	-1.2259	-1.2309
Overpotential contribution (η/V)	**0.558**	**0.540**	**0.520**	**0.503**	**0.497**	**0.487**	**0.473**
Cell overvoltage (*U*/V)	**2.226**	**2.198**	**2.159**	**2.123**	**2.108**	**2.088**	**2.059**

14.7 Actual Electrode Potentials

Knowing the anode and cathode overpotentials calculated previously, it is now possible to calculate the actual electrode potentials as the sum of the reversible electrode potential and the overpotential. The calculated figures vs. the temperature are listed in Table 107.

Table 107 – Electrode potential and cell voltage vs. temperature at 500 A/m^2

<table>
<tr><td>Electrode</td><td>Anode (+)</td><td>Cathode (-)</td></tr>
<tr><td>Current densities</td><td>$J_a = +500$ A.m^{-2}</td><td>$J_c = -500$ A.m^{-2}</td></tr>
<tr><td rowspan="2">Actual electrode potential</td><td>$2H_2O \rightarrow O_2(g) + 4H^+ + 4e^-$
$U_{O2}(40°C) = +1.611$ V/SHE
$U_{O2}(50°C) = +1.598$ V/SHE
$U_{O2}(60°C) = +1.584$ V/SHE</td><td>$Fe^{2+} + 2e^- \rightarrow Fe(s)$
$U_{Fe}(40°C) = -0.541$ V/SHE
$U_{Fe}(50°C) = -0.521$ V/SHE
$U_{Fe}(60°C) = -0.501$ V/SHE</td></tr>
<tr><td></td><td>$2H^+ + 2e^- \rightarrow H_2(g)$
$U_{H2}(40°C) = -1.216$ V/SHE
$U_{H2}(50°C) = -1.221$ V/SHE
$U_{H2}(60°C) = -1.226$ V/SHE</td></tr>
<tr><td>Actual cell voltage</td><td colspan="2">$U + \eta(40°C) = +2.152$ V
$U + \eta(50°C) = +2.119$ V
$U + \eta(60°C) = +2.085$ V</td></tr>
</table>

Close examination of the above tabulated data demonstrates clearly that selecting proper anode materials such as mixed metals oxides (MMO) coated-titanium anodes for oxygen evolution decreases significantly the overall cell voltage, and by selecting a proper cathode material such as chemically pure titanium, it suppresses the main cathode side reaction (i.e., H_2 evolution).

Table 108 – Composition and properties of anolyte and catholyte at 20°C

Electrode	Anolyte (+)		Catholyte (-)	
Composition	H_2SO_4	20 wt.% 227 g/L 2.317 M	$FeSO_4$ Fe pH	26.6 wt.% 334 g/L 2.437 M 2.50
Mass density	1,136 kg.m^{-3}		1,313 kg.m^{-3}	
Dynamic viscosity (60°C)	0.80 mPa.s		0.78 mPa.s	
Electrical conductivity (60°C)	98 S/m		12.3 S/m	
Molarities breakdown	$[H^+]$ $[SO_4^{2-}]$	4.634 M 2.317 M	$[H^+]$ $[Fe^{2+}]$ $[SO_4^{2-}]$	0.003 M 2.437 M 2.437 M
Osmolarity $(O_s = \Sigma c_i z_i)$	13.636 M		8.805 M	
Ionic strength $(I_M = 0.5\Sigma c_i z_i^2)$	6.818 M		8.803 M	
Notes: (*) the mass percentages listed in this table are those at the operating temperature. Upon cooling the solubility of iron (II) sulfate decreases significantly and the solid may crystallize out. (**) Optional supporting electrolyte50 g/L of $(NH_4)_2SO_4$.				

14.8 Ohmic Drop Contributions

Now that we now the actual electrode potentials and cell overvoltages, it is important to calculate the ***overall ohmic drop*** or simply *IR*, that corresponds to the summation of all the ohmic resistance contributions existing inside the electrolyzer.

These resistances are namely the electronic resistance of the anode, and cathode materials, the ionic resistance of the anion exchange membrane, the ionic resistance of the anolyte, and catholyte, plus the shielding resistance imparted by the oxygen gas bubbles evolving at the anode, and finally the electrical resistance of contacts as follows:

$$R_{total} = R_{anode} + R_{anolyte} + R_{gas} + R_{membrane} + R_{catholyte} + R_{cathode} + R_{contacts}$$

Each single resistance can be described by a single equation as follows:

$$R = \rho d/A = d/\kappa A$$

with R electrical resistance in Ω,

ρ electrical resistivity in Ω.m,

κ electrical conductivity in S.m^{-1},

d medium thickness in m,

A cross sectional area in m^2.

Then the overall ohmic drop is given by the following equation:

$$IR_{total} = (I/A)\ [d_{an}/\kappa_{an} + d_{anolyte}/\kappa_{anolyte} + d_{m}/\kappa_{m} + d_{catholyte}/\kappa_{catholyte} + d_{cath}/\kappa_{cath} + d_{contacts}/\kappa_{contacts}]$$

Moreover, it is important to take into account the temperature dependence of theses ohmic drops. For that purpose, the temperature coefficient of the resistivity is obtained from experimental or tabulated data. Usually, for pure metals and alloys, the electrical resistivity increases with temperature with a positive temperature coefficient A expressed in K^{-1}:

$$\rho = \rho_0\ [1 + A(T - T_0)]$$

For semiconductors (e.g., graphite, conductive ceramic oxides) and ionic conductors (e.g., electrolytes, membranes), the electrical conductivity (i.e., reciprocal of the resistivity) increases with the temperature with a positive temperature coefficient B expressed in K^{-1}:

$$\kappa = \kappa_0\ [1 + B(T - T_0)]$$

In the particular case of the electrical resistance of layered composite materials such as mixed metal oxides (MMO) coated-titanium anodes, the total electric resistance is the sum of the electrical resistance of the bare metal substrate, and that of the IrO_2-catalyst coating. Even for high catalyst loadings, the coating is only few micrometers thick. Thus, assuming that the IrO_2-coating exhibits an electrical resistivity of 30 μΩ.cm, it is safe to assume that the maximum resistivity of the anode is almost identical to that of titanium metal.

Finally, oxygen gas bubbles evolving at the anode create voidage, that is, void fraction denoted f, in the anolyte decreasing its effective electrical conductivity (κ_{gas}) relative to the bulk phase conductivity ($\kappa_{anolyte}$). Hence the ohmic drop related to the amount of gas bubbles near the anode surface can be calculated by means of the ***Bruggeman equation*** listed below:

$$\kappa_{gas} = \kappa_{anolyte}\ (1 - f)^{3/2}$$

The selected properties of anode, cathode, and membrane materials used for performing these electrochemical calculations are provided in Table 109.

Table 109 – Properties of electrodes and membrane materials

Electrodes and membrane performances	
Anode material	**MMO anode**
Manufacturer/supplier	Electrochem Technologies & Materials Inc
Electrical resistivity at 25°C	56.2 μΩ.cm
Temperature coefficient	0.0038 K^{-1}
Tafel slope for oxygen (*b*)	0.102 V/log
Tafel intercept (a)	0.130 V
Cathode material	**Titanium cathode**
Manufacturer/supplier	Titanium Industries Ltd.
Electrical resistivity at 25°C	56.2 μΩ.cm
Temperature coefficient	0.0038 K^{-1}
Tafel slope for hydrogen (*b*)	-0.519 V/log
Tafel intercept (a)	0.340 V
Membrane material	**Anion exchange membrane**
Manufacturer/supplier	
Electrical conductivityity at 25°C	1.78 $S.m^{-1}$
Membrane thickness	130 μm
Temperature coefficient	0.002 K^{-1}

An example for the calculations of each single ohmic drop contribution, at 60°C, and for a current density of 500 A/m^2 is presented in Table 110.

Table 110 – Ohmic drop contributions at 60°C and 500 $A.m^{-2}$

Electrodes	Anode (+): $Ti/Ta_2O_5\text{-}IrO_2$	Cathode (-): Ti (ASTM grade 2)
$A_{an} = A_{ca} =$ 1.548 m^2	d_{an} = 1/8 in = 3.175 x 10^{-3} m ρ_{an} = 56.3 μΩ.cm and A = 0.0038 K^{-1} R_{an} = 264.7 x 10^{-9} Ω IR_{an} = **8.92 x 10^{-7} V**	d_{ca} = 1/8 in = 3.175 x 10^{-3} m ρ_{ca} = 56.3 μΩ.cm and A = 0.0038 K^{-1} R_{ca} = 264.7 x 10^{-9} Ω IR_{ca} = **8.92 x 10^{-7} V**
Electrolytes	Anolyte	Catholyte
$A_{anolyte}$ = $A_{catholyte}$ = 1.548 m^2	$d_{anolyte}$ = ¼ in = 6.35 x 10^{-3} m $\kappa_{anolyte}$ = 98.4 $S.m^{-1}$ $R_{anolyte}$ = 41.7 x 10^{-6} Ω $IR_{anolyte}$ = **0.032 V**	$d_{catholyte}$ = 1 in = 25.4 x 10^{-3} m $\kappa_{catholyte}$ = 12.3 $S.m^{-1}$ $R_{catholyte}$ = 1.22 x 10^{-3} Ω $IR_{catholyte}$ = **0.941 V**
Separator A_m = 1.548 m^2	Anion exchange membrane (AEM) d_m = 130 μm = 1.39 x 10^{-4} m κ_m = 1.78 $S.m^{-1}$ and B = 0.002 K^{-1} R_m = 47.2 x 10^{-6} Ω IR_m = **0.035 V**	
Others (gas bubbles, contacts)	IR_{gas} = **0.059 V** IR_c = **0.002 V**	
Total	$IR_{an} + IR_{anolyte} + IR_{gas} + IR_m + IR_{catholyte} + IR_{cath} + IR_c$ = **1.083 V**	

Additional calculations regarding the ohmic drop contributions at several temperatures are reported in Table 111.

Table 111 – Breakdown of ohmic drop contributions vs. temperature

5_OHMIC DROPS	25°C	30°C	40°C	50°C	54°C	60°C
Anode resistivity ($\rho/\mu\Omega.cm$)	56.2	56.2	56.3	56.3	56.3	56.3
Anolyte conductivity ($\kappa_{an}/S.m^{-1}$)	72.59	76.27	83.63	90.99	93.93	98.35
Membrane conductivity ($\kappa_{m}/S.m^{-1}$)	1.78	1.79	1.81	1.83	1.84	1.85
Catholyte conductivity ($\kappa_{ca}/S.m^{-1}$)	5.15	5.74	6.93	8.12	8.60	9.31
Catholyte conductivity ($\kappa_{an}/S.m^{-1}$)[with supporting electrolyte]	7.74	8.48	10.41	11.95	12.57	13.49
Cathode resistivity ($\rho/\mu\Omega.cm$)	56.2	56.2	56.3	56.3	56.3	56.3
Average contact resistance (R_c/Ω)	0.0005	0.0005	0.0005	0.0005	0.0005	0.0005
Anode ohmic drop (V)	5.44E-03	5.44E-03	5.44E-03	5.45E-03	5.45E-03	5.45E-03
Anolyte ohmic drop (V)	0.044	0.042	0.038	0.035	0.034	0.032
Gas bubble ohmic drop (V)	0.080	0.076	0.069	0.064	0.062	0.059
Membrane ohmic drop (V)	0.037	0.036	0.036	0.036	0.035	0.035
Catholyte ohmic drop (V)	2.466	2.210	1.831	1.563	1.476	1.363
Catholyte ohmic drop (V)[with supporting electrolyte]	1.640	1.498	1.220	1.062	1.010	0.941
Cathode ohmic drop (V)	8.56E-03	8.56E-03	8.57E-03	8.58E-03	8.58E-03	8.58E-03
Contacts ohmic drop (V)	0.002	0.002	0.002	0.002	0.002	0.002
Overall ohmic drop (IR_{ohmic}/V)	**2.642**	**2.380**	**1.990**	**1.713**	**1.623**	**1.506**
Overall ohmic drop (IR_{ohmic}/V)[with supporting electrolyte]	**1.817**	**1.668**	**1.379**	**1.213**	**1.157**	**1.083**
6_LIQUID JUNCTION POTENTIAL	**25°C**	**30°C**	**40°C**	**50°C**	**54°C**	**60°C**
Liquid junction potential (activities)	-0.038	-0.038	-0.038	-0.038	-0.038	-0.039

From the above table, it can be seen clearly that the major contributions of the overall ohmic drop are in order of importance: (i) the poorly conductive catholyte, followed by (ii) the anion exchange membrane, (iii) the shielding effect of the gas bubbles, and finally (iv) the anolyte. For comparison, the contributions to the ohmic drop expressed as percentages for a catholyte with and without a supporting electrolyte are reported in Table 112.

Table 112 – Contributions to the ohmic drop with and without supporting electrolyte

Percent of ohmic drop without supporting electrolyte	
0.36	Anode ohmic drop (V)
2.14	Anolyte ohmic drop (V)
3.92	Gas bubble ohmic drop (V)
2.33	Membrane ohmic drop (V)
90.54	Catholyte ohmic drop (V)
0.57	Cathode ohmic drop (V)
0.13	Contacts ohmic drop (V)

Percent of ohmic drop with supporting electrolyte	
0.50	Anode ohmic drop (V)
2.98	Anolyte ohmic drop (V)
5.45	Gas bubble ohmic drop (V)
3.24	Membrane ohmic drop (V)
86.85	Catholyte ohmic drop (V)
0.79	Cathode ohmic drop (V)
0.18	Contacts ohmic drop (V)

14.9 Liquid-Junction Potential

Because the anolyte and catholyte are physically separated by an ion exchange membrane, a liquid junction exists between the two electrolytes. The ***Henderson's equation*** already established for a binary electrolyte in Section 6.7.5 is used for that purpose. As the system consists of sulfuric acid as anolyte and a solution of ferrous sulfate as catholyte, the Henderson' s equation becomes:

$$E_J = -(RT/F)\{t_{H+}\ln[a_{H+}(A)/a_{H+}(C)] + 0.5t_{Fe2+}\ln[a_{Fe2+}(A)/a_{Fe2+}(C)] - 0.5t_{SO42-}\ln[a_{SO42-}(A)/a_{SO42-}(C)]\}$$

The calculated liquid junction potentials vs. temperature are reported in Table 111 from which selected values are listed in Table 113.

Table 113 – Liquid junction potentials vs. temperature

Electrolyte	Anolyte		Catholyte	
Molarities of ions at 60°C	H^+ SO_4^{2-}	4.545 M 2.273 M	H^+ Fe^{2+} SO_4^{2-}	0.0032 M 2.197 M 2.204 M
Activities at 60°C	H^+ SO_4^{2-}	0.482 0.241	H^+ Fe^{2+} SO_4^{2-}	0.0032 2.197 2.204
Ions transference numbers	H^+ Fe^{3+} SO_4^{2-}	0.401 0.121 0.192	H^+ Fe^{2+} SO_4^{2-}	0.412 0.097 0.192
	E_J (40°C) = -0.038 V E_J (50°C) = -0.038 V E_J (60°C) = -0.039 V			

14.10 Overall Cell Voltage

Therefore after having calculated all the four contributions, we can finally calculate the overall cell voltage at various operating temperatures:

$$U_{cell} = (E_{anode} - E_{cathode}) + (\eta_{anode} - \eta_{cathode}) + \Delta E_J + \Sigma_k IR_k$$

Hence the overall cell voltage for the cell at various temperatures is given in and Table 114.

Table 114 – Overall cell voltage of three-compartment cell vs. temperature

U_{cell} (40°C) = 1.639 V + 0.520 V + 1.379 V – 0.038 V = 3.500 V

U_{cell} (50°C) = 1.620 V + 0.503 V + 1.213 V – 0.038 V = 3.297 V

U_{cell} (60°C) = 1.601 V + 0.487 V + 1.083 V – 0.039 V = 3.133 V

14.11 Cell Potential Breakdown

Based on the previously calculated contributions to the overall cell voltage at 60°C and for a current density of -500 A/m^2, it is then possible to represent graphically the various contributions as depicted in Figure 82.

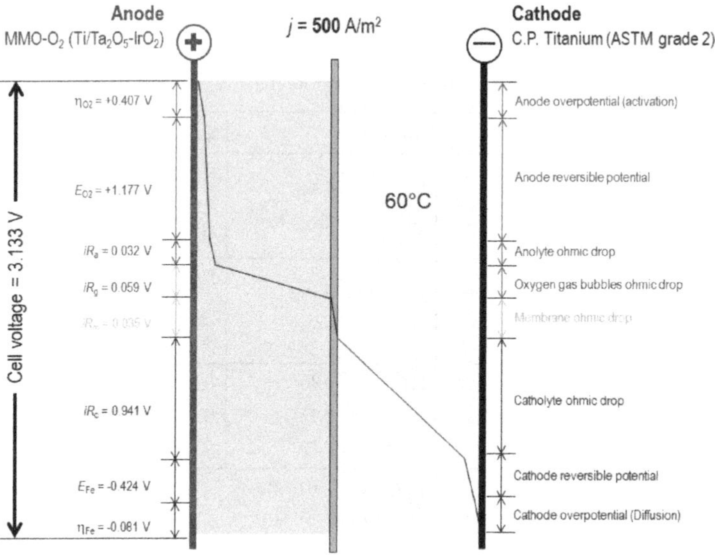

Figure 82 – Breakdown of the overall cell voltage for a current density of 500 A/m²

14.12 Faradaic, Voltaic, and Energy Efficiencies

These dimensionless quantities were already discussed more broadly in Section 8 and only the definitions and equation focussing on the electrowinning of iron will be presented hereafter.

14.12.1 Faradaic Current Efficiency

The ***faradaic cathode efficiency*** or ***cathode current efficiency*** denoted ε_I, or *CCE*, is the ratio of the electric charge consumed by the reduction of ferrous cations, Q_{Fe}, in C(Ah), to the total electric charge, Q, in C(Ah), that circulated inside the electrowinning cell.

$$CCE = \varepsilon_I = Q_{Fe}/Q$$

Thus it is the ratio of the actual mass of iron metal deposited at the cathode, m_{Fe}, in kg, to the theoretical mass of iron to be plated using the gravimetric electrochemical equivalent for iron, Ah.kg^{-1}, the cathode current density, j_c, in A/m^2, the cathode surface area, A_c, in m^2, and the duration of electrolysis, Δt, in hours:

$$CCE = \varepsilon_I = m_{Fe}Eq/j_cA_c\Delta t$$

The current efficiency increases with temperature as a higher temperature favors the mass transport, decreases the dynamic viscosity of the catholyte, and overpotentials. Two empirical linear equations were established for cathode and anode current efficiencies with temperature coefficients obtained from experiments. These are valid only within the narrow range of 90-100%:

$$CCE\ (t) = CCE_{25°C} + 0.002\ [t(°C) - 25] \qquad (1/\varepsilon_I)(\partial\varepsilon/\partial t) = 0.2\%/°C$$

$$ACE\ (t) = ACE_{25°C} + 0.00007\ [t(°C) - 25] \qquad (1/\varepsilon_I)(\partial\varepsilon/\partial t) = 7‰/°C$$

14.12.2 Voltaic or Potential Efficiency

The ***voltaic efficiency*** also called ***potential efficiency***, denoted by ε_U, is defined as the ratio of the thermodynamic or reversible cell voltage, U_{th}, in V, to the overall cell voltage, U_{cell}, in V, and it can be expressed as a fraction or a percentage.

$$\varepsilon_U = U_{th}/U_{cell}$$

14.12.3 Energy Efficiency

The ***energy efficiency***, denoted by ε_E, is the product of the faradaic current efficiency times the voltaic efficiency as follows:

$$\varepsilon_E = \varepsilon_U \times \varepsilon_I$$

14.13 Specific Energy Consumption

Based on the definition of the ***specific energy consumption*** described in Section 8.7 can be calculated from the following equation:

$$e_m = (E_q \times U_{cell})/\varepsilon_I$$

with

e_m	specific energy consumption in $J.kg^{-1}$ (Wh/kg),
ε_I	cathode current efficiency,
E_q	electrochemical equivalent in $C.kg^{-1}$ (Ah/kg),
U_{cell}	overall cell voltage in V.

Based on a Faradaic anode and cathode current efficiencies of 99.5 and 98.7 percent respectively, and the two gravimetric electrochemical equivalents of 3,350 Ah/kg for oxygen and 960 Ah/kg for iron, we obtain the following specific energy consumptions that are reported in Table 115.

Table 115 – Specific energy consumptions at 500 A.m^{-2}

Electrode	Anode (+)	Cathode (-)
Specific energy consumptions	11.773 kWh/kg of oxygen (40°C) 11.083 kWh/kg of oxygen (50°C) 10.524 kWh/kg of oxygen (60°C)	3.418 kWh/kg of iron (40°C) 3.213 kWh/kg of iron (50°C) 3.047 kWh/kg of iron (60°C)

14.14 Hourly Space-Time Yield

The ***space time yield***, denoted Y_t, or by the acronym *STY*, expresses the mass of product produced (i.e., iron, or oxygen) per unit surface active area of electrode (i.e., cathode, or anode) per unit time, it is expressed in in kg.m^{-2}.s^{-1} (kg.m^{-2}.h^{-1}). It is calculated using the equation already established in in Section 8.5.2:

$$STY = Y_t = (\varepsilon_I \times j)/E_q$$

Table 116 – Space time yield at 500 A.m^{-2}

Electrode	Anode (+) Anode current efficiency: 99.5%	Cathode (-) Cathode current efficiency: 98.7%
Space time yield	0.149 kg.m^{-2}.h^{-1} oxygen 0.104 m^3.m^{-2}.h^{-1} oxygen (NTP)	0.514 kg.m^{-2}.h^{-1} of iron

It is important to mention that the space time yield mainly depends on the current density for a given Faradaic current efficiency. Only the latter parameter can be influenced by the operating temperature and thus the space time yields varies slightly as the temperature increases.

Table 117 – Figures of merit and indices of performances vs. temperature

7_FIGURES OF MERITT	25°C	30°C	40°C	50°C	54°C	60°C
Overall cell voltage (U_{cell}/V)[with supporting electrolyte]	**4.004**	**3.827**	**3.500**	**3.297**	**3.227**	**3.133**
Faradaic current efficiency (cathode)	98.0%	98.1%	98.3%	98.5%	98.6%	98.7%
Faradaic current efficiency (anode)	99.5%	99.5%	99.6%	99.7%	99.7%	99.7%
Voltaic efficiency	41.9%	43.6%	47.4%	49.9%	50.9%	52.2%
Energy efficiency	41.0%	42.8%	46.6%	49.2%	50.2%	51.5%
O_2 specific energy consumption (e_m/kWh.kg^{-1})	13.483	12.883	11.773	11.083	10.843	10.524
Fe specific energy consumption (e_m/kWh.kg^{-1})	3.922	3.745	3.418	3.213	3.142	3.047
O_2 space time yield (/kg.m^{-2}.h^{-1})	0.148	0.149	0.149	0.149	0.149	0.149
O_2 space time yield (/m^3.m^{-2}.h^{-1})(NTP)	0.104	0.104	0.104	0.104	0.104	0.104
Fe space time yield (/kg.m^{-2}.h^{-1})	0.510	0.511	0.512	0.513	0.513	0.514

15 Laboratory, Prototype, and Pilot Testing

The laboratory, prototype, and pilot testing for electrowinning iron metal from iron sulfate(s), pregnant leach solutions, and spent pickling liquors was performed during the last thirteen years by *Electrochem Technologies & Materials Inc.* at the company facilities located in Boucherville, Quebec, Canada. This chapter provides a glimpse of the equipment designed, built, and used for that purpose.

15.1 Laboratory Electrolyzers

During the trials and screening tests performed in the laboratory, a small size rectangular divided cell was custom built. In its simplest form, the electrolyzer consisted of two or three rectangular compartments made of thick and clear plastic such as PMMA or polycarbonate (e.g., Plexiglas®, Lexan®) or PVC with a rectangular opening on each side for installing the ion exchange membranes.

The electrolyzer was equipped with rectangular plate electrodes together with anion and cation exchange membranes. The electrolyte solutions were poured into each compartment before electrolysis and circulated using peristaltic pumps. A custom built heat exchanger was used to prevent Joule's heating when performing the electrolysis over long period at high current densities.

Several generations of two- or three-compartment rectangular electrolyzers under the commercial name RECTLAB I, II, III, IV and V, were designed, and constructed in-house. These are depicted in Figure 83 to Figure 90.

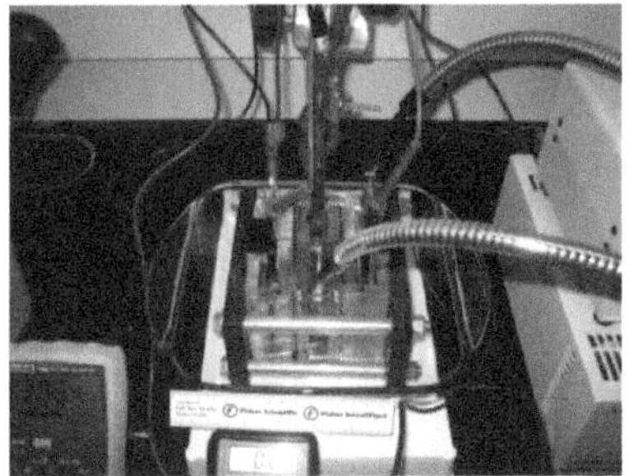

Figure 83 – Three-compartment laboratory electrolyzer RECTLAB II (2010)

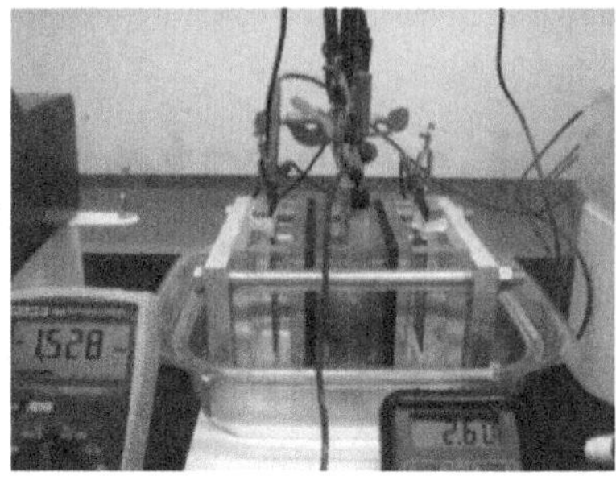

Figure 84 – Three-compartment laboratory electrolyzer RECTLAB III (2011)

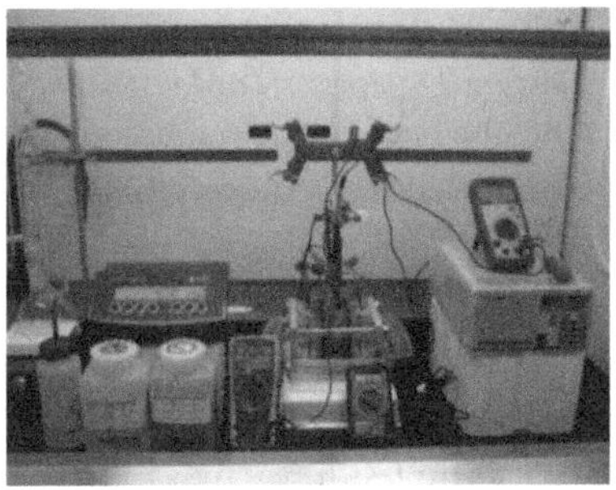

Figure 85 – Setup with RECTLAB III (2011)

Figure 86 – RECTLAB III with recirculation of anolyte and catholyte (2011)

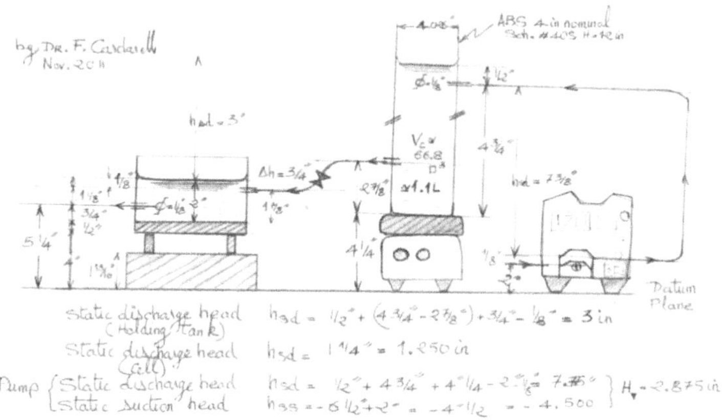

Figure 87 – Sketch of pump heads with recirculation of electrolyte (2011)

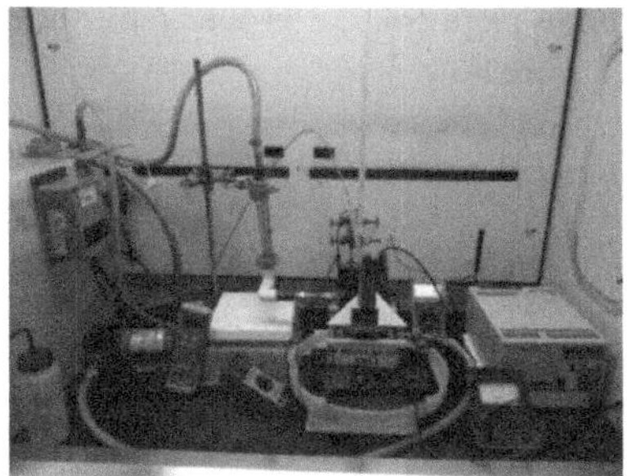

Figure 88 – Two-compartment laboratory electrolyzer RECTLAB IV (2012)

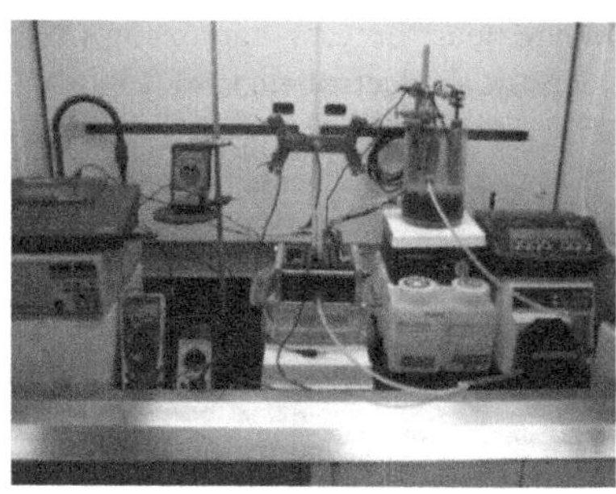

Figure 89 – Setup laboratory electrolyzer RECTLAB V (2013)

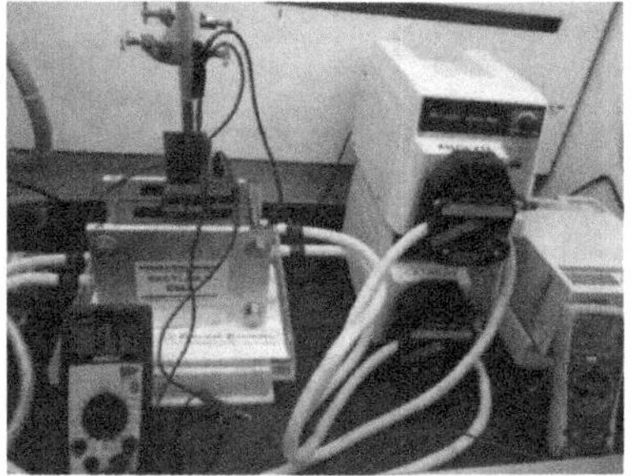

Figure 90 – Two-compartment laboratory electrolyzer RECTLAB V (2013)

Figure 91 – Hull cell (2014)

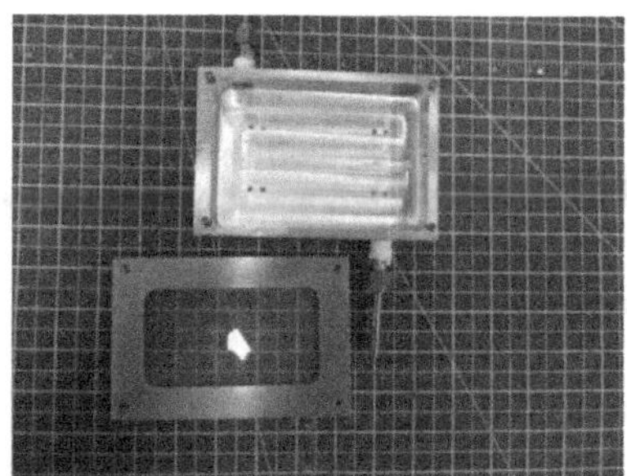

Figure 92 – Plate heat exchanger for RECTLAB cells

15.2 Prototype Electrolyzers

As soon as 2011, prototype experiments were also conducted with square or rectangular cathode plates having an active surface area of at least one square foot (929 cm^2). For that purpose, a series of open, plate and frame, divided electrolyzer named PROTOTYPE I (Figure 93), and PROTOTYPE II (Figure 94) were designed and constructed in-house. These versatile prototype scale electrolyzers allowed conducting experiment using a plethora of configurations including two- and three-compartment units, with forced circulation of anolyte, and catholyte, and the easy harvesting of the cathode plate for the proper removal of the deposit of electrolytic iron (Figure 95 and Figure 96).

Figure 93 – PROTOTYPE I electrolyzer (2011)

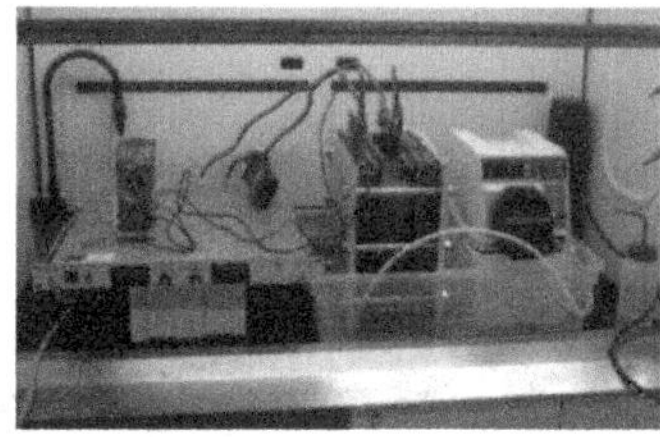

Figure 94 – PROTOTYPE II electrolyzer (2012)

Figure 95 – PROTOTYPE II electrolyzer with catholyte recirculation (2013)

Figure 96 – Close view of PROTOTYPE II electrolyzer (2013)

Totally enclosed divided plate and frame electrolyzers: FLOWPRO I (Figure 97) and II (Figure 98) were built for performing the electrochemical reduction and the dummying of large volumes of catholyte up to 60 L prior electrowinning. The sludge was removed continuously by a strainer (Figure 97).

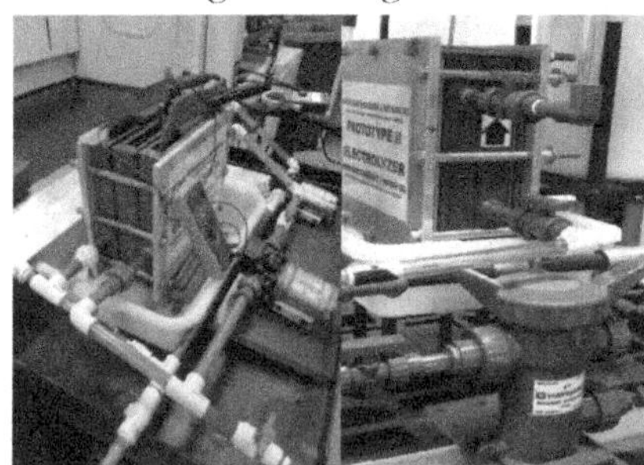

Figure 97 – FLOWPRO I electrolyzers for electrochemical reduction (2015)

Figure 98 – FLOWPRO II electrolyzer for electrochemical reduction (2016)

In 2012, for supporting the numerous prototype experiments, the manufacture of mild steel starter sheets (Figure 99) titanium cathode blanks (Figure 100), proprietary mixed metals oxides (MMO) coated-titanium anodes (Figure 102) was initiated.

Figure 99 – Prototype mild steel starter sheet

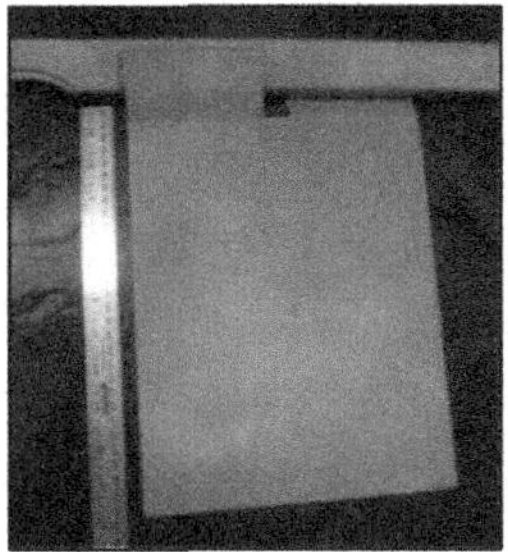

Figure 100 – Prototype titanium cathode blank

Figure 101 – Copper busbars

These electrodes were designed from the start with an intricate shape similar to the larger industrial electrodes they were supposed to mimic.

Figure 102 – Mixed metal oxides (MMO) anode

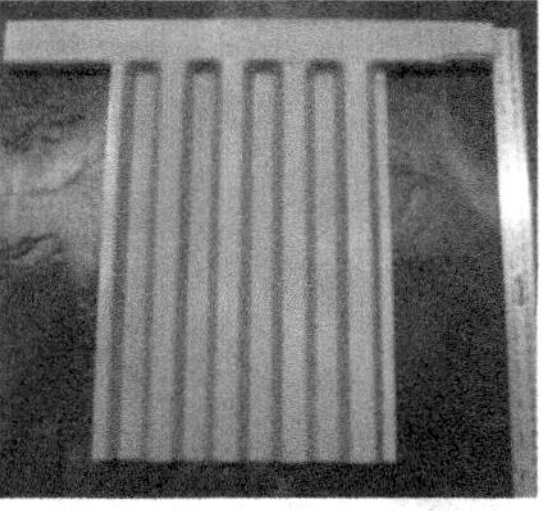

Figure 103 – Prototype MMO anode (Corrugated)

Figure 104 – Copper cathode

15.3 Semi-Pilot Electrolyzers

Larger semi-pilot scale electrolyzers with a total cathode surface area ranging from two square feet (2 x 929 cm^2) (Figure 107) up to twelve square feet (1.291 m^2) (Figure 106) were constructed for testing various electrowinning configurations, and to mimic the industrial electrolyzer. Particular attention was made to address the separate flow of the catholyte and the anolyte. For the latter, the utilization of disengagement vessels was used to separate the sulfuric acid from the oxygen gas. A particular attention was made to design and build a totally enclosed anode compartment hanging in the tank in between hanging cathodes plates.

When equipped with 60-L electrolytes holding tanks these electrolyzers allowed the recirculation of the electrolyte. Impellers, pumps, valves, rotameters, strainers, filters, were also installed. Internal or external heating was ensured by installing PTFE-coated or quartz immersed heaters resisting corrosion, and harsh operating conditions.

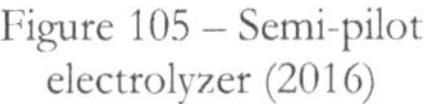

Figure 105 – Semi-pilot electrolyzer (2016)

Figure 106 – 10-square foot tank electrolyzer (2016)

Figure 107 – Two-square foot slot electrolyzer (2016)

Coaxial and cylindrical electrodes and membrane configurations (Figure 108) were also used for performing the electrochemical reduction, and dummying of large volume of catholyte containing high concentration of ferric cations along with the production of electrolytic iron metal powder.

Figure 108 – Cylindrical electrolyzers with coaxial design (2016)

For performing pilot test with industrial size electrodes, a larger rectangular electrolyzer consisting of a rectangular tank made of PP with a plate anode, a plate cathode, an anion-exchange membrane was constructed.

Table 118 – Pilot and prototype electrolyzer configurations

Types:	Rectangular or cylindrical tanks with conical bottom, plate and frames, tubular and coaxial with separator.
Cell construction material:	Polyvinylchloride (PVC), chlorinated-polyvinyl chloride (CPVC), polypropylene (PP), polycarbonate.
Piping material:	CPVC, PVC PFA.
Configuration:	Divided with two or more compartments
Compartment access:	open access, partially or entirely closed
Electrodes:	Plates, rods, tubes, three-dimensional (mesh, expanded metal)

Electrolyte circulation:	Anolyte and/or catholyte storage tanks with inlet and outlet
Electrodes assembly:	Monopolar, and bipolar
Heating & Cooling:	Immersed heaters, and heat exchangers
Pumping:	Air-operated diaphragm pumps, centrifugal pumps
Mixing:	Inert gas sparging, impeller, in-line static mixer. turbulent promoters
Purification of electrolyte:	Dummying or connection to strainers.
Electrolyte holding tanks:	From 10 gallons up to 55 gallons or connected to FIBC containers (252-279 gallons)
Solids removal:	Inline filters or strainers, filter-presses, or disk centrifuge
Instrumentation:	pH, ORP, temperature, conductivity probes, pressure gauges, rotameters.
Electrical connection:	Copper C101 busbars, copper cables AWG. No. "1/0" to No. "3/0" (106 to 212 kcmil)

15.4 Production of Electrolytic Iron Powder

15.4.1 Plate and Frame Electrolyzers

The production of high purity electrolytic iron powder was obtained by performing the electrowinning of iron inside a FLOWPRO IV type divided electrolyzer (see Figure 109) at high cathode current densities greater than -2,000 A/m^2 and/or with low concentration of ferrous iron. Under these operating conditions, the electrowinning process yields a poorly adherent and lousy fine iron metal powder easy to flush from the cathode surface by using a forced circulation of the catholyte. For that purpose, the enclosed plate and frame divided cell was build and used for electrowinning iron powder continuously at 50°C. The sludge was removed continuously by a strainer, rinsed, and filtered.

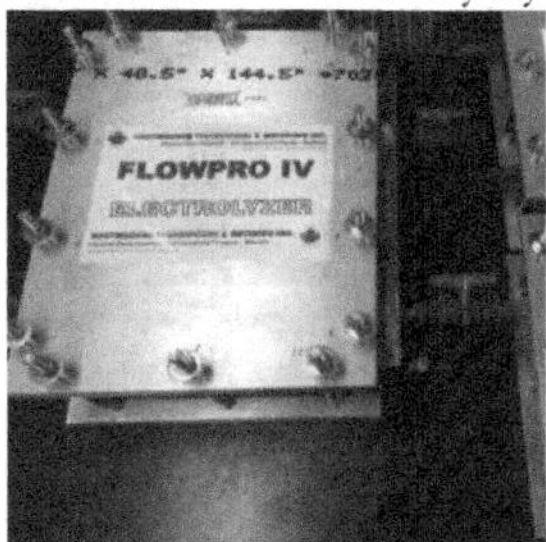

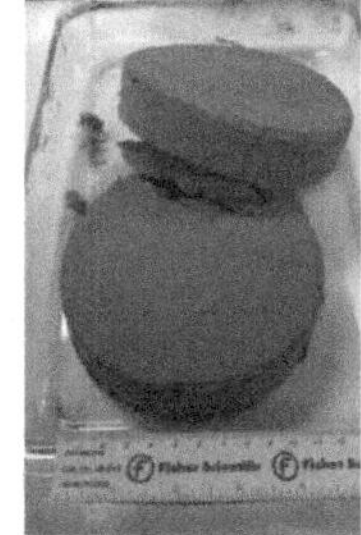

Figure 109 – FLOWPRO IV for producing iron powder (2016) and Fe-filter cake

15.4.2 Cylindrical and Tubular Electrolyzers

Large 50-L cylindrical electrolyzer (FLOWPRO III) with coaxial electrodes and membrane (Figure 110) was used for producing iron metal powder.

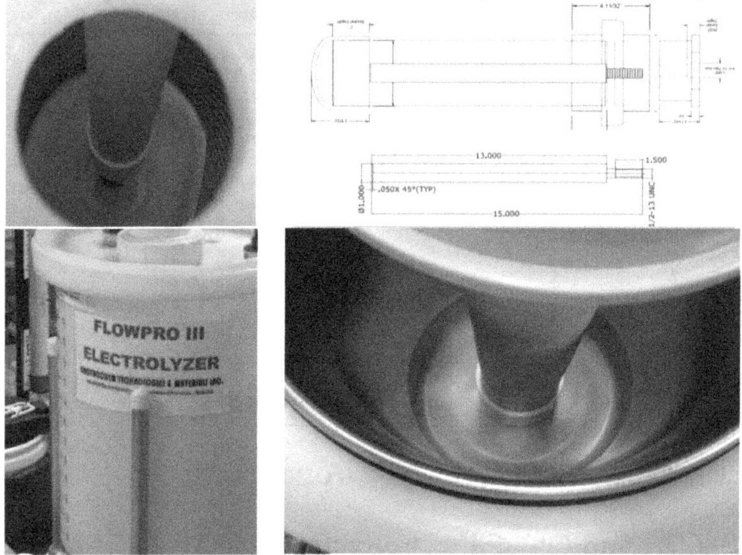

Figure 110 – FLOWPRO III electrolyzer for producing iron powder (2016)

Additionally a tall and narrow 4-foot tubular electrolyzer schematically depicted in Figure 111 was used for the same purpose but operated at a much higher cathode current density by using special rods of mixed metals oxides (MMO) anodes. For capturing the metallic particles from the suspension a hydro cyclone and a magnetic trap (Figure 111) and cartridge filters were used.

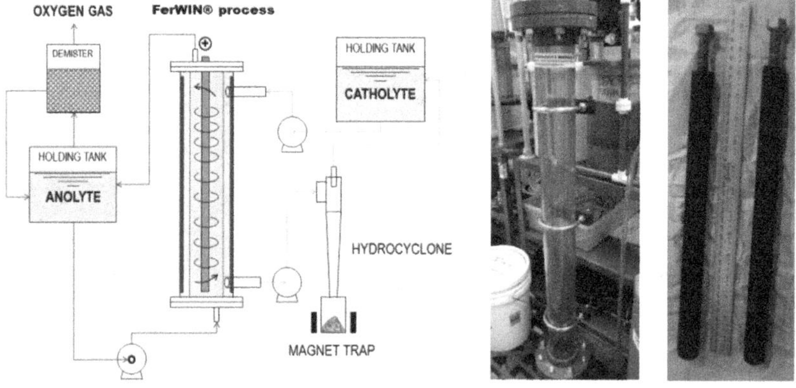

Figure 111 – Tubular electrolyzer for the production of electrolytic iron powder

15.5 Single Pilot Electrolyzer

To mimic the actual operating conditions for an industrial electrolyzer but restricting the size of the setup to one single cell to limit the burden of auxiliary equipment (e.g., DC power supply and holding tanks), we have designed and built a single cell electrolyzer with a 0.4 m² cathode surface area and the MMO mesh anode installed inside an enclosed compartment (Figure 113).

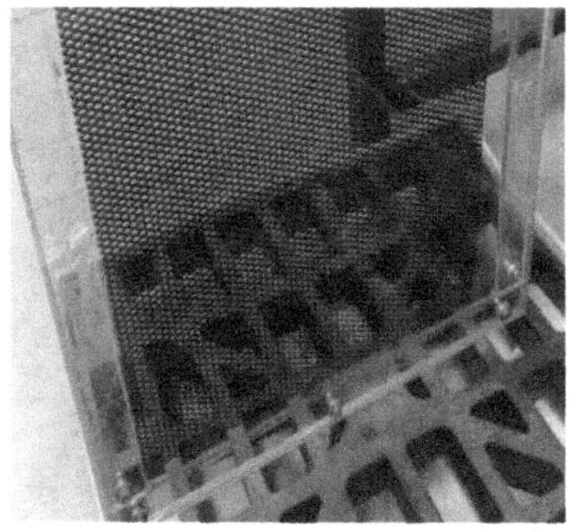

Figure 112 – MMO mesh anode

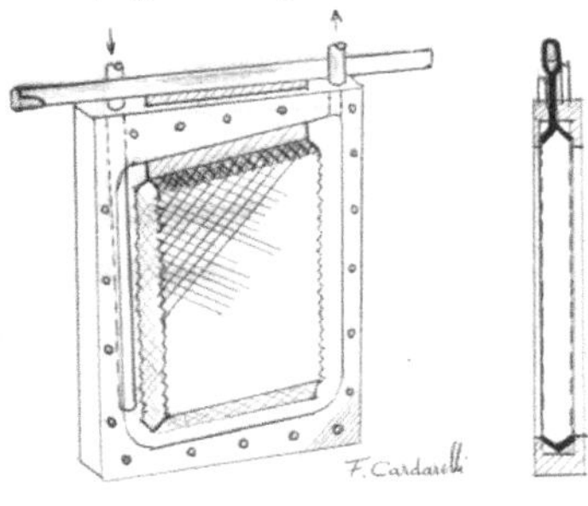

Figure 113 – Sketch anode compartment

A schematic P&ID for an electrowinning pilot plant comprising an electrolyzers with five cathodes is depicted in Figure 114 hereafter.

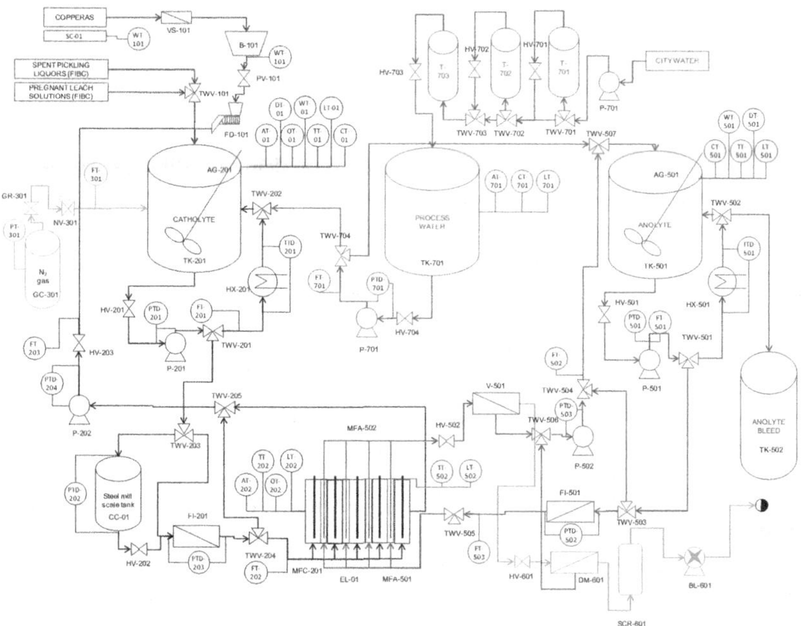

Figure 114 – Schematic P&ID for the pilot electrowinning plant

15.6 Electrolyzers Characteristics

We have summarized some of the characteristics of the major custom made laboratory, prototype, and pilot electrolyzers used for testing the electrowinning of iron in Table 119.

Table 119 – Rectangular electrolyzer characteristics

	RECTLAB V		PROTOTYPE II		PILOT		COMMERCIAL	
Electrolyzer type	SI units	US customary units	SI units	US customary units	SI units	US customary units	SI units	US customary units
Maximum number of cells per electrlyzer (N_{max})	1 cell(s)	1 cell(s)	5 cell(s)	5 cell(s)	10 cell(s)	10 cell(s)	66 cell(s)	66 cell(s)
Installed number of cells (N)	1 cell(s)	1 cell(s)	5 cell(s)	5 cell(s)	10 cell(s)	10 cell(s)	66 cell(s)	66 cell(s)
Cathode width (w)	0 1143 m	4 500 in	0 3048 m	12 000 in	0 3937 m	15.500 in	1.0160 m	40 000 in
Cathode height (L)	0 0889 m	3 500 in	0 4064 m	16 000 in	0 4445 m	17 500 in	1.5240 m	60 000 in
Cathode thickness (x)	3 175 mm	0 125 in	3 175 mm	0 125 in	3 175 mm	0 125 in	3 175 mm	0 125 in
Cathode effective surface area (A_e)(one side)	0 010 m^2	15 75 in^2	0 124 m^2	1 33 ft^2	0 175 m^2	1 88 ft^2	1 548 m^2	16 7 ft^2
Cathode-membrane gap (x_{CM})	25 4 mm	1 000 in	25 4 mm	1 000 in	25 4 m	1 000 in	25 4 mm	1 000 in
Cathode compartment volume (V_C)	0 037 m^3	1 31 in^3	0 003 m^3	0 11 ft^3	0 004 m^3	0.16 ft^3	0 039 m^3	1 39 ft^3
Cathode specific surface area (a_e)	m^{-1}	12 ft^2/ft^3	39 m^{-1}	12 ft^2/ft^3	39 m^{-1}	12 ft^{-1}	39 m^{-1}	12 ft^2/ft^3
Catholyte volume flow rate (Q_v)	1 9 L/min	0 50 gal/min	11 4 L/min	3 0 gal/min	66 8 L/min	15 0 gal/min	283 9 L/min	75 0 gal/min
Maximum cathode surface area ($A_{max} = N \times A_e$)	1 463 m^2	16 ft^2	0 619 m^2	7 ft^2	1 750 m^2	18.84 ft^2	102 2 m^2	1100 ft^2
Maximum current density (J_{max})	2691 A/m^2	250 A/ft^2	2691 A/m^2	250 A/ft^2	5382 A/m^2	500 A/ft^2	1615 A/m^2	150 A/ft^2
Maximum current (I)	27 A		333 A		942 A		2500 A	

15.7 Scale-up and Similarity Equations

Because the experimental results and cell performances were obtained during the experiments using the RECTLAB V laboratory cell, the PROTOTYPE II, and from a pilot electrolyzer, it is important to establish the mathematical similarity equations for calculating the performances of the commercial electrolyzer from the performances obtained at the laboratory, prototype, and pilot scale.

Since the electrolysis is performed under constant current (i.e., galvanostatic mode), the most important parameter is the overall cell voltage from which the specific energy consumption can be calculated directly. As already explained in Section 14.1.1, the overall cell voltage is the sum of all the potential contributions: the thermodynamic cell voltage, the activation, diffusion, and crystallization overpotentials, the ohmic drops due to the electrical resistance of electrodes, membranes, electrolytes, and bus bars:

$$U_{cell} = U_{th} + \Sigma\eta + j\,\Sigma_k\, R_k\, A_k + \Delta U_t$$

Because the compositions of the electrolytes, the cell operating temperature, and the electrode and membrane materials remains the same, hence only the geometric characteristics of the cell (i.e., electrode and membrane surface areas, electrode-membrane spacing, and the membrane thicknesses) will change with the electrolyzer design and have a direct impact on the overall ohmic drop. Therefore, because of the conservation of the total current circulating inside the electrolyzer:

$$j_c A_c = j_a A_a = I$$

We can express the variable ohmic drop consists to subtract the overpotential and thermodynamic cell voltage, and the aging term to the overall cell voltage when expressed as a function of the cathode current density as follows:

$$(U_{cell} - U_{th} + \Sigma\eta + \Delta U_t) = [j_c(A_c/A_a)\rho_a x_a + j_c\, \rho_c x_c + j_c(A_c/A_m)\rho_m x_m]$$

Hence, only the right side of the above equation will be impacted by changing the geometric characteristics of the electrolyzer. If we need to calculate the expected overall cell voltage for a new cell, U_2, from the overall cell voltage, U_1, measured with another rectangular cell with plate electrodes but having different geometric characteristics, both under a fixed cathode current density and operating temperature, we have:

$$(U_1 - U_{th} + \Sigma\eta + \Delta U_t) = [j_c(A_{c1}/A_{a1})\rho_a x_{a1} + j_c\, \rho_c x_{c1} + j_c(A_{c1}/A_{m1})\rho_m x_{m1}]$$

$$(U_2 - U_{th} + \Sigma\eta + \Delta U_t) = [j_c(A_{c2}/A_{a2})\rho_a x_{a2} + j_c\, \rho_c x_{c2} + j_c(A_{c2}/A_{m2})\rho_m x_{m2}]$$

The difference between the two cell voltages is obtained by the difference between above equations:

$$U_2 - U_1 = j_c\{\rho_a[(A_{c2}/A_{a2})x_{a2} - (A_{c1}/A_{a1})x_{a1}] + \rho_c(x_{c2}-x_{c1}) + \rho_m[(A_{c2}/A_{m2})x_{m2} - (A_{c1}/A_{m1})x_{m1}]\}$$

The numerical applications for the laboratory, prototype, and commercial electrolyzers are listed in Table 120.

Table 120 – Cell voltage similarity equations between electrolyzers

Prototype (2) vs. Laboratory (1)	Pilot (3) vs. Prototype (2)
Conditions: $x_{m1} = x_{m2} = x_m$ $x_{c1} = x_{a1} = x_1$ and $x_{c2} = x_{a2} = x_2$ $A_{c1} = A_{a1} = A_1$ and $A_{c2} = A_{a2} = A_2$	Conditions: $x_{m3} = x_{m2} = x_m$ $x_{c3} = x_{a3} = x_3$ and $x_{c2} = x_{a2} = x_2$ $A_{a3} = A_{m3}$ and $A_{c2} = A_{a2} = A_2$
$U_2 - U_1 = j_c\{(\rho_a+\rho_c)(x_2-x_1) + \rho_m x_m[(A_{c2}/A_{m2})-(A_{c1}/A_{m1})]\}$	$U_3 - U_2 = j_c\{x_3[\rho_a(A_{c3}/A_{a3}) + \rho_c] - [\rho_a(A_{c2}/A_{a2})+\rho_c]x_2 + \rho_m x_m[(A_{c3}/A_{m3})-(A_{c2}/A_{m2})]\}$
$U_2 = U_1 + 0.003$ V at 500 A/m² $U_2 = U_1 + 0.005$ V at 1000 A/m² $U_2 = U_1 + 0.008$ V at 1500 A/m²	$U_3 = U_2 - 0.401$ V at 500 A/m² $U_3 = U_2 - 0.803$ V at 1000 A/m² $U_3 = U_2 - 1.204$ V at 1500 A/m²
Between pilot (3) and laboratory (1) $U_3 = U_1 - 0.399$ V at 500 A/m² $U_3 = U_1 - 0.797$ V at 1000 A/m² $U_3 = U_1 - 1.196$ V at 1500 A/m²	

Numerical data:

Dimensions and geometric characteristics	① **RECTLAB V**	② **PROTOTYPE II**	③ **PILOT**
Cathode-membrane gap	$x_{c1} = 1.000$ in	$x_{c2} = 1.000$ in	$x_{c3} = 0.750$ in
Membrane-anode gap	$x_{a1} = 1.000$ in	$x_{a2} = 1.000$ in	$x_{a3} = 0.250$ in
Cathode surface area	$A_{c1} = 8.00$ in²	$A_{c2} = 192$ in²	$A_{c3} = 2{,}448$ in²
Membrane surface area	$A_{m1} = 9.00$ in²	$A_{m2} = 200$ in²	$A_{m3} = 3{,}312$ in²
Anode surface area	$A_{a1} = 8.00$ in²	$A_{c2} = 192$ in²	$A_{a3} = 2{,}784$ in²

Properties: $x_m = 130$ µm ; $\rho_a = (1/98)$ ohm.m, $\rho_c = (1/5.7)$ ohm.m, and $\rho_m = (1/1.78)$ ohm.m.

15.8 Electrowinning Parameters

From the figures and data described in the previous sections, and the comprehensive amount of experimental results gathered during laboratory, prototype, and pilot scale testing, it is then possible to devise the best range for operating conditions foreseen for an industrial production of electrolytic iron by electrowinning. These practical ranges are reported in Table 121.

Table 121 – Electrowinning operating conditions

Catholyte chemistry	**Electroactive species**	**Electroactive species**	Minimum	Average	Maximum
		$FeSO_4.7H_2O$	350.0 g/L	400.0 g/L	600.0 g/L
			28.2%	31.0%	44.1%
		$FeSO_4$	191.2 g/L	218.6 g/L	327.8 g/L
			15.4%	16.9%	24.1%
		Fe(II)	128.7 g/L	147.0 g/L	220.6 g/L
			10.4%	11.4%	16.2%
	Supporting electrolyte	**Supporting salts**	Maximum	Average	Minimum
		Na_2SO_4	100.0 g/L	88.0 g/L	80.0 g/L
			8.1%	6.8%	5.9%
		K_2SO_4	50.0 g/L	30.0 g/L	20.0 g/L
			4.0%	2.3%	1.5%
	Additives	**Complexing agent**	Maximum	Average	Minimum
		$(NH_4)_2SO_4$	100.0 g/L	70.0 g/L	50.0 g/L
			8.1%	5.4%	3.7%
		Lowering HER	Maximum	Average	Minimum
		Urea	30.0 g/L	15.0 g/L	10.0 g/L
			2.42%	1.16%	0.74%
		Buffering agent	Maximum	Average	Minimum
		H_3BO_3	20.0 g/L	15.0 g/L	10.0 g/L
			1.61%	1.16%	0.74%
		Surfactant	Maximum	Average	Minimum
		Lauryl sulfate	3.0 g/L	2.0 g/L	1.0 g/L
			0.24%	0.16%	0.07%
Catholyte properties		**Physical properties**	Minimum	Average	Maximum
		Mass density (kg/m^3)	1,240	1,290	1,360
		ORP (mV/AgCl)	-100	50	150
		Conductivity (mS/cm)	120	80	45
Electrowinning operating conditions		**Catholyte pH**	Minimum	Average	Maximum
		Low pH	2.00	2.60	2.75
		Cathode current density (A/m^2)	-1500	-1000	-775
		Temperature	27°C	25°C	20°C
		Cathode polarization (V/MSSA)	-1.486	-1.471	-1.462
		Medium pH	3.00	3.50	3.75
		Cathode current density (A/m^2)	-500	-250	-100
		Temperature	47°C	50°C	60°C
		Cathode polarization (V/MSSA)	-1.407	-1.352	-1.321
		High pH	4.00	3.50	5.5
		Cathode current density (A/m^2)	-500	-250	-1000
		Temperature	47°C	50°C	70°C
		Cathode polarization (V/MSSA)			
Cathodes		**Cathode materials**			
		Cathode blank	Titanium Gr.2	Titanium Gr.2	Titanium Gr.2
		Cathode starter sheet	Mild steel	Mild steel	Mild steel
Impurities and contaminants			Maximum	Maximum	Maximum
		Multivalencies	**Ti**	**V**	**Cr**
			10 mg/kg	5 mg/kg	5 mg/kg
		Depotits	**Cr**	**Mn**	**Cu**
			10 mg/kg	5 mg/kg	5 mg/kg
		Hydrogen evolution	**W**	**Au**	**Ni**
			2 mg/kg	1 mg/kg	1 mg/kg
			Se	**Te**	**Pt**
			1 mg/kg	1 mg/kg	1 mg/kg

16 Electrowinning Plant Calculations

16.1 Fundamental

The electrowinning process consists to electrolyze a warm iron-rich sulfate solution inside a divided electrolytic cell, also called electrolyzer, by means of an anion exchange membrane (AEM) as separator to prevent the mixing of both anolyte and catholyte while allowing the crossing of sulfate anions from the catholyte towards the anode compartment where they combine with the protons left behind from the oxygen evolution to form additional sulfuric acid. The electrodes consist of either a mild steel starter sheet or a titanium metal cathode blank, and a mixed metals oxides (MMO) iridium-coated titanium anode of the type (Ti/Ta_2O_5-IrO_2) that promotes the oxygen evolution reaction (OER).

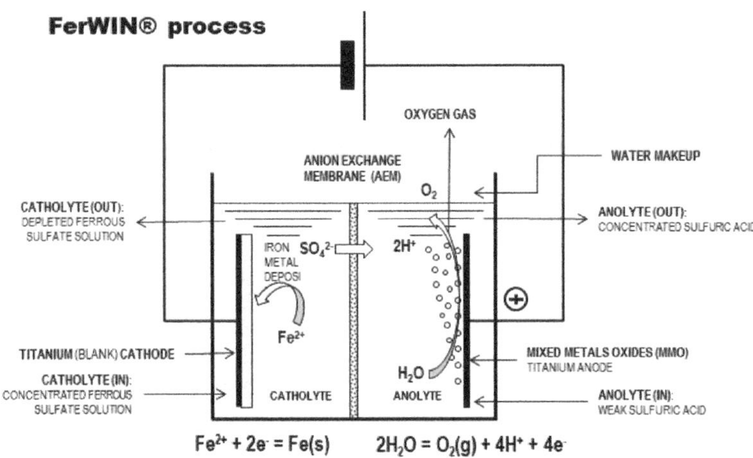

Figure 115 – Schematic of iron electrowinning with electrochemical reactions

The description of major (i.e., desired) and competitive (i.e., side or unwanted) electrochemical reactions occurring in each compartment are listed for convenience in Table 122.

Table 122 – Main and side electrochemical reactions

Electrode	Anode (+)	Cathode (-)
Major (desired) reactions	$2H_2O \rightarrow O_2(g) + 4H^+ + 4e^-$	$Fe^{2+} + 2e^- \rightarrow Fe(s)$
Competitive (side) reactions	$Fe^{2+} \rightarrow Fe^{3+} + e^-$	$2H^+ + 2e^- \rightarrow H_2(g)$ $Fe^{3+} + e^- \rightarrow Fe^{2+}$ $Fe^{3+} + 3e^- \rightarrow Fe(s)$

The combination of the two major half-reactions corresponds to the electrolysis of ferrous sulfate yielding electrolytic iron metal at the cathode, and sulfuric acid together with oxygen gas at the anode according to the overall electrochemical reaction involving anhydrous ferrous sulfate:

$$FeSO_4(s) + H_2O = Fe(s) + H_2SO_4 + 0.5O_2(g)$$

16.2 Process Flow Diagrams

Two schematic flow diagrams of the entire FerWIN® process are presented hereafter.

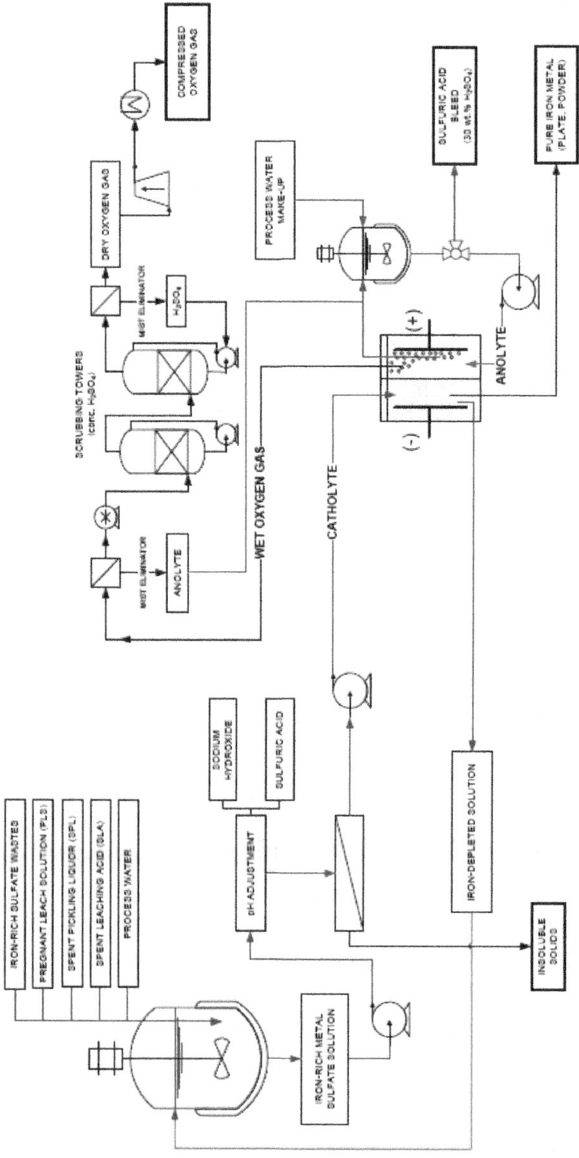

Figure 116 – Flow diagram of the FerWIN® process for electrowinning iron

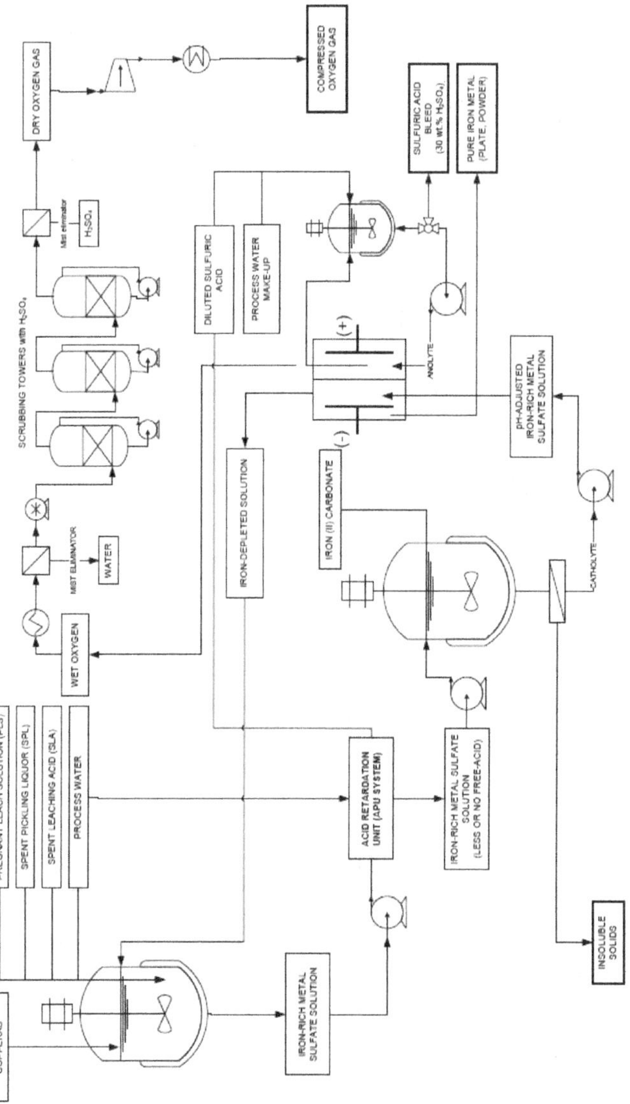

Figure 117 – Flow diagram of the FerWIN® process for electrowinning with APU unit

16.3 Electrowinning Plant Schedule

In this business case scenario, the iron electrowinning plant operates 350 days per year, 24 hours per day on three 8-hour shifts. Each year, the remaining 15 working days (i.e., two weeks) will be used for the ***annual shut down*** for preventive maintenance and inspection purposes.

Based on ***good manufacturing and processing practices*** (*GM&PP*) encountered in the mining, metallurgical, and chemical industries especially commercial plants for electrowinning zinc, copper, and nickel, we have adopted for these calculations, a ***processing losses***, denoted L, of five mass percent that will be applied to the processing of raw materials, products, and by-products. Thus the ***product recovery yield***, denoted R_Y, and defined as: $R_Y = (1 - L)$, is 95 mass percent. These figures are summarized in Table 123 hereafter.

Table 123 – Iron electrowinning plant schedule

PLANT SCHEDULE		
Production period	350 working day(s)/year	8,400 working hour(s)/year
Shutdown (maintenance)	2 week(s)/year	
	7 working days/week	24 hours/day
Processing losses (*L*)	3%	

16.4 Electrowinning Plant Nameplate Capacity

The preliminary engineering calculations and design criteria are based on a business case scenario for constructing an iron electrowinning plant having an annual nameplate production capacity, Ξ_{iron}, of **100,000 tonnes** of metallic iron per year. The iron-rich feedstock originates from either pure copperas or spent pickling liquors (SPLs) or pregnant leach solutions (PLS). This number was chosen to match half the production capacity of a mini-mill steel plant.

Theoretically, based on the overall electrochemical reaction, it is possible to calculate the ***mass equivalence factors*** assuming that the cathode and current efficiencies are 100% on both the anode and cathode electrochemical reactions. These figures rounded to the nearest unit are listed in Table 124.

Table 124 – Theoretical mass equivalence factors (100% current efficiency)

Mass equivalence factors	Iron metal	Oxygen gas	Sulfuric acid
1 tonne copperas	≡ **201** kg Fe	≡ **58** kg oxygen	≡ **353** kg H_2SO_4 (100%)
			≡ **379** kg H_2SO_4 (93%)
			≡ **1,176** kg H_2SO_4 (30%)
1 tonne $FeSO_4$ (anhydrous)	≡ **368** kg Fe	≡ **105** kg oxygen	≡ **646** kg H_2SO_4
			≡ **694** kg H_2SO_4 (93%)
			≡ **2,153** kg H_2SO_4 (30%)

These theoretical mass equivalence factors will be extensively used in combination with a given current efficiency, and recovery yields in all the mass balance calculations, and those pertaining to the calculations of plant capacities and greenhouse gases emissions.

The processing capacity of the feed per unit time, i.e., of copperas, denoted $\Xi_{copperas}$, in tonnes per year, that needs to be consumed to sustain such production capacity of pure metallic iron is calculated as follows:

$$\Xi_{copperas} = \Xi_{iron} (M_{FeSO4\cdot 7H2O}/M_{Fe}) \times \varepsilon_c \times R_Y$$

Similarly, the production capacity of sulfuric acid with strength, w_A, in mass fraction, pure oxygen gas, residual oxygen can be calculated from the targeted production capacity for iron as follows:

$$\Xi_{H2SO4} \text{ (wt.\%)} = \Xi_{iron} (M_{H2SO4}/M_{Fe}) \times \varepsilon_a \times R_Y \times (1/w_A)$$

$$\Xi_{O2} = \Xi_{iron} (M_{O2}/2M_{Fe}) \times \varepsilon_a \times R_Y$$

$$\Xi_{H2} = \Xi_{iron} (M_{H2}/M_{Fe}) \times (1 - \varepsilon_c) \times R_Y$$

Therefore, assuming a recovery yield, R_Y, of 97 percent and a cathode current efficiency, ε_c, of 98.7 percent, the iron electrowinning plant will need to process annually **519,990 tonnes** of copperas equivalents.

Conversely, using the same recovery yield of 97 percent and an anode current efficiency of 99.7 percent, the plant will produce annually **566,159 tonnes** of sulfuric acid (30 wt.% H_2SO_4) together with **27,707 tonnes** of pure oxygen (O_2) gas that can be either reused "on-site" in the adjacent steelmaking plant or simply released to the atmosphere provision the noxious sulfuric acid mists are first removed upstream by demisters and water scrubbers.

Finally, based on the previous cathode current efficiency, only **46 tonnes** per year (506,104 Nm^3/year) of hydrogen gas will evolve from the cathode compartment.

The detailed calculations for the consumption of copperas and the production of the above chemicals on a yearly, monthly, daily, and hourly basis are reported in Table 125.

Table 125 – Iron electrowinning plant nameplate capacity

NAMEPLATE PRODUCTION CAPACITY			
Ferrous sulfate heptahydrate (Copperas)	**FEED**	**519,990** tonne(s)/year	573,191 short ton(s)/year
		43,333 tonne(s)/month	47,766 short ton(s)/month
		1,486 tonne(s)/day	1,638 short ton(s)/day
		61.904 tonne(s)/hour	68.237 short ton(s)/hour
Production of metallic iron (Fe)		**100,000** tonne(s)/year	110,231 short ton(s)/year
Recovery yield	97.0%	8,333 tonne(s)/month	9,186 short ton(s)/month
Faradaic cathode efficiency	98.7%	286 tonne(s)/day	315 short ton(s)/day
		11.905 tonne(s)/hour	13.123 short ton(s)/hour
Production of sulfuric acid (H_2SO_4)		**169,848** tonne(s)/year	187,225 short ton(s)/year
Strength	100 wt.%	14,154 tonne(s)/month	15,602 short ton(s)/month
Recovery yield	97.0%	485 tonne(s)/day	535 short ton(s)/day
Faradaic anode efficiency	99.7%	20.220 tonne(s)/hour	22.289 short ton(s)/hour
Production of sulfuric acid solution		**566,159** tonne(s)/year	624,084 short ton(s)/year
Strength of the sulfuric acid solution (wt.% H_2SO_4)	30.0%	47,180 tonne(s)/month	52,007 short ton(s)/month
		1,618 tonne(s)/day	1,783 short ton(s)/day
		67.400 tonne(s)/hour	74.296 short ton(s)/hour
Production of oxygen gas (O_2)		27,707 tonne(s)/year	30,541 short ton(s)/year
Recovery yield	97.0%	**19,407,159** m^3(NTP)/year	685.4 MMft^3(NTP)/year
Faradaic anode efficiency	99.7%	1,617,263 m^3(NTP)/month	57.1 MMft^3(NTP)/month
		55,449 m^3(NTP)/day	1,958 Mft^3(NTP)/day
		2,310 m^3(NTP)/hour	81,590 ft^3(NTP)/hour
Production of hydrogen gas (H_2)		46 tonne(s)/year	50 short ton(s)/year
Recovery yield	97%	**506,104** m^3(NTP)/year	17.9 MMft^3(NTP)
Faradaic cathode efficiency for H_2	1.3%	42,175 m^3(NTP)/month	1.5 MMft^3(NTP)/month
		1,446 m^3(NTP)/day	51 Mft^3(NTP)/day
		60 m^3(NTP)/hour	2,128 ft^3(NTP)/hour

16.5 Mass Balances

In this section, we will provide the mass balances for both the anolyte and catholyte streams for a single commercial electrolyzer. The calculations are based on an iron electrowinning plant having an annual nameplate production capacity of 100,000 tonnes of electrolytic iron.

16.5.1 Catholyte Mass Balance Equations

On the cathode side, the catholyte circulates inside the cathode compartment and we must consider the inlet mass flow rate of catholyte, i.e., a concentrated solution of ferrous sulfate, C_1, and outflows such as the mass flow rate of the catholyte depleted in ferrous sulfate, C_2, the mass flow rate of the electrolytic iron deposited at the cathode (i.e., product), ***Fe***, the mass flow rate of sulfate anions leaving the cathode compartment by crossing the anion exchange membrane, ***S***, and finally the mass flow rate of water, ***WB***, that must be removed (i.e., bleed) to account from the water originating from the addition of ferrous sulfate heptahydrate (i.e., copperas), ***FS***. These are depicted in Figure 118.

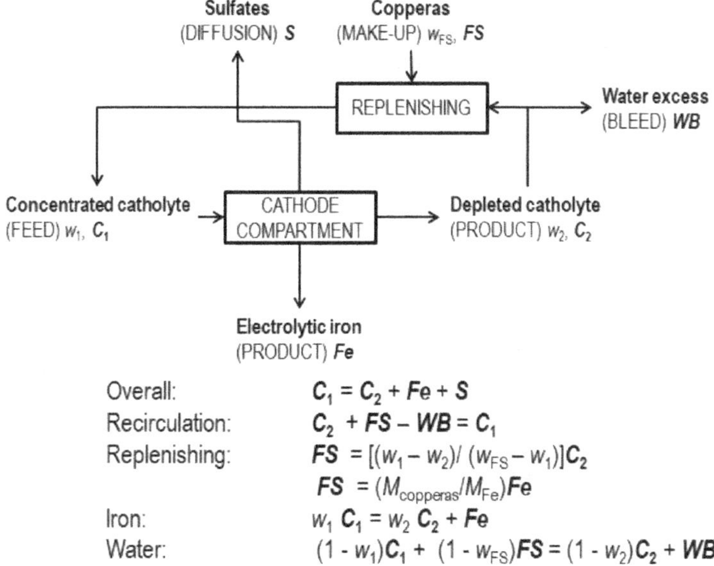

Figure 118 – Mass balance flow diagram for the catholyte stream (CCE 100%)

The overall mass balance is simply the algebraic sum of the mass flow rates for each stream:

$$C_1 = C_2 + Fe + S$$

The mass flow rates of the individual components (i.e., iron, sulfates, and water) can thus be written as follows using the mass fractions of each component as follows:

Iron: $w_1 C_1 = w_2 C_2 + Fe$

Sulfate anions: $w_{S1} C_1 = w_{S2} C_2 + S$

Water: $(1 - w_1)\ \boldsymbol{C_1} = (1 - w_2)\ \boldsymbol{C_2}$

Moreover, when assuming a cathode current efficiency and recovery yield of 100%, the relationship between ***Fe***, and ***S***, is simply based on the stoichiometry of the overall electrochemical reaction for electrowinning iron:

$$FeSO_4 + H_2O = Fe + H_2SO_4 + 0.5O_2$$

The production rate of electrolytic iron as a function of the electrowinning parameters is given by the Faraday's law:

$$\boldsymbol{Fe} = \varepsilon_c j_c A_c / E_{qFe}$$

Thus for a given mass flow rate of electrolytic iron deposited at the cathode, ***Fe***, (e.g., **2,268** kg/day) and the relative molar masses of each chemical species, we can calculate the following mass flow rates:

$$\boldsymbol{S} = (M_S/M_{Fe})\boldsymbol{Fe} = 3{,}901 \text{ kg/day}$$

From the linear combination of above equations, we can calculate the initial mass flow rate of the catholyte feed knowing the initial and final mass fractions of iron, and taking into account the production rate of electrolytic iron as follows:

$$\boldsymbol{C_2} = [(1 - w_2)/(w_1 - w_2)]\ \boldsymbol{Fe} = 38{,}880 \text{ kg/day}$$

Then the relation between the mass flow rate of the depleted catholyte vs. the mass flow rate of concentrated catholyte (i.e., feed) is calculated as follows:

$$\boldsymbol{C_2} = [(1 - w_1)/(1 - w_2)]\ \boldsymbol{C_1} = 36{,}898 \text{ kg/day}$$

Moreover, because the depleted catholyte, $\boldsymbol{C_2}$, is recirculated (i.e., recycled) to be used as catholyte feed, it must be replenished by adding ferrous sulfate heptahydrate, to keep the iron concentration constant, and simultaneously a bleed of water must be performed with the mass flow rate ***WB*** to account for the hydration of copperas.

$$\boldsymbol{C_2} = \boldsymbol{C_1} + \boldsymbol{FS} - \boldsymbol{WB}$$

The mass flow rate of added copperas, ***FS***, is calculated as follows:

$$\boldsymbol{FS} = (M_{copperas}/M_{Fe})\boldsymbol{Fe} = 11{,}289 \text{ kg/day}$$

$$\boldsymbol{FS} = [(w_1 - w_2)/(w_{FS} - w_1)]\ \boldsymbol{C_2}$$

For preventing the dilution, the bleed of water, ***WB***, is obtained by:

$WB = (7M_W/M_{copperas})FS = 5{,}121$ kg/day

16.5.2 Anolyte Mass Balance Equations

On the anode side, the anolyte circulates inside the anode compartment, and we must consider first the inlet streams with the mass flow rate for the anolyte feed, ***F***, consisting of the weak sulfuric acid solution, and the mass flow rate (i.e., source) of sulfate anions, ***S***, crossing the anion exchange membrane. Secondly, for the outlet, we need to consider the mass flow rate of the product (i.e., concentrated sulfuric acid), ***P***, from which a fraction is removed (i.e., bleed), ***B***, leaving a mass flow rate of a recycled fraction, ***R***, and the oxygen gas evolved, ***O***.

The dimensionless recycling ratio, denoted α of the mass flow rate of concentrated catholyte to be diluted with make-up water and to be recycled to the mass flow rate of the product, ***P***, is simply defined as follows: $\boldsymbol{R} = \alpha\boldsymbol{P}$ and thus $\boldsymbol{B} = (1 - \alpha)\boldsymbol{P}$. All the above mass flow rates are depicted schematically in Figure 119.

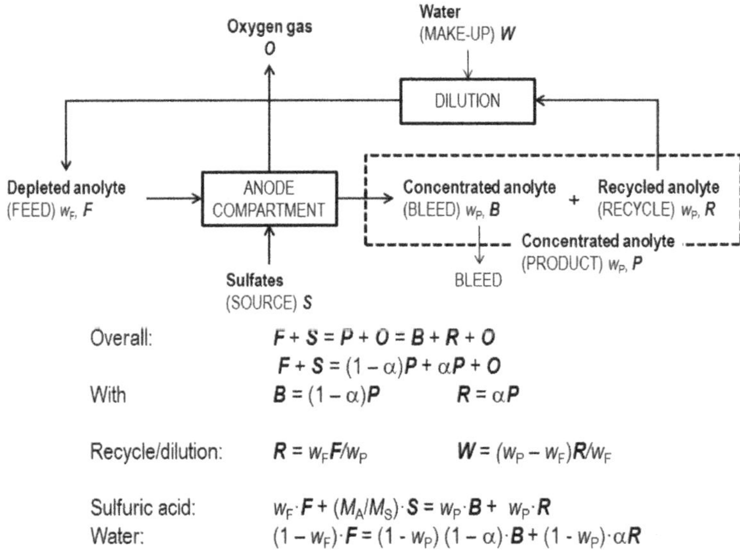

Figure 119 – Mass balance flow diagram for the anolyte stream (ACE 100%)

The overall mass balance is simply the algebraic sum of the mass flow rates for each stream:

$$\boldsymbol{F} + \boldsymbol{S} = \boldsymbol{P} + \boldsymbol{O} = (1 - \alpha)\boldsymbol{P} + \boldsymbol{R} + \boldsymbol{O}$$

The mass flow rates of the individual components (i.e., sulfuric acid and water) can thus be written as follows using the mass fractions of each component and the relative molar masses of sulfuric acid (M_A) and of sulfate anions (M_S):

Sulfuric acid: $w_F \boldsymbol{F} + (M_A/M_S)\boldsymbol{S} = w_P (1 - \alpha)\boldsymbol{P} + w_P \boldsymbol{R} = w_P \boldsymbol{P}$

Water: $(1 - w_F)\boldsymbol{F} = (1 - w_P)(1 - \alpha)\boldsymbol{P} + (1 - w_P)\boldsymbol{R} = (1 - w_P)\boldsymbol{P}$

From the linear combination of above equations, we can calculate the mass flow rate for the anolyte feed vs. the mass flow rate of the sulfate anions diffusing from the cathode compartment:

$$w_F(1 - w_P)\cdot \boldsymbol{F} + (M_A/M_S)(1 - w_P)\cdot \boldsymbol{S} = (1 - w_P)\, w_P \boldsymbol{P}$$

$$\underline{w_P (1 - w_F)\cdot \boldsymbol{F} = w_P(1 - w_P)\boldsymbol{P}}$$

$$(w_F - w_P)\boldsymbol{F} + (1 - w_P)(M_A/M_S)\boldsymbol{S} = 0$$

$$\boldsymbol{F} = [(1 - w_P)(M_A/M_S)\boldsymbol{S}]/(w_P - w_F) = 13{,}939 \text{ kg/day}$$

When assuming an anode current efficiency and recovery yield of 100%, the relationship between ***W***, ***S***, and ***O*** is simply based on the stoichiometry of the overall electrochemical reaction for electrowinning iron:

$$FeSO_4 + H_2O = Fe + H_2SO_4 + 0.5O_2$$

The production rate of sulfuric acid as a function of the electrowinning parameter is given by the Faraday's law as:

$$\boldsymbol{P} = (\varepsilon_a j_a A_a / E_{qH2SO4})$$

Thus for a given mass flow rate of electrolytic iron deposited at the cathode, ***Fe***, (e.g., **2,268** kg/day) and the relative molar masses of each chemical species, we can calculate the following mass flow rates:

$$\boldsymbol{S} = (M_S/M_{Fe})\boldsymbol{Fe} = 3{,}901 \text{ kg/day}$$

$$\boldsymbol{O} = (M_O/M_{Fe})\boldsymbol{Fe} = 650 \text{ kg/day}$$

The mass flow rate of the total product is obtained from the sum of the mass flow rate of sulfuric acid produced by electrolysis (3,969 kg/day) and the mass flow rate of sulfuric acid contained in the feed (w_F = 10 wt.%), that is, 1,394 kg/day) divided by the strength of the concentrated anolyte (w_P = 30 wt.%) with the following equation:

$$\boldsymbol{P} = [(M_A/M_{Fe})\boldsymbol{Fe}]/w_P + (w_F/w_P)\boldsymbol{F} = 17{,}921 \text{ kg/day}$$

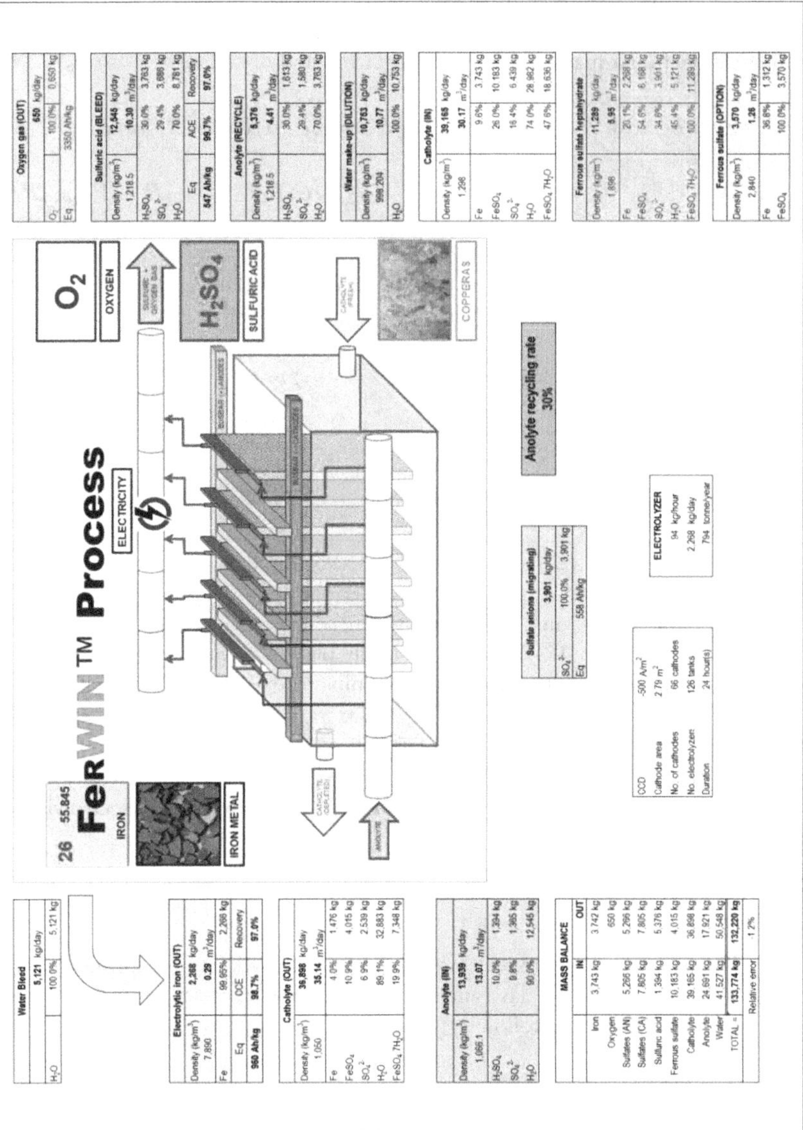

Figure 120 – Daily mass balance per single electrolyzer for electrowinning iron

Assuming a recycling ratio of 25 percent, the mass flow rates for the bleed and the recycled anolyte are:

$$\boldsymbol{R} = \alpha \boldsymbol{P} = 5{,}376 \text{ kg/day}$$

$\boldsymbol{B} = (1 - \alpha)\boldsymbol{P} = 12{,}545$ kg/day

These figures for daily mass flow rates (per single electrolyzer) for a 100,000 tonnes per annum iron electrowinning plant are summarized in Figure 120.Finally, it is possible to calculate the mass flow rate of make-up water to be added to the recycled anolyte in order to obtain the same composition of the feed by a simple equation for dilution:

$\boldsymbol{W} = (w_P - w_F)\boldsymbol{R}/w_F = 10{,}753$ kg/day

16.6 Electrochemical Performances and Figures of Merit

From the optimum operating parameters measured during the piloting trials and reported in Section 15.8 the performances and figures of merit obtained for the commercial electrolyzer are summarized in Table 126.

Table 126 – Electrochemical performances and figures of merit

ELECTROWINNING PERFORMANCES and FIGURES of MERIT				
Iron metal deposit (purity)		Fe 99.97%	V 0.01%	
		Cr 0.01%	Mn 0.01%	100.00%
Mass density (calc.)	ρ	7,874 kg/m^3	491.5 lb/ft^3	
Anode current density	j_a	500 A.m^{-2}	46 A/ft^2	
Cathode current density	j_c	500 A.m^{-2}	46 A/ft^2	
Cell voltage	U_{cell}	3.133 V		
Faradaic cathode efficiency	CCE	98.7%		
Faradaic anode efficiency	ACE	99.7%		
Electrochemical equivalent (Fe)	E_q	**960** Ah/kg	435 Ah/lb	
Electrochemical equivalent (H_2SO_4)	E_q	**547** Ah/kg	248 Ah/lb	
Electrochemical equivalent (O_2)	E_q	**3,350** Ah/kg	4,783 Ah/Nm^3	
Electrochemical equivalent (H_2)	E_q	**26,590** Ah/kg	2,392 Ah/Nm^3	
Specific energy consumption (Fe)	e_m	**3.047** kWh/kg	1.382 kWh/lb	
		3,047 kWh/tonne	2,764 kWh/ton	
Specific energy consumption (H_2SO_4)	e_m	**1.717** kWh/kg	0.779 kWh/lb	
		1,717 kWh/tonne	1,558 kWh/ton	
Specific energy consumption (O_2)	e_m	**10.528** kWh/kg	4.775 kWh/lb	
		10,528 kWh/tonne	9,551 kWh/ton	
Space time yield (Fe)	STY_{Fe}	**0.514** kg/m^2.h	0.105 lb/ft^2.h	
		12.34 kg/m^2.day	2.527 lb/ft^2.day	
Space time yield (H_2SO_4)	STY_{H2SO4}	**0.912** kg/m^2.h	0.187 lb/ft^2.h	
		21.89 kg/m^2.day	4.484 lb/ft^2.day	
Space time yield (O_2)	STY_{O2}	0.149 kg/m^2.h	0.0305 lb/ft^2.h	
		3.57 kg/m^2.day	0.731 lb/ft^2.day	
		0.105 Nm^3/m^2.h	0.343 ft^3/ft^2.h	
		2.509 Nm^3/m^2.day	0.014 ft^3/ft^2.day	
Space time yield (H_2)	STY_{H2}	0.00024 kg/m^2.h	0.0001 lb/ft^2.h	
		0.006 kg/m^2.day	0.001 lb/ft^2.day	
		0.003 Nm^3/m^2.h	0.009 ft^3/ft^2.h	
		0.065 Nm^3/m^2.day	0.000 ft^3/ft^2.day	

16.7 Electrolytes Flows and Conversion Rates

16.7.1 Catholyte Fractional Conversion Rate

The catholyte enters the electrolyzer with an elevate concentration of ferrous sulfate (C_{FSI}) intentionally kept below the saturation for reasons already mentioned in the previous sections. Upon leaving the electrolyzer, the concentration of ferrous sulfate decreases until a threshold value (C_{FSO}) which is chosen arbitrarily based on the electrolyzer performances. The ***fractional conversion rate*** of iron is given by:

$$X_{Fe}(\%) = 100(C_{FSI} - C_{FSO})/C_{FSI} = 100\ (C_{FeI} - C_{FeO})/C_{FeI}$$

16.7.2 Catholyte Circulation Mode

As already discussed in details in Section 16.5.1 without any additions and when the catholyte is electrolyzed as the iron metal plates onto the cathode, and sulfate anions cross the membrane the concentration of ferrous sulfate in the catholyte decreases continuously. In order to ensure a constant concentration, ferrous carbonate, ferrous sulfate monohydrate, or anhydrous ferrous sulfate must be added regularly to compensate the depletion. If copperas is used instead the 388 kg of water released per tonne of copperas must be removed. For that purpose, the cathode compartment must be connected to large jacketed storage tanks having a large volume (100 m^3) compared to the volume of the commercial electrolyzer.

16.7.3 Catholyte Volume Flow Rate

In order to determine the optimal mass and volume flow rates of the catholyte, we can assume that the cathode compartment of the electrochemical cell can be describe by the model of a Continuously Stirred Electrolyzer (CSE) (see Section 10.1.6), the overall mass balance can be written as follows:

$$V_{catholyte}\ (\partial C_{Fe}/\partial t) = (C_{FeI} - C_{FeO})Q_{catholyte} - \varepsilon_c j_c A_c/E_q$$

Where:

$V_{catholyte}$	volume of catholyte in m^3,
A_c	cathode active surface area in m^2,
C_{Fe}	mass concentration of iron in kg.m^{-3},
C_{FeI}, C_{FeO}	inlet and outlet mass concentration of iron, in kg.m^{-3},
$Q_{catholyte}$	volume flow rate of catholyte in m^3/hour,
$\varepsilon_C j_C A_c/E_q$	deposition rate of iron metal by electrolysis, in kg/hour.

Where the first term corresponds to the net time variation of iron, the second term the concentration changes between the inlet and outlet and finally the last term the net production rate of metallic iron by the electrochemical reaction. Using the fractional conversion rate, the specific cathode area, and the residence time of the catholyte in the cathode compartment, it is possible to draw a simplified equation:

$$\partial X_{Fe}/\partial t = - X_{Fe}/\tau + \varepsilon_c j_c a_c / E_q$$

Where:

$\tau = V_{CC}/Q_{catholyte}$ catholyte residence time in hours,

$a_{cc} = A_c/V_{catholyte}$ specific active cathode surface area in m^{-1}.

After integration, the fractional conversion rate vs. time is:

$$R_{Fe} = (\varepsilon_c j_c a_{cc} \tau / E_q)[1 - \exp(-t/\tau)]$$

Therefore the maximum conversion rate is given by:

$$X_{Fe,\,max} = (\varepsilon_c j_c a_{cc} \tau / E_q) = (\varepsilon_c j_c A_c / Q_{catholyte} E_q)$$

When a steady state establishes, between the mass of iron entering the cathode compartment, and the deposition rate of electrolytic iron onto the cathode, and knowing the electrowinning conditions (i.e., current efficiency and current density), the total amount of iron metal that must be plated daily, this allows us to calculate the minimum catholyte flow rate required in each cell:

$$Q_{catholyte} = (\varepsilon_c j_c a_{cc} \tau / E_q)/(C_{FeI} - C_{FeO})$$

On the other hand, this flow rate must also match with the amount of ferrous sulfate that has to be converted per cell and per unit time based on the nameplate capacity of the electrochemical plant using the simple equation:

$$Q_{catholyte} = (dm_{Fe}/dt)/(C_{FeI} - C_{FeO}) = (dm_{FS}/dt)/(C_{FSI} - C_{FSO})$$

Both approaches are identical and yield the mass and volume flow rates of catholyte in the cathode compartment of each individual cell. The variation of the total iron concentration in the catholyte ranges from 4 up to 9.6 mass percent during electrolysis and it is replenished by addition and iron source.

Table 127 – Inlet and outlet catholyte composition and properties

CATHOLYTE			
Catholyte flow rates (Electrowinning plant)	$\partial M_C/\partial t$	2,989 tonne(s)/day	3,295 ton(s)/day
		125 tonne(s)/hour	137 ton(s)/hour
	$Q_{catholyte}$	2,278 m³/day	601,878 gal/day
		95 m³/hour	25,078 gal/hour
		1.582 m³/min	418 gal/min
Operating temperature	T	60°C	140°F
Concentration of copperas (Feed)	C_{CPI}	624 g/L	47.58%
Concentration of ferrous sulfate (Feed)	C_{FSI}	341 g/L	26.00%
Concentration of total iron (Feed)	C_{FeIN}	125 g/L	9.56%
Catholyte mass density (Feed)	r_{CI}	1,312 kg/m³	81.9 lb/ft³
Concentration of total iron (Out)	C_{FeOUT}	41 g/L	4.00%
Catholyte mass density (Out)	ρ_{CO}	1,017 kg/m³	63.5 lb/ft³
Cathode conversion rate	R_{CP}	68%	

16.7.4 Anolyte Fractional Conversion Rate

The fractional conversion rate of sulfuric acid at the anode is given by the equation:

$$X_{H2SO4}(\%) = 100\ (C_{AF} - C_{AO})/C_{AI}$$

16.7.5 Anolyte Circulation Modes

There are two options for operating the circulation of the anolyte during electrowinning.

16.7.5.1 Continuous Increase of the Acid Concentration

The first approach consists to perform the ***batch recirculation*** by recirculating the anolyte in closed loop from a large storage tank. After reaching the maximum concentration threshold, a bleed of the fraction of the anolyte can be performed and water is added accordingly. The weak anolyte is usually a sulfuric acid solution with a mass percentage of 10 wt.% H_2SO_4. Because the initial electrical conductivity of the 10 wt.% anolyte is roughly 50 percent lower than that of the final anolyte (i.e., 30 wt.% H_2SO_4) there is a continuous and beneficial increase of the electrical conductivity during electrowinning, with a continuous drop in the overall cell voltage over time.

16.7.5.2 Constant Concentration Operation

If the size of the anolyte holding tank allows, the second option consists to perform the electrowinning maintaining the concentration of sulfuric acid constant at 20 wt.% by continuously adding weak sulfuric acid or water until the total volume of anolyte exceeds the maximum anolyte tank capacity. Then a bleed must be conducted. Actually, running the electrolysis according to the previous option, the variation of the anolyte conductivity makes the control and monitoring of the cell voltage tedious.

16.7.6 Anolyte Mass and Volume Flow Rates

As for the catholyte, we can assume that upon electrolysis a steady state establishes. That is, the disappearing rate of sulfate anions leaving the cathode compartment, the rate of mass transfer of sulfate anions across the anion exchange membrane, and the production rate of protons left behind by the electrolysis of water with the evolution of oxygen are balanced. Hence knowing all the electrowinning operating conditions (i.e., current density, Faradaic current efficiency, and anode surface area), the electrochemical equivalents for sulfuric acid, the total production rate of sulfuric acid to be regenerated, this allows to calculate the equation for the mass flow rate of the anolyte entering the anode compartment of each cell that were provided in Section 16.5.2.

Table 128 – Inlet and outlet anolyte composition and properties

ANOLYTE			
Anolyte flow rates (Electrowinning plant)	$\partial M_{AF}/\partial t$	4,787 tonne(s)/day	5,277 ton(s)/day
		199 tonne(s)/hour	220 ton(s)/hour
	Q_{AF}	4,490 m^3/day	1,186,130 gal/day
		187 m^3/hour	49,422 gal/hour
		3.118 m^3/min	824 gal/min
Concentration of sulfuric acid (Feed)	C_{AF}	107 g/L	10.0% H_2SO_4
Mass density of anolyte (Feed) (20°C)	ρ_{AF}	1,066.1 kg/m^3	66.6 lb/ft^3
Concentration of sulfuric acid (Product)	C_{AP}	366 g/L	30.0% H_2SO_4
Mass density of sulfuric acid (Product) (20°C)	ρ_{AP}	1,218.5 kg/m^3	76.1 lb/ft^3
Anode conversion rate	R_A	70.8%	

16.8 Electrolyzer Design

16.8.1 Cathodes

16.8.1.1 Cathode Materials

Two options are available industrially: (1) ***Starter sheets*** made of pure iron can be used with a mass density of 7,840 kg/m^3 (0.283 lb/in^3). It is worth to mention, that starter sheets require labor intensive operations in order to prepare the starter sheets, high machinery maintenance, and lower productivity. On the other hand, once metallic iron is plated onto the started sheet there is no need to perform the stripping and the cathodes can be simply melted inside an electric arc furnace. (2) Another suitable option is to use ***blank cathodes*** made of stainless steel or better commercially pure titanium (i.e., ASTM grade 1 or 2) with a mass density of 4,540 kg/m^3 (0.164 lb/in^3). C.P. titanium is preferred because of its high overpotential for the hydrogen evolution reaction, and also because upon harvesting of the cathode, it facilitates the stripping of the iron plate at the end of each electrowinning cycle and finally it does not corrodes inside the catholyte especially during shut down periods.

Moreover, the overall cathode always consists of a cathode plate made of one of the metal above and a hanger bar made of oxygen-free high conductivity copper such as the grade C110 with a mass density of 8,960 kg/m^3 (0.324 lb/in^3) or better of titanium-clad copper to prevent corrosion.

16.8.1.2 Total Number of Cathodes per Electrolyzer

The ***total number of cathodes per electrolyzer***, denoted N_{CT}, is usually selected as a function of the annual tonnage of iron metal to be produced by the electrochemical plant. For instance, some practical figures are provided in Table 129.

Table 129 – Total number of cathodes per cell vs. annual tonnage of iron

Range of annual plant nameplate capacity for iron metal (P/tonnes)	Recommended volume of the polymer concrete cell (V_T/m^3)	Total number of cathodes per cell (N_{CT})
5,000 to 15,000	5-8	30-36
20,000 to 40,000	8-10	39-45
>40,000	10-20	60-66

Because it is important to minimize the footprint and capital cost of the future cell house, it was decided to utilize the maximum number of cathodes.

Moreover, based on the common harvesting design used in both copper and zinc electrowinning, in which every third cathode is harvested per pull, the total number of cathodes per cell must be always a multiple of three. Therefore, a configuration with a maximum of **66 cathodes per cell** was adopted for the iron electrowinning plant.

16.8.1.3 Rectangular Cathode Shape and Dimensions

The cathodes are usually rectangular metal plates in shape but they exhibit a larger and thicker T-shaped upper portion usually made of titanium-clad copper acting both as hanging and bus bar as depicted in Figure 100 with key dimensions reported in Figure 121 hereafter.

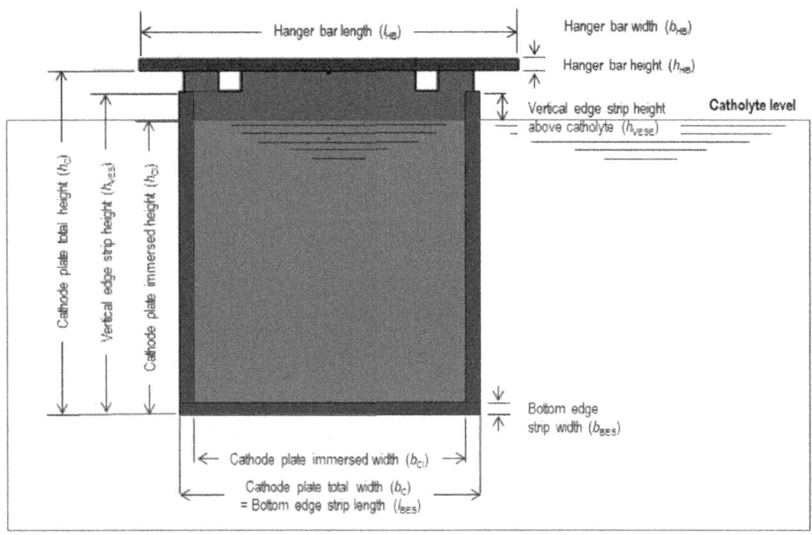

Figure 121 – Titanium cathode blank shape and dimensions with edge strips

The proper cathode design must allow the easy hooking achieved by the lifting crane for harvesting the cathodes. Thus this can be achieved in large electrowinning plants by designing either square or rectangular cut-outs from the cathode surface beneath the hanger bar and above the liquid level. In some instances especially for small scale production or pilot plants this is achieved by simply utilizing titanium eye-bolts attached to the hanger bars.

The overall cathode plate dimensions are: (1) the total height of the cathode plate, denoted h_C, the total width of the cathode plate, b_C, and finally the thickness of the cathode plate, t_C all in m (in).

From these dimensions, it is then simple to calculate the cathode plate geometric surface area, denoted A_C, in m^2 (ft^2) along with the volume of the cathode plate, denoted V_C, in m^3 (in^3) as follows:

$$A_C = b_C \times h_C$$

$$V_C = b_C \times h_C \times t_C$$

Afterwards, the mass of the rectangular cathode plate, m_C, in kg (lb.) can be calculated from the mass density of the cathode material, ρ_C, in kg/m^3 (lb/in^3):

$$m_C = \rho_C (b_C \times h_C \times t_C)$$

16.8.1.4 Shape and Dimensions of Hanger Bar

On the other hand, the hanger bar is characterized by a total length, denoted l_{HB}, its width, denoted b_{HB}, and its height, denoted h_{HB}. Because the hanger bar must be much longer than the total width of the cathode plate to be able to hang over the busbars with the same excess length, denoted l_{XS}, on each side, the length is related to the cathode plate width by the simple equation:

$$l_{HB} = b_C + 2 \times l_{XS}$$

For hanger bars exhibiting a rectangular cross section, the cross section area, denoted A_{HBS}, in m^2 (in^2) and the volume, denoted V_{HBS}, m^3 (in^3) are:

$$A_{HBS} = b_{HB} \times h_{HB} \quad \text{and} \quad V_{HBS} = (l_{HB} \times b_{HB} \times h_{HB})$$

The mass of the hanger bar, denoted m_{HB}, in kg (lb.) is using the mass density for the composite titanium-clad copper denoted $\rho_{Ti\text{-}Cu}$, in kg/m^3 (lb/in^3) is:

$$m_{HB} = \rho_{Ti\text{-}Cu} (l_{HB} \times b_{HB} \times h_{HB})$$

The characteristics and dimensions of hanger bars are listed in Table 130.

Table 130 – Cathode hanger bar dimensions and characteristics

HANGER BAR			
Hanging bar material		Titanium-clad copper C110	
Mass density of copper	ρ_{HB}	8,900 kg/m^3	555.6 lb/ft^3
Hanging bar length	l_{HB}	1.34620 m	53.000 in
Hanging bar excess length on each side	l_{XS}	0.12700 m	5.000 in
Hanging bar width	b_{HB}	0.02540 m	1.000 in
Hanging bar height	h_{HB}	0.03810 m	1.500 in
Hanging bar cross section area	A_{HB}	0.00097 m^2	0.0104 ft^2
Hanging bar volume	V_{HB}	0.00130 m^3	0.046 ft^3
Hanging bar mass	m_{HB}	11.6 kg	26 lb

16.8.1.5 Overall T-Shape Cathode Mass

The total mass of the T-shape cathode plate with hanger bar, denoted m_{CTS}, in kg (lb.) is given by:

$$m_{CTS} = m_C + m_{HB}$$

16.8.1.6 Insulating Edge Strips or Slotted Plastic Edges

In order to ensure that each iron plate on the two sides of the cathodes are not intergrowth nor develop dendrites, insulating ***edge strips*** must be installed.

In practice, ***electroplating tape*** is only suitable for cathodes having a relatively small cathode surface (e.g., few square feet) and thus are restricted to prototype and pilot electrolyzer while ***slotted plastic edges*** made of polypropylene are commonly used with a **"*cross-slot*"** configuration.

Two ***vertical edge strips*** with a width, b_{VES}, and a height, h_{VES}, in m (in) must be installed on the two cathode edges. On the other hand, a ***bottom edge strip*** with a width, b_{BES}, and a total length, l_{BES}, in m (in) is inserted at bottom of each cathode. Because, the bottom strip overlaps the two vertical strips, it length is simply: $l_{BES} = b_C$

It is also important that the two vertical edge strips are long enough so that they end well above the catholyte level in the cell. Usually an excess height equivalent to the width of the strip, h_{excess}, usually 1.5 in (3.81 cm) seems enough. Actually, any introduction of catholyte between the edge strip and the cathode will cause the electrodeposition of iron and compromise the deposition, and stripping process.

16.8.1.7 Actual Immersed Cathode Characteristics

Based on the previous edge strips dimension, it is possible to calculate the actual cathode immersed width, denoted b_{CI}, as follows:

$$b_{CI} = b_C - 2b_{VES}$$

On the other hand, introducing the height of the cathode plate above the electrolyte level, $h_{electrolyte}$, we can calculate the immersed height, denoted h_{CI}, of the active cathode sheet taking also into account the width of the bottom edge strip:

$$h_{CI} = h_C - h_{electrolyte} - b_{BES}$$

Therefore total active surface area of the immersed cathode is simply:

$$A_{CI} = b_{CI} \times h_{CI} = (b_C - 2b_{VES})(h_C - h_{electrolyte} - b_{BES})$$

16.8.1.8 Cathode Buttons

Because automated harvesting operation and narrow inter-electrode gaps are not necessarily compatible, when necessary up to five anode buttons made of PVC or PTFE can be installed at each corner and one at the center of the cathode plate to prevent mechanical damages during lifting to the anion exchange membrane especially by dendrites.

16.8.1.9 Cathode Active Surface Area

Because the cathodes are used on both sides, the ***cathode active surface area***, denoted A_c, in m^2 (ft^2) is twice the single immersed geometric surface area, A_{CI}, of the immersed portion of the cathode plate less the total surface area covered by the insulating edge strips. It is easy to calculate it using the following equation:

$$A_c = 2(b_{CI} \times h_{CI}) = 2(b_C - 2b_{VES}) \times (h_C - h_{electrolyte} - b_{BES})$$

16.8.1.10 Cathode Specific Active Surface Area

The ***cathode specific active surface area***, denoted a_c, expressed in m^{-1}, corresponds to the dimensionless ratio of the total cathode active surface area over the total volume of the cathode space, that is, the cathode-membrane gap, e_{gcm}, in m (in) times the cathode active surface, A_c, as follows:

$$a_c = A_c/(e_{gcm}A_c) = 1/e_{gcm}$$

16.8.1.11 Cathode Surface Velocity

The ***cathode surface velocity***, denoted u_{SC}, expressed in m/s (m/h), corresponds to the velocity of the catholyte flowing parallel to the cathode surface. It can be calculated by dividing the volume flow rate of catholyte inside the narrow cathode-membrane channel by the total active surface area of the cathode as follows by dividing the overall volume flow rate of the catholyte inside the entire electrowinning plant, $Q_{catholyte}$, by the number of cathodes per cell defined in Section 16.8.1.2 and the total number of electrolytic cells (i.e., electrolyzers) per plant that will be defined later in Section 16.9.2:

$$u_{SC} = [Q_{catholyte}/(N_{CT} \times N_E)]/A_c$$

It is obvious that this parameter influences the adhesion and quality of the iron metal deposit by reducing the thickness of the Nernst diffusion layer. However, if the surface velocity of the catholyte is too high, it can prevent the plating by flushing the nuclei from the surface and creating an area near the catholyte entrance were no plating can occur. Based on practical observation made in most copper and zinc electrowinning plants, the cathode surface velocity must range between 0.05 and 0.12 m/h.

The selected characteristics and dimensions of the cathodes are reported in Table 131.

Table 131 – Cathodes characteristics, sizes and dimensions

CATHODE(S)			
Cathode material		C.P. Titanium (ASTM B265 Grade 2)	
Number of cathodes per tank	N_{CT}	**66** cathodes	
Mass density of cathode material	ρ_C	4,540 kg/m³	283.4 lb/ft³
Cathode-anode spacing	e_{gca}	0.032 m	1.250 in
Cathode-membrane gap (spacing)	e_{gcm}	0.025 m	1.000 in
Cathode plate width (total)	b_C	1.0922 m	43.000 in
Cathode plate height (total)	h_C	1.6701 m	65.750 in
Cathode plate thickness	t_C	0.00635 m	0.250 in
Cathode geometric surface area (one side)	A_C	1.824 m²	20 ft²
Cathode plate volume	V_C	0.012 m³	0.409 ft³
Cathode plate mass	m_C	53 kg	116 lb
Cathode mass (T-shaped with hanging bar)	m_{CTS}	66 kg	145 lb
Edge strips width (vertical)	b_{ESV}	0.0381 m	1.500 in
Edge strips height (vertical)	h_{ESV}	1.5621 m	61.500 in
Edge strips width (bottom)	b_{ESB}	0.0381 m	1.500 in
Edge strips length (bottom)	l_{ESB}	1.4478 m	57.000 in
Height above catholyte level	$h_{electrolyte}$	0.10795 m	4.250 in
Cathode plate width (immersed)	b_{CI}	1.0160 m	40.000 in
Cathode plate height (immersed)	h_{CI}	1.5240 m	60.000 in
Cathode plate volume (immersed)	V_{CI}	0.0098 m³	0.347 ft³
Cathode immersed surface area (both sides with strips)	A_{CE}	2.793 m²	30.1 ft²
Cathode immersed surface area (one side with strips)	A_{CI}	1.396 m²	15.0 ft²
Specific cathode active surface area	a_{CE}	39.37 m⁻¹	424 ft⁻¹
Cathode surface velocity	u_{SC}	0.002 m/s	0.005 ft/s
		0.094 m/h	0.308 ft/h

16.8.2 Anodes

16.8.2.1 Anode Materials

Two options are available: (1) the first option used in these calculations consists to utilize long lasting mixed metal oxides coated-titanium anodes for evolving oxygen (MMO-O_2). The chemically pure titanium metal substrate (ASTM grade 2) is coated with an electro-catalyst consisting of a mixture of iridium dioxide and tantalum pentoxide (Ti/IrO_2-Ta_2O_5). They have a proven anode service life expectancy in some instance up to 5 years which is equivalent to a circulated charge per unit surface area of 21 MAh/m^2. (2) The second option for anode current densities below +300 A/m^2 consists to utilize cold rolled lead-silver or lead-tin-calcium anodes with a proven anode service life expectancy from 3 to 4 years.

16.8.2.2 Total Number of Anodes per Electrolyzer

Because each cathode must be surrounded by two anodes, the ***total number of anodes per electrolyzer*** N_{AT}, is an increment more than the total number of cathodes:

$$N_{AT} = N_{CT} + 1$$

In our case, the total number of anodes per tank is therefore equal to **67 anode plates**.

16.8.2.3 Cathode-Anode Overlap

For preventing the edge effects, when electrowinning zinc or copper without using separators, the cathodes are always designed larger than anodes with a ***cathode-anode overlap*** L_{CAO}. Overlaps of 30-50 mm (1.125-2.000 in) on the cathode edge are typical for a smooth plating finish at the edges, and usually **an overlap of 31.75 mm** (1.25 in) is adopted. However in the particular case of divided electrolyzer, we can neglect the overlap ($L_{CAO} = 0$) as the actual open surface of the membrane smaller than the cathode surface will play the preventing role.

16.8.2.4 Anode Shape and Dimensions

Like cathodes, MMO coated-titanium anodes are T-shaped with the upper portion made of titanium-clad copper acting both as hanger and bus bar.

The active surface area is either made of: (1) a plain rectangular MMO-coated titanium plate with an inclined bottom or (2) made of a MMO-coated trapezoidal expanded metal (raised mesh type) welded to an incline plain MMO coated-titanium plate.

In both cases, the anodes exhibit a slightly inclined bottom with a small plane angle, denoted θ. The inclined design of the enclosed anode compartment will be discussed later in Section 16.8.4.

In case, of a ***plain rectangular MMO-coated titanium anode plate***, with a width, denoted b_A, a height, denoted h_A, and a plate thickness, t_A, all dimensions are expressed in m (in) (see Figure 122).

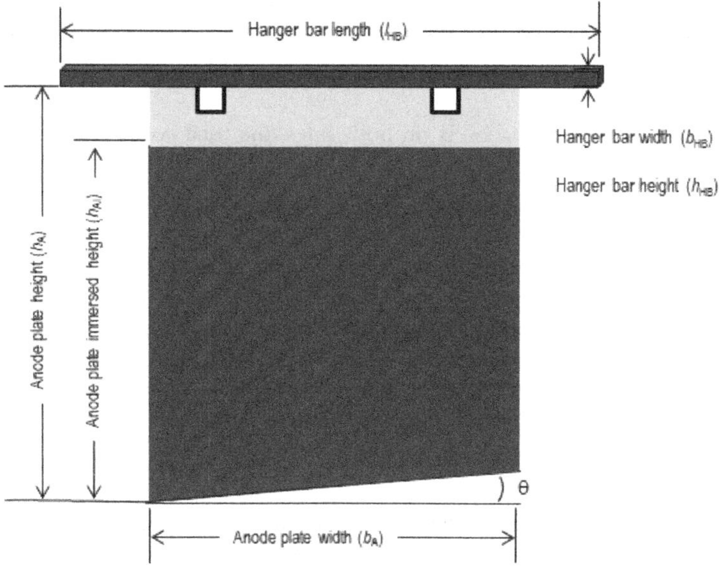

Figure 122 – MMO plate anode shape and dimensions with inclined bottom

Taking into account the overlaps between anodes and cathodes, the height, and width of the immersed portion of are related as follows:

$$h_{\mathrm{A}} = h_{\mathrm{C}} - 2L_{\mathrm{CAO}} \quad \text{and} \qquad b_{\mathrm{A}} = b_{\mathrm{C}} - 2L_{\mathrm{CAO}}$$

Therefore, the geometric surface area of the anode plate is simply:

$$A_{\mathrm{A}} = (b_{\mathrm{A}} \times h_{\mathrm{A}}) = (h_{\mathrm{C}} - 2L_{\mathrm{CAO}}) \times (b_{\mathrm{C}} - 2L_{\mathrm{CAO}})$$

Additionally, to be more accurate, the reduction of active surface area due to the inclined bottom must be accounted for and the actual geometric surface area of the anode, denoted A_{A}^*, is calculated as follows:

$$A_{\mathrm{A}}^* = (b_{\mathrm{A}} \times h_{\mathrm{A}}) - b_{\mathrm{A}}(b_{\mathrm{A}}\tan\theta)/2$$

The mass of each anode plate can be calculated using the mass density of the anode material, denoted ρ_{A}, in kg/m^3 (lb/in^3) is:

$$m_{\mathrm{A}} = \rho_{\mathrm{A}}\, t_{\mathrm{A}}\, [(b_{\mathrm{A}} \times h_{\mathrm{A}}) - b_{\mathrm{A}}(b_{\mathrm{A}}\tan\theta)/2]$$

The true active surface area is the anode coated surface area, denoted A_{coated}. With the anode width, b_{A}, and the immersed height wetted by the anolyte, denoted h_{AI} while the immersed width is irrelevant as it is equal to $b_{AI} = b_A$, taking into account the inclined bottom, the actual coated anode surface area is given by:

$$A_{coated} = (b_A \times h_{AI}) - b_A(b_A \tan\theta)/2$$

Because the MMO coating is on both sides, the total coated surface area is twice the above area:

$$2A_{coated} = 2[(b_A \times h_{AI}) - b_A(b_A \tan\theta)/2]$$

In case, of a ***MMO-coated expanded metal mesh anode***, with a width, denoted b_A, a height, denoted h_A, and a mesh thickness, t_A, all dimensions are expressed in m (in) and having a given open area OA in percent (see Figure 123) and taking into account the reduction of active surface area due to the inclined bottom, the actual geometric surface area of the anode mesh, denoted A_A^* is simply:

$$A_A^* = (OA/100)\ [(b_A \times h_A) - b_A(b_A \tan\theta)/2]$$

The mass of each mesh anode plate can be calculated approximately using the mass density of the anode material, denoted ρ_A, in kg/m^3 (lb/in^3):

$$m_A^* = \rho_A\ t_A\ (OA/100)\ [(b_A \times h_A) - b_A(b_A \tan\theta)/2]$$

Then the ***mesh anode coated surface area***, A_{coated}^*, in m^2 (ft^2) is:

$$A_{coated}^* = (OA/100)\ [(b_A \times h_{AI}) - b_A(b_A \tan\theta)/2]$$

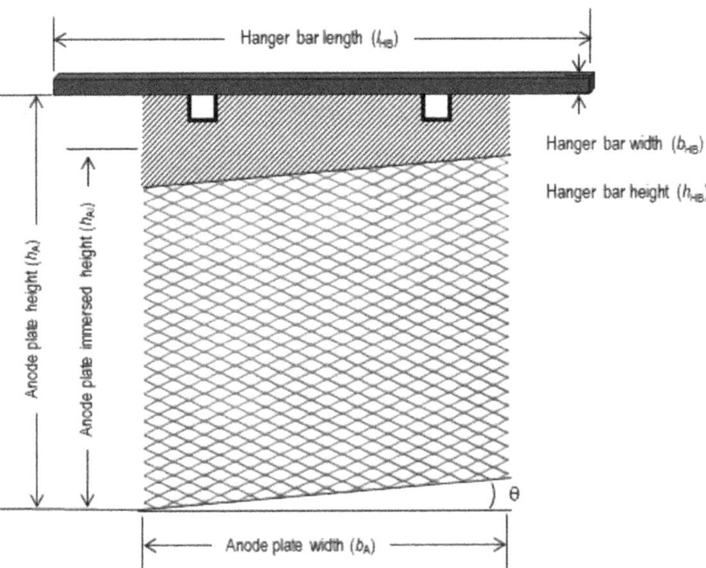

Figure 123 – MMO mesh anode shape and dimensions with inclined top and bottom

16.8.2.5 Anode Specific Active Surface Area

The ***anode specific active surface area***, denoted a_A, expressed in m^{-1}, corresponds to the dimensionless ratio of the total anode active surface area over the total volume of the anode compartment, that is, twice the anode-membrane gap, e_{gam}, in m (in) times the anode active surface, A_a, as follows:

$$a_a = A_a/(2e_{gam}A_a) = 0.5/e_{gam}$$

16.8.2.6 Anode Surface Velocity

The ***anode surface velocity***, denoted u_{SA}, expressed in m/s (m/h), corresponds to the velocity of the anolyte flowing parallel to the anode surface. It is calculated by dividing the volume flow rate of anolyte inside the narrow anode compartment by the total active surface area of the anode. The volume flow rate per anode compartment is obtained by dividing the overall volume flow rate of the anolyte in the electrowinning plant, $Q_{anolyte}$, by the number of anodes per cell defined in Section 16.8.1.2 and the total number of electrolytic cells (i.e., electrolyzers) per plant defined later in Section 16.9.2:

$$u_{SA} = [Q_{anolyte}/(N_{AT} \times N_E)]/A_a$$

It is obvious that this parameter influences the mass transfer along with the disengagement of the oxygen gas bubbles. The surface velocity of the anolyte must be as high as possible. The selected characteristics of the MMO anode are reported in Table 132.

Table 132 – MMO coated-titanium anodes characteristics, sizes and dimensions

ANODE(S)			
Mixed metal oxide anode material		Ti/IrO_2-Ta_2O_5 (EMMO-IRO-TI2-HD)	
Mass density of anode material		4,540 kg/m³	283.4 lb/ft³
Number of anodes per cell (both sides)	N_a	**67** MMO anodes	
Anode-cathode overlap	L_{CAO}	0.000 m	0.000 in
Anode-membrane gap (spacing)	e_{gam}	0.006 m	0.250 in
Anode plate width	b_A	1.0922 m	43.000 in
Anode plate height	h_A	1.6701 m	65.750 in
Anode plate thickness	t_A	0.00318 m	0.125 in
Anode inclined bottom plane angle	θ	0.052 rad	3.0 °
Anode plate mass	m_A	29 kg	65 lb
Anode plate geometric surface area (one side)	A_a	1.824 m²	19.63 ft²
Anode plate (actual) geometric surface area (one side)	A_a*	1.699 m²	18.29 ft²
Anode plate (actual) volume	V_A	0.005 m³	0.190 ft³
Anode coated width	b_{coat}	1.092 m	43.000 in
Anode coated height	h_{coat}	1.670 m	65.750 in
Anode (coated) surface area (one side)	A_{coated}	1.699 m²	18.29 ft²
Anode (coated) surface area (both sides)	A_a	3.398 m²	37 ft²
Specific anode active surface area	a_{CE}	78.74 m⁻¹	848 ft⁻¹
Anode surface velocity	u_{SC}	0.012 m/s	0.039 ft/s
		0.706 m/h	2.317 ft/h

16.8.3 Membranes

The anodes are totally enclosed or bagged inside a frame with the anion exchange membranes. The ***total number of membranes per electrolyzer*** is twice the number of anodes:

$$N_{MT} = 2\ N_{AT}$$

In order to reduce the ohmic drop and prevent leakage of sulfuric acid, each anode and two membranes are enclosed inside a specifically designed anode compartment allowing the maximum flow rate of the anolyte and the fast removal of the oxygen gas. The total surface area of each membrane separator must be therefore about 20% smaller than that of the geometric area of each cathode. The selected characteristics of the membranes are reported in Table 133.

Table 133 – Anion exchange membrane characteristics

MEMBRANE(S)			
Membrane material		ANION EXCHANGE MEMBRANE	
Number of membranes with PP frame	N_{MT}	**134** membranes	
Membrane exposed width	b_m	1.016 m	40.000 in
Membrane exposed height	h_m	1.524 m	60.000 in
Membrane thickness	x_m	163 μm	0.006 in
Membrane open surface area	A_m	1.548 m²	17 ft²

16.8.4 Anode Compartment

The MMO anode is contained inside a parallelepiped compartment with frames of anion exchange membrane on both sides. The inlet for the anolyte is a deep tube embedded in one frame reaching the bottom while the anolyte outlet consists of a short tube installed at the top of the compartment inside the other frame (Figure 124).

The frame of the anode compartment is built with a slightly inclined bottom (Figure 125) with a plane angle, denoted θ, in order to prevent the regions with low velocities and to promote the proper flushing of the anode and enhance the rapid detachment of the oxygen gas bubbles. The ceiling of the anode compartment is also inclined with the same angle as the bottom to perform the rapid disengagement of the mixture sulfuric acid-oxygen gas mixture. The narrow gap existing between the bottom of the compartment and the anode is denoted e_{wa}.

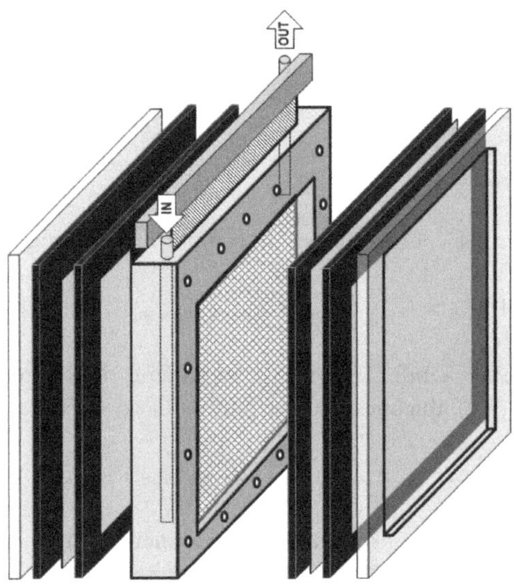

Figure 124 – Cut-off view of anode compartment with membranes and frames

Moreover, in order to maintain a narrow gap between the MMO anode and the anion exchange membrane on both sides of the anode compartment, it is worth to use two embossed mesh plates welded together to the top plate.

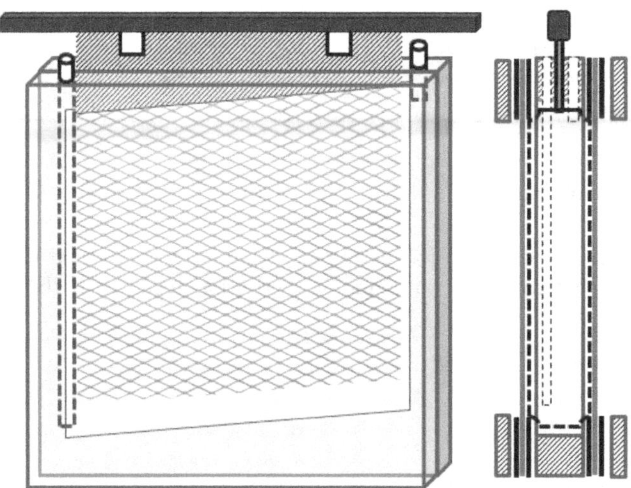

Figure 125 – Anode compartment with MMO mesh anode

The length, denoted l_{comp}, and height, denoted h_{comp}, of the inside of the anode compartment must accommodate the shape and dimensions of the anode active area while the width, denoted b_{comp},.must fit with the embossed design of the mesh anode to ensure a nearly zero-gap.

$$l_{comp} = b_{coated} + 2e_{wa}$$

$$b_{comp} = b_{coated} + e_{wa}$$

The total inner volume the anode compartment is simply given by:

$$V_{comp} = b_{comp} \left[(l_{comp} \times h_{comp}) - b_{comp}(b_{comp}\tan)\right]$$

On the other hand, the total outer volume of the anode compartment assuming a constant wall thickness for the plastic frame, denoted t_{wall}, in m (in.)

$$V_{outer} = b_{comp}(l_{comp} + 2t_{wall})(h_{comp} + 2t_{wall})$$

The characteristics of the anode compartment are reported in Table 134.

Table 134 – Dimensions of the anode compartment

ANODE COMPARTMENT			
Membrane-Anode compartment width	b_{comp}	0.051 m	2.000 in
Membrane-Anode compartment outer volume	V_{outer}	0.114 m^3	4.012 ft^3
Plastic wall thickness	t_{wall}	0.051 m	2.000 in
Wall to anode gap	e_{wa}	0.025 m	1.000 in
Membrane-Anode inner compartment length	l_{comp}	1.143 m	45.000 in
Membrane-Anode inner compartment height	h_{comp}	1.695 m	66.750 in
Membrane-Anode inner compartment volume	V_{comp}	0.098 m^3	3.477 ft^3
Membrane support frame thickness	t_M	0.005 m	0.197 in

16.8.5 Electrolyzer

A schematic of the parallelepiped electrolyzer is depicted in Figure 126 showing the countercurrent configuration, and separate flows of the anolyte and catholyte.

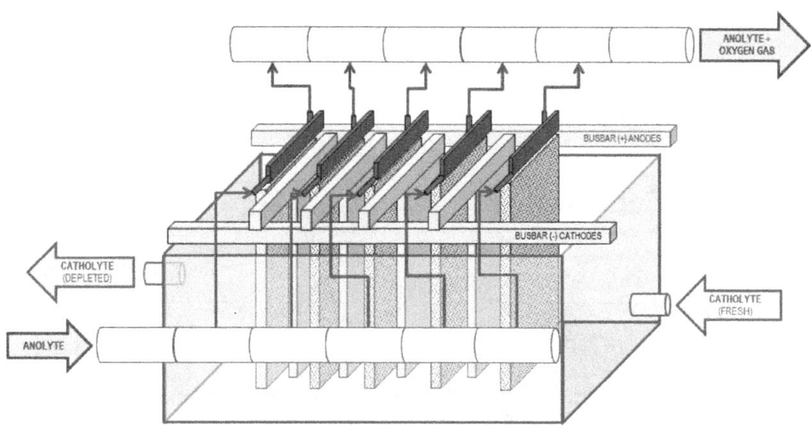

Figure 126 – Schematic of the iron electrowinning electrolyzer

16.8.5.1 Polymer Concrete Electrolyzer

The ***polymer-concrete tank*** electrolyzer is most affordable and resistant construction material for electrowinning iron as it is similar to the one used in copper electro-refineries, zinc and nickel electrowinning plants. It consists to a monolithic and reinforced vinyl ester-based polymer concrete. In certain cases, an additional inner liner made of CPVC could be installed to prevent leaks. Commercially, the Unicell® type II tank concept (Figure 127) was introduced by the Belgian company *Corrosion Technology International Group* or simply *CTI Ancor* that was later acquired by *Steuler GmbH.*

The Unicell® design offer several advantages compared to former traditional construction materials such as thermoplastics (e.g., PP and HDPE), lead-lined concrete, or even fiberglass reinforced polymers (FRP). (1) Its monolithic casting specifically designed to provide superior chemical resistance and mechanical durability offers an acid proof and homogeneous structure withstanding the extreme environment of an electrowinning tank house; (2) it has integrated inlets and overflow piping; (3) the electrolyzer stands as a structural unit where walkways, piping, valves can be attached to inserts embedded in the concrete wall structure; (4) The thick walls are designed to support large and heavy electrodes and can contain up to 10 m^3 of electrolyte with minimum buckling. (5) Moreover a sloped bottom allows separating solids by gravity settling followed by the ease of removing slimes and sludge during maintenance and shutdown.

As an illustration, a sketch of a jumbo size polymer concrete electrolyzer is depicted in Figure 127.

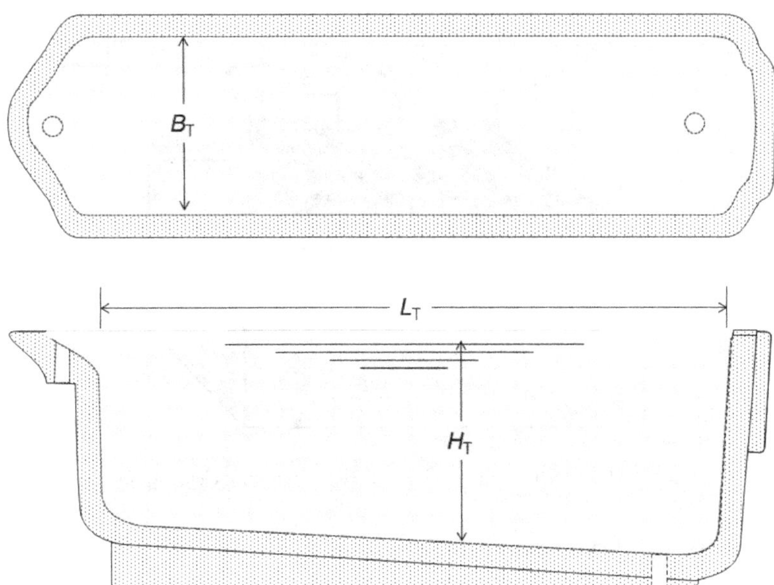

Figure 127 – Sketch of polymer concrete cell

16.8.5.2 Electrolyzer Design and Dimensions

The electrolyzer consists of a parallelepiped shaped tank. The inside dimensions of each tank are dictated by the number, size, and spacing of cathodes, anodes, and separators. Therefore, these dimensions can be easily calculated as follows for the inner width and depth:

$$B_T = b_{comp} + 2e_{AW} \quad \text{and} \quad H_T = h_{comp} + e_{AB}$$

B_T	inside width of the tank in m (in),
H_T	inside depth of the tank in m (in),
b_{comp}	width of the anode compartment in m (in),
h_{comp}	height of the anode compartment in m (in),
e_{gcm}	cathode-membrane spacing or gap in m (in),
e_{AW}	clearance between anode compartment and wall in m (in),
e_{AB}	clearance between anode compartment and bottom in m (in).

The total tank inner length must also take into account the total number and width of anodes compartment frames, number and thicknesses of the cathodes along with the clearance between the two end anode compartments and the end walls into the equation:

$$L_T = N_{CT}\,(2e_{gcm} + t_c) + (N_{AT} + 1)b_{comp} + 2e_{AW}$$

The empty volume of the parallelepiped tank, denoted V_T, in m³, excluding anode compartments and cathodes is given by:

$$V_T = B_T \times H_T \times L_T$$

The volume occupied by the cathodes, anode compartment, taking into account the cathode-membrane spacing, is:

$$V_{CAC} = [N_{CT}\,(2e_{gcm} + t_c) + (N_{AT} + 1)b_{comp} + 2e_{AW}](b_{comp} + 2e_{AW})(b_{comp} + e_{AB})$$

The actual volume of catholyte filling the void, $V_{catholyte}$, is simply obtained by subtracting the volume occupied by the cathodes and anode compartments to the empty volume of the tank as follows:

$$V_{catholyte} = V_T - (N_{AT} \times V_{comp} + N_{CT} \times V_{CI})$$

Finally, the outside dimensions of the parallelepiped tank takes into account a concrete wall with a thickness, denoted w.

Table 135 – Characteristics of the parallelepiped electrolyzer

ELECTROLYZER PRODUCTION CAPACITY					
Production of electrolytic iron per cell		2,275	kg/day	796	tonnes/year
Production of sulfuric acid per cell	30%	16,613	kg/day	5,814	tonnes/year
Production of oxygen gas per cell		571	Nm³/day	199,911	Nm³/year
ELECTROLYTES FLOW RATES					
Volume flow rate of catholyte (per cathode-membrane space)	Q_{CE}	0.0029	m³/min	0.75	gal/min
Volume flow rate of anolyte (per anode-membrane space)	Q_{AE}	0.0400	m³/min	10.57	gal/min
NUMBERS OF ELECTRODES & MEMBRANES					
Number of cathodes per electrolyzer	N_{CT}	**66**	cathodes/electrolyzer		
Number of anodes per cell (both sides)	N_{AT}	**67**	anodes/electrolyzer		
Number of membranes (framed)	N_{MT}	**134**	membranes/electrolyzer		
Total anode immersed surface area	A_{TA}	228	m²/electrol	2,451	ft²/electrolyzer
Total cathode immersed surface area	A_{TC}	184	m²/electrol	1,984	ft²/electrolyzer
SIZE & DIMENSIONS					
Cell concrete wall thickness	w	0.152	m	6.000	in
Edge clearance between cathode and tank wall	e_{CW}	0.051	m	2.000	in
Edge clearance between cathode and tank bottom	e_{CB}	0.102	m	4.000	in
Edge clearance between anode compartment and tank wall	e_{AW}	0.051	m	2.000	in
Edge clearance between anode compartment and tank bottom	e_{AB}	0.102	m	4.000	in
Tank inside width	B_T	1.245	m	4.08	ft
Tank inside depth	H_T	1.797	m	5.90	ft
Tank inside length	L_T	10.732	m	35.21	ft
Tank footprint	A_T	25.6	m²	276	ft²
Tank inside volume (totally empty)	V_T	24.002	m³	6,341	gallons
Volume of electrolyte	V_E	15.741	m³	4,158	gallons

16.8.5.3 Electrical Requirements

The electrical requirements, namely the total current per electrolyzer, denoted $I_{electrolyzer}$, in A, the overall voltage per electrolyzer, denoted $U_{electrolyzer}$, in V, and the total power per electrolyzer, denoted P_{cell}, in W depends on the type of electrical connection between the anode and cathodes (i.e., parallel or series) and hence are related to the individual cell voltage, denoted U_{cell}, in V, the cathode active surface area, A_c, in m^2, the cathode current density, j_c, in A/m^2, and the cathode current efficiency, ε_c as described in Table 136 hereafter.

Table 136 – Electrical requirement vs. electrodes arrangement

Electrode connection	Parallel	Series
Voltage	$U_{electrolyzer} = U_{cell}$	$U_{electrolyzer} = N_{CT} \cdot U_{cell}$
Current	$I_{electrolyzer} = N_{CT} I_{cell} = (N_{CT} \cdot A_c \cdot j_c)/\varepsilon_c$	$I_{electrolyzer} = I_{cell} = A_c \cdot j_c/\varepsilon_c$
Power	$P_{electrolyzer} = N_{CT} U_{cell} I_{cell} = (N_{CT} \cdot U_{cell} A_c \cdot j_c)/\varepsilon_c$	

Usually, the preferred layout to connect electrically anodes and cathodes inside the parallelepiped electrolyzer is in parallel in order to keep a minimum voltage while having a high current flowing as depicted in Figure 128.

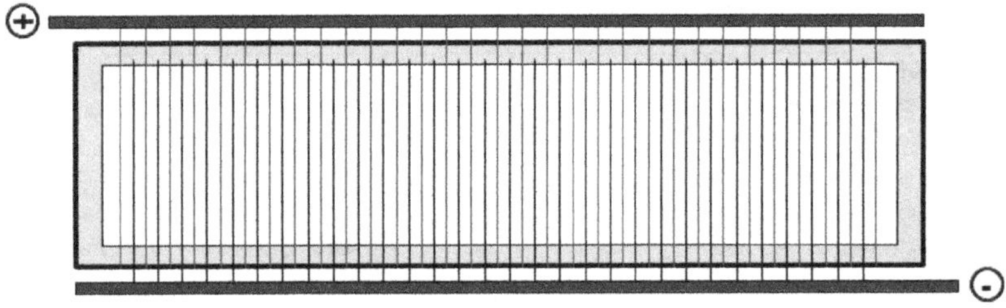

Figure 128 – Electrolyzer with anode and cathodes connected in parallel

Therefore the overall voltage per electrolyzer will be equal to the cell voltage of 3.133 V and the total current required will be 93.4 kA, this yields a total power 293 kW.

Table 137 – Electrolyzer electrical requirements

ELECTROLYZER ELECTRICAL REQUIREMENTS				
Type of cell		Polymer concrete rectangular tank		
Electrodes inside arrangement	series	0	parallel	1
Number of cell connected in parallel	Np	66 cell(s)		
Number of cell connected in series	Ns	0 cell(s)		
Total voltage per electrolyzer	$U_{electrolyzer}$	3.133 V		
Total current intensity per electrolyzer	$I_{electrolyzer}$	93.4 kA		
Total electric power per electrolyzer	$P_{electrolyzer}$	293 kW		

16.9 Cell House

The plant where all the electrolyzers (i.e., cells) are installed side by side and connected is called the electrowinning ***cell house***.

16.9.1 Total Cathode Surface Area

The first important parameter for sizing the tank house is to calculate the ***total cathode surface area***, denoted A_{TC} and expressed in m^2 (ft^2), which is required to plate the total amount of iron metal, M_{Fe} in kg (lb), to be recovered during a given period of time, denoted Δt, and usually expressed in hours.

Based on the electrochemical equivalent of iron, E_q in Ah/kg (Ah/lb), and assuming an operating cathode current efficiency ε_C and a cathode current density j_c in A/m^2 (A/ ft^2), the total cathode surface area is given by the following simple equation:

$$A_{TC} = [(M_{Fe}/\Delta t) \times E_q)]/(\varepsilon_c \times j_c) = M_{Fe}/Y_{Fe}$$

16.9.2 Total Number of Electrolyzers

Based on the total cathode surface area required per electrowinning plant, the total cathode surface area inside each electrolyzer, and the number of cathodes, the ***total number of electrolyzers*** (i.e., cells) is obtain after rounding-up the number by the equation:

$$N_E = A_{TC}/(N_{CT}A_{CE})$$

For preventing unexpected shutdown of electrolyzers for repair, it is advise to perform maintenance of the cells by a banks of ten cells every six months.

The foot print occupied by all the electrolyzers, A_{EFP}, in m^2 (ft^2) is:

$$A_{EFP} = N_E \times A_T.$$

Table 138 – Cell house

CELL HOUSE			
Number of electrolyzers (**rounded**)	N_E	**126.0** cell(s)	
Plant (electrolyzer footprint)	A_{EFP}	3,232 m^2	34,787 ft^2
Total cathode surface area required	A_{TC}	23,226 m^2	250,000 ft^2

16.9.3 Number of Harvesting Cycles

Because the cathodes must be removed periodically to harvest the iron plate deposit to be removed by mechanical stripping, it is necessary to calculate the ***harvesting cycle time***.

The total mass of electrodeposited iron per electrolyzer, m_{Fe}, in kg (lb.), with a mass density, ρ_{Fe} of 7,890 kg/m^3 (0.285 lb/in^3) on the total cathode surface area, A_{TC}, to reach a desired thickness, t_{Fe}, in m (in.), is given by:

$$m_{Fe} = \rho_{Fe} \cdot \times t_{Fe} \cdot \times A_{TC}$$

Based either on the hourly production rate of electrolytic iron, M_{Fe}, in kg/h (lb/hour) or on the hourly space time yield, Y_{Fe}, in kg.m^{-2}.h^{-1} (lb.m^{-2}.h^{-1}), the harvesting time, Δt, in hours, to reach a given thickness is:

$$\Delta t = m_{Fe}/M_{Fe} = (\rho_{Fe} \cdot \times t_{Fe} \cdot \times A_{TC})/M_{Fe} = (\rho_{Fe} \times \cdot t_{Fe})/Y_{Fe}$$

Only a third of the cathodes are lifted all at once, the maximum mass (i.e., load) to be lifted including a safety factor, ***SF***, determines the crane capacity. The mass of each cathode at the end of a cycle, m_{EPC}, kg (lb.) is the sum of the mass of the T-shaped cathode, m_{CTS}, plus the mass of plated iron, m_{Fe}. The load lifted is:

$$SF \times (N_{CT}/3)m_{EPC} = SF \times (N_{CT}/3)(m_{CTS} + m_{Fe})$$

Table 139 – Harvesting cycle

HARVESTING CYCLE			
Production rate of electrolytic iron per electrolyzer	M_{Fe}	2,275 kg/day	5,014 lb/day
		95 kg/hour	209 lb/hour
Targeted thickness of electrolytic iron (one side)	t_{Fe}	0.0064 m/cycle	0.250 in/cycle
Duration of harvesting cycle	Δt	97.2 hour(s)	4.05 day(s)
Total mass of electrolytic iron per electrolyzer per cycle	m_{Fe}	9,216 kg/cycle/cell	20,318 lb
Mass of electrolytic iron per cathode (both sides)	m_{Fe}	140 kg/cycle	308 lb/cycle
Mass of each T-shaped cathode with hanger bar	m_{CTS}	66 kg	145 lb
Mass of electroplated T-shaped cathode	m_{EPC}	205 kg/cycle	453 lb/cycle
Number of cathodes lifted per batch	N_{CLIFT}	22 cathodes	
Minimum load to be lifted per batch		4,518 kg/load	9,961 lb/load
Mass safety factor	SF	1.15	
Maximum load to be lifted per batch		5,196 kg/load	11,455 lb/load

The cathode harvesting cycle is designed as to accommodate a given deposit thickness on each cathode side. The thickness depends on the capability of the stripping machines (see Section 16.9.13) to separate the metallic iron plate from the titanium cathode blanks. Depending on the cathode current density, the harvesting cycle can vary from few days up to ten days in some instances.

16.9.4 Rectifier Specifications

The electrical specifications for selecting a suitable DC power supply (i.e., rectifier) for the cell house are the total current (I), the total voltage (U) and total power (P). They all rely on the electrical arrangement of the electrolyzers and hence are related to the electrolyzer total current ($I_{electrolyzer}$) and total voltage ($U_{electrolyzer}$). As described in Section 16.8.5.3 all the anodes and cathodes are connected in parallel. Afterwards, the rectifier requirements depend on the connection of the electrolyzers together in banks. Because, in practice, it is not suitable to have all the electrolyzers connected in parallel or all electrolyzers connected in series, it is recommended utilize a mixed cell arrangement.

Table 140 – Bank electrical requirements vs. electrolyzer arrangement

Electrolyzer connection	Parallel	Parallel-Series	Series
Voltage	$U = U_{electrolyzer}$	$U = N_{CP}\cdot U_{electrolyzer}$	$U = N_{CS}\cdot U_{electrolyzer}$
Current	$I_{banks} = N_{CP}\ I_{electrolyzer}$	$I = N_{banks}\ I_{electrolyzer}$	$I = I_{electrolyzer}$
Power	$P_{banks} = N_{CP}\cdot N_{CS}\cdot U_{electrolyzer}\ I_{electrolyzer}$		

Actually, the practical solution consists to connect a certain number of electrolyzers in parallel, denoted N_{CP}, and called banks this allows to design main copper busbars having a reasonable cross section, while the banks of such electrolyzers, N_{banks}, are then connected in series with a total DC voltage usually kept below ten times the individual cell voltage.

For instance, in this case study, we have a total 126 electrolyzers can have banks of 32 electrolyzers connected in parallel (N_{CP} = 32) with the following electrical requirements:

$$U_{bank} = U_{electrolyzer} = U_{cell}$$

$$I_{bank} = N_{CP} \times I_{electrolyzer} = N_{CP} \times N_{CT} \times I_{cell}$$

Then the four banks are connected in series (N_{banks} = 4) as depicted schematically in Figure 129 hereafter and the electrical requirement for the entire cell house becomes:

$$U_{total} = N_{banks}\ U_{bank} = N_{banks}\ U_{electrolyzer} = N_{banks}\ U_{cell}$$

$$I_{total} = I_{bank} = N_{CP} \times I_{electrolyzer} = N_{CP} \times N_{CT} \times I_{cell}$$

Finally, the maximum practical voltage will be equal to the total voltage times a ***voltage safety factor***, denoted *VSF*, of 1.5 to account for surges and spikes in the electrowinning plant voltage that might occur because of the potential drift of each single cell due to the aging of membranes, and passivation of the mixed metals oxides (MMO) coated-titanium anodes at the end of their service life:

$$U_{max} = VSF \times U_{total} = 1.5\ U_{total}$$

While the total current required will be at least the total current times a ***current safety factor***, denoted *ISF*, of 1.50.

$$I_{max} = ISF \times I_{tot} = 1.25\ I_{tot}$$

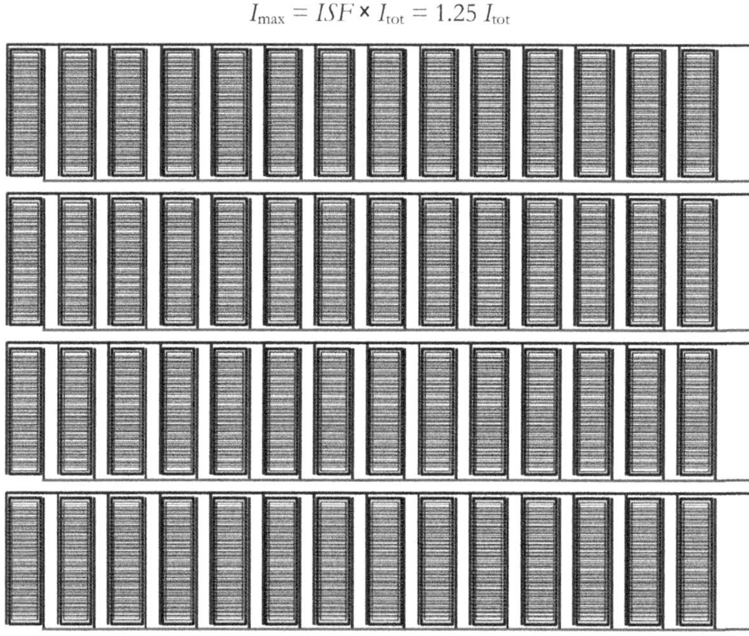

Figure 129 – Cell house with electrolyzers connected in parallel and series

The maximum electric power requirement for the entire cell house is then:

$$P_{max} = VSF \times ISF \times U_{total} \times I_{total} = 1.875\ U_{total} \times I_{total}$$

Finally, the rectifiers may be sized also to consider future expansions.

Table 141 – Rectifiers specifications

RECTIFIER (DC power supply requirements)		
Total voltage per electrolyzer	$U_{electrolyzer}$	3.133 V
Total current intensity per electrolyzer	$I_{electrolyzer}$	93.4 kA
Number of electrolyzers (**rounded**)	N_E	**126.0** electrolyzer(s)
Number of electrolyzers connected in parallel	N_{CP}	**31.50**
Number of banks connected in series	N_{banks}	**4.00**
Voltage safety factor	VSF	1.50
Maximum voltage (VSF x voltage)	U_{max}	18.8 V
Current safety factor	*ISF*	1.25
Maximum current (ISF x current)	I_{max}	3,677 kA
Minimum power required	P_{min}	69 MW

16.9.5 Busbars Ampacities and Design

16.9.5.1 Ampacity

The ***maximum carrying current*** of an electrical conductor in the form of a wire or cable is called either ***current rating*** or ***ampacity*** by electrical engineers. Ampacities are closely related to the maximum temperature elevation the wire or cable can sustain without affecting its electrical resistivity, and damaging the insulating protective sheath.

Therefore, the ampacity of a given conductor strongly depends on the intrinsic properties of the constituting material such as its electrical resistivity, its temperature coefficient, its thermal conductivity, its specific heat capacity, its temperature of fusion, and also external factors such as the nature of the insulating sheath materials, the type of external cooling (e.g., natural or forced cooling).

The calculation of ampacities is extremely important for sizing the current collectors in the secondary circuit of the transformer as large electric current of several thousand amperes circulate. Primarily for reasons of safety, and mostly based on practice and experiments, electrical engineers have developed guidance for selecting proper wire or cable to carry safely an electrical current and established certain standards for electrical wiring such as those specified in the *National Electrical Code* (NEC) in the United States. Typical NEC wire ampacity tables will show allowable maximum currents for different sizes and applications.

Although the melting point of copper theoretically imposes a limit on wire ampacity, the materials commonly employed for insulating conductors melt at temperatures far below the melting point of copper, and so practical ampacity ratings are based on the thermal limits of the insulation. Voltage dropped as a result of excessive wire resistance is also a factor in sizing conductors for their use in circuits, but this consideration is better assessed through more complex means. Practical rules to evaluate the ampacities of bare copper conductors such as those used in electrochemical and electro-thermal equipment are discussed hereafter.

For instance, for bare copper wires or cables, the adopted value for a maximum carrying current is given as **one ampere** for a wire having a cross section of **700 circular mils** (i.e., a wire diameter of 0.0265 in), that is, a maximum current density of 2.82 A/mm^2. However, if the copper wire or cable is water cooled the ampacity can be increased up to **one ampere** for a wire having a cross section of **438.5 cmils** (i.e., a wire of diameter 0.021 in) that is, a maximum current density of 4.50 A/mm^2. Usually, a conservative approach consists to adopt an ampacity of 1.0 A/mm^2 (0.500 A/kcmil), while companies are normally quite comfortable designing busbars withstanding current density up to 1.2 A/mm^2 (0.608 A/kcmil).

Therefore, it is recommended to design composite main bus bars made of several parallel copper strips with a rectangular or triangular section assembled together with spacers to ensure a sufficient air gap in-between to allow air cooling by natural convection.

Each individual electrolyzer requires a total current of about 93.4 kA, the proper busbars design consists to assemble a main busbars with 9 individual strips, each of size 450 mm x 20 mm, separated by a 20 mm air gap between each busbars. This fulfilled the above 1.2 A/mm^2 requirement.

Table 142 – Main busbars design and characteristics

BUSBARS			
Copper grade		Oxygen free pitch copper (OFPC)	
Maximun carrying current density (Ampacity)		1.2 A/mm^2	0.61 A/kcmil
Maximum curent per cell		93.4 kA	
Total cross section area of copper required	A_{Cu}	0.07782 m^2	186,954 in^2
Number of single copper strips per busbar	N_{Cu}	9	154 MMCM
Copper strip thickness	d_{Cu}	0.0192 m	0.756 in
Copper strip width	b_{Cu}	0.450 m	17.717 in
Air gap between adjacent strips	d_{Air}	0.0192 m	0.756 in

16.9.5.2 Busbars and Contact Ohmic Drop

Busbars are current collectors intended to ensure the proper and even distribution of the electric current between the rectifier and the anodes and cathodes. As busbars are responsible for a significant portion of the power costs great efforts have been made to minimize the contact resistance between the cathodes (resp. anodes) hanger bars.

Actually, the contact resistance is a function of electrode weight while the busbars resistance is a function of the, resistivity of copper, in Ω.m, the cross-sectional area, in m^2, and conductor length, in m, ($R = \rho l/A$) as for any electrical conductor carrying current. For instance, for electrowinning iron the contact resistance is 0.060 mΩ for a cathode current density of -500 A/m^2 with a total surface area of 1.851 m^2 at two contact points per cell thus produces an ohmic drop of about 56 mV.

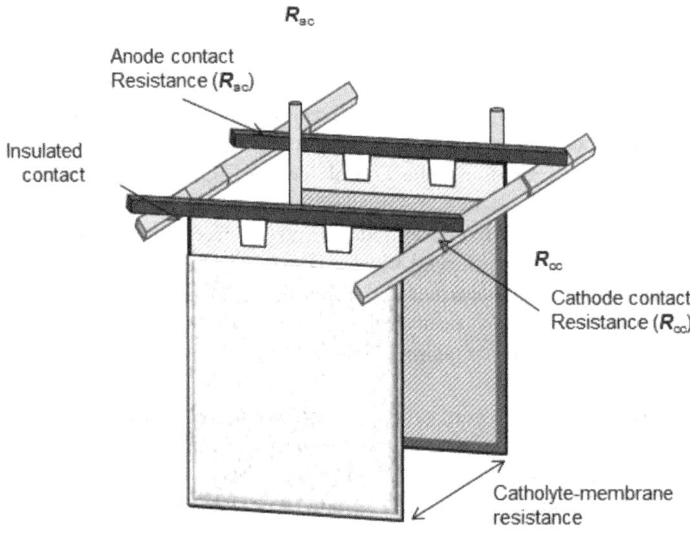

Figure 130 – Contact resistance in busbars

For these reasons, industrially busbars that carry the current from the power supply to the electrodes can vary widely in design [127, 128]. The possible designs used extensively in the copper, nickel and zinc electrowinning are: (i) dogbone, (ii) triangular, (iii) double contact, and finally (iv) Optibar.

Dogbone busbars. This option exhibits the simplest design and offers a cheap solution and was used in earlier copper electro refining plants and still used today in some older plants. It consists of two flat copper busbars acting as main electrical contacts. This symmetrical electrode design allows carrying more electric current. However, the fabrication requires larger amount of oxygen free copper metal making them more expensive than the triangular design. From a maintenance

[127] WIECHMANN, E.; AQUEVEQUE, P.; VIDAL, G.; and HENRIQUEZ, J. (2013) Contact system design to improve energy efficiency in copper electrowinning processes. *Industry Applications, IEEE Transactions*, 49(2013) 2461-2465.

[128] BOON, C.; FRASER, R.; JOHNSTON, T.; and ROBINSON, D. (2013) Comparison of intercell contact bars for electrowinning plants. *ALTA Ni-Co-Cu 2013*, Perth, Western Australia, pp.177-189.

standpoint, it is difficult to keep the contact surface clean as creeping of the catholyte and crystallization often occurs.

Triangular busbars. This option uses an asymmetric hanger bar that exhibit lower current carrying capacity than the other designs. Triangular busbars are a more viable option, provided that proper consideration is given to the design and layout of contact points between hanger bar (cathode and anode) and triangular busbars. The difference in elevation between the cathode and anode hanger bars requires using a bullhorn anode hanger bar design.

Double contacts busbars. The innovative **DoubleContact™** (Trademarks of *Outotec Oy*) inter-cell bus bar assembly was designed originally by *Outokumpu Oy* (now *Outotec Oy*). In this design both anodes and cathodes have an electrical contact on both sides. The Double contact bus bar assembly consists of one main inter cell bus bar, two equalizing bus bars, one main insulator, and one auxiliary insulator. The bus bars are made of oxygen free copper and all insulators of high quality fiberglass reinforced vinyl ester resin. The principal benefit of this technology is a more even current distribution, which in turn leads to reduced energy consumption, a more even cathode weight distribution, and fewer short circuits and less shut down for maintenance.

Optibar intercell contact. The ***optibar intercell busbars*** resembles a common multipole electrical connector. It uses as many contact segments as anode-cathode pairs to be connected. The current is directly injected from a cathode to a corresponding next cell anode. The load is connected as current source elements and the cell voltage is no longer equipotential

16.9.6 Electrolytes Pumping and Manifolding

16.9.6.1 Catholyte Flow

Based on common practice for copper, nickel, and zinc electrowinning plants, we recommend that the circulation of the catholyte in each electrolyzer is performed from the bottom to top. Moreover, the electrolyzer catholyte feed inlet ducts will need to be installed along the centre of the cell house, allowing for only five feed manifolds for each catholyte to feed the entire cell house.

The catholyte feed manifolds enter the cell house at the electrical neutral point. As common practice, the catholyte drain pipes must be located at the centre of the building, thus allowing the civil slope of the plant floor (i.e., change in elevation divided by the horizontal distance covered) to act as a run-off trench for possible electrolyzer overflow and spillages.

16.9.6.2 Anolyte and Oxygen Gas Flow

Due to the specific utilization of an anode compartment with each anode enclosed within two plastic frames according to the design described in Section 16.8.4, a separate flow anolyte must be considered.

Actually, the anolyte feed enter the anode compartment from a dip tube installed on one side at the bottom of the compartment while the anolyte froth consisting of sulfuric acid with nascent oxygen gas evolved at the anodes exit from a tube at the opposite side and on top of the compartment. The froth from each anode compartment is collected inside a large manifold and then directed to a disengaging tank where the oxygen gas is separated from the entrained anolyte, and the anolyte is then returned to the electrolyzer or to a holding storage tank. Such operating mode ensures that the anolyte exhibits at all times a high concentration of sulfuric acid with a low concentration of oxygen gas are maintained under conditions of high anode current density.

Moreover, because of the pressure differential existing between the catholyte and anolyte, it is important to keep the structural integrity of the membrane at all times by carefully monitoring the pressure differential.

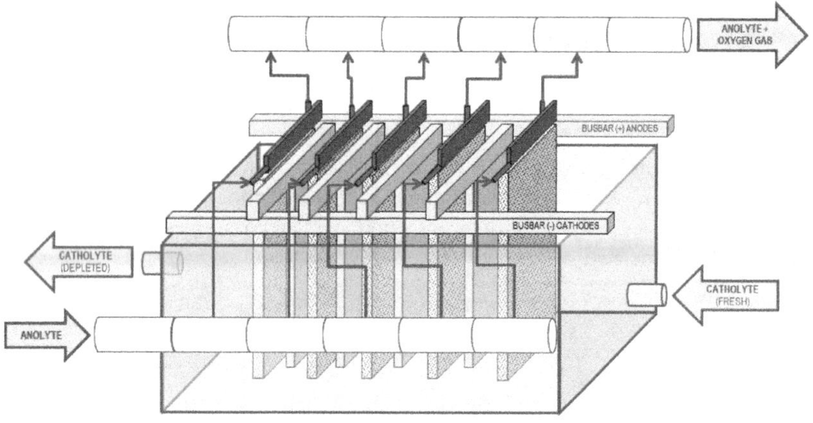

Figure 131 – Iron electrowinning cell with anolyte and catholyte flows

16.9.7 Electrolyzer Elevation

In order to facilitate the gravity overflow of cells to the circulation the electrolyzers need to be elevated above the ground. When elevation is already a necessity, it is then useful to elevate the cells high enough allowing for regular inspection by personnel. It is common practice, in copper, nickel, and zinc electrowinning plants across North America, that electrolyzers are erected 5 feet (1.524 m) above the ground of the cell house.

16.9.8 Mist Suppression

16.9.8.1 Anolyte

The major difference and great technical advantage when operating an iron electrowinning plant, compared with copper, nickel, and zinc electrowinning installations, is the fact that the oxygen evolving anodes are framed inside a compartment thus preventing the release of noxious mists of corrosive sulfuric acid droplets as the anolyte and oxygen gas streams are totally enclosed. This unique design thus prevents serious occupational health and safety issues for the workplace and corrosion of the building structure and surrounding equipment.

16.9.8.2 Catholyte

On the catholyte side, the fine mists released by the catholyte due to some unavoidable traces hydrogen gas evolution that accompanies the deposition of iron can be easily prevented by using frothing agents forming thick layer of foam that blankets the catholyte, and at the same times prevents air oxidation. This abatement method is combined with proper ventilation and using floating hollow polypropylene balls and beads also called demister balls.

16.9.9 Oxygen-gases Scrubber

In case, the oxygen gas needs to be recovered and sold as compressed gas, the role of the scrubber is to remove any traces of water and sulfuric acid from the pure oxygen gas coming from the anode compartment. The wet oxygen gas passes through a demister, then three scrubbing tower using concentrated sulfuric acid remove the last traces of water then a second demister removes the droplets of concentrated sulfuric acid

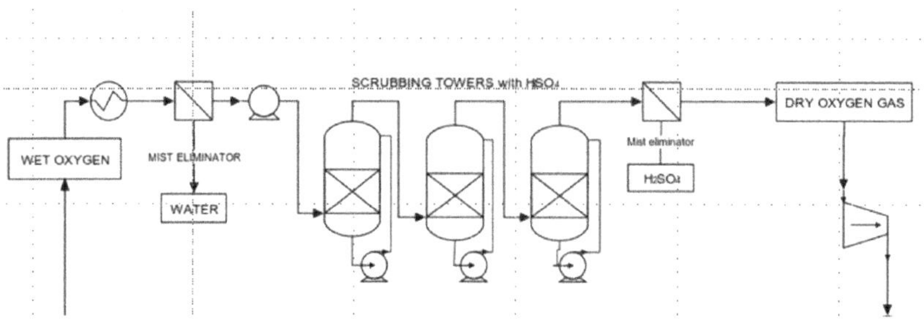

Figure 132 – Oxygen-gas scrubber

16.9.10 Catholyte Continuous Filtration

In practice, ***Scheibler polishing filters*** (*Larox*, Finland) are employed in the industry to aid in the filtration of circulating electrolyte, reducing the need to clean electrolyzers. Actually, these filter are based on the principle of adsorption filtration and are constructed to an advanced filter design, these filters cost-effectively reduce suspended solids to very low levels of parts per million in the filtrate.

16.9.11 Temperature Management and Control

Feed to the cell house could be heated using immersed or plate and frame heat exchangers, the optimum temperature is in the range of 40°C to 60°C.

16.9.12 Cathodes Harvesting Machinery

The sizing of a cathode harvesting machine can be calculated as follows:

$$M_{\text{capacity}} = N_{\text{E}} \times N_{\text{CLIFT}} \times m_{\text{EPC}} \times S$$

M_{capacity}	machine capacity in kg (lb),
N_{CLIFT}	number of cathodes harvested per cycle per electrolyzer,
N_{E}	number of electrolyzers,
m_{EPC}	mass of T-shaped cathode with deposit in kg (lb),
S	mass safety factor.

Based on a thickness of 6.35 mm (250 mils) on each sides of the cathode and a harvesting cycle of 4.1 days, the capacity including a safety factor of 115% is about 5.2 tonnes per cycle per electrolyzer. When cathodes, from four electrolyzers are harvested per cycle, this requires a 25-tonnes capacity overhead bridge crane.

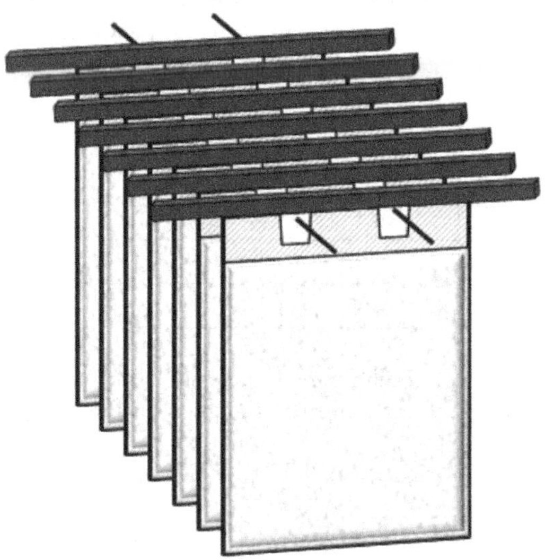

Figure 133 – Harvesting cathodes

16.9.13 Cathode Two-stage Rinsing and Passivation

Upon harvesting the wet cathodes from the electrolyzer, some catholyte solution is still wetting the electrolytic iron plate surface, and hence the solution must be removed by rinsing the iron plate. In practice, this is achieved by immersing the harvested cathode plate inside a first rinsing tank containing suitable additives (e.g., cleaning, etching, passivating agents) followed by a second tank containing hot deionized water. This two-stage rinsing is depicted schematically in Figure 134. However during this process the volume flow rates due to the drag-out of the catholyte ending in the first tank and drag-over of the rinsing bath into the final rinsing tank, and finally the drag-out of water out of the rinsing tank must be known for performing a continuous operation.

At a given operating temperature, pH, and mass percentage of copperas, the drag-out or retention of the catholyte solution corresponds to the ratio of the volume of catholyte solution retained, $V_{\text{catholyte}}$, per unit cathode active surface area (i.e., the wetted area and totalizing both sides), and it is defined by the following simple formula:

$$\text{Drag-out (catholyte)} = V_{\text{catholyte}}/A_c$$

Because the mass density, the surface tension, and the dynamic viscosity of most electrolytes usually decrease with a temperature increase, the drag-out of the catholyte is a strongly dependent on the operating temperature.

For instance, we have listed in Table 143 rounded figures for the drag-out of the catholyte at various temperatures for smooth and bright deposits of electrolytic iron from a catholyte containing 350 g/L $FeSO_4$ at pH 2.5,

Table 143 – Drag-out of the catholyte at various temperatures

Catholyte temperature	Drag-out (L/m^2)
30°C	0.7
40°C	0.6
60°C	0.5

Therefore, once equilibrium is reached and assuming a maximum concentration threshold of total iron in the two rinsing tank, it is possible to calculate the volume flow rates.

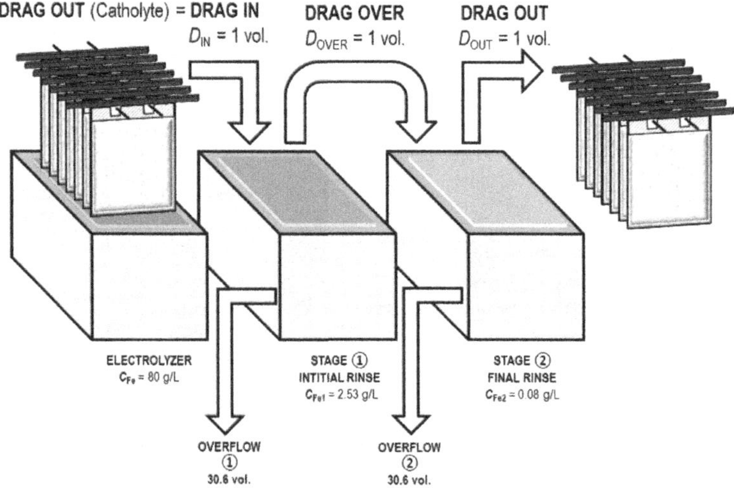

Figure 134 – Schematic of the two-stage rinsing of the harvested cathode

Initially, the drag-out flow rate, D_{OUT}, in m^3/hour, of the catholyte leaving the electrolyzer with a total iron concentration C_{Fe}, in g/L is equal to the drag-in flow rate D_{IN}, in m^3/hour, of the catholyte entering the first rinsing tank where the total iron concentration must be kept at a maximum threshold C_{Fe1}, in g/L while the rinsing tank losses liquid due to the drag-over flow rate, D_{OVER}, in m^3/hour, of the first rinsing solution.

For this first rinsing stage, the overflow rate of liquid, OVF_1, in m^3/hour, required to maintain a constant level in the first rinsing tank, can be calculated using the individual mass balance for the iron species written as follows:

$$D_{OUT}\ C_{Fe} = D_{IN}\ C_{Fe} = D_{OVER}\ C_{Fe1} - OVF_1\ C_{Fe1}$$

Therefore, after rearranging the above equation, the overflow rate of liquid in the first rinsing tang is is simply given by:

$$OVF_1 = (D_{IN}\ C_{Fe} - D_{OVER}\ C_{Fe1})/C_{Fe1}$$

Similarly, regarding the second rinsing stage, where the final drag-out flow rate of the second tank is OVF_2 we have:

$$OVF_2 = (D_{OVER}\ C_{Fe1} - D_{OUT}\ C_{Fe2})/C_{Fe2}$$

Often, the drag-in, drag-over and drag-out retention are very close for the same surface conditions. These calculations are provided in Table 142.

Table 144 – Two-stage rinsing of cathodes

TWO-STAGE RINSING			
Number of cathodes lifted per batch	N_{CLIFT}	22 cathodes	
Cathode active surface area (both sides)			
Cathode immersed surface area (both sides with strips)	A_{CE}	2.7929 m^2	30.1 ft^2
Total cathode surface area	A_{TC}	61 m^2	661 ft^2
Drag-out catholyte		0.500 L/m^2	0.0123 gal/ft^2
Drag-out of catholyte per harvest	D_{OUT}	0.031 m^3/min	8 gallon(s)/min
Drag-in of catholyte per harvest	D_{IN}	0.031 m^3/min	8 gallon(s)/min
Initial concentration of total iron in the catholyte	C_{Fe0}	80.0 g/L Fe	
Allowable concentration of total iron in the first rinsing tank	C_{Fe1}	2.53 g/L Fe	
Allowable concentration of total iron in the second rinsing tank	C_{Fe2}	0.08 g/L Fe	
Overflow rate for first rinsing solution	OVF_1	0.940 m^3/min	248 gallon(s)/min
Drag-over of first solution per harvest	D_{OVER}	0.031 m^3/min	8 gallon(s)/min
Overflow rate of second rinsing solution	OVF_2	0.941 m^3/min	249 gallon(s)/min
Drag-out volume of second liquid per harvest	D_{OUT}	0.031 m^3/min	8 gallon(s)/min

16.9.14 Cathodes Stripping Machine

Various suppliers (Table 145) can custom design stripping machines for the electrowinning operation. Options include fully automatic machines, semi-automatic machines, and options for water spray rinsing booths.

Table 145 – Vendors for cathode stripping machines

Vendor	Location
CAID Industries	Tucson, USA
MESCO	Japan
METSO (Outotec)	Pori, Finland

16.9.15 Cell House Layout

The cell house building consists of three parallel bays, the two of which contain the electrolyzers served by two 25 tons overhead crane that can be moved from one aisle to the other as required. The third bay or machinery bay contains the auxiliary equipment and is served by a 10 tons overhead crane.

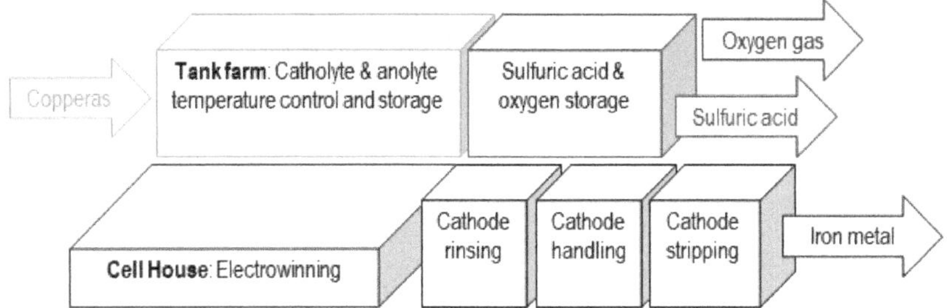

Figure 135 – Schematic block diagram for the electrowinning

The cell house consists of 126 individual electrolyzers. The way each cell is arranged in the cell house is as follows: (i) banks or blocks consist of assemblies of 32 cells all connected in parallel with a total current of 94 kA and voltage of 3.133 V. (ii) A section of four blanks connected in series (94 kA and 12.5 V). (iii) The cell house needs a floor space of at least 34,787 ft^2 (3,232 m^2). The size of the tank farm is determined based on the volumes of both anolyte and catholyte required daily.

17 Costs and Benefits Analysis

17.1 Business Case

This conceptual costs estimate calculations for a green field plant for electrowinning iron located in a friendly jurisdiction are performed as Class 5: order of magnitude with an accuracy ranging of between -20% and +50% with all the costs and prices expressed in 2023 US dollars.

17.1.1 Targeted Geographical Locations

We tried in this chapter to remain agnostic regarding the exact plant geographical location. However, we have used a hypothetical jurisdiction qualifying with the following economic requirements:

- Having access to affordable electricity tariffs below $0.05USD/kWh originating from hydropower or nuclear energy,
- Local availability of large tonnages of copperas from the titanium pigment industry, spent pickling liquors from steelmaking operations, pregnant leach solutions from metallurgical industries, or waste streams containing high concentration of iron-rich sulfates,
- Local access to sulfuric acid originating from nearby copper, zinc, or nickel smelters,
- Close proximity with established iron- and steelmakers capable to re-melt and convert the electrolytic iron produced into high quality steel,
- Highly qualified and trained operators personnel, and affordable labor costs and competitive wages,
- Friendly, jurisdiction regarding the implementation of grass root metallurgical and chemical operations.

From a business standpoint, the best countries satisfying the above requirements are: Canada (e.g., Quebec, Ontario, Manitoba), Scandinavia (e.g., Sweden, Norway, and Finland), Brazil, Russia, India, South Africa, and China.

17.1.2 Electrowinning Plant Nameplate Capacity

The capacity of the iron electrowinning plant is the one adopted in Section 16, that is, **519,990** tonnes of copperas equivalent processed annually, **100,000** tonnes of electrolytic iron produced along with **566,159** tonnes of sulfuric acid (30 wt.%) and **19.4** million of Nm^3 of pure oxygen gas.

17.1.3 Plant History

As no such iron electrowinning plant exists commercially in the world for that business case, a green field plant is the only scenario considered here.

17.2 Capital Expenses (CAPEX)

All possible care was taken to include the relevant items and to ensure that adequate provision was made to allow for the Canadian or Scandinavian winter for instance the proper insulation costs of the facilities and utilization of concentrated "winter acid" sulfuric acid with a maximum concentration of 93 wt.% in order to prevent crystallization during shipping, storage, and handling. Most of these calculations are based on conceptual studies using conceptual drawings for quantities, in-house data, and budgetary quotations from suppliers for major equipment, and input and feedback from customers who assessed the FerWIN® process. Moreover, it is important to list the main exclusions to the capital cost estimated:

- Land cost has not been included in the capital and operating cost estimate,
- The costs beyond the boundary fence are also excluded,
- Local sales taxes,
- Plant commissioning and training of operators,
- Project development costs prior to the definitive design and cost estimate.

The capital investment needed to supply the manufacturing and plant facilities is called the ***fixed capital investment*** (FC) while the capital for the operation of the plant is the ***working capital*** (WC).

The sum of the fixed-capital investment and the working capital is known as the ***total capital expenditures*** often denoted by the acronym CAPEX or sometimes TCI.

$$\text{CAPEX} = \text{TCI} = \text{FC} + \text{WC}$$

Because of the numerous assumptions, and short cuts in this conceptual economic evaluation, the numbers must be considered as ball park figures. If some parties want to use it as working document for evaluating the FerWIN® process, it is recommended to hire chartered accountants and professional engineers or a reputable engineering firm to perform a preliminary study at their plant location.

17.2.1 CAPEX Cost Estimation Categories

The estimation of the capital expenditures of an electrochemical plant is generally divided in several categories that are listed in Table 146.

Table 146 – CAPEX costs estimation categories

Capital equipment expenses (CAPEX)	Direct costs	Equipment purchased and installation Land acquisition
	Indirect costs	Engineering services Project services Site preparation Administrative fees
	Working capital	Amount of money needed to sustain the beginning of production during the first three or six months • Inventories • Spare parts
	Contingency	Amount of money to be available to mitigate any unexpected expenses occurring during the early project life

17.2.2 Costs Estimates Types and Accuracy

Cost estimates fall into five classes with accepted corresponding accuracy according to the *American Association of Costs Estimators* (AACE) (see Table 147).

Table 147 – Cost estimate classification (AACE)

Estimate class	Name	Purpose	Project definition level (Overall engineering)	Accuracy range	Correspondence with stock market reports
Class 5	Order of magnitude	Screening or conceptual	0% to 2%	L: -20% to -50% H: +30 to +100%	Conceptual economic assessment
Class 4	Intermediate	Concept study or preliminary feasibility	1% to 15%	L: -15% to -30% H: +20 to +50%	Preliminary economic assessment (PEA)
Class 3	Preliminary	Budget, authorization, or control	10% to 40%	L: -10% to -20% H: +10 to +30%	Preliminary feasibility study (PFS)
Class 2	Substantive	Control or bid/tender	30% to 70%	L: -5% to -15% H: +5 to +20%	Bankable feasibility study (BFS)
Class 1	Definitive	Check estimate or bid/tender	50% to 100%	L: -3% to -10% H: +3 to +15%	

As the names imply, the main difference between these types of estimates is their degree accuracy. The first three types serve as a cost indicator at a very early stage of the project. They are developed with a minimum amount of detailed engineering and provide a client or a management group with that first look at project cost. The preparation of a preliminary estimate is done by an estimator based on his assessment of the design, past cost estimates, in-house estimating information, and previous contracts and purchase orders.

It is not required to obtain formal quotations from equipment manufacturers in support of a preliminary estimate. Informal budgetary quotations on known major equipment are acceptable. However, even these types of quotations can prove to be time consuming to obtain. Definitive and substantive estimates require formal, firm equipment cost quotations from equipment manufacturers and suppliers.

17.2.3 The Six-tenth Rule

In the absence of data, the ***rule of six-tenths***, first mentioned in 1947 [129], is a rule of thumb extensively used in chemical engineering that was developed over the years, and it can be used if the cost of a similar equipment or plant of different size or capacity is known. The rule of six-tenths gives very satisfactory results when only an approximate cost within plus or minus 20% is required. At any rate, the following equation expresses the rule of six-tenths.

$$C_E(2) = C_E(1) \times (Q_2/Q_1)^{0.6}$$

$C_E(1)$ and $C_E(2)$ Cost of equipment 1 and 2,

Q_2 and Q_1 Capacity or size of equipment 1 and 2.

17.2.4 The "n" exponent

An analysis of the cost of individual pieces of equipment shows that the cost exponent (n) varies from 0.3 to 1.2, but the average is very near to 0.6, thus if unknown for a particular piece of equipment the recommended n value is usually taken equal to 0.6. If, during preliminary estimation, a higher degree of sophistication is sought, professional tables can be used. They usually list the value of a size exponent for various types of process equipment [130]. Using the size exponents transforms, the previously formula becomes:

$$C_E(2) = C_E(1)\ (Q_2/Q_1)^n$$

---

[129] WILLIAMS Jr.,R. (1947) Six-tenths factor aids in approximating costs. *Chemical Engineering* December 1947

[130] GUTHRIE, K.M. (1969) Data and techniques for preliminary capital cost estimating. *Chemical Engineering*, March 24, 1969.

$C_E(1)$ and $C_E(2)$	Cost of equipment 1 and 2 respectively,
Q_2 and Q_1	Capacities of equipment 1 and 2 respectively,
n	Cost exponent varying between 0.3 to 1.2.

It is also convenient to use charts called nomograms that can be found in specialized textbooks listed in the bibliography (see Section 20.6) or in a lesser extend in the technical literature from manufacturers.

17.2.5 Plant Location Adjustment

The CAPEX and OPEX for the iron electrowinning plant are intentionally calculated for a hypothetical North American location. Because the labor and energy cost vary with geographical location along with the transportation cost for import of raw materials and equipment and export of the products and co-products, the cost of a similar electrowinning plant at another location can be made using geographical adjustment factors such as those reported in Table 148. Moreover, the plant cost must be increased by at least 6% for each 1000 kilometers that a new plant location is distant from a major manufacturing hub or import facilities (e.g., deep harbor).

Table 148 – Geographical adjustment factor for electrowinning plants

Country	U.S. = 1.0
Australia	1.3
Canada	1.0
China	0.60
France and Germany	1.1
India	0.60
Scandinavia	1.15
South Africa	1.2
United Kingdom	1.1
United States	1.0

17.2.6 Determination of the Present Costs

Because no costs remain stable for long period of time, and because the cost of equipment provided in the specialized technical literature always depends on the publication date of the document, the costs must be updated prior to be used into the calculations. In order to calculate the present cost of equipment from its cost for a given date, two calculation methods can be used: (i) use of price deflators, and (ii) cost indices.

17.2.6.1 Price Deflator

The first method consists to use ***price deflator*** values extracted from depreciation tables such as those provided by the *U.S. Department of Labor Statist* with the year 1992 taken as reference. Thus the cost of the equipment is determined employing the simple equation:

$$C_E(\text{year Y}) = C_E(\text{year X})(D_X/D_Y)$$

With

C_E(year Y and X)	present and past cost of equipment,
D_x and D_Y	price deflators of years X and Y respectively.

17.2.6.2 Cost Indices

Another way for estimating the present cost use ***cost indices***. Actually, a cost index is a table of values that relates the costs of specific items at various dates to a specific time in the past. Cost indices are useful to adjust costs for inflation over time. The journal *Chemical Engineering* (CE) publishes several useful cost indices at the back of the magazine each month. Of particular importance to the chemical process industry are the *CE plant Cost Index* and the *Marshall & Swift Equipment Cost Index*.

Table 149 – Cost index sources

Index name	Basis	Base year of 100	Publication
Marshall-Swift	Installed equipment costs (chemical industry process industry).	1926	Chemical Engineering Magazine
Engineering News Record	Construction costs	1913 1949 or 1967	Engineering News-Record
Chemical Engineering	Chemical plant construction costs plant cost index	1957-1959	Chemical Engineering Magazine

The *chemical engineering cost index* provides values for several plant-related costs, including various types of equipment, buildings, construction labor and engineering fees. These values relate costs of overall plants over time, using the 1957-1959 timeframe as the base period (i.e., value = 100). The *Marshall & Swift indices* provide equipment-cost-index values arranged in accordance to the process industry in which the unit is used. This index uses the year 1926 as the base period. To use one of these indices to account for cost escalation, multiply the cost to be escalated by the ratio of the index values for the years in question using the following equation:

$$C_E(\text{present}) = C_E(\text{past}) \times (I_2/I_1)$$

C_E(present and past)	present and past cost of equipment,
I_2 and I_1	present and past indices values.

17.3 Fixed Capital Investment

Fixed capital may be defined as the total price to purchase equipment, get them installed, and tested, and it includes processing installations, buildings, auxiliary services, construction and engineering involved in the construction of the new plant. Among the several methods used to estimate the fixed capital investment, we used a method that requires the cost factors by considering the proportional costs of each purchased piece of equipment. The cost factors presented are based on modern industrial experience.

17.3.1 Direct Costs

Direct costs are costs related to tangible things or products such as process equipment.

17.3.1.1 Purchased Equipment Costs

The ***purchased equipment costs*** are based on cost capacity data and budgetary quotations received from equipment manufacturers and vendors. Cost data originating from old sources are brought up to date by the use of inflation indexes or cost indices (see Section 17.2.6).

The major equipment's to be purchased and installed are the Jumbo size polymer concrete tank to be used as electrolyzer fully equipped with manifolds, pumps, busbars, cathodes, and anode compartments, the overhead bridge crane, and hoisting for harvesting cathodes and their displacement, the cathode stripping machines, the rectifier and DC electric power supply, the control unit, the off-gas scrubbing system, and sulfuric acid demister for pure oxygen gas.

17.3.1.2 Equipment Installation Costs

The ***installation costs*** of process equipment may be estimated as being an amount equivalent to 43 percent of the purchased equipment cost. Further details may be made based on percentages reported in Table 150.

Table 150 – Installation costs

Items	Materials	Labor	Total
Foundations	4%	3%	7%
Structures	7%	4%	11%
Erection of equipment	w/o	25%	25%
Total installation	11%	32%	43%

17.3.1.3 Piping Costs

The ***piping costs*** cover labor, valves, fittings, pipe, supports, and other terms involved in the complete erection of all piping used directly in the process. The cost of piping depending upon the type of process involved may be estimated at amounts equal to percentages of the purchased equipment value (Table 151).

Table 151 – Piping costs

Processing plant	Percentage of purchased equipment			Percentage of fixed capital
	Materials	Labor	Total	
Solids	9%	7%	16%	4%
Solids-fluids	17%	14%	31%	7%
Fluids	36%	30%	66%	13%

17.3.1.4 Instrumentation and Controls

Instrumentation is the major part of the capital investment which actually includes not only the instruments but also all the auxiliaries (PLCs) for a complete system. ***Instrumentation costs*** may be calculated from the purchased equipment as equivalent percentages (Table 152).

Table 152 – Instrumentation costs

	Materials	Labor	Total
Few controls	4%	1%	5%
Medium controls	12%	3%	15%
Extensive controls	24%	6%	30%

17.3.1.5 Insulation Costs

Insulation costs can become important for an iron electrowinning plant in cold winter locations such as Canada, Northern United States, Scandinavia, inner Mongolia in China, and Siberia in Russia, and hence it may be necessary to estimate insulation costs with a great deal of care. The total cost for the labor and materials required for insulating equipment and piping in ordinary chemical plants is approximately 8 to 10 percent of the purchased equipment cost.

17.3.1.6 Electrical Installation Costs

For most an iron electrochemical plants, the ***electrical installation costs*** consists of four major components those are power wiring, lighting, transformation, service, and instrument and control wiring. The complete installed cost of electrical may be estimated as being equivalent to 10 to 15 percent of the purchased equipment.

17.3.1.7 Building Costs

In estimating the ***building costs***, it depend construction and existence of plant site. Costs for plumbing, heating, lighting, ventilation, and similar building services are list the erected unit costs of buildings and building components and the installed cost of service. The cost of buildings, including services for different types of process plants, is shown in Tables 8 as equal to a percentage of the purchased equipment price.

Table 153 – Buildings with services costs

	Greenfield plant	Brownfield plant	Plant expansion
Solids	68%	25%	15%
Solids-fluids	47%	29%	7%
Fluids	35%	5-18%	6%

17.3.1.8 Yard Improvements

The ***yard improvements costs*** consist of constructions for fencing, grading, roads, sidewalks, railroad sidings, landscaping, and similar items. The cost of yard improvements for large electrochemical plants may be estimated as an amount equivalent to 2 to 5 percent of the purchased equipment price.

17.3.1.9 Services Facilities

Service facilities include utilities for supplying steam, water, power, compressed air, and fuel. Waste disposal, fire protection, and miscellaneous service items are also included under the general heading of service facilities cost. The total cost for service facilities in electrochemical plants may be determined as amounts equivalent to percentages of the purchased equipment cost.

17.3.1.10 Land

The value of land is a highly fluctuating item. It will vary extensively with so many factors that it should be checked for each location of the property and may vary by a cost factor per hectare (acre) as high as thirty to fifty between a rural district and a highly industrialized area. As a rough average, land costs for industrial plants amount to 4 to 8 percent of the purchased equipment cost. Because the value of land usually does not decrease with time, this cost should not be included in the fixed capital investment when estimating cash flow, such as depreciation.

Table 154 – Land and site preparation costs

Land cost (building and services)	$\$/m^2$	$	996.00
Site preparation	$\$/m^2$	$	59.00
Waste water treatment	$\$/m^3$	$	1.22
Building lease	$\$/m^2$	$	65.00

The hourly labor rate for construction and installation manpower includes the following costs: salaries, benefits, mobilization and demobilization, operation of construction equipment, consumables, supervision, miscellaneous and profit. The cost for construction equipment rental is estimated on the basis of the requirements and the duration of the work to be performed. An allowance of $105 per day applicable to 50% of the workforce is included for travelling, room and board.

Table 155 – Fixed capital investment calculations (Direct costs)

Costs breakdown	Factors	Explanations
Purchased equipment		
Total purchased equipment cost =	$________	
Direct costs		
Land	1% to 2%	Percentage of total purchased cost
Yard improvements	2% to 5%	Percentage of total purchased cost
Foundations	15%	Percentage of total purchased cost individually estimated for each piece of equipment, and a factor for the entire section is calculated from the total
Buildings (including services)	25% to 35%	Percentage of total purchased cost
Structures	7%	Percentage of total purchased cost
Insulation (installed)	15% to 30%	Percentage of total purchased cost
Piping (installed)	15% to 66%	Percentage of total purchased cost
Instrumentation & controls (installed)	2% to 10%	Percentage of total purchased cost
Electrical (installed)	2% to 10%	Percentage of total purchased cost based on motor horsepower requirements for each section
Painting	1% to 2%	Percentage of total purchased cost
Miscellaneous	10%	Percentage of total purchased cost to cover minor equipment and construction costs that are not shown with the equipment list
Total direct costs prior taxes =	$________	
Sales taxes		
Total direct costs after taxes =	$________	

The breakdown of direct costs for a green field electrowinning plant producing **100,000 tonnes per year** of electrolytic iron, are reported in Table 156.

Table 156 – Direct costs

Electrowinning plant (Greenfield) Production capacity for electrolytic iron	(order of magnitude ± 30%) 100,000 tonnes/year	USD 2023	
10. IRON ELECTROWINNING PLANT	**Quantity per year**	**Unit cost (delivered)**	**Total cost (delivered)**
Polymer concrete tank (Jumbo size)	126 system(s)	$ 10,000	$ 1,260,000
Manifolding (Bottom)	126 system(s)	$ 15,000	$ 1,890,000
Copper busbars (Double contact)	252 busbar(s)	$ 15,000	$ 3,780,000
Overhead bridge crane and bale	1 system(s)	$ 450,000	$ 450,000
DC Power supply (Rectifier)	1 system(s)	$ 17,970,384	$ 17,970,384
Cathode stripping machines	2 system(s)	$ 250,000	$ 500,000
Acid mist eliminator and scrubber	1 system(s)	$ 485,000	$ 485,000
Process control and instrumentation	1 system(s)	$ 1,000,000	$ 1,000,000
	Total purchased cost =	**$ 27,335,384**	**$ 27,335,384**
	Installation costs 43.00%	$ 11,754,215	
	Total installed cost =	**$ 39,089,600**	
	Land 4.00%	$ 1,093,415	
	Yard improvements 10.00%	$ 2,733,538	
	Foundations 5.00%	$ 1,366,769	
	Buildings 35.00%	$ 9,567,385	
	Structures 7.00%	$ 1,913,477	
	Insulation 8.00%	$ 2,186,831	
	Instrumentation 15.00%	$ 4,100,308	
	Electrical 15.00%	$ 4,100,308	
	Piping 13.00%	$ 3,553,600	
	Painting 2.00%	$ 546,708	
	Miscellaneous 10.00%	$ 2,733,538	
	Total electrowinning section cost =	**$ 72,985,476**	
	Sales taxe 0.000%	$ -	
	Total direct costs =	**$ 72,985,476**	
	PLANT SECTION	**USD**	
	10. IRON ELECTROWINNING PLANT	$ 72,985,476	
	A. DIRECT COSTS		
	Total direct costs =	**$ 72,985,476**	

17.3.2 Indirect Costs

Indirect costs are costs related to intangible items, such as engineering and supervision, and project management expenses.

17.3.2.1 Engineering and Supervision Costs

The ***engineering and supervision costs*** include the costs of detailed design and other engineering services required to carry out the project construction design and engineering, drafting, purchasing, accounting, construction and cost engineering, travel, reproductions, communications. This cost is approximately 30 percent of the purchased equipment cost or 8 percent of the total direct costs.

17.3.2.2 Construction Expenses

Construction expenses cover construction and operation, construction tools and rentals, home office personnel located at the construction site, construction payroll, travel and living, taxes and insurance, and other construction overhead. This expense item is occasionally included under equipment installation, or more often under engineering, supervision, and construction. If construction or field expenses are to be estimated separately, the construction expenses average roughly 10 percent of the total direct costs for ordinary chemical process plants.

17.3.2.3 Contractor's fee

The ***contractor's fee*** depends upon the size, complexity, and location of the plant. It may be estimated as being equivalent to 2 to 8 percent of direct plant cost, which is the sum of the physical plant cost and engineering and construction expense.

The ***Owner's costs*** consist of salaries and expenses of the client personnel assigned to the project during the preparation, construction, training, and start-up phases, costs for the metallurgical testing, for the environmental impact study, and for value engineering studies.

17.3.2.4 Contingency

Contingency charges are extra costs added into the project budget to allow for variation from the cost estimate. In order to compensate for unpredictable expense, minor process changes, price changes, and estimating errors, a contingency charge is applied against the direct plant cost. It may be estimated as equivalent to a percentage of the direct plant cost. A new development where there is no previous similar experience and rather limited information will carry a high contingency, whereas a simpler installation similar to other construction will need only a minimum contingency

Table 157 – Fixed capital investment calculations (Indirect costs)

Indirect costs		
Engineering & constructions	5% to 25%	Percentage of plant cost
Administration & overhead	5%	Percentage of plant cost
Total direct & indirect costs =	**$**_______	
Contingency	15%	Percentage of direct plant cost
Contractor's fees	5%	Percentage of direct plant cost
Total fixed capital costs =	**$**_______	

The indirect costs for a green field iron electrowinning plant producing **100,000 tonnes per year** of electrolytic iron are reported in Table 158.

Table 158 – Indirect and fixed costs

B. INDIRECT COSTS			
Field or construction costs	3.00%	$	2,189,564
Administration & Overhead	5.00%	$	3,649,274
Sub-total overhead	8.00%	**$**	**5,838,838**
Consulting & engineering costs			
Preliminary engineering	0.50%	$	364,927
Basic engineering	1.50%	$	1,094,782
Detail engineering	3.00%	$	2,189,564
PCM	10.00%	$	7,298,548
Sub-total EPCM	15.00%	**$**	**10,947,821**
Temporary facilities	2.00%	$	1,459,710
Freight	1.00%	$	729,855
Commissioning	5.00%	$	3,649,274
Owner's cost	6.00%	$	4,379,129
Sub-total	14.00%	**$**	**10,217,967**
Total EPCM	29.00%	**$**	**21,165,788**
Contractors's fees	5.00%	**$**	**3,649,274**
Total indirect costs =		**$**	**30,653,900**
Total direct & indirect costs =		**$**	**103,639,376**
C. FIXED COSTS			
Contingency	15.00%	$	15,545,906
Total fixed capital cost =		**$**	**119,185,283**

17.4 Working Capital

The ***working capital*** is the amount of capital required for meeting expenses to start the plant after start-up of operations and before revenue becomes available and finance ordinarily amounts to the production cost for one month of operation before revenues from the process start.

Therefore, the working capital corresponds to the amount of money tied up in the raw materials and supplies carried in stock, intermediate and finished products in stocks, and semi-finished products in the process of being manufactured, accounts receivable, as well as cash needed to operate the plan on a day-do-day basis, cash kept on hand for monthly payment of operating expenses, such as salaries, wages, and raw-material purchases, accounts payable, and taxes.

Table 159 – Fixed capital investment calculations (Working capital)

Working capital		
Raw material inventory	(see note)	One month supply at purchased value
In-process inventory	(see note)	One-half the total manufacturing expense during a period to the total hold-up time
Product inventory	(see note)	One month production value at operating cost
Extended credit	(see note)	One month production at sales value or twice the operating cost
Available cash	(see note)	One month manufacturing expenses
Working capital =	$_______	Or 10 to 20% of the fixed capital investment or 25% of annual product sales value
Total capital expenditure (CAPEX) =	$_______	Fixed Capital + Working Capital

In general, it will be found to be an amount equal to 10 to 20% of the fixed capital investment or 25% of annual product sales value, and it will be financed from a short-term loan until sufficient cash flow is generated. The breakdown for a green field iron electrowinning plant producing **100,000 tonnes per year** of electrolytic iron is reported in Table 160.

Table 160 – Working capital

D. WORKING CAPITAL		
Raw material inventory	$	754,088
In-proces inventory	$	1,542,863
Product inventory	$	2,756,840
Extended credit	$	6,428,665
Available cash	$	3,214,333
Total working capital =	**$**	**14,696,789**

Therefore, based on the direct and indirect costs, the contingency and the working capital, the total capital expenditures for a green field iron electrowinning plant producing **100,000 tonnes per year** of electrolytic iron are reported in Table 161.

Table 161 – Total capital expenditures (CAPEX)

A. DIRECT COSTS	$ 72,985,476
B. INDIRECT COSTS	$ 30,653,900
C. CONTIGENCY	$ 15,545,906
FIXED CAPITAL COST	**$ 119,185,283**
D. WORKING CAPITAL	$ 14,696,789
Capital expenses (CAPEX) =	**$ 133,882,072**

17.5 Operation Costs (OPEX)

17.5.1 OPEX Cost Estimation Categories

The estimation the operating costs of an electrochemical plant denoted by the acronym OPEX is generally divided in several categories such as variable production costs, and fixed costs that are listed in Table 162.

Table 162 – OPEX costs estimation categories

Operating expenses (OPEX)	Variable operating costs (i.e., manufacturing or production costs)	Proportional to production rate • Raw materials • Utilities • Plant supplies • Labour • Packaging • Shipping • Royalties
	Fixed operating costs	Independent of production rate • Maintenance • Pay-roll Overhead • Plant Overhead • Depreciation • Insurance

17.5.2 Variable Costs

Variable costs also called ***direct costs***, ***manufacturing costs*** or ***production costs*** are expenses directly tied to the manufacturing or the production of a product (e.g., electrolytic iron). These include the costs of purchasing raw materials, process materials, various utilities, operating labor, and the rent for a production plant. Material and energy balances must be use to quantify the consumption of materials, and energy requirements. For the labor and maintenance requirements, staffing charts are used for each plant location, to account for regional differences in labor efficiencies.

17.5.2.1 Raw Materials

The annual consumptions of chemicals are based on mass balances obtained from prototype and pilot scale testing. The major raw material is ferrous sulfate heptahydrate (copperas). Considering that the copperas is often dissolved in effluents, and wastes, we have arbitrarily excluded its cost from the OPEX.

17.5.2.2 Process Materials

Process materials are for instance, urea, sodium sulfate anhydrous, magnesium sulfate heptahydrate, potassium sulfate, ammonium sulfate, sodium hydroxide, sodium carbonate (anhydrous), and sulfuric acid along with process and cooling water, and steam.

17.5.2.3 Utilities, Energy and Fuels

Electrical costs are estimated based on a typical industrial power charge ($27/MWh) following application of a utilization factor to the horsepower of the operating equipment.

Table 163 – Costs of raw materials, process materials, and utilities

Electricity	\$/kWh	\$	0.027
Natural gas (NG)	\$/MMBtu	\$	2.90
Petroleum	\$/bbl(US)	\$	85.20
Water (cooling)	\$/m³	\$	0.33
Water (process)	\$/m³	\$	0.11
Steam (265°C)	\$/tonne	\$	9.71
Air (compressed)	\$/m³	\$	0.05
Hydrogen	\$/m³	\$	1.79
Oxygen	\$/m³	\$	0.71
Ammonia (anhydrous)	\$/tonne	\$	595.00
Ammonium sulfate	\$/tonne	\$	400.00
Urea	\$/tonne	\$	335.00
Ferrous sulfate heptahydrate	\$/tonne	\$	150.00
Iron metal scrap	\$/tonne	\$	650.00
Iron plate (Electrolytic)	\$/tonne	\$	1,250.00
Potassium carbonate (Potash)	\$/tonne	\$	800.00
Potassium hydroxide (85 wt.% KOH)	\$/tonne	\$	700.00
Potassium hydroxide lye (52 wt.% KOH)	\$/tonne	\$	500.00
Sodium carbonate anhydrous	\$/tonne	\$	660.00
Sodium hydroxide flakes (98 wt.% NaOH)	\$/tonne	\$	415.00
Sodium hydroxide lye (50 wt.% NaOH)	\$/tonne	\$	260.00
Sodium sulfate (anhydrous)	\$/tonne	\$	125.00
Sulfuric acid (93 wt.% H_2SO_4)	\$/tonne	\$	50.00

Table 164 – Other costs

Byproducts taxes (CO_2)	\$/tonne	\$	65.00
Hazardous wastes disposal	\$/tonne	\$	500.00
Wastes disposal cost	\$/tonne	\$	10.00
Freight & duty	\$/tonne	\$	20.00
Non hazardous waste disposal	\$/tonne	\$	100.00
Anode 1/8" (MMO-O_2)	\$/m^2	\$	6,000.00
Cathode 1/4" (Titanium Gr. 2)	\$/m^2	\$	1,200.00
Cathode 1/8" (SS 316)	\$/m^2	\$	495.00
Cathode 1/8" (AISI 1030)	\$/m^3	\$	100.00
Cathode 1/4" (Aluminum 1000)	\$/m^2	\$	100.00
Membrane AEM	\$/m^2	\$	200.00

17.5.3 Fixed Costs

The estimated management and administration personnel along with the operating and plant staff must be established for a given nameplate capacity. Hourly rates were given for some categories of staff and estimates were made for those excluded. For dayshift staff **2,080 hours per annum** were provided for all staff. The same was applied to continuous shift workers where a single shift post was assumed to require four to five personnel, to cover leave and sickness.

17.5.4 Allotment of Workers and Staff

The electrowinning plant will be operated 350 days a year with 15 days of shutdown expected for preventive maintenance and repair. The cell house is operated 24 hours per day and seven days a week with three shifts daily. The allotment of worker and staff is provided in Table 165. In the initial years of operation 17 staff and 39 hourly employees totaling 56 will be required (see Table 165). Over time due to the automation and modernization less mine manpower is expected.

Table 165 – Allotment of workers and staff

Position	First shift	Second shift	Third shift	Total
Workers and operators (Hourly employees)				
Shipping and Receiving	2	2	0	**4**
Starter sheet stripping	1	1	1	**3**
Crane operation	1	1	1	**3**
Machine operation	1	1	1	**3**
Electrode replacement	1	1	1	**3**
Control room operator	1	1	1	**3**
Cell inspection	1	1	1	**3**
Tank farm	2	2	1	**5**
			Sub-total =	**27**
Engineering, maintenance & repair (Hourly employees)				
Electrician	1	1	1	**3**
Mechanical foreman	1	1	1	**3**
Instrumentation technician	1	1	1	**3**
Pipe fitters	1	1	1	**3**
			Sub-total =	**12**
Management personnel and office Staff				
Supervisor of operations	1	1	1	**3**
Laboratory technician	1	1	0	**2**
Laboratory Manager	1	0	0	**1**
Metallurgical clerck	1	0	0	**1**
Chief Metallurgist	1	0	0	**1**
Manager engineering	1	0	0	**1**
Manager EH&S	1	0	0	**1**
Manager HR	1	0	0	**1**
Secretary	1	0	0	**1**
Chief buyer	1	0	0	**1**
Chief Accountant	1	0	0	**1**
Information Technology	1	0	0	**1**
Plant manager	1	0	0	**1**
General manager	1	0	0	**1**
			Sub-total =	**17**
			Total =	**56**

17.5.5 Labor Costs

The labor costs used in this study are reported in Table 166 hereafter.

Table 166 – Labor costs

Labor cost (operator)	\$/hour	$	17.38
Labor cost (maintenace)	\$/hour	$	19.75
Labor cost (supervision)	\$/hour	$	31.60
Labor cost (engineer)	\$/hour	$	35.55
Labor cost (admin)	\$/hour	$	19.75
Labor cost (management)	\$/hour	$	55.30

17.5.6 Maintenance

For new plants this can be as low as 3% of capital cost per annum. However, this increases as the plant ages, and a good safe average figure over a 15 year depreciation period normally used for economic evaluation, is 5% per annum.

17.5.7 Indirect Costs

Typically indirect costs are 40% of total direct costs as per standard policy on order-of-magnitude estimates.

17.5.8 Contingencies

Typically contingencies are 30% of total direct plus indirect costs as per standard company policy on order-of-magnitude estimates.

17.5.9 Administration and Overhead Costs

General and Administration costs cover: (1) Administration building maintenance and utilities; (2) Offices and IT supplies; (3) Mining leases and municipal taxes; (4) Site insurance and fire protection; (5) Recruiting and training costs; (6) Safety equipment and medical supplies; (7) Environmental supplies; (8) Telecommunication fees; and finally (9) Other miscellaneous items (association dues etc.).

Annual maintenance supplies and parts costs have been factored based on an annual cost of six percent of the total mechanical equipment costs. Based on all the assumptions, definitions, and factors described above, the operating expense can be calculated and reported in the Table 167 hereafter.

Table 167 – Operating expenditures (OPEX)

2. OPERATING COSTS (OPEX)	PROCESSING LOSSES	10%	COSTS		
COST BREAKDOWN	**CALCULATION BASIS**	**QUANTITY PAR YEAR**	**COST (DELIVERED)**	**ANNUAL COST**	**COST (IRON)**
2.1 RAW MATERIALS					
Freight and duty		100,000 tonnes	0.0 $/tonne	$ -	$ - $/tonne
Total				$ -	**$ - $/tonne**
2.2 PROCESS MATERIALS					
Cathode blanks (Titanium Gr. 2)	5 years service life	1 663 plates	1 200.00 $/plates	$ 1,995,840	$ 19.96 $/tonne
MMO-O_2 anodes (Ti/Ta_2O_5-IrO_2)	5 years service life	1 688 plates	6 000.00 $/plates	$ 10,130,400	$ 101.30 $/tonne
Anion exchange membranes	5 years service life	3 377 sheets	200.00 $/plates	$ 135,072	$ 1.35 $/tonne
Total				**$ 12,261,312**	**$ 122.61 $/tonne**
2.3 UTILITIES					
Electricity (Electrowinning)	3.047 kWh/tonne	304 681 935 kWh	0.027 $/kWh	$ 8,226,412	$ 82.26 $/tonne
Electricity (other equipment)	10% of electricity	30 468 193 kWh	0.027 $/kWh	$ 822,641	$ 8.23 $/tonne
Electricity (billing demand)	HQ billing demand	86 396 kW	9.500 $/kW	$ 820,763	$ 8.21 $/tonne
Total				**$ 9,869,816**	**$ 98.70 $/tonne**
2.4 LABOR & MANPOWER					
Workers & Operators	21 shifts per week, 52 weeks a year	56,160 hours	17.38 $/hour	$ 976,061	$ 9.76 $/tonne
Maintenance & Repair (mechanical & electrical & instrumentation)	21 shifts per week, 52 weeks a year	24,960 hours	19.75 $/hour	$ 492,960	$ 4.93 $/tonne
Laboratory technicians	21 shifts per week, 52 weeks a year	4,160 hours	19.75 $/hour	$ 82,160	$ 0.82 $/tonne
Supervision & Engineers	21 shifts per week, 52 weeks a year	6,240 hours	31.60 $/hour	$ 197,184	$ 1.97 $/tonne
Secretary & Clercks	full time	4,160 hours	19.75 $/hour	$ 82,160	$ 0.82 $/tonne
Chief Accountant	full time	2,080 hours	40.00 $/hour	$ 83,200	$ 0.83 $/tonne
Laboratory Manager	full time	2,080 hours	31.60 $/hour	$ 65,728	$ 0.66 $/tonne
Chief Buyer	full time	2,080 hours	19.75 $/hour	$ 41,080	$ 0.41 $/tonne
Chief Metallurgist	full time	2,080 hours	35.55 $/hour	$ 73,944	$ 0.74 $/tonne
Manager Engineering	full time	2,080 hours	55.30 $/hour	$ 115,024	$ 1.15 $/tonne
Manager EH&S	full time	2,080 hours	35.55 $/hour	$ 73,944	$ 0.74 $/tonne
Manager HR	full time	2,080 hours	31.60 $/hour	$ 65,728	$ 0.66 $/tonne
Plant Manager	full time	2,080 hours	55.30 $/hour	$ 115,024	$ 1.15 $/tonne
General Manager	full time	2,080 hours	69.13 $/hour	$ 143,780	$ 1.44 $/tonne
Total				**$ 2,607,977**	**$ 26.08 $/tonne**
2.5 MANUFACTURING OVERHEAD					
G&A and maintenance, lighting, heating and indirect services	5% fixed capital			$ 5,959,264	$ 59.59 $/tonne
Total				**$ 5,959,264**	**$ 59.59 $/tonne**
2.6 GENERAL PLANT OVERHEAD					
Labor					
Expenses	included				
2.7 LOCAL TAXES & INSURANCES	2% of fixed capital			**$ 2,383,706**	**$ 23.84 $/tonne**
2.8 TECHNICAL & ADMINISTRATION EXPENSES	included				
2.9 MARKETING & SALES	included				
2.10 RESEARCH & DEVELOPMENT	included				
2.11 OTHER OPERATING COSTS					
Depreciation of equipments (without MMOs)	25 years life			**$ 4,767,411**	**$ 47.67 $/tonne**
Building lease	none	$ 10.00 $/ft^2	GRR 0.00%		$ - $/tonne
Royalties and licences payments (Electrolytic iron)	mass balance (Product)	100,000 tonnes	0.0 $/tonne	$ -	$ - $/tonne
Wastewater treatment	mass balance	m^3	1.22 $/m^3	$ -	$ - $/tonne
Wastes disposal and recycling	mass balance	tonnes	100 $/tonne	$ -	$ - $/tonne
Total operating costs (OPEX)				**$ 37,849,486**	**$ 378.50 $/tonne**
				Without	**$ 330.82 $/tonne**

For convenience, and clarity, we have extracted the major figures from the Table 167 into a more concise tabulated format provided in Table 170 hereafter.

Table 168 – OPEX breakdown

•PROCESS MATERIALS		$ 122.61
•UTILITIES		$ 98.70
•LABOUR		$ 26.08
•OVERHEAD(S)		$ 83.43
•ROYALTIES		$ -
•WASTES DISPOSAL & RECYCLING		$ -
TOTAL =		**$ 330.82**
Cathodes	6.0%	$ 19.96
Membranes	0.4%	$ 1.35
MMO anodes	**30.6%**	$ 101.30
Electricity	**29.8%**	$ 98.70
Labour	7.9%	$ 26.08
Overheads	25.2%	$ 83.43
		$ 330.82

VARIABLE COSTS	$ 22,131,128	$ 221.31	$ 221.31
FIXED COSTS	$ 10,950,947	$ 109.51	$ 109.51
DEPRECIATION	$ 4,767,411	$ 47.67	$ -
	$ 37,849,486	**$ 378.50**	**$ 330.82**

Close examination of the above tables, shows two major contributors on the operating cost for producing electrolytic iron. (1) First, the cost of mixed metals oxides (MMO) anodes for evolving oxygen that accounts for $101.30/tonne of iron produced. Thus with an OPEX of $330.82 per tonne this represents 30.6 percent of the entire production cost. (2) Secondly, with an electricity tariff of $27/MWh, the electricity costs accounts for $98.70/tonne of iron, that is, 29.8 percent. This appears even clearer when using the pie chart depicted in Figure 136.

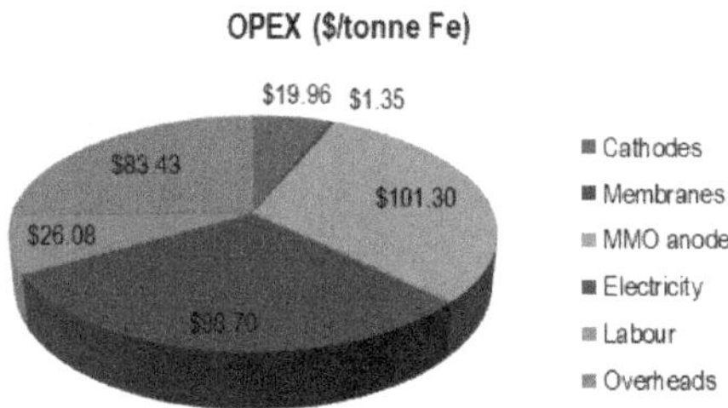

Figure 136 – Breakdown of the operating expenses

Therefore as these two costs both taken together, they represent 60.5 percent of the operating costs for producing iron thus any departure from the prices of electricity and industrial anodes will have a significant impact of the profitability of the entire process and this aspect will be discussed briefly in Section 19.

18 Financial Analysis

The purpose of this section is to assess the economic viability of a plant for electrowinning the iron with a production capacity of **100,000 tonnes** of electrolytic iron per annum. The financial evaluation will be carried out by the preparation of a discounted cash flow model to which the capital and operating cost estimates as well as the production schedule provided in the previous Chapter 17 are input data. The aim is to calculate key financial indicators such as the internal rate of return on the total investment, the net present worth resulting from the net cash flows generated by the project along with the payback time.

18.1 Basis of Evaluation

This section defines both the fundamental financial quantities and indicators along with assumptions that have been utilized in the financial model.

18.1.1 Operating Life or Useful Life

The financial evaluation was carried out over an expected ***operating plant life*** or ***useful plant life*** (N) of **25 years** for the plant. The construction phase is assumed to start in **January 2025** after additional pilot testing and to take two years and it will be completed in 2027. Afterwards, the plant will be operated continuously between 2027 and 2052.

18.1.2 Sales Revenue

The ***sales revenue*** or ***annual income***, denoted R, refers to an increase in equity resulting from the total annual sales of the two products (i.e., electrolytic iron, and concentrated sulfuric acid).

18.1.3 Operating and Production Costs

The annual ***production costs*** denoted C, are expenses directly related to the production of electrolytic iron. These include the costs of for purchasing raw materials, process materials, and various utilities, and the cost of operating labor. The annual, ***operating costs*** denoted O, are the sum of all production costs plus other ***general expenses*** or ***fixed costs***, E, such as the social and unemployment taxes, overhead and G&A, land taxes and property insurances, marketing expenses, and royalties.

$$O = C + E$$

18.1.4 Fixed-Capital Investment

The ***fixed-capital investment*** denoted I, is the initial capital investment, I_0, in both facilities and equipment plus all the ***additional capital investments*** I_k made during the entire operating life of the project to extend the service life of equipment or to replace damaged or obsolete assets.

$$I = I_0 + \Sigma_k I_k$$

The initial capital investment can be made all at once the first year or distributed as follows: 50% the first year, 25% the second year, and 25% the third year.

18.1.5 Working Capital

The **working capital**, denoted WC, is the amount of money tied up in the raw materials, intermediate and finished products, accounts receivable, as well as cash needed to operate the plan on a day-do-day basis. Working capital is required to meet expenses after start-up of operations before revenue becomes available. In our case, the working capital is **15 percent** of the original capital investment less the cost of anodes and membranes, and will be financed from a short-term loan until sufficient cash flow is generated.

$$WC = 0.15\,[I_0 - (C_{ano} + C_{mem})]$$

18.1.6 Total Capital Investment

The ***total capital investment***, denoted CI, or by its acronym CAPEX is the sum of the fixed-capital investment and ***working capital***.

$$TCI = FCI + WC$$

18.1.7 Gross Profit

The **Gross Profit** or ***Operating Income***, denoted G, is the yearly earning from the plant through its operating life. It is equal to sales revenue minus the production costs (C). However, it does not include deductions for the depreciation and income tax:

$$G = R - C$$

18.1.8 Gross Profit margin

The ***gross profit margin***, denoted GPM, is a profitability ratio that measures what percentage of revenue is left after subtracting the cost of goods sold. The cost of goods sold refers to the direct cost of production and does not include operating expenses, interest, or taxes. Therefore, the gross profit margin measures the profitability without accounting for overheads.

Gross Profit Margin = 100 (Revenue - Cost of Sales)/Revenue

18.1.9 Net Profit Margin

The ***net profit margin***, denoted NPM, is a profitability ratio that measures what percentage of revenue and other income is left after subtracting all costs for the business, including costs of goods sold, operating expenses, interest, and taxes. Net profit margin differs from gross profit margin as a measure of profitability for the business in general, taking into account not only the cost of goods sold, but all other related expenses.

Net Profit Margin = 100 Net Profit / Revenue

18.1.10 Interest Rate or Discount Rate

The ***interest rate***, denoted i, consists to the charge for the use of borrowed money. In this business case an interest rate of 6 percent and a half was used (6½%).

18.1.11 Income Tax Rate

The ***income tax rate***, denoted, t, is the sum of federal and state or province income tax rate. It is assumed to be 48%. Therefore, the income after taxes, denoted by the acronym IAT, is given by:

$$IAT = I\ (1 - t)$$

18.1.12 Salvage Value

The ***residual value*** or ***salvage value***, denoted S, is the market value of the plant and its assets at the end of the useful life of the project. That means that the assets can still be reused or capable to provide further service and it is worth more than its ***scrap value*** or ***junk value***. In this preliminary study, the salvage value is determined as the cost of the building and land plus the scrap value of the electrode materials which is close to **22.5 percent** of the initial fixed-capital investment.

$$S = 0.225\ I_0$$

18.1.13 Annual Depreciation

The ***annual depreciation***, denoted D, consists of a fixed annual charge on the facility or equipment investment which will results in recovery of the initial investment at the end of the useful life less the salvage value. The annual depreciation is determined in this report arbitrarily by the ***straight-line method*** given by:

$$D = (I_0\text{-}S)/N$$

18.1.14 EBITDA

The ***earnings, before income tax, depreciation, and amortization***, denoted by the acronym EBITDA, is the difference between the gross profit and total capital investment:

$$EBITDA = G - CI$$

18.1.15 Taxable Income

The ***taxable income***, denoted TI, is the EBITDA less the annual depreciation.

$$TI = EBITDA - D$$

18.1.16 Annual Cash Flow Equivalent

The ***annual cash flow equivalent*** worth denoted AEC, corresponds to the present worth distributed on the entire life time of the plant into equal annual payments, it is calculated by dividing the present worth by the capital recovery factor as follows:

$$AEC = PW/\{[(1 + i)^N - 1]/[i(1+i)^N]\}$$

18.1.17 Net Profit

The ***net profit***, denoted P, is equal to gross profit minus depreciation, interests, and income tax.

$$P = G - i\,(I + W) - t\,[G - D] - D$$

18.1.18 Present and Net Present Value

The ***present value*** denoted PV, or ***present worth*** denoted PW, is the principal which would have to be invested at the present time at a given compound interest i to yield a total amount at the end of the operating life of the plant equal to the amount of profit:

$$PV = PW = P_1/(1+i) + P_2/(1+i)^2 + P_3/(1+i)^3 + \ldots P_N/(1+i)^N = \Sigma_k^N [P_k/(1+i)^k]$$

The ***net present value*** or ***net present worth*** is the difference between the present value and the total capital investment:

$$NPV = NPW = \Sigma_k [P_k/(1+i)^k] - (I + W)$$

18.1.19 Internal Rate of Return

The ***internal rate of return***, denoted IRR, is the compound interest determined when the present worth and the total capital investment are equals that is when the NPV equal zero.

$$\Sigma_k [P_k/(1 + IRR)^k] = (I + W)$$

18.1.20 Return-on-Investment

The ***return-on-investment***, denoted, ROI, and usually expressed as percentage relates to the project's anticipated net profit to the total amount of capital invested.

$$ROI = 100\ P/(I + W)$$

18.1.21 Payback Time

The ***payback time*** denoted PB, is the time required for the annual cash flow to become positive.

18.1.22 Selling Prices of Metallic Iron and Sulfuric Acid

For the basis of this conceptual study, a selling price of $950.00 per tonne of rectangular plate of electrolytic iron, and $35.00 per tonne of sulfuric acid (30 wt.%) was utilized for the first year of the project and was incremented at 3% increase over the entire life of the project to take into account the escalation of prices and commodities. These prices were based on current market conditions.

18.1.23 Taxation, Duties and Royalties

This financial evaluation was carried out on a before-tax basis whereby taxes and duties were not considered. The project is subject to royalties expressed as a gross smelter return (GSR) based on a percentage of the production.

18.1.24 Project Discount Rate

The financial plan assumes owner equity will be utilized to cover 100% of the project capital requirements. For this project, a discount rate of 8% was used as the base case.

18.1.25 Minimum Acceptable Rate of Return

The ***minimum acceptable rate of return***, with the acronym MARR, is the minimum profit an investor expects to make from an investment, taking into account the risks of the investment and the opportunity cost of undertaking it instead of other investments.

18.1.26 Other Assumptions

The other premises and assumptions applied in the preparation of the financial projections are outlined below: Costs and prices expressed in US dollars with the following currency exchange rate: 1 USD = **1.35** CAD.

Table 169 – Assumptions

INVESTMENT		
Total investment required (CAPEX = FC + WC)	$	133,984,667
Fixed costs (FC)	$	119,185,283
Working capital (WC)	$	14,718,575
Preproduction costs (0.15 FC)	$	2,009,770
Ratio building/land		1.0
FINANCING		
Borrowed bank loan (B)	$	33,000,000
Debt ratio (B/(FC-B))		28%
Nominal (annual) interest rate (R)		8.0%
Compounding periods per year (M = C x K)		12.0
Compounding period per payments period (C)		1.0
Payment periods per year (K)		12.0
Effective interest rate (I)		0.7%
PROJECT		
Deflation production rate (Deflator)		-1.0%
Inflation rate (Inflator)		3%
Project life or Year depeciation (N)		25 years
Ramp-up factor		1.050
Minimum attractive rate of return (MARR 1)		8.0%
Minimum attractive rate of return (MARR 2)		12.0%
TAXES		
Marginal taxe rates		31%
MARKETABLE PRODUCTS		**USD/tonne**
SULFURIC ACID (30 wt.%)	$	35.00
ELECTROLYTIC IRON (99.995 wt.% Fe)	$	950.00
OXYGEN GAS	$	40.00
OPERATING & MAINTENANCE COSTS (O&Ms)	$	330.82
ELECTRICITY COSTS		$27 per MWh
SHIPPING FREIGHT COSTS	$	20.00
COPPERAS PRICE	$	30.00
ROYALTIES		5.0%

18.2 Discounted Cash Flow Analysis

The ***discounted cash flow analysis*** is a financial model to determine the present value of an investment today, based on projections of how much money that capital investment will generate in the future. Owing to lack of space, only an excerpt of the discounted cash flow analysis for an electrowinning plant producing 100,000 tonnes per annum of electrolytic iron, for the first seven years, is presented in Table 170.

Table 170 – Discounted cash flow analysis

	Year 0	Year 1	Year 2	Year 3	Year 4	Year 5	Year 6	Year 7
Book value of assets (Bn)		$ 119,185,282.73	$ 110,450,460	$ 106,083,049	$ 101,715,637	$ 97,348,226	$ 92,980,815	$ 88,613,404
Salvage value (S)								
Year	0	1	2	3	4	5	6	7
PRODUCTION								
Annual electrowinning of copperas		519,990 tonnes	519,990 tonnes	545,990 tonnes	573,289 tonnes	601,953 tonnes	632,051 tonnes	663,654 tonnes
Annual production capacity (Electrolytic iron)		100,000 tonnes	100,000 tonnes	105,000 tonnes	110,250 tonnes	115,762 tonnes	121,550 tonnes	127,628 tonnes
Annual production capacity (Sulfuric acid 30%)		566,159 tonnes	169,848 tonnes	178,340 tonnes	187,257 tonnes	196,620 tonnes	206,451 tonnes	216,774 tonnes
Annual production capacity (Oxygen gas)		27,707 tonnes	27,707 tonnes	29,092 tonnes	30,547 tonnes	32,074 tonnes	33,678 tonnes	35,362 tonnes
CASH INFLOWS (REVENUES)								
Sales revenue of electrolytic iron		$ 97,849,791	$ 100,785,284	$ 108,999,285	$ 117,882,727	$ 127,490,169	$ 137,880,618	$ 149,117,888
Sales revenue of sulfuric acid		$ 20,410,039	$ 6,306,702	$ 6,820,698	$ 7,376,585	$ 7,977,777	$ 8,627,966	$ 9,331,145
Sales revenue of oxygen gas		$ 1,141,518	$ 1,175,763	$ 1,271,588	$ 1,375,222	$ 1,487,303	$ 1,608,518	$ 1,739,612
Total sales revenues (annual income) =		**$ 119,401,347**	**$ 108,267,749**	**$ 117,091,571**	**$ 126,634,534**	**$ 136,955,249**	**$ 148,117,101**	**$ 160,188,645**
CASH OUTFLOWS (EXPENSES)								
Purchase of copperas (**inflated**)		$ (16,067,691)	$ (16,549,722)	$ (17,898,524)	$ (19,357,254)	$ (20,934,870)	$ (22,641,062)	$ (24,486,308)
Licensee maintenance fees and technical support		$ (250,000)	$ (250,000)	$ (250,000)	$ (250,000)	$ (250,000)	$ (250,000)	$ (250,000)
Royalties		$ (5,970,067)	$ (5,413,387)	$ (5,854,579)	$ (6,331,727)	$ (6,847,762)	$ (7,405,855)	$ (8,009,432)
Shipping costs		$ (1,999,996)	$ (1,999,996)	$ (2,099,996)	$ (2,204,995)	$ (2,315,245)	$ (2,431,007)	$ (2,552,558)
Operating & maintenance costs (O&Ms)(**deflated**)		$ (32,751,254)	$ (32,423,742)	$ (33,704,479)	$ (35,036,806)	$ (36,419,721)	$ (37,858,300)	$ (39,353,702)
Bank loan annual interest paid (In)		$ (2,640,000)	$ (2,603,888)	$ (2,564,887)	$ (2,522,766)	$ (2,477,275)	$ (2,428,145)	$ (2,375,085)
Total production & maintenace costs =		**$ (59,679,008)**	**$ (59,240,734)**	**$ (62,372,464)**	**$ (65,702,548)**	**$ (69,244,873)**	**$ (73,014,369)**	**$ (77,027,086)**
Gross Profit (operating income) =		**$ 59,722,339**	**$ 49,027,015**	**$ 54,719,107**	**$ 60,931,986**	**$ 67,710,375**	**$ 75,102,732**	**$ 83,161,559**
CAPITAL INVESTMENT								
Preproduction costs	$ (2,009,770)							
Initial investment	$ (100,984,667)							
Working capital (WC)	$ (14,718,575)							
Bank loan annual payment on principal (PPn)		$ (451,400)	$ (487,512)	$ (526,513)	$ (568,634)	$ (614,124)	$ (663,254)	$ (716,315)
Extension and replacement of assets								
Total capital investment =	**$ (117,713,012)**	**$ (451,400)**	**$ (487,512)**	**$ (526,513)**	**$ (568,634)**	**$ (614,124)**	**$ (663,254)**	**$ (716,315)**
Earnings before Income Tax & Depreciation (EBITDA)	$ (117,713,012)	$ 59,270,939	$ 48,539,503	$ 54,192,594	$ 60,363,352	$ 67,096,251	$ 74,439,478	$ 82,445,245
Annual depreciation straightline (CCA)		$ 4,367,411	$ 4,367,411	$ 4,367,411	$ 4,367,411	$ 4,367,411	$ 4,367,411	$ 4,367,411
Losses recoverable	$ -	$ (117,713,012)	$ (62,809,484)	$ (18,637,392)	$ -	$ -	$ -	$ -
Taxable income	**$ (117,713,012)**	**$ (62,809,484)**	**$ (18,637,392)**	**$ 31,187,791**	**$ 55,995,941**	**$ 62,728,840**	**$ 70,072,067**	**$ 78,077,833**
PRE-TAX								
Annual cash flow (PRE-TAX) =	$ (117,713,012)	$ (58,442,072)	$ (14,269,980)	$ 35,555,202	$ 60,363,352	$ 67,096,251	$ 74,439,478	$ 82,445,245
Discounted cash flow (MARR 1)	$ (117,713,012)	$ (54,113,030)	$ (12,234,208)	$ 28,224,866	$ 44,368,866	$ 45,664,581	$ 46,909,498	$ 48,106,008
Discounted cash flow (MARR 2)	$ (117,713,012)	$ (52,180,422)	$ (11,375,941)	$ 25,307,491	$ 38,362,002	$ 38,072,215	$ 37,713,356	$ 37,294,042
Income after tax	**$ (117,713,012)**	**$ (62,809,484)**	**$ (18,637,392)**	**$ 21,675,515**	**$ 38,917,179**	**$ 43,596,544**	**$ 48,700,086**	**$ 54,264,094**
AFTER TAX								
Annual cash flow (AFTER-TAX) =	$ (117,713,012)	$ (58,442,072)	$ (14,269,980)	$ 26,042,926	$ 43,284,590	$ 47,963,955	$ 53,067,498	$ 58,631,506
Discounted cash flow (MARR 1)	$ (117,713,012)	$ (54,113,030)	$ (12,234,208)	$ 20,673,714	$ 31,815,466	$ 32,643,462	$ 33,441,525	$ 34,210,920
Discounted cash flow (MARR 2)	$ (117,713,012)	$ (52,180,422)	$ (11,375,941)	$ 18,536,840	$ 27,508,140	$ 27,216,036	$ 26,885,646	$ 26,521,916

18.3 Key Financial Indicators

Based on the previous discounted cash flow analysis, the key financial indicators are summarized in the Table 171 using two minimum acceptable rates of return (MARR) of 8 percent and 12 percent respectively.

Table 171 – Key financial indicators

		MARR			AFTER-TAX
Net present value	NPV	**8.0%**	**$**	**639,938,256**	
Net future value	NFV	8.0%	$	4,382,601,273	
Internal rate of return	IRR	8.0%		**23.3%**	
Return on investment	ROI	8.0%		**36.2%**	1
Payback period	PBP	8.0%		**2 years**	
Annual equivalent	AE	8.0%	$	59,948,634	
Capitat recovery	CR	8.0%	$	9,428,344	
AEC			$	18,594,327	

		MARR			PRE-TAX
Net present value	NPV	**8.0%**	**$**	**979,786,387**	
Net future value	NFV	8.0%	$	6,710,042,768	
Internal rate of return	IRR	8.0%		**28.2%**	
Return on investment	ROI	8.0%		**36.2%**	1
Payback period	PBP	8.0%		**2 years**	
Annual equivalent	AE	8.0%	$	91,785,192	

		MARR			AFTER-TAX
Net present value	NPV	**12.0%**	**$**	**306,535,861**	
Net future value	NFV	12.0%	**$**	**5,211,129,386**	
Internal rate of return	IRR	12.0%		**23.34%**	
Return on investment	ROI	12.0%		**36%**	1
Payback period	PBP	12.0%		**2 years**	
Annuel equivalent	AE	12.0%	$	28,715,905	

		MARR			PRE-TAX
Net present value	NPV	**12.0%**	**$**	**501,555,805**	
Net future value	NFV	12.0%	**$**	**8,526,480,990**	
Internal rate of return	IRR	12.0%		**28.22%**	
Return on investment	ROI	12.0%		**36%**	1
Payback period	PBP	12.0%		**2 years**	
Annuel equivalent	AE	12.0%	$	46,985,135	

19 Sensitivity Analysis

The previous key financial indicators obtained from the preliminary financial analysis are highly dependent on various variables such as the production cost for electrowinning iron, the electrowinning plant nameplate capacity, the market price of electrolytic iron, the price of copperas, and finally the price and availability of sulfuric acid. For that purpose, running a ***sensitivity analysis*** also referred to as a ***"what-if" analysis*** will determine how different values of these independent variables affect the net present worth for the project under a given set of assumptions listed hereafter.

19.1 Plant Nameplate Capacity

The plant nameplate capacity has a huge impact of the key financial indicators as larger the production is, lower is the operating cost. Therefore, we believe that targeting a production capacity greater than at least 100,000 tonnes of electrolytic iron metal annually which is half the average output of most steel mini-mills, will allow to obtain profitability with a shorter payback time, and higher return on investment. Because the technology is modular, it will be straightforward to perform the expansion of the plant incrementally to obtain a higher capacity.

Table 172 – Financial indicators vs. production cost and nameplate capacity

Electrolytic iron selling prices ($/tonne)			$650.00	$800.00	$950.00
PLANT CAPACITY & COST (M$)	Production cost ($/tonne of iron)		$320.00	$320.00	$320.00
	$134M USD 100,000 tonnes Fe	NPV	$72M	$385M	$559M
		ROI	14%	25%	33%
		IRR	10%	17%	21%
		PB	5 years	3 years	2 years
	Production cost ($/tonne of iron)		$343.00	$343.00	$343.00
	$74M USD 50,000 tonnes Fe	NPV	$30M	$192M	$320M
		ROI	9%	19%	29%
		IRR	9%	18%	26%
		PB	5 years	3 years	2 years

19.2 Price of Electrolytic Iron Metal

The market fluctuations, and recent volatility for the prices for most iron metal products (e.g., pig iron, steel) including electrolytic iron exert a huge constrain on the profitability of the FerWIN® process (Figure 137). In this regards, we believe that for a successful commercial roll-out of the electrowinning of iron, the selling price for electrolytic iron must match with that of high quality steels. Actually, even if the selling price for electrolytic iron can reach in some instance as high as $1,900/tonne, the market for electrolytic iron is only a niche market with nearly 60,000 tonnes produced per year that must be compared to the huge 1.9 billion tonnes of crude steel produced. Thus, the only way to sell iron is to compete with steel or high quality iron scrap, the latter is rather scarce nowadays as most commercial steel scrap is contaminated by zinc due to ubiquitous galvanized steel.

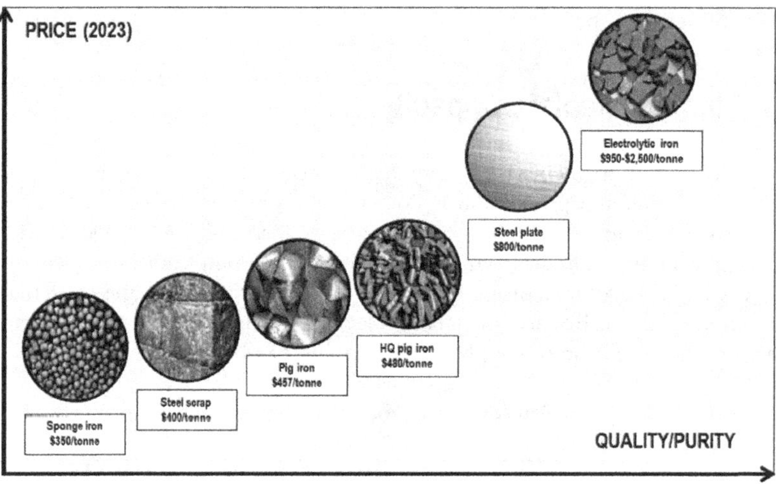

Figure 137 – Prices of selected iron product vs. purity and quality

19.3 Price of Copperas

Despite clean and pure copperas can be sold up to $150/tonne for wastewater treatment purposes or for the production red iron oxide pigment, most of the time tainted copperas is offered at less than $35/tonne. Moreover, for the copperas contained in pregnant leach solutions, spent pickling liquors, and metallurgical effluents as these sources always implies neutralization and disposal costs, that are prohibitive in certain locations, it can be shipped at no costs when by-produced to offset the previous costs. Therefore, we believe that the price of copperas has very little impact on the profitability.

19.4 Price and Oversupply of Sulfuric Acid

By contrast with the price of copperas, the price and supply for sulfuric acid strongly depend on the geographical location and the proximity to nearby copper, nickel, zinc smelters from which it is produced on a large scale. This explains the wide range of prices ranging from $50/tonne up to $150/tonne.

19.5 "What if" Analysis

For that purpose, we have conducted a sensitivity (i.e., "what if" analysis) on the net present worth from the four previous variables namely, the production cost, the selling price of iron and sulfuric acid, and finally, the price of copperas. The results from the calculations, using departures ranging from -20 up to +25 percent from the base case scenario adopted for the preliminary financial analysis, are tabulated in Table 172.

Table 173 – Sensitivity analysis

Sensitivity analysis								
Departure	**OPEX** (/tonne)	**NPV(12%)**	**Fe** (/tonne)	**NPV(12%)**	H_2SO_4 (/tonne)	**NPV(12%)**	**Copperas** (/tonne)	**NPV(12%)**
-20%	$265	$411,863,018	$760	-$311,230,989	$28	$264,869,180	$24	$378,767,505
-15%	$281	$376,945,494	$808	-$23,969,305	$30	$277,880,227	$26	$352,229,767
-10%	$298	$341,929,506	$855	$144,548,277	$32	$289,360,563	$27	$328,814,116
-5%	$314	$315,991,737	$903	$250,615,247	$33	$297,864,515	$29	$311,469,189
0%	**$331**	**$302,340,280**	**$950**	**$302,340,280**	**$35**	**$302,340,280**	**$30**	**$302,340,280**
5%	$347	$288,688,823	$998	$354,065,313	$37	$306,816,044	$32	$293,211,371
10%	$364	$260,020,762	$1,045	$456,611,336	$39	$316,215,150	$33	$274,040,663
15%	$380	$210,810,025	$1,093	$614,146,982	$40	$331,723,674	$35	$242,408,993
20%	$397	$122,722,598	$1,140	$855,701,639	$42	$355,503,410	$36	$193,074,698
25%	$413	-$45,376,467	$1,188	$1,196,890,216	$44	$388,135,925	$38	$108,146,038

Moreover, for convenience, we have also plotted the tabulated data that are depicted graphically in Figure 138.

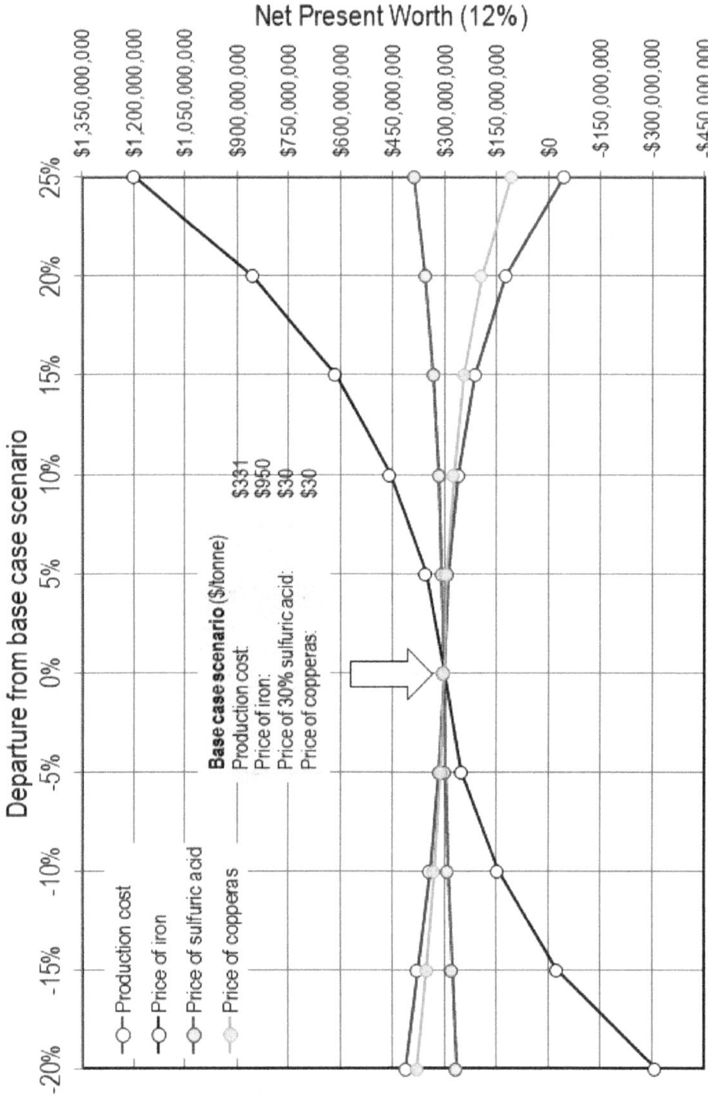

Figure 138 – Sensitivity analysis of the net present worth

19.6 Fluctuation of the Price of Iridium

The construction of an iron electrowinning plant involves a certain degree of risk that even a combination of careful assessment, experience and know how cannot eliminate. In this section we will review briefly one of the major technical and economic risks and propose solutions to mitigate it.

Actually, the profitability of the commercial iron electrowinning plant is directly related to the market price of iridium, and in a lesser extent on the prices of other platinum group metals (PGMs) used for the fabrication of the industrial mixed metals oxides (MMO) coated-titanium anodes.

Actually, the cost of mixed metals oxides (MMO) coated-titanium anodes for evolving oxygen accounts for $110/tonne of electrolytic iron produced. Thus with an OPEX of $330.00 per tonne this represents 30 percent of the entire production cost. This demonstrates the strong impact of the fluctuations of the price of iridium

Since the summer of 2020, the prices of iridium and ruthenium metals experienced a spectacular not to say historical increase. Actually, the prices of iridium and ruthenium have climbed to a record high of $6,400 and $550 per troy ounce respectively on May 14, 2021 from $1,660 and $280 respectively on August 17, 2020. At the time of completing the manuscript, the current prices are $4,950 and $475 per troy ounce respectively (October 18, 2023). The plot of the daily price of iridium metal over the last thirty years obtained from reputable sources (e.g, *BASF Bullion prices*, and *Johnson Matthey PGMs prices*) is depicted in Figure 139.

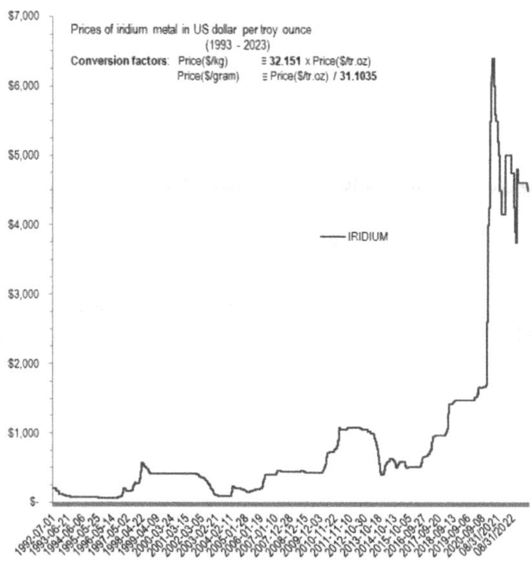

Figure 139 – Prices of iridium metal from 1992 to 2023

According to experts of platinum group metals (PGMs) this is mostly related to supply shortages due to the closure in 2020 of mines and production facilities in South Africa, and a lesser extend to the utilization of large iridium crucibles for growing high purity silicon ingots by the Czochralski crystal pulling technique. However, this could be only the tip of the iceberg as the recent fever for the production of green hydrogen gas by electrolysis especially using the proton exchange membrane (PEM) technology will fuel-up the iridium demand even further.

More importantly, mixed metals oxides (MMO) coated-titanium anodes, for evolving oxygen gas also use iridium, and are the preferred anodes several electrowinning processes. This peculiar situation is followed carefully as it could become unbearable for future end users to purchase expensive MMO-O_2 anodes in the near future.

Considering that both iridium, and ruthenium are treated as by-products in the production of PGMs mostly driven by the three metals namely platinum, palladium and rhodium, it is not certain that producers will ramp-up production to match the growing demand anytime soon and some experts say it can even worsen for the years to come.

Of course, the refurbishing of spent MMO anodes is sometimes offered to end users in order to extend the anode service life. However, the impact of refurbishing on the supply is rather limited. The major alternative to mitigate the cost of iridium-based anodes is to go back to the utilization of lead anodes. However, the latter solution is not ideal as lead anodes cannot withstand elevate anode current densities, and corrode over time generating hazardous sludge's inside the anode compartment.

Finally, it is worth to mention that *Electrochem Technologies & Materials Inc.* is a manufacturer of industrial anodes particularly mixed metals oxides (MMO) coated-titanium anodes. Thus during the last 14 years of extensive testing of the FerWIN® process, the company manufactured and tested all the MMO anodes, and thus collected a huge amount of information on the best mixed metals oxides formulations, the optimized catalyst loading, the service life under harsh acidic condition, and high current densities. Moreover, new iridium depleted coatings and modified substrates were succesfully commercialized to address the above issue. Finally, cheaper alternate precursors where also identified.

20 Bibliography

20.1 Electrochemical Data

ANTELMAN, M.S.; and HARRIS F.J. (1982) *The Encyclopedia of Chemical Electrode Potentials.* Plenum Press, New York, NY.

BARD, A.J.; PARSONS, R.; and JORDAN, J. (eds.) (1985) *Standard Potentials in Aqueous Solutions.* Marcell Dekker, New York.

BARD, A.J. (ed.)(1973-1986) *Encyclopedia of Electrochemistry of the Elements, 15 vol.* Marcel Dekker, New York, NY.

CHARLOT, G.; COLLUMEAU, A.; and MARCHON, J.C. (1971) *Selected Constants: Oxidation-reduction Potentials of Inorganic Substances in Aqueous Solution.* Butterworths, London, UK.

CONWAY, B.E. (1969) *Electrochemical Data.* Greenwood Press, Westport.

DOBOS, D. (1975) *Electrochemical Data: a Handbook for Electrochemists in Industry and Universities.* Elsevier, New York, NY.

DRAPER, C.R.; and PORTCULLIS (1975) *Tables and Operating Data for Electroplaters.* Redhill, England, UK.

GIBSON, J.G.; and SUDWORTH, J.L. (1973) *Specific Energies of Galvanic Reactions and Related Thermodynamic Data.* Chapman Hall, London, UK.

HAMPEL, C.A. (1964) *The Encyclopedia of Electrochemistry.* Reinhold, New York, NY.

HARNED. H.S.; and OWEN, B.B. (1958) *The Physical-Chemistry of Electrolytic Solutions, Third Edition.* American Chemical Society Monograph Series, Reinhold, New York, NY, pp. 592.

LOBO V.M.M. (1989) *Handbook of electrolyte solutions, 2 volumes (Part A and Part B)* Elsevier, New York, NY.

HORVATH, A.L. (1985) *Handbook of Aqueous Electrolyte Solutions: Physical Properties, Estimation and Correlation Methods.* Ellis Horwood Series in Physical Chemistry, Ellis Horwood Limited, Hemel Hempstead, UK.

MANSFIELD, C.W. (1960) *Oxidation and Reduction Potentials of Organic Systems.* William and Wilkins, Publishers, Baltimore, MD.

MILAZZO, G.; and CAROLI, S. (1978) *Tables of Standard Electrode Potentials.* John Wiley & Sons, New York, NY.

PARSONS, R. (1959) *Handbook of Electrochemical Constants.* Butterworths, London, UK, and Academic Press, New York, NY.

PITZER, K.S. (ed.) (1991) *Activity Coefficients in Electrolyte Solutions, Second Edition.* CRC Press, Boca Raton, FL.

POURBAIX, M. (1966) *Atlas of Electrochemical Equilibria.* Pergamon Press, New York, NY.

TAMAMUSHI, R. (1975) *Kinetic Parameters of Electrode Reactions of Metallic Compounds.* Butterworths, London, UK.

ZAYTSEV, I.D.; and ASEYEV, G.G. (eds.) (1992) *Properties of Aqueous Solutions of Electrolytes.* CRC Press, Boca Raton, FL.

ZEMAITIS, J.F.; CLARK, D.M.; RAFAL, M.; and SCRIVNER, N.C. (1986) *Handbook of Aqueous Electrolyte Thermodynamics: Theory and Applications.* Design Institute for Physical Property Data (DIPPD), *American Institute of Chemical Engineers* (AIChE), New York, NY.

20.2 Electrochemistry and Electrode Kinetics

ALBERY, J. (1975) *Electrode Kinetics.* Oxford University Press, London, NY.

ANTROPOV, L.I. (1977) *Theoretical Electrochemistry.* Mir Editions, Moscow, USSR.

BAGOTZKY, V.S. (1993) *Fundamentals of Electrochemistry.* Plenum Publishing Corporation, New York, NY.

BARD, A. J.; and FAULKNER, L.R. (1980) *Electrochemical Methods: Fundamentals and Applications.* John Wiley & Sons, New York, NY.

BESSON, J. (1984) *Précis de thermodynamique & cinétique électrochimiques.* Éditions Ellipses, Paris, France.

BESSON, J.; and Guitton, J. (1972) *Manipulations d'Électrochimie. Introduction a la théorie et a la pratique de la cinétique électrochimique.* Masson & Cie, Paris, France.

BOCKRIS, J.O'M.; and DRAZIC, D.M. (1972) *Electrochemical Science.* Taylor and Francis, London, U.K.

BRETT, C. M. A.; and BRETT, A. M. O. (1993) *Electrochemistry: Principles, Methods, and Applications.* Oxford University Press, U.K.

BUTLER, J.A.V. (1951) *Electrical phenomena at interfaces, in chemistry, physics and biology.* Methuen, London 1951.

CONWAY, B.E. (1965) *Theory and principles of electrode processes.* Ronald, New York, NY.

CROW, D. R. (1973) *Principles and Applications of Electrochemistry.* Chapman & Hall, London, U.K.

FRIED, I. (1973) *The Chemistry of Electrode Processes.* Academic Press, New York, NY.

FUOSS, R.M. and ACCASCINA, F. (1959) *Electrolytic Conductance.* Interscience, New York., NY

GILEADI, E. (1993) *Electrode Kinetics for Chemists, Chemical Engineers, and Materials Scientists.* VCH, New York, NY.

IVES, D.J.G.; and JANZ, G.J. (eds.)(1961) *Reference Electrodes: Theory and Practice.* Academic Press, New York, NY.

KORYTA, J.; and DVORAK, J. (1987) *Principles of Electrochemistry.* Wiley, New York, NY.

KORTÜM, G. (1965) *Treatise in Electrochemistry, Second Edition.* Elsevier, New York, NY.

LEVICH, V.G. (1962) *Physico-Chemical Hydrodynamics.* Prentice-Hall, Englewood Cliffs, NJ.

MACDONALD, D.D. (1977) *Transient techniques in electrochemistry.* Plenum Press, New York, NY.

MACINNES, D.A. (1961) *The principles of Electrochemistry.* Dover Publications, New York, NY.

MILAZZO, G. (1963) *Electrochemistry; Theoretical Principles and Practical Applications.* Elsevier, New York, NY.

MANSFIELD, D. (1974) *Electrochemistry.* Heinemann, London, U.K.

NEWMAN, J.S. (1973) *Electrochemical Systems.* Prentice-Hall, Englewood Cliffs, NJ.

OLDHAM, K.B.; and MYLAND, J.C. (1993) *Fundamentals of Electrochemical Science.* Academic Press, New York, NY.

RIEGER, P.H. (1987) *Electrochemistry.* Prentice-Hall, Englewood Cliffs, NJ.

ROCHOW, R. (1965) *Electrochemistry.* Reinhold, New York, NY.

TAMAMUSHI, R. (1975) *Kinetic Parameters of Electrode Reactions of Metallic Compounds.* Butterworths, London, U.K.

VETTER, K.J. (1967) *Electrochemical Kinetics: Theoretical and Experimental Aspects.* Academic Press, New York, NY.

WEST, J.M. (1973) *Basic Electrochemistry.* Van Nostrand Reinhold, London, U.K.

20.3 Electrochemical Engineering

DECONINCK, J. (1992) *Current Distributions and Electrode Shape Changes in Electrochemical Systems.* Springer-Verlag, Berlin, Germany.

FAHIDY, T.Z. (1985) *Principles of Electrochemical Reactor Analysis.* Elsevier (Chemical Engineering Monographs, Vol. 18), New York, NY.

GALLONE, P. (1973) *Trattato di ingegneria elettrochimica.* Tamburini editore, Milan, Italy.

GOODRIDGE, F.; and SCOTT, K. (1995) *Electrochemical Process Engineering: a Guide to the Design of Electrolytic Plant.* Plenum Press, New York, NY.

HINE, F. (1985) *Electrode Processes and Electrochemical Engineering.* Plenum, New York, NY.

ISMAIL, M.I.(ed)(1989) *Electrochemical Reactors: Science and Technology.* Elsevier, New York, NY.

MANTELL, C.L. (1960) *Electrochemical Engineering, Fourth edition.* McGraw-Hill Book Company, New York, NY.

PICKETT, D.J. (1977) *Electrochemical Reactor Design.* Elsevier (Chemical Engineering Monographs, Vol. 9), New York, NY.

ROUSAR, I.; MICKA, K.; and KIMLA, A. (1986) *Electrochemical Engineering, 2 vol. (Part. A-D, Part. D-F).* Elsevier (Chemical Engineering Monographs, 21B), New York, NY.

SCOTT, K. (1991) *Electrochemical Reaction Engineering.* Academic Press, New York, NY.

WENDT, H., and KREYSA, G. (1999) *Electrochemical Engineering: Science and Technology in Chemical and other Industries.* Springer, Berlin, Germany.

20.4 Industrial Electrochemistry and Electrosynthesis

GENDERS, J.D.; and PLETCHER, D. (1991) *Electrosynthesis from Laboratory, to Pilot, to Production.* Electrosynthesis Company Inc., East Amherst, NY.

GENDERS, J.D.; and WEINBERG, N.L. (1992) *Electrochemistry for a Cleaner Environment.* Electrosynthesis Company Inc., East Amherst, NY.

HALE, A.J. (1919) *The Manufacture of Chemicals by Electrolysis.* Constable, London, UK

KUHN, A.T. (Ed) (1971) *Industrial Electrochemical Processes.* Elsevier, New York, NY.

MANTELL, C.L. (1950) *Industrial Electrochemistry, Third Edition.* McGraw-Hill Book Company, New York, NY.

OTTEWILL, R.K.; LYKLEMA, J.; and PARSONS, R. (1972) *Industrial Electrochemistry.* Elsevier, New York, NY.

MILAZZO, G. (1963) *Electrochemistry; Theoretical Principles and Practical Applications.* Elsevier, New York, NY.

PLETCHER, D.; and WALSH, F.C. (1990) *Industrial Electrochemistry*, Second Edition. Chapman Hall, London, UK.

REGNER, A. (1957) *Electrochemical Processes in Chemical Industries.* Constable, London, UK

RIDEAL, E.K. (1918) *Industrial Electrometallurgy including Electrolytic and Electrothermal Processes.* Baliere, Tindall and Cox, London, UK.

20.5 Electroplating and Electrodeposition

AVERKIN, V.A.; and DAVEY, R. (1965) *Electrolytic Deposition of Alloys.* Mir Editions, New York, NY.

BOCKRIS, J.O'M.; and RAZUMNEY, G.A. (1967) *Fundamental Aspects of Electrocrystallization.* Plenum Press, New York, NY.

BRENNER, A. (1963) *Electrodeposition of Alloys: Principles and Practice (2 Vol).* Academic Press, New York, NY.

CANNING, W. (ed.)(1978) *Handbook of electroplating.* W. Canning Limited, London, UK.

DUFFY, J.I. (1982) *Electrodeposition Processes, Equipment, and Compositions.* Noyes Data Corp., Park Ridge, NJ.

DURNEY, L.J. (ed.)(1984) *Electroplating Engineering Handbook, Fourth Edition.* Van Nostrand Reinhold, New York, NY.

GRAHAM A.K. (ed.)(1962) *Electroplating Engineering Handbook.* Reinhold, New York, NY.

GRAY, A.G. (1953) *Modern Electroplating.* John Wiley and Sons, New York, NY.

KISS, L. (1988) *Kinetics of Electrochemical Metal Dissolution.* Elsevier, New York, NY.

LOWENHEIM, F.A. (ed.)(1974) *Modern Electroplating, Third Edition.* Wiley, New York, NY.

RAUB, E.; and MULLER, K. (1967) *Fundamentals of Metal Deposition.* Elsevier, New York, NY.

RODGERS, T.M. (1959) *Handbook of Practical Electroplating.* Macmillan, New York, NY.

SAFRANEK, W.H.(ed.)(1974) *The Properties of Electrodeposited Metals and Alloys.* Elsevier, New York, NY.

20.6 Plant Economics and Financial Analysis

ARIES, R.S., and NEWTON, R.D, K.D. (1955) *Chemical Engineering Cost Estimation.* (McGraw-Hill Chemical Engineering Series) McGraw-Hill Book Company, Inc., New York, NY.

CHILTON, C.H. (1960) *Cost Engineering in the Process Industries.* McGraw-Hill Book Company, New York, NY.

HUMPHREYS, K.K. (1991) *Jelen's Cost and Optimization Engineering, Third Edition.* McGraw-Hill, New York, NY.

PARK, C.S; ZUO, M.J.; and PELOT, R. (2012) *Contemporary Engineering Economics, a Canadian Perspective, Third Canadian Edition.* Pearson Canada, Toronto, Canada.

PETERS, M.S., and TIMMERHAUS, K.D. (1980) *Plant Design and Economics for the Chemical Engineers, Third Edition.* (McGraw-Hill Chemical Engineering Series) McGraw-Hill Book Company, Nbrandtew York, NY.

VILBRANDT, F.C. (1949) *Chemical Engineering Plant Design.* (McGraw-Hill Chemical Engineering Series) McGraw-Hill Book Company, New York, NY.

21 Appendices

21.1 Scientific and Technical Acronyms

Table 174 – List of scientific and technical acronyms

Acronyms	Description
ACD	Anode current density
ACE	Anode current efficiency
AEM	Anion exchange membrane
APU	Acid retardation unit
ATH	Aluminum trihydrate
BRs	Bauxite residues
BSE	Batch stirred electrolyzer
CAS No.	Chemical Abstract Service Registry Number
CCD	Cathode current density
CCE	Cathode current efficiency
CEM	Cation exchange membrane
CPVC	Chlorinated-polyvinylchloride
CSE	Continuous stirred electrolyzer
emf	Electromotive force
EPDM	Ethylene propylene diene monomer
GHGs	Greenhouse gases
gpm	Gallons (US) per minute
HDPE	High density polyethylene
HER	Hydrogen gas evolution reaction
HX	Heat exchanger
IEC	*International Electrotechnical Commission*
IR	Infrared electromagnetic radiation
MMO	Mixed metals oxides coated anodes
mpy	mils per year
O.V.	Oil of Vitriol
OER	Oxygen gas evolution reaction
ORP	Oxidation-reduction potential
P&ID	Process and instrumentation diagram
PE	Polyethylene
PFA	Perfluoroalkoxy
PFE	Plug flow electrolyzer
pH	Potential hydrogen
PLS	Pregnant leach solution
PP	Polypropylene

Acronyms	Description
PPE	Personal protective equipment
PTFE	Polytetrafluoroethylene
PVC	Polyvinylchloride
PVDF	Polyvinylidene fluoride
RM	Red mud
S.G.	Specific gravity
SEC	Specific energy consumption
SHE	Standard hydrogen electrode
SI	*Système International d'Unités*
SPL	Spent pickling liquor
STP	Standard temperature and pressure conditions
STY	Space time yield
tpa	Tonnes per annum
USCS	*U.S. Customary System*
YSZ	Yttria stabilized zirconia

21.2 Economic and Financial Acronyms

Table 175 – List of economic and financial acronyms

Acronyms	Description
AEC	Annual cash equivalent
C	Production cost
CAPEX	Capital expenditures
D	Annual depreciation
E	Fixed cost or operating expenses
EBITDA	Earnings, before income tax, depreciation, and amortization
EH&S	Environmental, Health & Safety
FCI	Fixed capital investment
G	Gross profit, operating income
GPM	Gross profit margin
I	Fixed capital investment
i	Interest rate
IAT	Income after taxes
IRR	Internal rate of return
MARR	Minimum acceptable rate of return
NP	Net profit
NPM	Net profit margin
NPV	Net present value
NPW	Net present worth
O	Operating cost
OPEX	Operating cost
PB	Payback time
PV	Present value
PW	Present worth

Acronyms	Description
R	Revenue
ROI	Return on investment
S	Salvage value
TCI	Total capital investment
TI	Taxable income
WC	Working capital

21.3 Latin and Greek Symbols

Table 176 – Latin symbols

Symbol and acronym	Physical Quantity	SI unit (Practical)	USCS unit
°Bé	Baume degree	none	none
A	Active electrode surface area	m^2	ft^2
a_A	First Tafel's anode coefficient	V	V
a_C	First Tafel's cathode coefficient	V	V
ACD	Anode current density	A/m^2	A/ft^2
ACE	Faradaic anode current efficiency	none	none
a_e	Electrode specific surface area	m^{-1}	ft^{-1}
a_k	Activity	none	none
b_A	Second Tafel's anode coefficient	$V/\log_{10}\|j\|$	$V/\log_{10}\|j\|$
b_C	Second Tafel's cathode coefficient	$V/\log_{10}\|j\|$	$V/\log_{10}\|j\|$
b_k	Molality of solute k	mol/kg	lb-mol/lb
B_k	Absolute electrical (ionic) mobility	s/kg	s/lb
CCD	Cathode current density	A/m^2	A/ft^2
CCE	Faradaic cathode current efficiency	none	none
CE	Faradaic current efficiency	none	none
c_k	Molarity of species k	$mol.m^{-3}$	$lb\text{-}mol.ft^{-3}$ (lb-mol/gal)
C	Capacitance	F	F
C_k	Mass concentration of species k	$kg.m^{-3}$	$lb.ft^{-3}$ (lb/gal)
c_p	Specific heat capacity (isobar)	J/kg/K	Btu/lb/°R
D_H	Hydrodynamic diameter	m	ft
D_k	Diffusion coefficient of species k	$m^2.s^{-1}$	$ft^2.s^{-1}$
D_T	Thermodiffusion coefficient of species k	$m^2.s^{-1}.K^{-1}$	$ft^2.s^{-1}.°R^{-1}$
E	Nernst electrode potential	V/SHE	V/SHE
$\mathbf{E}$	Electric field strength	V/m	V/ft
E_F	Fermi energy	J(eV)	Btu
e_{gap}	Inter electrode gap	m	ft (in)

Symbol and acronym	Physical Quantity	SI unit (Practical)	USCS unit
e_m	Specific energy consumption	J/kg(kWh/kg)	kWh/lb
e_v	Volumetric energy consumption	J/m³(kWh/m³)	kWh/ft³(kWh/gal)
$E^0_{298.15K}$	Nernst standard electrode potential	V/SHE	V/SHE
E_{qm}	Gravimetric (specific) electrochemical equivalent	C/kg (Ah/kg)	C/lb (Ah/lb)
E_{qv}	Volumetric electrochemical equivalent	C/m³ (Ah/m³)	C/ft³ (Ah/gal)
g	Specific Gibbs enthalpy	J/kg	Btu/lb
G	Molar Gibbs enthalpy	J/mol	Btu/mol
G	Molar Gibbs free enthalpy	J/mol	Btu/lb-mol
g	Specific Gibbs free enthalpy	J/kg	Btu/lb
G_k	Mass velocity of species k	$mol.m^{-2}.s^{-1}$	$lb.ft^{-2}.s^{-1}$
g_n	Standard acceleration of gravity	$9.80665\ m.s^{-2}$	$31.17405\ ft.s^{-2}$
h	Specific enthalpy	J/kg	Btu/lb
H	Molar enthalpy	J/mol	Btu/mol
H	Molar enthalpy	J/mol	Btu/lb-mol
h	Specific enthalpy	J/kg	Btu/lb
I	Electric current	A	A
I_C	Ionic strength (molar basis)	mol/m^3	lb-mol/gal
I_m	Ionic strength (molality basis)	mol/kg	lb-mol/lb
j	Electric current density	A/m^2	A/ft^2
j_a	Anode current density	A/m^2	A/ft^2
j_c	Cathode current density	A/m^2	A/ft^2
J_k	Molar flux of species k	$mol.m^{-2}.s^{-1}$	$lb\text{-}mol.ft^{-2}.s^{-1}$
k	Thermal conductivity	W/m/K	(Btu/h)/ft/°R
K_a	Acidity constant	none	none
k_D	Specific refractivity (λ_D = 589.3 nm)	m^3/kg	ft^3/lb
K_D	Specific refraction (λ_D = 589.3 nm)	m^3/kg	ft^3/lb
k_m	Mass transfer coefficient	s^{-1}	s^{-1}
Kp	Equilibrium constant	none	none
Kw	Autoprotolysis constant for water	none	none
M	Molar mass	kg/kmol	lb/lb-mol
m	Mass flow rate	kg/s	lb/s
m_k	Molality	mol/kg	lb-mol/lbm
m_k	Mass of particle k	kg	lb
M_r	Relative molar mass (^{12}C = 12.000)	none	none
n_D	Refractive index (λ_D = 589.3 nm)	none	none
n_k	Particle density of species k	m^{-3}	ft^{-3}
pH	Potential hydrogen	none	none

Symbol and acronym	Physical Quantity	SI unit (Practical)	USCS unit
q	Electrostatic (electric) charge	C	Ah
Q	Quantity of heat	J	Btu
Q_v	Volume flow rate	m^3/s (L/min)	ft^3/s (gal/min)
R	Electrical resistance	Ω	ohm
n_D	Molar refractivity (λ_D = 589.3 nm)	m^3/mol	ft^3/lb-mol
R_p	Resistance of polarization	Ω/m^2	ohm/in^2
s	Specific entropy	J/kg/K	Btu/lb-m/°R
S	Molar entropy	J/mol/K	Btu/lb-mol/°R
S	Entropy	J/K	Btu/°R
s	Solubility (molar)	mol/m^3	$lb\text{-}mol/ft^3$
s	Specific entropy	J/kg/K	Btu/lb/°R
S_A	Solubility	g/100 g solvent	lb/lb of solvent
SEC	Specific energy consumption	J/kg (kWh/kg)	kWh/lb
S_T	Soret coefficient	K^{-1}	$°R^{-1}$
STY	Space time yield	$kg.m^{-2}.s^{-1}$ ($kg.m^{-2}.h^{-1}$)	$lb.ft^{-2}.h^{-1}$
T	Thermodynamic (absolute) temperature	K	°R
T_b, *b.p.*	Boiling (vaporizing) point	K	°R
t_k	Transport number of species k	none	none
T_m, *m.p.*	Melting (freezing) point	K	°R
u	Fluid velocity	m/s	ft/s
U	Overall heat transfer coefficient	$W.m^{-2}.K^{-1}$	$(Btu/h).ft^{-2}.°R^{-1}$
U	Molar internal energy	J/mol	Btu/lb-mol
u	Specific internal energy	J/kg	Btu/lb
U_{cell}	Overall cell voltage	V	V
u_k	Electrical (ionic) mobility	$m^2.s^{-1}.V^{-1}$	$ft^2.s^{-1}.V^{-1}$
u_k	Terminal velocity of species k	m/s	ft/s
U_{th}	Thermodynamic cell voltage	V	V
VEC	Volumetric energy consumption	$J/m^3(kWh/m^3)$	kWh/ft^3(kWh/gal)
W	Work	J	$lb.ft^{-2}.s^{-2}$ (lb_f-ft)
w_k	Mass fraction of species k	none	none
W_S	Electron work function	J (eV)	$lb.ft^{-2}.s^{-2}$ (lb_f-ft)
x_k	Molar fraction of species k	none	none
X_k	Fractional conversion rate	none	none
Y_m	Space time yield	$kg.m^{-2}.s^{-1}$ ($kg.m^{-2}.h^{-1}$)	$lb.ft^{-2}.h^{-1}$
Z	Impedance	Ω	ohm

Table 177 – Greek symbols

Greek symbol	Physical Quantity	SI unit	USCS unit
α	Degree of ionization	none	none
χ_α	Electrochemical potential	V	V
δ	Thickness of the Nernst diffusion layer	m	m
ΔE_J	Liquid junction potential	V	V
ΔT_{LMTD}	Logarithmic mean temperature difference	K	°R
ΔU_{cell}	Overall cell voltage	V	V
ΔU_τ	Cell potential drift	V	V
ΔU_{th}	Thermodynamic (Reversible) cell voltage	V	V
ε	Dielectric permittivity	none	none
ε_E	Energy efficiency	none	none
ε_I	Faradaic (current) efficiency	none	none
ε_U	Voltaic (potential) efficiency	none	none
ϕ_k	Particle flux density of species k	$mol.m^{-2}.s^{-1}$	$lb\text{-}mol.ft^{-2}.s^{-1}$
Φ	Galvani (inner) electric potential	V	V
Λ_0	Equivalent electrical conductivity (Equivalent conductance) at infinite dilution	$S.m^2.eq^{-1}$	$S.ft^2.eq^{-1}$
Λeq	Equivalent electrical conductivity (Equivalent conductance)	$S.m^2.eq^{-1}$	$S.ft^2.eq^{-1}$
Λm	Molar electrical conductivity (molar conductance)	$S.m^2.mol^{-1}$	$S.ft^2.lb\text{-}mol^{-1}$
η	Dynamic (absolute) viscosity	Pa.s	$lbf\text{-}s/ft^2$
η	Overvoltage (overpotential)	V	V
κ	Electrical conductivity	S/m	S/ft
Ψ	Volta (outer) electric potential	V	V
$\mu(a_k)$	Standard chemical potential (molar basis)	J/mol	Btu/lb-mol
$\mu(m_k)$	Standard chemical potential (molality basis)	J/mol	Btu/lb-mol
$\mu(n_k)$	Standard chemical potential (particle basis)	J/mol	Btu/lb-mol
μ^0	Standard chemical potential	J/mol	Btu/lb-mol
ν	Kinematic viscosity	$m^2.s^{-1}$	$ft^2.s^{-1}$
π	Vapor pressure	Pa	lbf/ft^2
ρ	Mass density	kg/m^3	lb/ft^3
σ	Surface tension	J/m^2	Btu/ft^2

Greek symbol	Physical Quantity	SI unit	USCS unit
τ_R	Residence time	s	s
ω_k	Absolute electrical (ionic) mobility	mol.s/kg	lb-mol.s/lb

21.4 Selected Universal Constants (CODATA, 2018)

The 2018 CODATA recommended values of the constants provided hereafter in Table 178 are recommended for international use by CODATA and are the latest available.

Table 178 – Selected universal constants (CODATA, 2018)

Constant	Symbol	SI value
atomic mass unit	u, uma, m_u	u = 1.66053906660(50) × 10^{-27} kg u = 931.49410242(28) MeV/c^2
Avogadro's constant	N_A, L	N_A = 6.02214076 × 10^{23} mol^{-1}
Bohr magneton (B.M., μ_B)	$\mu_B = eh/4\pi m_e$	μ_B = 9.2740100783(28) × 10^{-24} $J.T^{-1}$ μ_B = 5.7883818060(17) × 10^{-5} $eV.T^{-1}$
Boltzmann's constant	$k = R/N_A$	k = 1.380649 × 10^{-23} $J.K^{-1}$ k = 8.617333262 × 10^{-5} $eV.K^{-1}$
Celerity of light in vacuum	c, c_0	c_0 = 2.99792458 × 10^8 $m.s^{-1}$(defined)
Electron rest mass	m_e	m_e = 9.1093837015(28) × 10^{-31} kg m_e = 5.48579909065(16) × 10^{-4} u m_e = 0.51099895000(15) MeV/c^2
Elementary electric charge	e	e = 1.602176634 × 10^{-19} C
Faraday's constant	$F = N_A e$	F = 96,485.33212 $C.mol^{-1}$
First Bohr atomic radius	$a_0 = 4\pi\varepsilon_0 h^2/m_e e^2$	a_0 = 5.29177210903(80)(57) × 10^{-11} m
First radiation constant	$c_1 = 2\pi hc^2$	c_1 = 3.741771852 × 10^{-16} $W.m^2$
Ideal gas molar constant	R	R = 8.314462618 $J.mol^{-1}.K^{-1}$
molar Planck's constant	$N_A h$	$N_A h$ = 3.990312712 × 10^{-10} $J.s.mol^{-1}$
Newtonian constant of gravitation	G	G = 6.67430(15) × 10^{-11} $N.kg^{-2}.m^2$
Permeability of vacuum	$\mu_0 = 1/(\varepsilon_0 c^2)$	μ_0 = 4π × 10^{-7} $H.m^{-1}$ (defined)

Constant	Symbol	SI value
		$\mu_0 = 1.25663706212 \times 10^{-6}$ H.m^{-1}
Permittivity of vacuum	$\varepsilon_0=1/(\mu_0 c^2)$	$\varepsilon_0 = 8.85418781758 \times 10^{-12}$ F.m^{-1}
Planck's constant	h	$h = 6.62607015 \times 10^{-34}$ J.s $h = 4.135667696 \times 10^{-15}$ eV.s
Planck's constant (rationalized)	$\hbar=h/2\pi$	$\hbar = 1.054571817 \times 10^{-34}$ J.s $\hbar = 6.582119569 \times 10^{-16}$ eV.s
proton rest mass	m_p	$m_p = 1.67262192369(51) \times 10^{-27}$ kg
Second radiation constant	$c_2=hc/k$	$c_2 = 1.438776877 \times 10^{-3}$ K
Speed of light in vacuum	c	$c = 2.99792458 \times 10^{8}$ m.s^{-1} (defined)
Standard acceleration of gravity	g_n	$g_n = 9.80665$ m.s^{-2} (defined)
Standard atmosphere	p_0	$p_0 = 101{,}325$ Pa (defined)
standard molar volume (STP) (ideal gas) [273.15K, 101325 Pa]	$V_0=RT_0/p_0$	$V_0 = 22.41396954 \times 10^{-3}$ m^3.mol^{-1}
standard molar volume (STP) (ideal gas) [273.15K, 100 kPa]	$V_0=RT_0/p_0$	$V_0 = 22.\ 71095464 \times 10^{-3}$ m^3.mol^{-1}
Stefan-Boltzmann's constant	$\sigma=(\pi^2/60)(k^4/\hbar^3c^2)$	$\sigma = 5.670374419 \times 10^{-8}$ W.m^{-2}.K^{-4}

21.5 Conversion Factors

Table 179 – Selected conversion factors

Physical quantity	SI unit	Conversion factor(s)
Mass [M]	kg	1 atomic mass unit (u) = (1/12) m_{12C} = 1.66053873 x 10^{-27} kg 1microgram (μg) = 10^{-9} kg (E) 1 gamma (γ) = 10^{-9} kg (E) 1 milligram (mg) = 10^{-6} kg (E) 1 gram (g) = 10^{-3} kg (E) 1 pennyweight (dwt) = 1/20 oz tr (E) = 1.55517384 x 10^{-3} kg 1 drachm (dr. tr.) = 1/8 ounce troy (E) = 3.8879346 x 10^{-3} kg 1 ounce troy (oz tr) = 1/12 lb (troy) (E) = 31.1034768 x 10^{-3} kg 1 pound troy (lb tr) = 5760 grains (E) = 0.3732417216 kg 1 pound avdp (lb) = 7000 grains (E) = 0.45359237 kg (E) 1 kilopond (kip) = 1 TMU (E) = 9.80665 kg (E) 1 metric ton unit (mtu) = 1/10 tonne (E)= 10 kg (E) 1 short ton unit (shtu) = 1/10 short ton (E) = 20 lb (E) = 9.0718474 kg 1 long ton unit (lgtu) = 1/10 long ton (E) = 22.4 lb (E) = 10.16046909 kg 1 slug (gee-pound) = 14.5939029372 kg 1 flask (UK, mercury) = 76 lb (E) = 34.47302012 kg 1 bag (UK, cement) = 94 lb (E) = 42.63768278 kg (E) 1 hundredweight (short) = 100 lb (E) = 45.359237 kg (E) 1 bag (US, cement) = 100 lb (E) = 45.359237 kg (E) 1 hundredweight (gross) = 112 lb (E) = 50.80234544 kg 1 quintal (metric) = 100 kg (E) 1 short ton (sht)= 2000 lb (E) = 907.1847 kg 1 tonne (t) = 1 metric ton = 1000 kg (E) 1 long ton (lgt)= 2240 lb (E) = 1016.0469 kg
Length [L]	m	1 Angstrom (A) = 10^{-10} m (E) 1 nanometer (nm) = 10^{-9} m (E) 1 micrometer (μm) = 10^{-6} m (E) 1 millinch = 1 mil = 1 thou = 10^{-3} inch (E) = 25.4 μm (E) 1 caliber = 10^{-2} inch (E) = 2.54 x 10^{-4} m (E) 1 millimeter (mm) = 10^{-3} m 1 centimeter (cm)= 10^{-2} m (E) 1 inch (in) = 2.54 x 10^{-2} m (E) 1 inch (US, Survey) = (1/39.37) m (E) = 2.54000508001 x 10^{-2} m 1 foot (ft) = 12 inches (E) = 0.3048 m (E) 1 foot (US, Survey) = 12 inches (US, Survey) (E) = 0.30480060696 m 1 cubit (cu) = 18 inches (E) = 0.4572 m (E) 1 yard (yd) = 3 feet (E) = 36 inches (E) = 0.9144 m 1 mile (statute) = 5,280 feet (E) = 1609.344 m (E) 1 mile (nautical international) = 1852 m (E) 1 mile (nautical UK) = 6080 feet (E) = 1853.184 m (E)
Surface area [L^2]	m^2	1 square inch (in^2) = 645.16 x 10^{-6} m^2 (E) 1 square foot (ft^2) = 92.9034 x 10^{-3} m^2 (E) 1 acre = 4,840 square yards (E) = 43,560 ft^2 (E) = 4,046.856422 m^2 1 acre (US, Survey) = 4,840 square yards (US, Survey) (E) = 4,046.87261 m^2
Volume,	m^3	1 cubic millimetre (mm^3) = 10^{-9} m^3 (E)

Physical quantity	SI unit	Conversion factor(s)
capacity $[L^3]$		1 microlitre (μL) = 10^{-9} m^3 (E) 1 lambda (λ) = 10^{-9} m^3 (E) 1 drop (drp) = 1/480 fl oz (E) = 61.61152 x 10^{-9} m^3 1 cubic centimetre (cm^3) = 10^{-6} m^3 (E) 1 millilitre (mL) = 10^{-6} m^3 (E) 1 cubic inch (in^3) = 16.387064 x 10^{-6} m^3 1 fluid ounce (US fl oz) = 1/128 gal (US liq) (E) = 29.57352956 x 10^{-6} m^3 1 fluid ounce (UK fl oz) = 1/160 gal (UKS liq) (E) = 28.413075 x 10^{-6} m^3 1 litre (L) = 1 dm^3 (E) = 10^{-3} m^3 (E) 1 board foot measure (bfm) = 1/12 ft^3 (E) = 2.359737216 x 10^{-3} m^3 1 gallon (US, liq) = 231 in^3 (E) = 3.785411784 x 10^{-3} m^3 1 gallon (US, dry) = 268.8025 in^3 (E) = 4.40488377086 x 10^{-3} m^3 1 gallon (UK) = 4.546092 x 10^{-3} m^3 1 cubic foot (ft^3) = 28.316846592 x 10^{-3} m^3 1 barrel (US, oil) = 42 gal (US, liq) = 158.987294928 x 10^{-3} m^3
Time [T]	s	1 minute (min) = 60 s (E) 1 hour (h) = 60 min (E) = 3600 s (E) 1 day (d) = 24 h (E) = 86400 s (E) 1 year (a) = 365 days (E) = 3.1536 x 10^7 s (E)
Density $[ML^{-3}]$	kg.m^{-3}	1 pound per cubic foot (lb.ft^{-3}) = 16.0184634 kg.m^{-3} 1 pound per gallon (lb.gal^{-1}) = 119.826427 kg.m^{-3} 1 gee-pound per cubic foot (slug.ft^{-3}) = 515.3788184 kg.m^{-3} (E) 1 gram per cubic centimeter (g.cm^{-3}) = 1000 kg.m^{-3} (E) 1 kilogram per cubic centimeter (kg.dm^{-3}) = 1000 kg.m^{-3} (E) 1 tonne per cubic meter (tonne.m^{-3}) = 1000 kg.m^{-3} (E) 1 pound per cubic inch (lb.in^{-3}) = 27,679.90447102 kg.m^{-3} (E)
Pressure, stress $[ML^{-1}T^{-2}]$	Pa	1 barye = 1 dyn.cm^{-2} (E) = 0.1 Pa (E) 1 micrometer of mercury (μmHg) = 0.133322368421 Pa 1 newton per square metre (N.m^{-2}) = 1 Pa (E) 1 Torr = 1 mmHg(0°C) = 133.322368421 Pa 1 kilopascal (kPa) = 10^6 Pa (E) 1 centimeter of mercury (cmHg) = 1.33322368421 kPa 1 inch of mercury (inHg) = 3.38638815789 kPa 1 pound-force per square inch (psi) = 1 lb$_f$.in^{-2} (E) = 6.89475527293 kPa 1 kilogram-force per square centimeter (kg$_f$.cm^{-2}) = 98.0665 kPa (E) 1 bar = 100 kPa (E) 1 technical atmosphere (at) = 100 kPa (E) 1 atmosphere (atm) = 101.325 kPa (E) 1 megapascal (MPa) = 10^6 Pa (E) 1 kilopound per square inch (ksi) = 1 kip.in^{-2} (E) = 1000 psi (E) = 6.8947529317 MPa 1 ton per square inch (tsi) = 1 ton.in^{-2} (E) = 2000 psi (E) = 13.7895145863 MPa 1 gigapascal (GPa) = 10^9 Pa (E)
Energy, work $[ML^2T^{-2}]$	J	1 electron-volt (eV) = 1.602176462 x 10^{-19} J 1 erg = 1 dyne.cm (E) = 10^{-7} J (E) 1 calorie (therm) = 4.1840 J (E) 1 calorie (15°C) = 4.1855 J 1 calorie (IT) = 4.18674 J 1 calorie (mean) = 4.19002 J

Physical quantity	SI unit	Conversion factor(s)
		1 kilojoule (kJ) = 1000 J (E) 1 British thermal unit (39°F) = 1059.67 J 1 British thermal unit (60°F) = 1054.678 J 1 British thermal unit (ISO) = 1055.06 J (E) 1 British thermal unit (IT) = 1055.05585262 J (E) 1 British thermal unit (mean) = 1055.87 J 1 British thermal unit (therm) = 1054. 35026449 J 1 pound centigrade unit (pcu) = 1.8 Btu (IT) (E) = 1.8991008 kJ 1 watt-hour (Wh) = 3600 J (E) 1 kilowatt-hour (kWh) = 3.6 MJ (E) 1 therm (EEG) = 10^5 Btu (IT)(E) = 105.505585262 M J 1 million Btu (MMBtu) = 10^6 Btu (IT) (E) = 1.055056 GJ (E) 1tonne of TNT = 4.184 GJ 1 barrel oil equivalent (bboe) = 6.12 GJ 1 tonne coal equivalent (tce) = 7 Gigacalories (therm) (E) = 29.288 GJ (E) 1 tonne oil equivalent = 10 Gigacalories (therm) (E) = 41.840 GJ (E) 1 quadrillion Btu (quad) = 10^{15} Btu (IT) (E) = 1.05505585262 E J 1 Q-unit = 10^{18} Btu(IT) (E) = 1.05505585262 ZJ
Power	W	1 cheval-vapeur (CV) = 75 kg_f.m/s (E) = 735.49875 W (E) 1 horsepower (hp) = 550 lb_f.ft/s (E) = 745.699871581 W 1 kilowatt = 1000 W (E) 1 horsepower (boiler) = 1000 kg_f.m/s (E) = 9,806.65 W (E)
CARDARELLI, F. (2005) *Encyclopaedia of Scientific Units, Weights and Measures. Their SI equivalences and Origins.* Springer, New York, Heidelberg, London.		

21.6 Standard Relative Atomic Masses

Table 180 – Standard Relative Atomic Masses

1	H	hydrogen	1.00794	24	Cr	chromium	51.99610	47	Ag	silver	107.86820	70	Yb	ytterbium	173.04000
2	He	helium	4.00260	25	Mn	manganese	54.93805	48	Cd	cadmium	112.41100	71	Lu	lutetium	174.96700
3	Li	lithium	6.94100	26	Fe	iron	55.84500	49	In	indium	114.81800	72	Hf	hafnium	178.49000
4	Be	beryllium	9.01218	27	Co	cobalt	58.93320	50	Sn	tin	118.71000	73	Ta	tantalum	180.94790
5	B	boron	10.81100	28	Ni	nickel	58.69340	51	Sb	antimony	121.76000	74	W	tungsten	183.84000
6	C	carbon	12.01100	29	Cu	copper	63.54600	52	Te	tellurium	127.60000	75	Re	rhenium	186.20700
7	N	nitrogen	14.00674	30	Zn	zinc	65.39000	53	I	iodine	126.90447	76	Os	osmium	190.23000
8	O	oxygen	15.99940	31	Ga	gallium	69.72300	54	Xe	xenon		77	Ir	iridium	192.22000
9	F	fluorine	18.99840	32	Ge	germanium	72.61000	55	Cs	caesium	132.90545	78	Pt	platinum	195.08000
10	Ne	neon	20.17970	33	As	arsenic	74.92160	56	Ba	barium	137.32700	79	Au	gold	196.96659
11	Na	sodium	22.98977	34	Se	selenium	78.96000	57	La	lanthanum	138.90550	80	Hg	mercury	200.59000
12	Mg	magnesium	24.30500	35	Br	bromine	79.90400	58	Ce	cerium	140.11600	81	Tl	thallium	204.38330
13	Al	aluminium	26.98154	36	Kr	krypton	83.80000	59	Pr	praseodymiu	140.90765	82	Pb	lead	207.20000
14	Si	silicon	28.08550	37	Rb	rubidium	85.46780	60	Nd	neodymium	144.24000	83	Bi	bismuth	208.98038
15	P	phosphorus	30.97376	38	Sr	strontium	87.62000	61	Pm	promethium	145.00000	84	Po	polonium	
16	S	sulfur	32.06600	39	Y	yttrium	88.90590	62	Sm	samarium	150.36000	85	At	astatine	
17	Cl	chlorine	35.45270	40	Zr	zirconium	91.22400	63	Eu	europium	151.96400	86	Rn	radon	222.00000
18	Ar	argon	39.94800	41	Nb	niobium	92.90638	64	Gd	gadolinium	157.25000	87	Fr	francium	
19	K	potassium	39.09830	42	Mo	molybdenum	95.94000	65	Tb	terbium	158.92534	88	Ra	radium	
20	Ca	calcium	40.07800	43	Tc	technetium		66	Dy	dysprosium	162.50000	89	Ac	actinium	
21	Sc	scandium	44.95910	44	Ru	ruthenium	101.07000	67	Ho	holmium	164.93032	90	Th	thorium	232.03810
22	Ti	titanium	47.86700	45	Rh	rhodium	102.90550	68	Er	erbium	167.26000	91	Pa	protactinium	
23	V	vanadium	50.94150	46	Pd	palladium	106.42000	69	Tm	thulium	168.93421	92	U	uranium	238.02890

21.7 Periodic Table of the Elements

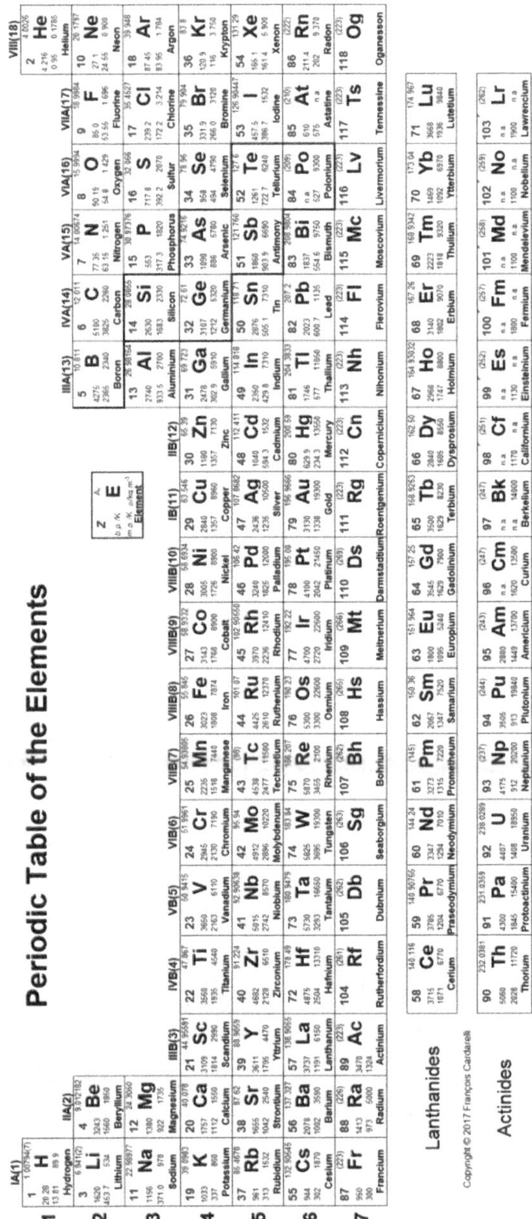

Figure 140 – Periodic chart of the elements

21.8 Selected Oxidation-Reduction Potentials

A selected list of oxidation-reduction potentials of electroactive species occurring in effluents containing iron sulfate(s) are reported in Table 181.

Table 181 – Selected oxidation-reduction potentials

Electrochemical reaction	Standard electrode potential (V/SHE)	Electrochemical reaction	Standard electrode potential (V/SHE)
$Ti^{2+} + 2e^- = Ti(s)$	−1.630	$HSO_4^- + 3H^+ + 2e^- = SO_2(aq) + 2H_2O$	0.16
$Ti^{3+} + 3e^- = Ti(s)$	−1.210	$SO_4^{2-} + 4H^+ + 2e^- = SO_2(aq) + 2H_2O$	0.17
$Mn^{2+} + 2e^- = Mn(s)$	−1.185	$TiO^{2+} + 2H^+ + e^- = Ti^{3+} + H_2O$	0.19
$V^{2+} + 2e^- = V(s)$	−1.130	$VO^{2+} + 2H^+ + e^- = V^{3+} + H_2O$	0.34
$Zn^{2+} + 2e^- = Zn(s)$	−0.7618	$Cu^{2+} + 2e^- = Cu(s)$	0.34
$Cr^{3+} + 3e^- = Cr(s)$	−0.740	$Cu^+ + e^- = Cu(s)$	0.52
$Fe^{2+} + 2e^- = Fe(s)$	−0.440	$S_2O_3^{2-} + 6H^+ + 4e^- = 2S(s) + 3H_2O$	0.60
$Cr^{3+} + e^- = Cr^{2+}$	−0.420	$O_2(g) + 2H^+ + 2e^- = H_2O_2(aq)$	0.70
$Cd^{2+} + 2e^- = Cd(s)$	−0.400	$Fe^{3+} + e^- = Fe^{2+}$	0.77
$Co^{2+} + 2e^- = Co(s)$	−0.280	$O_2(g) + 4H^+ + 4e^- = 2H_2O$	1.23
$V^{3+} + e^- = V^{2+}$	−0.260	$MnO_2(s) + 4H^+ + 2e^- = Mn^{2+} + 2H_2O$	1.23
$Ni^{2+} + 2e^- = Ni(s)$	−0.250	$Cl_2(g) + 2e^- = 2Cl^-$	1.36
$Sn^{2+} + 2e^- = Sn(s)$	−0.130	$\beta\text{-}PbO_2(s) + 4H^+ + 2e^- = Pb^{2+} + 2H_2O$	1.46
$Pb^{2+} + 2e^- = Pb(s)$	−0.130	$H_2O_2(aq) + 2H^+ + 2e^- = 2H_2O$	1.78
$2H^+ + 2e^- = H_2(g)$	**0.000**	$Co^{3+} + e^- = Co^{2+}$	1.82
$S(s) + 2H^+ + 2e^- = H_2S(g)$	0.14	$HSO_5^- + 2H^+ + 2e- = HSO_4^- + H_2O$	1.85
$Sn^{4+} + 2e^- = Sn^{2+}$	0.15	$S_2O_8^{2-} + 2e^- = 2SO_4^{2-}$	2.01
$Cu^{2+} + e^- = Cu^+$	0.16		

22 Index

About the Author

Dr. François Cardarelli, President and Owner of the Canadian company *Electrochem Technologies & Materials Inc.*, is an industrial chemist with a strong physical-chemistry background and a doctorate in chemical engineering from the University Paul Sabatier (UPS) Toulouse III. He is the inventor and co-inventor of 16 patents, and the sole author of three reference handbooks published worldwide by Springer since 1996 and two monographs.

He has over 34 years of industrial experience in North America and Europe in developing electrochemical, chemical, and metallurgical processes for winning, refining or producing a variety of metals, alloys, and inorganic chemicals either from aqueous solutions or molten salts media.

A particular area of his professional expertise is the chemical, and electrochemical processing of mining residues, metallurgical wastes, and industrial effluents, the manufacture of industrial electrodes, the electrochemical production of vanadium electrolyte, the pyro- and hydrometallurgical production of vanadium, niobium, tantalum, and tungsten compounds and chemicals, and finally the manufacture of novel industrial materials. All these processes are covered by patents enforced in many jurisdictions.

Dr. François Cardarelli is a member in good standing of the following professional organizations and societies: *American Institute of Chemical Engineers* (AIChE)[Lifetime member], *American Chemical Society* (ACS), *Chemical Institute of Canada* (CIC), *Canadian Society for Chemical Engineering* (CSChE), *The Electrochemical Society* (ECS), *Mineralogical Society of America* (MSA), *Ordre des Chimistes du Québec* (OCQ), The *Oughtred Society* (OS), and *The Minerals, Metals and Materials Society* (TMS).

Made in the USA
Monee, IL
09 November 2023